Intermediate Algebra
Math 118

Custom Edition for
Community College of Philadelphia

Taken from:
Intermediate Algebra, Fifth Edition
by Elayn Martin-Gay

Learning Solutions

New York Boston San Francisco
London Toronto Sydney Tokyo Singapore Madrid
Mexico City Munich Paris Cape Town Hong Kong Montreal

Cover Art: *Umedas1*, by Barry Cronin

Taken from:

Intermediate Algebra, Fifth Edition
by Elayn Martin-Gay
Copyright © 2009, 2005, 2001, 1997, 1993 by Pearson Education, Inc.
Published by Prentice Hall
Upper Saddle River, New Jersey 07458

This special edition published in cooperation with Pearson Learning Solutions.

All trademarks, service marks, registered trademarks, and registered service marks are the property of their respective owners and are used herein for identification purposes only.

Pearson Learning Solutions, 501 Boylston Street, Suite 900, Boston, MA 02116
A Pearson Education Company
www.pearsoned.com

Printed in the United States of America

6 7 8 9 10 V312 15 14 13 12 11

0002000102705722102

LB

ISBN 10: 0-558-75684-0
ISBN 13: 978-0-558-75684-0

Contents

CHAPTER

7

RATIONAL EXPONENTS, RADICALS, AND COMPLEX NUMBERS   378

CHAPTER

8

QUADRATIC EQUATIONS AND FUNCTIONS   445

APPENDICES   484

Community College of Philadelphia

Math 118 Students

To access your MyLabsPlus account:

1. Go to www.ccp.mylabsplus.com – You must use IE as your browser
2. In the Log In space, enter your J number – use upper case J
3. In the Password space, enter "password"
4. Click on Log In
5. At the Welcome Screen, find and click on MyProfile in the upper right

6. In the Old Password space, enter "password"
7. Create and Verify a New Password for your account

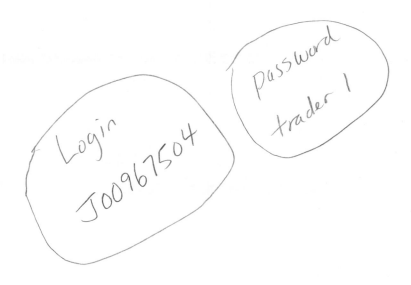

Login
J00967504

Password
trader 1

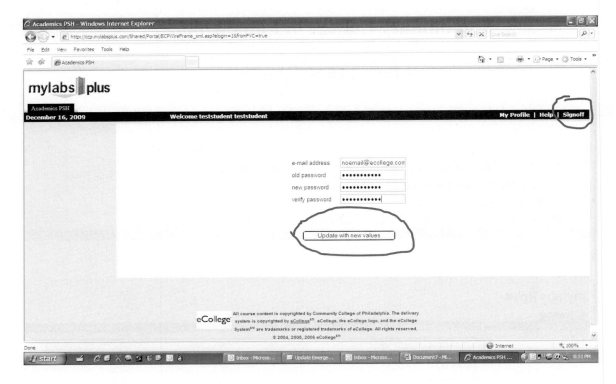

8. Click Update with new Values
9. Click Sign off
10. Enter your Log In (CCP Student ID with the upper case J) and your NEW Password
11. Click on Log In
12. Click on Math 118 (your appropriate section number will be listed as well)

13. On the left side, click on Study Plan
14. Click on the MML Study Plan link in the middle of the screen

15. You will see the Licensing agreement, scroll to the bottom and click on: I Accept.
16. You will be prompted for an access code, click on Access Code and enter the access code packaged with your Textbook.
    -If you do not have an Access Code you purchase one on line, click on Buy Access Now
    -The Access code will look something like this:
    HSEMSA-QUIPU-PRAYS-ADMAN-TANIS-MOLES

Once you have entered the Access Code successfully, you will not need it again. You will have full access to all the on line materials for your course.

Once in the course materials, click on the Study Plan, Tools for Success and Multimedia Library to find tutorials, tools and practice problems that will help you understand the material covered in this class.

CHAPTER

1

Real Numbers and Algebraic Expressions

A common definition of *tourism* is travel for mainly recreational or leisure purposes. The terms *tourist* and *tourism* were first used as official terms in 1937 by the League of Nations. Another interesting fact about tourism is that in 1841, Thomas Cook organized the first tour package in history. He arranged a per-person flat rate for a group of campaigners to travel by rail to a rally in Loughborough, England, in exchange for a share of the fares charged.

Tourism is vital for many countries because income is generated by the consumption of goods and services by tourists. In addition, there is the opportunity for employment in these service industries that depend on tourists. In Section 1.2, page 16, Exercises 97–100, you will have the opportunity to estimate the number of tourists predicted for selected countries.

In arithmetic, we add, subtract, multiply, divide, raise to powers, and take roots of numbers. In algebra, we add, subtract, multiply, divide, raise to powers, and take roots of variables. Letters, such as x, that represent numbers are called **variables.** Understanding these algebraic expressions depends on your understanding of arithmetic expressions. This chapter reviews the arithmetic operations on real numbers and the corresponding algebraic expressions.

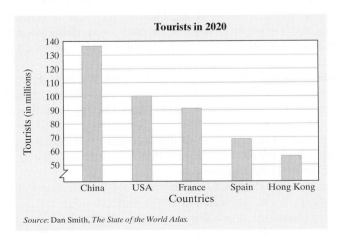

Source: Dan Smith, *The State of the World Atlas.*

1.1 TIPS FOR SUCCESS IN MATHEMATICS

OBJECTIVES

1 Get ready for this course.

2 Understand some general tips for success.

3 Understand how to use this text.

4 Get help as soon as you need it.

5 Learn how to prepare for and take an exam.

6 Develop good time management.

Before reading this section, remember that your instructor is your best source for information. Please see your instructor for any additional help or information.

OBJECTIVE 1 ▶ Getting ready for this course. Now that you have decided to take this course, remember that a *positive attitude* will make all the difference in the world. Your belief that you can succeed is just as important as your commitment to this course. Make sure you are ready for this course by having the time and positive attitude that it takes to succeed.

Next, make sure you have scheduled your math course at a time that will give you the best chance for success. For example, if you are also working, you may want to check with your employer to make sure that your work hours will not conflict with your course schedule. Also, schedule your class during a time of day when you are more attentive and do your best work.

On the day of your first class period, double-check your schedule and allow yourself extra time to arrive in case of traffic problems or difficulty locating your classroom. Make sure that you bring at least your textbook, paper, and a writing instrument. Are you required to have a lab manual, graph paper, calculator, or some other supply besides this text? If so, also bring this material with you.

OBJECTIVE 2 ▶ General tips for success. Below are some general tips that will increase your chance for success in a mathematics class. Many of these tips will also help you in other courses you may be taking.

Exchange names and phone numbers with at least one other person in class. This contact person can be a great help if you miss an assignment or want to discuss math concepts or exercises that you find difficult.

Choose to attend all class periods and be on time. If possible, sit near the front of the classroom. This way, you will see and hear the presentation better. It may also be easier for you to participate in classroom activities.

Do your homework. You've probably heard the phrase "practice makes perfect" in relation to music and sports. It also applies to mathematics. You will find that the more time you spend solving mathematics problems, the easier the process becomes. Be sure to schedule enough time to complete your assignments before the next class period.

Check your work. Review the steps you made while working a problem. Learn to check your answers to the original problems. You may also compare your answers with the answers to selected exercises section in the back of the book. If you have made a mistake, try to figure out what went wrong. Then correct your mistake. If you can't find what went wrong, don't erase your work or throw it away. Bring your work to your instructor, a tutor in a math lab, or a classmate. It is easier for someone to find where you had trouble if they look at your original work.

Learn from your mistakes and be patient with yourself. Everyone, even your instructor, makes mistakes. (That definitely includes me—Elayn Martin-Gay.) Use your errors to learn and to become a better math student. The key is finding and understanding your errors.

Was your mistake a careless one, or did you make it because you can't read your own math writing? If so, try to work more slowly or write more neatly and make a conscious effort to carefully check your work.

Did you make a mistake because you don't understand a concept? Take the time to review the concept or ask questions to better understand it.

Did you skip too many steps? Skipping steps or trying to do too many steps mentally may lead to preventable mistakes.

Know how to get help if you need it. It's all right to ask for help. In fact, it's a good idea to ask for help whenever there is something that you don't understand. Make sure you know when your instructor has office hours and how to find his or her office. Find out whether math tutoring services are available on your campus. Check out the hours, location, and requirements of the tutoring service. Videotapes and software are available with this text. Learn how to access these resources.

Organize your class materials, including homework assignments, graded quizzes and tests, and notes from your class or lab. All of these items will be valuable references throughout your course especially when studying for upcoming tests and the final exam. Make sure that you can locate these materials when you need them.

Read your textbook before class. Reading a mathematics textbook is unlike leisure reading such as reading a novel or newspaper. Your pace will be much slower. It is helpful to have paper and a pencil with you when you read. Try to work out examples on your own as you encounter them in your text. You should also write down any questions that you want to ask in class. When you read a mathematics textbook, some of the information in a section may be unclear. But when you hear a lecture or watch a videotape on that section, you will understand it much more easily than if you had not read your text beforehand.

Don't be afraid to ask questions. Instructors are not mind readers. Many times we do not know a concept is unclear until a student asks a question. You are not the only person in class with questions. Other students are normally grateful that someone has spoken up.

Hand in assignments on time. This way you can be sure that you will not lose points for being late. Show every step of a problem and be neat and organized. Also be sure that you understand which problems are assigned for homework. You can always double-check this assignment with another student in your class.

OBJECTIVE 3 ▶ Using this text. There are many helpful resources that are available to you in this text. It is important that you become familiar with and use these resources. They should increase your chances for success in this course.

- The main section of exercises in each exercise set is referenced by an example(s). Use this referencing if you have trouble completing an assignment from the exercise set.
- If you need extra help in a particular section, look at the beginning of the section to see what videotapes and software are available.
- Make sure that you understand the meaning of the icons that are beside many exercises. The video icon 📹 tells you that the corresponding exercise may be viewed on the videotape that corresponds to that section. The pencil icon ✎ tells you that this exercise is a writing exercise in which you should answer in complete sentences. The triangle icon △ tells you that the exercise involves geometry.
- Practice exercises are located immediately after a worked-out example in the text. This exercise is similar to the previous example and is a great way for you to immediately reinforce a learned concept. All answers to the practice exercises are found in the back of the text.
- Integrated Reviews in each chapter offer you a chance to practice—in one place—the many concepts that you have learned separately over several sections.
- There are many opportunities at the end of each chapter to help you understand the concepts of the chapter.

    Chapter Highlights contain chapter summaries and examples.

    Chapter Reviews contain review problems organized by section.

    Chapter Tests are sample tests to help you prepare for an exam.

    Cumulative Reviews are reviews consisting of material from the beginning of the book to the end of that particular chapter.

- *The Bigger Picture.* This feature contains the directions for building an outline to be used throughout the course. The purpose of this outline is to help you make the transition from thinking "section by section" to thinking about how the mathematics in this course is part of a bigger picture.

- *Study Skills Builder.* This feature is found at the end of many exercise sets. In order to increase your chance of success in this course, please read and answer the questions in the Study Skills Builder. For your convenience, the table below contains selected Study Skills Builder titles and their location.

Study Skills Builder Title	*Page of First Occurrence*
Learning New Terms	Page 16
Are You Preparing for a Test on Chapter 1?	Page 39
What to Do the Day of an Exam?	Page 265
Have You Decided to Complete This Course Successfully?	Page 55
Organizing a Notebook	Page 67
How Are Your Homework Assignments Going?	Page 75
Are You Familiar with Your Textbook Supplements?	Page 215
How Well Do You Know Your Textbook?	Page 129
Are You Organized?	Page 154
Are You Satisfied with Your Performance on a Particular Quiz or Exam?	Page 241
Tips for Studying for an Exam	Page 185
Are You Getting All the Mathematics Help That You Need?	Page 291
How Are You Doing?	Page 366
Are You Prepared for Your Final Exam?	Page 625

See the preface at the beginning of this text for a more thorough explanation of the features of this text.

OBJECTIVE 4 ▶ Getting help. If you have trouble completing assignments or understanding the mathematics, get help as soon as you need it! This tip is presented as an objective on its own because it is so important. In mathematics, usually the material presented in one section builds on your understanding of the previous section. This means that if you don't understand the concepts covered during a class period, there is a good chance that you will not understand the concepts covered during the next class period. If this happens to you, get help as soon as you can.

Where can you get help? Many suggestions have been made in the section on where to get help, and now it is up to you to do it. Try your instructor, a tutoring center, or a math lab, or you may want to form a study group with fellow classmates. If you do decide to see your instructor or go to a tutoring center, make sure that you have a neat notebook and are ready with your questions.

OBJECTIVE 5 ▶ Preparing for and taking an exam. Make sure that you allow yourself plenty of time to prepare for a test. If you think that you are a little "math anxious," it may be that you are not preparing for a test in a way that will ensure success. The way that you prepare for a test in mathematics is important. To prepare for a test,

1. Review your previous homework assignments. You may also want to rework some of them.
2. Review any notes from class and section-level quizzes you have taken. (If this is a final exam, also review chapter tests you have taken.)
3. Review concepts and definitions by reading the Highlights at the end of each chapter.
4. Practice working out exercises by completing the Chapter Review found at the end of each chapter. (If this is a final exam, go through a Cumulative Review. There is

one found at the end of each chapter except Chapter 1. Choose the review found at the end of the latest chapter that you have covered in your course.) *Don't stop here!*

5. It is important that you place yourself in conditions similar to test conditions to find out how you will perform. In other words, as soon as you feel that you know the material, get a few blank sheets of paper and take a sample test. There is a Chapter Test available at the end of each chapter. During this sample test, do not use your notes or your textbook. Once you complete the Chapter Test, check your answers in the back of the book. If any answer is incorrect, there is a CD available with each exercise of each chapter test worked. Use this CD or your instructor to correct your sample test. Your instructor may also provide you with a review sheet. If you are not satisfied with the results, study the areas that you are weak in and try again.

6. Get a good night's sleep before the exam.

7. On the day of the actual test, allow yourself plenty of time to arrive at where you will be taking your exam.

When taking your test,

1. Read the directions on the test carefully.

2. Read each problem carefully as you take the test. Make sure that you answer the question asked.

3. Pace yourself by first completing the problems you are most confident with. Then work toward the problems you are least confident with. Watch your time so you do not spend too much time on one particular problem.

4. If you have time, check your work and answers.

5. Do not turn your test in early. If you have extra time, spend it double-checking your work.

OBJECTIVE 6 ▶ Managing your time. As a college student, you know the demands that classes, homework, work, and family place on your time. Some days you probably wonder how you'll ever get everything done. One key to managing your time is developing a schedule. Here are some hints for making a schedule:

1. Make a list of all of your weekly commitments for the term. Include classes, work, regular meetings, extracurricular activities, etc. You may also find it helpful to list such things as laundry, regular workouts, grocery shopping, etc.

2. Next, estimate the time needed for each item on the list. Also make a note of how often you will need to do each item. Don't forget to include time estimates for reading, studying, and homework you do outside of your classes. You may want to ask your instructor for help estimating the time needed.

3. In the following exercise set, you are asked to block out a typical week on the schedule grid given. Start with items with fixed time slots like classes and work.

4. Next, include the items on your list with flexible time slots. Think carefully about how best to schedule some items such as study time.

5. Don't fill up every time slot on the schedule. Remember that you need to allow time for eating, sleeping, and relaxing! You should also allow a little extra time in case some items take longer than planned.

6. If you find that your weekly schedule is too full for you to handle, you may need to make some changes in your workload, classload, or in other areas of your life. You may want to talk to your advisor, manager or supervisor at work, or someone in your college's academic counseling center for help with such decisions.

Note: In this chapter, we begin a feature called Study Skills Builder. The purpose of this feature is to remind you of some of the information given in this section and to further expand on some topics in this section.

1.1 EXERCISE SET

    PRACTICE   WATCH   DOWNLOAD   READ   REVIEW

1. What is your instructor's name?

2. What are your instructor's office location and office hours?

3. What is the best way to contact your instructor?

4. What does the ＼ icon mean?

5. What does the 🖳 icon mean?

6. What does the △ icon mean?

7. Where are answers located in this text?

8. What Exercise Set answers are available to you in the answers section?

9. What Chapter Review, Chapter Test, and Cumulative Review answers are available to you in the answer section?

10. Search after the solution of any worked example in this text. What are Practice exercises?

11. When might be the best time to work a Practice exercise?

12. Where are the answers to Practice exercises?

13. List any similarities between a Practice exercise and the worked example before it.

14. Go to the Highlights section at the end of this chapter. Describe how this section may be helpful to you when preparing for a test.

15. Do you have the name and contact information of at least one other student in class?

16. Will your instructor allow you to use a calculator in this class?

17. Are videotapes, CDs, and/or tutorial software available to you? If so, where?

18. Is there a tutoring service available? If so, what are its hours?

19. Have you attempted this course before? If so, write down ways that you might improve your chance of success during this second attempt.

20. List some steps that you can take if you begin having trouble understanding the material or completing an assignment.

21. Read or reread objective 6 and fill out the schedule grid below.

22. Study your filled-out grid from Exercise 21. Decide whether you have the time necessary to successfully complete this course and any other courses you may be registered for.

	Monday	*Tuesday*	*Wednesday*	*Thursday*	*Friday*	*Saturday*	*Sunday*
4:00 A.M.							
5:00 A.M.							
6:00 A.M.							
7:00 A.M.							
8:00 A.M.							
9:00 A.M.							
10:00 A.M.							
11:00 A.M.							
12:00 P.M.							
1:00 P.M.							
2:00 P.M.							
3:00 P.M.							
4:00 P.M.							
5:00 P.M.							
6:00 P.M.							
7:00 P.M.							
8:00 P.M.							
9:00 P.M.							
10:00 P.M.							
11:00 P.M.							
Midnight							
1:00 A.M.							
2:00 A.M.							
3:00 A.M.							

1.2 ALGEBRAIC EXPRESSIONS AND SETS OF NUMBERS

OBJECTIVES

1 Identify and evaluate algebraic expressions.

2 Identify natural numbers, whole numbers, integers, and rational and irrational real numbers.

3 Find the absolute value of a number.

4 Find the opposite of a number.

5 Write phrases as algebraic expressions.

OBJECTIVE 1 ▶ Evaluating algebraic expressions. Recall that letters that represent numbers are called **variables.** An **algebraic expression** is formed by numbers and variables connected by the operations of addition, subtraction, multiplication, division, raising to powers, and/or taking roots. For example,

$$2x + 3, \quad \frac{x + 5}{6} - \frac{z^2}{y^2}, \quad \text{and} \quad \sqrt{y} - 1.6$$

are algebraic expressions or, more simply, expressions.

Algebraic expressions occur often during problem solving. For example, the B747-400 aircraft costs $8443 per hour to operate. (*Source: The World Almanac*) The algebraic expression $8443t$

gives the total cost to operate the aircraft for t hours. To find the cost to operate the aircraft for 5.2 hours, for example, we replace the variable t with 5.2 and perform the indicated operation. This process is called **evaluating** an expression, and the result is called the **value** of the expression for the given replacement value.

In our example, when $t = 5.2$ hours,

$$8443t = 8443(5.2) = 43,903.60$$

Thus, it costs $43,903.60 to operate the B747-400 aircraft for 5.2 hours.

> ▶ **Helpful Hint**
> Recall that $8443t$ means $8443 \cdot t$.

△ **EXAMPLE 1**   **Finding the Area of a Tile**

The research department of a flooring company is considering a new flooring design that contains parallelograms. The area of a parallelogram with base b and height h is bh. Find the area of a parallelogram with base 10 centimeters and height 8.2 centimeters.

Solution   We replace b with 10 and h with 8.2 in the algebraic expression bh.

$$bh = 10 \cdot 8.2 = 82$$

The area is 82 square centimeters

PRACTICE

1   The tile edging for a bathroom is in the shape of a triangle. The area of a triangle with base b and height h is $A = \frac{1}{2}bh$. Find the area of the tile if the base measures 3.5 cm and the height measures 8 cm.

Algebraic expressions simplify to different values depending on replacement values. (Order of operations is needed for simplifying many expressions. We fully review this in Section 1.3.)

EXAMPLE 2 Evaluate: $3x - y$ when $x = 15$ and $y = 4$.

Solution We replace x with 15 and y with 4 in the expression.

$$3x - y = 3 \cdot 15 - 4 = 45 - 4 = 41$$

□

PRACTICE
2 Evaluate $2p - q$ when $p = 17$ and $q = 3$.

When evaluating an expression to solve a problem, we often need to think about the kind of number that is appropriate for the solution. For example, if we are asked to determine the maximum number of parking spaces for a parking lot to be constructed, an answer of $98\frac{1}{10}$ is not appropriate because $\frac{1}{10}$ of a parking space is not realistic.

OBJECTIVE 2 ▶ Identifying common sets of numbers. Let's review some common sets of numbers and their graphs on a number line. To construct a number line, we draw a line and label a point 0 with which we associate the number 0. This point is called the **origin.** Choose a point to the right of 0 and label it 1. The distance from 0 to 1 is called the **unit distance** and can be used to locate more points. The **positive numbers** lie to the right of the origin, and the **negative numbers** lie to the left of the origin. The number 0 is neither positive nor negative.

Concept Check ☑

Use the definitions of positive numbers, negative numbers, and zero to describe the meaning of *nonnegative numbers.*

A number is **graphed** on a number line by shading the point on the number line that corresponds to the number. Some common sets of numbers and their graphs include:

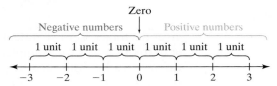

The symbol ... is used in each set above. This symbol, consisting of three dots, is called an **ellipsis** and means to continue in the same pattern.

The members of a set are called its **elements.** When the elements of a set are listed, such as those displayed in the previous paragraph, the set is written in **roster** form. A set can also be written in **set builder notation,** which describes the members of a set but does not list them. The following set is written in set builder notation.

$$\{x \mid x \text{ is a natural number less than 3}\}$$

▶ Helpful Hint

Use { } or ∅ to write the empty set. {∅} is **not** the empty set because it has one element: ∅.

This same set written in roster form is $\{1, 2\}$.

A set that contains *no* elements is called the **empty set** (or **null set**) symbolized by { } or ∅. The set

$$\{x \mid x \text{ is a month with 32 days}\} \text{ is } \varnothing \text{ or } \{\ \}$$

because no month has 32 days. The set has no elements.

EXAMPLE 3   List the elements in each set.

a. $\{x \mid x \text{ is a natural number greater than } 100\}$

b. $\{x \mid x \text{ is a whole number between 1 and 6}\}$

Solution

a. $\{101, 102, 103, \dots\}$ **b.** $\{2, 3, 4, 5\}$

PRACTICE
  3   List the elements in each set.

a. $\{x \mid x \text{ is a whole number between 5 and 10}\}$

b. $\{x \mid x \text{ is a natural number greater than 40}\}$

The symbol ∈ is used to denote that an element is in a particular set. The symbol ∈ is read as "is an element of." For example, the true statement

$$3 \text{ is an element of } \{1, 2, 3, 4, 5\}$$

can be written in symbols as

$$3 \in \{1, 2, 3, 4, 5\}$$

The symbol ∉ is read as "is not an element of." In symbols, we write the true statement "p is not an element of $\{a, 5, g, j, q\}$" as

$$p \notin \{a, 5, g, j, q\}$$

EXAMPLE 4   Determine whether each statement is true or false.

a. $3 \in \{x \mid x \text{ is a natural number}\}$ **b.** $7 \notin \{1, 2, 3\}$

Solution

a. True, since 3 is a natural number and therefore an element of the set.

b. True, since 7 is not an element of the set $\{1, 2, 3\}$.

PRACTICE
  4   Determine whether each statement is true or false.

a. $7 \in \{x \mid x \text{ is a natural number}\}$ **b.** $6 \notin \{1, 3, 5, 7\}$

We can use set builder notation to describe three other common sets of numbers.

Identifying Numbers

Real Numbers: $\{x \mid x \text{ corresponds to a point on the number line}\}$

0

Rational numbers: $\left\{ \dfrac{a}{b} \;\middle|\; a \text{ and } b \text{ are integers and } b \neq 0 \right\}$

Irrational numbers: $\{x \mid x \text{ is a real number and } x \text{ is not a rational number}\}$

> ▶ **Helpful Hint**
> Notice from the definition that all real numbers are either rational or irrational.

Every rational number can be written as a decimal that either repeats or terminates. For example,

Rational Numbers

$$\frac{1}{2} = 0.5 \qquad\qquad \frac{5}{4} = 1.25$$

$$\frac{2}{3} = 0.6666666\ldots = 0.\overline{6} \qquad \frac{1}{11} = 0.090909\ldots = 0.\overline{09}$$

An irrational number written as a decimal neither terminates nor repeats. For example, π and $\sqrt{2}$ are irrational numbers. Their decimal form neither terminates nor repeats. Decimal approximations of each are below:

Irrational Numbers

$$\pi \approx 3.141592\ldots \qquad \sqrt{2} \approx 1.414213\ldots$$

Notice that every integer is also a rational number since each integer can be written as the quotient of itself and 1:

$$3 = \frac{3}{1}, \quad 0 = \frac{0}{1}, \quad -8 = \frac{-8}{1}$$

Not every rational number, however, is an integer. The rational number $\frac{2}{3}$, for example, is not an integer. Some square roots are rational numbers and some are irrational numbers. For example, $\sqrt{2}$, $\sqrt{3}$ and $\sqrt{7}$ are irrational numbers while $\sqrt{25}$ is a rational number because $\sqrt{25} = 5 = \frac{5}{1}$. The set of rational numbers together with the set of irrational numbers make up the set of real numbers. To help you make the distinction between rational and irrational numbers, here are a few examples of each.

Real Numbers		
Rational Numbers		**Irrational Numbers (Decimal Form Neither Terminates Nor Repeats)**
Numbers	**Equivalent Quotient of Integers, $\frac{a}{b}$ (Decimal Form Terminates or Repeats)**	
$-\frac{2}{3}$	$\frac{-2}{3}$ or $\frac{2}{-3}$	$\sqrt{5}$
$\sqrt{36}$	$\frac{6}{1}$	$\frac{\sqrt{6}}{7}$
5	$\frac{5}{1}$	$-\sqrt{13}$
0	$\frac{0}{1}$	π
1.2	$\frac{12}{10}$	$\frac{2}{\sqrt{3}}$
$3\frac{7}{8}$	$\frac{31}{8}$	

Some rational and irrational numbers are graphed below.

Earlier we mentioned that every integer is also a rational number. In other words, all the elements of the set of integers are also elements of the set of rational numbers. When this happens, we say that the set of integers, set Z, is a subset of the set of rational numbers, set Q. In symbols,

$$Z \subseteq Q$$

$\underbrace{}_{\text{is a subset of}}$

The natural numbers, whole numbers, integers, rational numbers, and irrational numbers are each a subset of the set of real numbers. The relationships among these sets of numbers are shown in the following diagram.

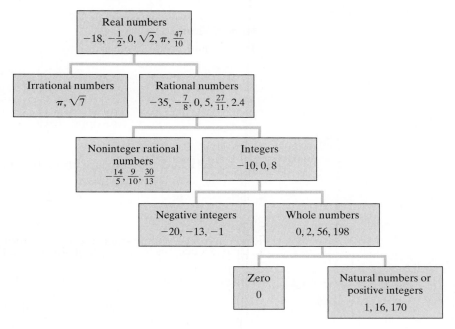

EXAMPLE 5 Determine whether the following statements are true or false.

a. 3 is a real number.

b. $\dfrac{1}{5}$ is an irrational number.

c. Every rational number is an integer.

d. $\{1, 5\} \subseteq \{2, 3, 4, 5\}$

Solution

a. True. Every whole number is a real number.

b. False. The number $\dfrac{1}{5}$ is a rational number, since it is in the form $\dfrac{a}{b}$ with a and b integers and $b \neq 0$.

c. False. The number $\dfrac{2}{3}$, for example, is a rational number, but it is not an integer.

d. False. Since the element 1 in the first set is not an element of the second set. □

PRACTICE

5 Determine whether the following statements are true or false.

a. -5 is a real number.

b. $\sqrt{8}$ is a rational number.

c. Every whole number is a rational number.

d. $\{2, 4\} \subset \{1, 3, 4, 7\}$

OBJECTIVE 3 ▶ Finding the absolute value of a number. The number line can also be used to visualize distance, which leads to the concept of absolute value. The **absolute**

value of a real number a, written as $|a|$, is the distance between a and 0 on the number line. Since distance is always positive or zero, $|a|$ is always positive or zero.

Using the number line, we see that

$$|4| = 4 \qquad \text{and also} \qquad |-4| = 4$$

Why? Because both 4 and -4 are a distance of 4 units from 0.

An equivalent definition of the absolute value of a real number a is given next.

Absolute Value

The absolute value of a, written as $|a|$, is

$$|a| = \begin{cases} a \text{ if } a \text{ is 0 or a positive number} \\ -a \text{ if } a \text{ is a negative number} \end{cases}$$

the opposite of

EXAMPLE 6 Find each absolute value.

a. $|3|$ **b.** $\left|-\dfrac{1}{7}\right|$ **c.** $-|2.7|$ **d.** $-|-8|$ **e.** $|0|$

Solution

a. $|3| = 3$ since 3 is located 3 units from 0 on the number line.

b. $\left|-\dfrac{1}{7}\right| = \dfrac{1}{7}$ since $-\dfrac{1}{7}$ is $\dfrac{1}{7}$ units from 0 on the number line.

c. $-|2.7| = -2.7$. The negative sign outside the absolute value bars means to take the opposite of the absolute value of 2.7.

d. $-|-8| = -8$. Since $|-8|$ is 8, $-|-8| = -8$.

e. $|0| = 0$ since 0 is located 0 units from 0 on the number line. □

PRACTICE
6 Find each absolute value.

a. $|4|$ **b.** $\left|-\dfrac{1}{2}\right|$ **c.** $|1|$ **d.** $-|6.8|$ **e.** $-|-4|$

Concept Check ☑

Explain how you know that $|14| = -14$ is a false statement.

OBJECTIVE 4 ▶ Finding the opposite of a number. The number line can also help us visualize opposites. Two numbers that are the same distance from 0 on the number line but are on opposite sides of 0 are called **opposites.**

See the definition illustrated on the number lines below.

The opposite of 6.5 is -6.5

The opposite of $\dfrac{2}{3}$ is $-\dfrac{2}{3}$.

The opposite of -4 is 4.

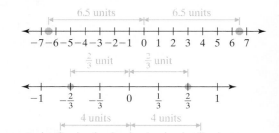

> **Opposite**
> The opposite of a number a is the number $-a$.

Above we state that the opposite of a number a is $-a$. This means that the opposite of -4 is $-(-4)$. But from the number line above, the opposite of -4 is 4. This means that $-(-4) = 4$, and in general, we have the following property.

> **Double Negative Property**
> For every real number a, $-(-a) = a$.

EXAMPLE 7   Write the opposite of each number.

a. 8   **b.** $\dfrac{1}{5}$ **c.** -9.6

Solution

a. The opposite of 8 is -8.

b. The opposite of $\dfrac{1}{5}$ is $-\dfrac{1}{5}$.

c. The opposite of -9.6 is $-(-9.6) = 9.6$.

PRACTICE
7   Write the opposite of each number.

a. 5.4   **b.** $-\dfrac{3}{5}$ **c.** 18

OBJECTIVE 5 ▶ Writing phrases as algebraic expressions. Often, solving problems involves translating a phrase to an algebraic expression. The following is a partial list of key words and phrases and their usual direct translations.

Selected Key Words/Phrases and Their Translations			
Addition	*Subtraction*	*Multiplication*	*Division*
sum	difference of	product	quotient
plus	minus	times	divide
added to	subtracted from	multiply	into
more than	less than	twice	ratio
increased by	decreased by	of	
total	less		

EXAMPLE 8   Translate each phrase to an algebraic expression. Use the variable x to represent each unknown number.

a. Eight times a number

b. Three more than eight times a number

c. The quotient of a number and -7

d. One and six-tenths subtracted from twice a number

e. Six less than a number

f. Twice the sum of four and a number

Solution

a. $8 \cdot x$ or $8x$

b. $8x + 3$

c. $x \div -7$ or $\dfrac{x}{-7}$

d. $2x - 1.6$ or $2x - 1\dfrac{6}{10}$

e. $x - 6$

f. $2(4 + x)$

□

PRACTICE

8   Translate each phrase to an algebraic expression. Use the variable x to represent the unknown number.

a. The product of 3 and a number

b. Five less than twice a number

c. Three and five-eighths more than a number

d. The quotient of a number and 2

e. Fourteen subtracted from a number

f. Five times the sum of a number and ten

VOCABULARY & READINESS CHECK

Use the choices below to fill in each blank. Not all choices will be used.

whole numbers	integers	rational number	a
natural numbers	value	irrational number	$-a$
absolute value	expression	variables	

1. Letters that represent numbers are called _____.

2. Finding the _____ of an expression means evaluating the expression.

3. The _____ of a number is that number's distance from 0 on the number line.

4. A(n) _____ is formed by numbers and variables connected by operations such as addition, subtraction, multiplication, division, raising to powers, and/or taking roots.

5. The _____ are $\{1, 2, 3, \ldots\}$.

6. The _____ are $\{0, 1, 2, 3, \ldots\}$.

7. The _____ are $\{\ldots -3, -2, -1, 0, 1, 2, 3, \ldots\}$.

8. The number $\sqrt{5}$ is a(n) _____.

9. The number $\dfrac{5}{7}$ is a(n) _____.

10. The opposite of a is _____.

1.2 | EXERCISE SET

Find the value of each algebraic expression at the given replacement values. See Examples 1 and 2.

1. $5x$ when $x = 7$

2. $3y$ when $y = 45$

3. $9.8z$ when $z = 3.1$

4. $7.1a$ when $a = 1.5$

5. ab when $a = \dfrac{1}{2}$ and $b = \dfrac{3}{4}$

6. yz when $y = \dfrac{2}{3}$ and $z = \dfrac{1}{5}$

7. $3x + y$ when $x = 6$ and $y = 4$

8. $2a - b$ when $a = 12$ and $b = 7$

9. The aircraft B737-400 flies an average speed of 400 miles per hour.

The expression 400*t* gives the distance traveled by the aircraft in *t* hours. Find the distance traveled by the B737-400 in 5 hours.

10. The algebraic expression 1.5*x* gives the total length of shelf space needed in inches for *x* encyclopedias. Find the length of shelf space needed for a set of 30 encyclopedias.

△ **11.** Employees at Wal-Mart constantly reorganize and reshelve merchandise. In doing so, they calculate floor space needed for displays. The algebraic expression *l* · *w* gives the floor space needed in square units for a display that measures length *l* units and width *w* units. Calculate the floor space needed for a display whose length is 5.1 feet and whose width is 4 feet.

12. The algebraic expression $\frac{x}{5}$ can be used to calculate the distance in miles that you are from a flash of lightning, where *x* is the number of seconds between the time you see a flash of lightning and the time you hear the thunder. Calculate the distance that you are from the flash of lightning if you hear the thunder 2 seconds after you see the lightning.

13. The B737-400 aircraft costs $2948 dollars per hour to operate. The algebraic expression 2948*t* gives the total cost to operate the aircraft for *t* hours. Find the total cost to operate the B737-400 for 3.6 hours.

14. Flying the SR-71A jet, Capt. Elden W. Joersz, USAF, set a record speed of 2193.16 miles per hour. At this speed, the algebraic expression 2193.16*t* gives the total distance flown in *t* hours. Find the distance flown by the SR-71A in 1.7 hours.

List the elements in each set. See Example 3.

15. $\{x \mid x \text{ is a natural number less than } 6\}$

16. $\{x \mid x \text{ is a natural number greater than } 6\}$

17. $\{x \mid x \text{ is a natural number between } 10 \text{ and } 17\}$

18. $\{x \mid x \text{ is an odd natural number}\}$

19. $\{x \mid x \text{ is a whole number that is not a natural number}\}$

20. $\{x \mid x \text{ is a natural number less than } 1\}$

21. $\{x \mid x \text{ is an even whole number less than } 9\}$

22. $\{x \mid x \text{ is an odd whole number less than } 9\}$

Graph each set on a number line.

23. $\{0, 2, 4, 6\}$

24. $\{-1, -2, -3\}$

25. $\left\{\frac{1}{2}, \frac{2}{3}\right\}$

26. $\{1, 3, 5, 7\}$

27. $\{-2, -6, -10\}$

28. $\left\{\frac{1}{4}, \frac{1}{3}\right\}$

29. In your own words, explain why the empty set is a subset of every set.

30. In your own words, explain why every set is a subset of itself.

List the elements of the set $\left\{3, 0, \sqrt{7}, \sqrt{36}, \frac{2}{5}, -134\right\}$ *that are also elements of the given set. See Example 4.*

31. Whole numbers

32. Integers

33. Natural numbers

34. Rational numbers

35. Irrational numbers

36. Real numbers

Place ∈ *or* ∉ *in the space provided to make each statement true. See Example 4.*

37. -11 $\{x \mid x \text{ is an integer}\}$

38. 0 $\{x \mid x \text{ is a positive integer}\}$

39. -6 $\{2, 4, 6, \dots\}$

40. 12 $\{1, 2, 3, \dots\}$

41. 12 $\{1, 3, 5, \dots\}$

42. 0 $\{1, 2, 3, \dots\}$

43. $\frac{1}{2}$ $\{x \mid x \text{ is an irrational number}\}$

44. 0 $\{x \mid x \text{ is a natural number}\}$

Determine whether each statement is true or false. See Examples 4 and 5. Use the following sets of numbers.

$$N = \text{set of natural numbers}$$
$$Z = \text{set of integers}$$
$$I = \text{set of irrational numbers}$$
$$Q = \text{set of rational numbers}$$
$$\mathbb{R} = \text{set of real numbers}$$

45. $Z \subseteq \mathbb{R}$

46. $\mathbb{R} \subseteq N$

47. $-1 \in Z$

48. $\frac{1}{2} \in Q$

49. $0 \in N$

50. $Z \subseteq Q$

51. $\sqrt{5} \notin I$

52. $\pi \notin \mathbb{R}$

53. $N \subseteq Z$

54. $I \subseteq N$

55. $\mathbb{R} \subseteq Q$

56. $N \subseteq Q$

57. In your own words, explain why every natural number is also a rational number but not every rational number is a natural number.

58. In your own words, explain why every irrational number is a real number but not every real number is an irrational number.

Find each absolute value. See Example 6.

59. $-|2|$

60. $|8|$

61. $|-4|$

62. $|-6|$

63. $|0|$

64. $|-1|$

65. $-|-3|$

66. $-|-11|$

67. Explain why $-(-2)$ and $-|-2|$ simplify to different numbers.

68. The boxed definition of absolute value states that $|a| = -a$ if a is a negative number. Explain why $|a|$ is always nonnegative, even though $|a| = -a$ for negative values of a.

Write the opposite of each number. See Example 7.

69. -6.2

70. -7.8

71. $\dfrac{4}{7}$

72. $\dfrac{9}{5}$

73. $-\dfrac{2}{3}$

74. $-\dfrac{14}{3}$

75. 0

76. 10.3

Write each phrase as an algebraic expression. Use the variable x to represent each unknown number. See Example 8.

77. Twice a number.

78. Six times a number.

79. Five more than twice a number.

80. One more than six times a number.

81. Ten less than a number.

82. A number minus seven.

83. The sum of a number and two.

84. The difference of twenty-five and a number.

85. A number divided by eleven.

86. The quotient of a number and thirteen.

87. Twelve, minus three times a number.

88. Four, subtracted from three times a number.

89. A number plus two and three-tenths.

90. Fifteen and seven-tenths plus a number.

91. A number less than one and one-third.

92. Two and three-fourths less than a number.

93. The quotient of five and the difference of four and a number.

94. The quotient of four and the sum of a number and one.

95. Twice the sum of a number and three.

96. Eight times the difference of a number and nine.

CONCEPT EXTENSIONS

Use the bar graph below to complete the given table by estimating the millions of tourists predicted for each country. (Use whole numbers.)

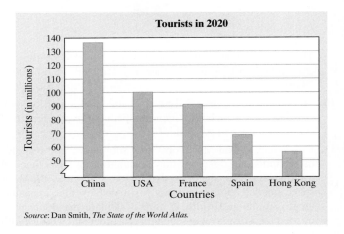

Source: Dan Smith, *The State of the World Atlas.*

97. China	
98. France	
99. Spain	
100. Hong Kong	

101. In your own words, explain why every natural number is also a rational number but not every rational number is a natural number.

102. In your own words, explain why every irrational number is a real number but not every real number is an irrational number.

📖 **STUDY SKILLS BUILDER**

Learning New Terms

Many of the terms used in this text may be new to you. It will be helpful to make a list of new mathematical terms and symbols as you encounter them and to review them frequently. Placing these new terms (including page references) on 3 × 5 index cards might help you later when you're preparing for a quiz.

Answer the following.

1. Name one way you might place a word and its definition on a 3 × 5 card.

2. How do new terms stand out in this text so that they can be found?

1.3 OPERATIONS ON REAL NUMBERS

OBJECTIVE 1 ▶ Adding and subtracting real numbers. When solving problems, we often have to add real numbers. For example, if the New Orleans Saints lose 5 yards in one play, then lose another 7 yards in the next play, their total loss may be described by $-5 + (-7)$.

The addition of two real numbers may be summarized by the following.

> **Adding Real Numbers**
>
> **1.** To add two numbers with the *same sign*, add their absolute values and attach their common sign.
>
> **2.** To add two numbers with *different signs*, subtract the smaller absolute value from the larger absolute value and attach the sign of the number with the larger absolute value.

For example, to add $-5 + (-7)$, first add their absolute values.

$$|-5| = 5, |-7| = 7, \quad \text{and} \quad 5 + 7 = 12$$

Next, attach their common negative sign.

$$-5 + (-7) = -12$$

(This represents a total loss of 12 yards for the New Orleans Saints in the example above.)
To find $(-4) + 3$, first subtract their absolute values.

$$|-4| = 4, |3| = 3, \quad \text{and} \quad 4 - 3 = 1$$

Next, attach the sign of the number with the larger absolute value.

$$(-4) + 3 = -1$$

EXAMPLE 1   Add.

a. $-3 + (-11)$ **b.** $3 + (-7)$ **c.** $-10 + 15$

d. $-8.3 + (-1.9)$ **e.** $-\dfrac{2}{3} + \dfrac{3}{7}$

Solution

a. $-3 + (-11) = -(3 + 11) = -14$ **b.** $3 + (-7) = -4$

c. $-10 + 15 = 5$ **d.** $-8.3 + (-1.9) = -10.2$

e. $-\dfrac{2}{3} + \dfrac{3}{7} = -\dfrac{14}{21} + \dfrac{9}{21} = -\dfrac{5}{21}$

PRACTICE

1   Add.

a. $-6 + (-2)$ **b.** $5 + (-8)$ **c.** $-4 + 9$

d. $(-3.2) + (-4.9)$ **e.** $-\dfrac{3}{5} + \dfrac{2}{3}$

Subtraction of two real numbers may be defined in terms of addition.

Subtracting Real Numbers

If a and b are real numbers,
$$a - b = a + (-b)$$

In other words, to subtract a real number, we add its opposite.

EXAMPLE 2 Subtract.

a. $2 - 8$ **b.** $-8 - (-1)$ **c.** $-11 - 5$ **d.** $10.7 - (-9.8)$

e. $\dfrac{2}{3} - \dfrac{1}{2}$ **f.** $1 - 0.06$ **g.** Subtract 7 from 4.

Solution   Add the opposite   Add the opposite

a. $2 - 8 = 2 + (-8) = -6$ **b.** $-8 - (-1) = -8 + (1) = -7$

c. $-11 - 5 = -11 + (-5) = -16$ **d.** $10.7 - (-9.8) = 10.7 + 9.8 = 20.5$

e. $\dfrac{2}{3} - \dfrac{1}{2} = \dfrac{2 \cdot 2}{3 \cdot 2} - \dfrac{1 \cdot 3}{2 \cdot 3} = \dfrac{4}{6} + \left(-\dfrac{3}{6}\right) = \dfrac{1}{6}$

f. $1 - 0.06 = 1 + (-0.06) = 0.94$ **g.** $4 - 7 = 4 + (-7) = -3$ ☐

PRACTICE
2 Subtract.

a. $3 - 11$ **b.** $-6 - (-3)$ **c.** $-7 - 5$ **d.** $4.2 - (-3.5)$

e. $\dfrac{5}{7} - \dfrac{1}{3}$ **f.** $3 - 1.2$ **g.** Subtract 9 from 2.

To add or subtract three or more real numbers, add or subtract from left to right.

EXAMPLE 3 Simplify the following expressions.

a. $11 + 2 - 7$ **b.** $-5 - 4 + 2$

Solution

a. $11 + 2 - 7 = 13 - 7 = 6$ **b.** $-5 - 4 + 2 = -9 + 2 = -7$ ☐

PRACTICE
3 Simplify the following expressions.

a. $13 + 5 - 6$ **b.** $-6 - 2 + 4$

OBJECTIVE 2 ▶ Multiplying and dividing real numbers. In order to discover sign patterns when you multiply real numbers, recall that multiplication by a positive integer is the same as repeated addition. For example,

$$3(2) = 2 + 2 + 2 = 6$$
$$3(-2) = (-2) + (-2) + (-2) = -6$$

Notice here that $3(-2) = -6$. This illustrates that the product of two numbers with different signs is negative. We summarize sign patterns for multiplying any two real numbers as follows.

> **Multiplying Two Real Numbers**
> The product of two numbers with the *same* sign is positive.
> The product of two numbers with *different* signs is negative.

Also recall that the product of zero and any real number is zero.

$$0 \cdot a = 0$$

> **Product Property of 0**
> $0 \cdot a = 0$ Also $a \cdot 0 = 0$

EXAMPLE 4   Multiply.

a. $(-8)(-1)$ **b.** $-2\left(\dfrac{1}{6}\right)$ **c.** $-1.2(0.3)$ **d.** $0(-11)$

e. $\dfrac{1}{5}\left(-\dfrac{10}{11}\right)$ **f.** $(7)(1)(-2)(-3)$ **g.** $8(-2)(0)$

Solution

a. Since the signs of the two numbers are the same, the product is positive. Thus $(-8)(-1) = +8$, or 8.

b. Since the signs of the two numbers are different or unlike, the product is negative. Thus $-2\left(\dfrac{1}{6}\right) = -\dfrac{2}{6} = -\dfrac{1}{3}$.

c. $-1.2(0.3) = -0.36$

d. $0(-11) = 0$

e. $\dfrac{1}{5}\left(-\dfrac{10}{11}\right) = -\dfrac{10}{55} = -\dfrac{2}{11}$

f. To multiply three or more real numbers, you may multiply from left to right.
$$
\begin{aligned}
(7)(1)(-2)(-3) &= 7(-2)(-3) \\
&= -14(-3) \\
&= 42
\end{aligned}
$$

g. Since zero is a factor, the product is zero.
$$(8)(-2)(0) = 0$$

PRACTICE
4   Multiply.

a. $(-5)(3)$ **b.** $(-7)\left(-\dfrac{1}{14}\right)$ **c.** $5.1(-2)$ **d.** $14(0)$

e. $\left(-\dfrac{1}{4}\right)\left(\dfrac{8}{13}\right)$ **f.** $6(-1)(-2)(3)$ **g.** $5(-2.3)$

> ▶ **Helpful Hint**
> The following sign patterns may be helpful when we are multiplying.
>
> **1.** An odd number of negative factors gives a negative product.
> **2.** An even number of negative factors gives a positive product.

Recall that $\dfrac{8}{4} = 2$ because $2 \cdot 4 = 8$. Likewise, $\dfrac{8}{-4} = -2$ because $(-2)(-4) = 8$. Also, $\dfrac{-8}{4} = -2$ because $(-2)4 = -8$, and $\dfrac{-8}{-4} = 2$ because $2(-4) = -8$. From these examples, we can see that the sign patterns for division are the same as for multiplication.

> **Dividing Two Real Numbers**
> The quotient of two numbers with the *same* sign is positive.
> The quotient of two numbers with *different* signs is negative.

Also recall that division by a nonzero real number b is the same as multiplication by $\frac{1}{b}$. In other words,

$$\frac{a}{b} = a \cdot \frac{1}{b}$$

This means that to simplify $\frac{a}{b}$, we can divide by b or multiply by $\frac{1}{b}$. The nonzero numbers b and $\frac{1}{b}$ are called **reciprocals.** Notice that b *must* be a nonzero number. We do not define division by 0. For example, $5 \div 0$, or $\frac{5}{0}$, is undefined. To see why, recall that if $5 \div 0 = n$, a number, then $n \cdot 0 = 5$. This is not possible since $n \cdot 0 = 0$ for any number n, and never 5. Thus far we have learned that we cannot divide 5 or any other nonzero number by 0.

Can we divide 0 by 0? By the same reasoning, if $0 \div 0 = n$, a number, then $n \cdot 0 = 0$. This is true for any number n so that the quotient $0 \div 0$ would not be a single number. To avoid this, we say that

> Division by 0 is undefined.

EXAMPLE 5   Divide.

a. $\dfrac{20}{-4}$ **b.** $\dfrac{-9}{-3}$ **c.** $-\dfrac{3}{8} \div 3$ **d.** $\dfrac{-40}{10}$ **e.** $\dfrac{-1}{10} \div \dfrac{-2}{5}$ **f.** $\dfrac{8}{0}$

Solution

a. Since the signs are different or unlike, the quotient is negative and $\dfrac{20}{-4} = -5$.

b. Since the signs are the same, the quotient is positive and $\dfrac{-9}{-3} = 3$.

c. $-\dfrac{3}{8} \div 3 = -\dfrac{3}{8} \cdot \dfrac{1}{3} = -\dfrac{1}{8}$ **d.** $\dfrac{-40}{10} = -4$

e. $\dfrac{-1}{10} \div \dfrac{-2}{5} = -\dfrac{1}{10} \cdot -\dfrac{5}{2} = \dfrac{1}{4}$ **f.** $\dfrac{8}{0}$ is undefined.   □

PRACTICE
5   Divide.

a. $\dfrac{-16}{8}$ **b.** $\dfrac{-15}{-3}$ **c.** $-\dfrac{2}{3} \div 4$

d. $\dfrac{54}{-9}$ **e.** $-\dfrac{1}{12} \div \left(-\dfrac{3}{4}\right)$ **f.** $\dfrac{0}{-7}$

With sign rules for division, we can understand why the positioning of the negative sign in a fraction does not change the value of the fraction. For example,

$$\frac{-12}{3} = -4, \quad \frac{12}{-3} = -4, \quad \text{and} \quad -\frac{12}{3} = -4$$

Since all the fractions equal -4, we can say that

$$\frac{-12}{3} = \frac{12}{-3} = -\frac{12}{3}$$

In general, the following holds true.

If a and b are real numbers and $b \neq 0$, then $\dfrac{a}{-b} = \dfrac{-a}{b} = -\dfrac{a}{b}$.

OBJECTIVE 3 ▶ Evaluating expressions containing exponents. Recall that when two numbers are multiplied, they are called **factors.** For example, in $3 \cdot 5 = 15$, the 3 and 5 are called factors.

A natural number *exponent* is a shorthand notation for repeated multiplication of the same factor. This repeated factor is called the **base,** and the number of times it is used as a factor is indicated by the **exponent.** For example,

$$4^3 = 4 \cdot 4 \cdot 4 = 64$$

4 is a factor 3 times.

Exponents

If a is a real number and n is a natural number, then the **nth power of a,** or **a raised to the nth power,** written as a^n, is the product of n factors, each of which is a.

$$a^n = \underbrace{a \cdot a \cdot a \cdot a \cdot \cdots \cdot a}_{a \text{ is a factor } n \text{ times.}}$$

It is not necessary to write an exponent of 1. For example, 3 is assumed to be 3^1.

EXAMPLE 6   Evaluate each expression.

a. 3^2 **b.** $\left(\dfrac{1}{2}\right)^4$ **c.** -5^2

d. $(-5)^2$ **e.** -5^3 **f.** $(-5)^3$

Solution

a. $3^2 = 3 \cdot 3 = 9$ **b.** $\left(\dfrac{1}{2}\right)^4 = \left(\dfrac{1}{2}\right)\left(\dfrac{1}{2}\right)\left(\dfrac{1}{2}\right)\left(\dfrac{1}{2}\right) = \dfrac{1}{16}$

c. $-5^2 = -(5 \cdot 5) = -25$ **d.** $(-5)^2 = (-5)(-5) = 25$

e. $-5^3 = -(5 \cdot 5 \cdot 5) = -125$ **f.** $(-5)^3 = (-5)(-5)(-5) = -125$

PRACTICE
6   Evaluate each expression.

a. 2^3 **b.** $\left(\dfrac{1}{3}\right)^2$ **c.** -6^2

d. $(-6)^2$ **e.** -4^3 **f.** $(-4)^3$

▶ **Helpful Hint**

Be very careful when simplifying expressions such as -5^2 and $(-5)^2$.

$$-5^2 = -(5 \cdot 5) = -25 \quad \text{and} \quad (-5)^2 = (-5)(-5) = 25$$

Without parentheses, the base to square is 5, not -5.

OBJECTIVE 4 ▶ Finding roots of numbers. The opposite of squaring a number is taking the **square root** of a number. For example, since the square of 4, or 4^2, is 16, we say that a square root of 16 is 4. The notation $\sqrt{a}$ is used to denote the **positive, or principal, square root** of a nonnegative number a. We then have in symbols that $\sqrt{16} = 4$. The negative square root of 16 is written $-\sqrt{16} = -4$. The square root of a negative number, such as $\sqrt{-16}$ is not a real number. Why? There is no real number, that when squared gives a negative number.

EXAMPLE 7   Find the square roots.

a. $\sqrt{9}$ **b.** $\sqrt{25}$ **c.** $\sqrt{\dfrac{1}{4}}$ **d.** $-\sqrt{36}$ **e.** $\sqrt{-36}$

Solution

a. $\sqrt{9} = 3$ since 3 is positive and $3^2 = 9$.   **b.** $\sqrt{25} = 5$ since $5^2 = 25$.

c. $\sqrt{\dfrac{1}{4}} = \dfrac{1}{2}$ since $\left(\dfrac{1}{2}\right)^2 = \dfrac{1}{4}$.   **d.** $-\sqrt{36} = -6$

e. $\sqrt{-36}$ is not a real number.

PRACTICE
7   Find the square roots.

a. $\sqrt{49}$ **b.** $\sqrt{\dfrac{1}{16}}$ **c.** $-\sqrt{64}$ **d.** $\sqrt{-64}$ **e.** $\sqrt{100}$

We can find roots other than square roots. Since 2 cubed, written as 2^3, is 8, we say that the **cube root** of 8 is 2. This is written as

$$\sqrt[3]{8} = 2.$$

Also, since $3^4 = 81$ and 3 is positive,

$$\sqrt[4]{81} = 3.$$

EXAMPLE 8   Find the roots.

a. $\sqrt[3]{27}$ **b.** $\sqrt[5]{1}$ **c.** $\sqrt[4]{16}$

Solution

a. $\sqrt[3]{27} = 3$ since $3^3 = 27$.
b. $\sqrt[5]{1} = 1$ since $1^5 = 1$.
c. $\sqrt[4]{16} = 2$ since 2 is positive and $2^4 = 16$.

PRACTICE
8   Find the roots.

a. $\sqrt[3]{64}$ **b.** $\sqrt[5]{-1}$ **c.** $\sqrt[4]{10,000}$

Of course, as mentioned in Section 1.2, not all roots simplify to rational numbers. We study radicals further in Chapter 7.

OBJECTIVE 5 ▶ Using the order of operations. Expressions containing more than one operation are written to follow a particular agreed-upon **order of operations.** For example, when we write $3 + 2 \cdot 10$, we mean to multiply first, and then add.

> **Order of Operations**
>
> Simplify expressions using the order that follows. If grouping symbols such as parentheses are present, simplify expressions within those first, starting with the innermost set. If fraction bars are present, simplify the numerator and denominator separately.
>
> 1. Evaluate exponential expressions, roots, or absolute values in order from left to right.
> 2. Multiply or divide in order from left to right.
> 3. Add or subtract in order from left to right.

EXAMPLE 9   Simplify.

a. $20 \div 2 \cdot 10$

b. $1 + 2(1 - 4)^2$

c. $\dfrac{|-2|^3 + 1}{-7 - \sqrt{4}}$

Solution

a. Be careful! Here, we multiply or divide in order from left to right. Thus, divide, then multiply.

$$20 \div 2 \cdot 10 = 10 \cdot 10 = 100$$

b. Remember order of operations so that you are *not* tempted to add 1 and 2 first.

$$
\begin{aligned}
1 + 2(1 - 4)^2 &= 1 + 2(-3)^2 &&\text{Simplify inside grouping symbols first.} \\
&= 1 + 2(9) &&\text{Write } (-3)^2 \text{ as 9.} \\
&= 1 + 18 &&\text{Multiply.} \\
&= 19 &&\text{Add.}
\end{aligned}
$$

c. Simplify the numerator and the denominator separately; then divide.

$$
\begin{aligned}
\frac{|-2|^3 + 1}{-7 - \sqrt{4}} &= \frac{2^3 + 1}{-7 - 2} &&\text{Write } |-2| \text{ as 2 and } \sqrt{4} \text{ as 2.} \\
&= \frac{8 + 1}{-9} &&\text{Write } 2^3 \text{ as 8.} \\
&= \frac{9}{-9} = -1 &&\text{Simplify the numerator, then divide.} \quad \square
\end{aligned}
$$

PRACTICE
9   Simplify.

a. $14 - 3 \cdot 4$

b. $3(5 - 8)^2$

c. $\dfrac{|-5|^2 + 4}{\sqrt{4} - 3}$

Besides parentheses, other symbols used for grouping expressions are brackets [ ] and braces { }. These other grouping symbols are commonly used when we group expressions that already contain parentheses.

EXAMPLE 10   Simplify: $3 - [(4 - 6) + 2(5 - 9)]$

Solution
$$
\begin{aligned}
3 - [(4 - 6) + 2(5 - 9)] &= 3 - [-2 + 2(-4)] &&\text{Simplify within the innermost sets of parentheses.} \\
&= 3 - [-2 + (-8)] \\
&= 3 - [-10] \\
&= 13 \quad \square
\end{aligned}
$$

> ▶ **Helpful Hint**
> When grouping symbols occur within grouping symbols, remember to perform operations on the innermost set first.

PRACTICE
10   Simplify: $5 - [(3 - 5) + 6(2 - 4)]$.

EXAMPLE 11   Simplify: $\dfrac{-5\sqrt{30-5}+(-2)^2}{4^2+|7-10|}$

Solution   Here, the fraction bar, radical sign, and absolute value bars serve as grouping symbols. Thus, we simplify within the radical sign and absolute value bars first, remembering to calculate above and below the fraction bar separately.

$$\frac{-5\sqrt{30-5}+(-2)^2}{4^2+|7-10|} = \frac{-5\sqrt{25}+(-2)^2}{4^2+|-3|} = \frac{-5\cdot 5+4}{16+3} = \frac{-25+4}{16+3}$$

$$= \frac{-21}{19} \text{ or } -\frac{21}{19}$$ □

PRACTICE
11   Simplify: $\dfrac{-2\sqrt{12+4}-(-3)^2}{6^2+|1-9|}$

Concept Check ☑

True or false? If two different people use the order of operations to simplify a numerical expression and neither makes a calculation error, it is not possible that they each obtain a different result. Explain.

OBJECTIVE 6 ▶ Evaluating algebraic expressions. Recall from Section 1.2 that an algebraic expression is formed by numbers and variables connected by the operations of addition, subtraction, multiplication, division, raising to powers, and/or taking roots. Also, if numbers are substituted for the variables in an algebraic expression and the operations performed, the result is called **the value of the expression** for the given replacement values. This entire process is called **evaluating an expression.**

EXAMPLE 12   Evaluate each expression when $x = 4$ and $y = -3$.

a. $3x - 7y$ **b.** $-2y^2$ **c.** $\dfrac{\sqrt{x}}{y} - \dfrac{y}{x}$

Solution   For each expression, replace x with 4 and y with -3.

a. $3x - 7y = 3\cdot 4 - 7(-3)$ Let $x = 4$ and $y = -3$.
$\qquad\qquad = 12 - (-21)$ Multiply.
$\qquad\qquad = 12 + 21$ Write as an addition.
$\qquad\qquad = 33$ Add.

b. $-2y^2 = \underbrace{-2(-3)^2}$ Let $y = -3$.

$\qquad = -2(9)$ Write $(-3)^2$ as 9.

$\qquad = -18$ Multiply.

> ▶ **Helpful Hint**
> In $-2(-3)^2$, the exponent 2 goes with the base of -3 only.

c. $\dfrac{\sqrt{x}}{y} - \dfrac{y}{x} = \dfrac{\sqrt{4}}{-3} - \dfrac{-3}{4}$

$\qquad = -\dfrac{2}{3} + \dfrac{3}{4}$ Write $\sqrt{4}$ as 2.

$\qquad = -\dfrac{2}{3}\cdot\dfrac{4}{4} + \dfrac{3}{4}\cdot\dfrac{3}{3}$ The LCD is 12.

$\qquad = -\dfrac{8}{12} + \dfrac{9}{12}$ Write each fraction with a denominator of 12.

$\qquad = \dfrac{1}{12}$ Add.   □

Answer to Concept Check:
true; answers may vary

PRACTICE
12   Evaluate each expression when $x = 16$ and $y = -5$

a. $2x - 7y$ **b.** $-4y^2$ **c.** $\dfrac{\sqrt{x}}{y} - \dfrac{y}{x}$

Sometimes variables such as x_1 and x_2 will be used in this book. The small 1 and 2 are called **subscripts.** The variable x_1 can be read as "x sub 1," and the variable x_2 can be read as "x sub 2." The important thing to remember is that they are two different variables. For example, if $x_1 = -5$ and $x_2 = 7$, then

$$x_1 - x_2 = -5 - 7 = -12.$$

EXAMPLE 13   The algebraic expression $\dfrac{5(x - 32)}{9}$ represents the equivalent temperature in degrees Celsius when x is the temperature in degrees Fahrenheit. Complete the following table by evaluating this expression at the given values of x.

Degrees Fahrenheit	x	-4	10	32
Degrees Celsius	$\dfrac{5(x - 32)}{9}$			

Solution   To complete the table, evaluate $\dfrac{5(x - 32)}{9}$ at each given replacement value.
When $x = -4$,

$$\frac{5(x - 32)}{9} = \frac{5(-4 - 32)}{9} = \frac{5(-36)}{9} = -20$$

When $x = 10$,

$$\frac{5(x - 32)}{9} = \frac{5(10 - 32)}{9} = \frac{5(-22)}{9} = -\frac{110}{9}$$

When $x = 32$,

$$\frac{5(x - 32)}{9} = \frac{5(32 - 32)}{9} = \frac{5 \cdot 0}{9} = 0$$

The completed table is

Degrees Fahrenheit	x	-4	10	32
Degrees Celsius	$\dfrac{5(x - 32)}{9}$	-20	$-\dfrac{110}{9}$	0

Thus, $-4°F$ is equivalent to $-20°C$, $10°F$ is equivalent to $-\dfrac{110°}{9}$ C, and $32°F$ is equivalent to $0°C$.

PRACTICE
13   The algebraic expression $\dfrac{9}{5}x + 32$ represents the equivalent temperature in degrees Fahrenheit when x is the temperature in degrees Celsius. Complete the following table by evaluating this expression at the given values of x.

Degrees Celsius	x	-5	10	25
Degrees Fahrenheit	$\dfrac{9}{5}x + 32$			

VOCABULARY & READINESS CHECK

Choose the fraction(s) equivalent to the given fraction. (There may sometimes be more than one correct choice.)

1. $-\dfrac{1}{7}$ a. $\dfrac{-1}{-7}$ b. $\dfrac{-1}{7}$ c. $\dfrac{1}{-7}$ d. $\dfrac{1}{7}$

2. $\dfrac{-x}{y}$ a. $\dfrac{x}{-y}$ b. $-\dfrac{x}{y}$ c. $\dfrac{x}{y}$ d. $\dfrac{-x}{-y}$

3. $\dfrac{5}{-(x+y)}$ a. $\dfrac{5}{(x+y)}$ b. $\dfrac{-5}{(x+y)}$ c. $\dfrac{-5}{-(x+y)}$ d. $-\dfrac{5}{(x+y)}$

4. $-\dfrac{(y+z)}{3y}$ a. $\dfrac{-(y+z)}{3y}$ b. $\dfrac{-(y+z)}{-3y}$ c. $\dfrac{(y+z)}{3y}$ d. $\dfrac{(y+z)}{-3y}$

5. $\dfrac{-9x}{-2y}$ a. $\dfrac{-9x}{2y}$ b. $\dfrac{9x}{2y}$ c. $\dfrac{9x}{-2y}$ d. $-\dfrac{9x}{2y}$

6. $\dfrac{-a}{-b}$ a. $\dfrac{a}{b}$ b. $\dfrac{a}{-b}$ c. $\dfrac{-a}{b}$ d. $-\dfrac{a}{b}$

Use the choices below to fill in each blank. Some choices may be used more than once and some used not at all.

exponent	undefined	base	1	$\dfrac{-a}{-b}$	$\dfrac{a}{b}$
square root	reciprocal	0	9	$\dfrac{-a}{b}$	$\dfrac{a}{-b}$

7. $0 \cdot a = $ _____ .

8. $\dfrac{0}{4}$ simplifies to _____ while $\dfrac{4}{0}$ is _____ .

9. The _____ of the nonzero number b is $\dfrac{1}{b}$.

10. The fraction $-\dfrac{a}{b} = $ _____ $= $ _____ .

11. A(n) _____ is a shorthand notation for repeated multiplication of the same number.

12. In $(-5)^2$, the 2 is the _____ and the -5 is the _____ .

13. The opposite of squaring a number is taking the _____ of a number.

14. Using order of operations, $9 \div 3 \cdot 3 = $ _____ .

1.3 EXERCISE SET

MyMathLab   *Powered by CourseCompass™ and MathXL®*   Math XL   PRACTICE   WATCH   DOWNLOAD   READ   REVIEW

Add or subtract as indicated. See Examples 1 through 3

1. $-3 + 8$

 3. $-14 + (-10)$

5. $-4.3 - 6.7$

 7. $13 - 17$

9. $\dfrac{11}{15} - \left(-\dfrac{3}{5}\right)$

11. $19 - 10 - 11$

13. $-\dfrac{4}{5} - \left(-\dfrac{3}{10}\right)$

15. Subtract 14 from 8.

2. $12 + (-7)$

4. $-5 + (-9)$

6. $-8.2 - (-6.6)$

8. $15 - (-1)$

10. $\dfrac{7}{10} - \dfrac{4}{5}$

12. $-13 - 4 + 9$

14. $-\dfrac{5}{2} - \left(-\dfrac{2}{3}\right)$

16. Subtract 9 from -3.

Multiply or divide as indicated. See Examples 4 and 5.

 17. $-5 \cdot 12$

19. $-17 \cdot 0$

18. $-3 \cdot 8$

20. $-5 \cdot 0$

 21. $\dfrac{0}{-2}$

23. $\dfrac{-9}{3}$

 25. $\dfrac{-12}{-4}$

27. $3\left(-\dfrac{1}{18}\right)$

29. $(-0.7)(-0.8)$

31. $9.1 \div (-1.3)$

33. $-4(-2)(-1)$

 22. $\dfrac{-2}{0}$

24. $\dfrac{-20}{5}$

26. $\dfrac{-36}{-6}$

28. $5\left(-\dfrac{1}{50}\right)$

30. $(-0.9)(-0.5)$

32. $22.5 \div (-2.5)$

34. $-5(-3)(-2)$

Evaluate each expression. See Example 6.

 35. -7^2

37. $(-6)^2$

39. $(-2)^3$

 36. $(-7)^2$

38. -6^2

40. -2^3

41. $\left(-\dfrac{1}{3}\right)^3$

42. $\left(-\dfrac{1}{2}\right)^4$

Find the following roots. See Examples 7 and 8.

43. $\sqrt{49}$

44. $\sqrt{81}$

45. $-\sqrt{\dfrac{4}{9}}$

46. $-\sqrt{\dfrac{4}{25}}$

47. $\sqrt[3]{64}$

48. $\sqrt[5]{32}$

49. $\sqrt[4]{81}$

50. $\sqrt[3]{1}$

51. $\sqrt{-100}$

52. $\sqrt{-25}$

MIXED PRACTICE

Simplify each expression. See Examples 1 through 11.

53. $3(5-7)^4$

54. $7(3-8)^2$

55. -3^2+2^3

56. -5^2-2^4

57. $\dfrac{3.1-(-1.4)}{-0.5}$

58. $\dfrac{4.2-(-8.2)}{-0.4}$

59. $(-3)^2+2^3$

60. $(-15)^2-2^4$

61. $-8\div4\cdot2$

62. $-20\div5\cdot4$

63. $-8\left(-\dfrac{3}{4}\right)-8$

64. $-10\left(-\dfrac{2}{5}\right)-10$

65. $2-[(7-6)+(9-19)]$

66. $8-[(4-7)+(8-1)]$

67. $\dfrac{(-9+6)(-1^2)}{-2-2}$

68. $\dfrac{(-1-2)(-3^2)}{-6-3}$

69. $(\sqrt[3]{8})(-4)-(\sqrt{9})(-5)$

70. $(\sqrt[3]{27})(-5)-(\sqrt{25})(-3)$

71. $25-[(3-5)+(14-18)]^2$

72. $10-[(4-5)^2+(12-14)]^4$

73. $\dfrac{(3-\sqrt{9})-(-5-1.3)}{-3}$

74. $\dfrac{-\sqrt{16}-(6-2.4)}{-2}$

75. $\dfrac{|3-9|-|-5|}{-3}$

76. $\dfrac{|-14|-|2-7|}{-15}$

77. $\dfrac{3(-2+1)}{5}-\dfrac{-7(2-4)}{1-(-2)}$

78. $\dfrac{-1-2}{2(-3)+10}-\dfrac{2(-5)}{-1(8)+1}$

79. $\dfrac{\frac{1}{3}\cdot9-7}{3+\frac{1}{2}\cdot4}$

80. $\dfrac{\frac{1}{5}\cdot20-6}{10+\frac{1}{4}\cdot12}$

81. $3\{-2+5[1-2(-2+5)]\}$

82. $2\{-1+3[7-4(-10+12)]\}$

83. $\dfrac{-4\sqrt{80+1}+(-4)^2}{3^3+|-2(3)|}$

84. $\dfrac{(-2)^4+3\sqrt{120-20}}{4^3+|5(-1)|}$

Evaluate each expression when $x=9$ and $y=-2$. See Example 12.

85. $9x-6y$

86. $4x-10y$

87. $-3y^2$

88. $-7y^2$

89. $\dfrac{\sqrt{x}}{y}-\dfrac{y}{x}$

90. $\dfrac{y}{2x}-\dfrac{\sqrt{x}}{3y}$

91. $\dfrac{3+2|x-y|}{x+2y}$

92. $\dfrac{5+2|y-x|}{x+6y}$

93. $\dfrac{y^3+\sqrt{x-5}}{|4x-y|}$

94. $\dfrac{y^2+\sqrt{x+7}}{|3x-y|}$

See Example 13.

95. The algebraic expression $8+2y$ represents the perimeter of a rectangle with width 4 and length y.

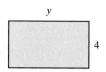

a. Complete the table that follows by evaluating this expression at the given values of y.

Length	y	5	7	10	100
Perimeter	$8+2y$				

b. Use the results of the table in part **a** to answer the following question. As the width of a rectangle remains the same and the length increases, does the perimeter increase or decrease? Explain how you arrived at your answer.

96. The algebraic expression πr^2 represents the area of a circle with radius r.

a. Complete the table below by evaluating this expression at given values of r. (Use 3.14 for π.)

Radius	r	2	3	7	10
Area	πr^2				

b. As the radius of a circle increases, (see the table) does its area increase or decrease? Explain your answer.

97. The algebraic expression $\dfrac{100x+5000}{x}$ represents the cost per bookshelf (in dollars) of producing x bookshelves.

a. Complete the table below.

Number of Bookshelves	x	10	100	1000
Cost per Bookshelf	$\dfrac{100x+5000}{x}$			

b. As the number of bookshelves manufactured increases, (see the table) does the cost per bookshelf increase or decrease? Why do you think that this is so?

98. If c is degrees Celsius, the algebraic expression $1.8c+32$ represents the equivalent temperature in degrees Fahrenheit.

a. Complete the table below.

Degrees Celsius	c	-10	0	50
Degrees Fahrenheit	$1.8c+32$			

b. As degrees Celsius increase (see the table), do degrees Fahrenheit increase or decrease?

CONCEPT EXTENSIONS

Find the value of the expression when $x_1 = 2$, $x_2 = 4$, $y_1 = -3$, $y_2 = 2$.

99. $\dfrac{y_2 - y_1}{x_2 - x_1}$

100. $\sqrt{(x_2 - x_1)^2 + (y_2 - y_1)^2}$

Each circle below represents a whole, or 1. Determine the unknown fractional part of each circle.

101.

$\frac{1}{5}$

$\frac{3}{7}$

102.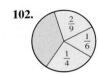

$\frac{2}{9}$

$\frac{1}{6}$

$\frac{1}{4}$

103. Most of Mauna Kea, a volcano on Hawaii, lies below sea level. If this volcano begins at 5998 meters below sea level and then rises 10,203 meters, find the height of the volcano above sea level.

Sea level

?

10,203 m

5998 m

Mauna Kea

104. The highest point on land on Earth is the top of Mt. Everest in the Himalayas, at an elevation of 29,028 feet above sea level. The lowest point on land is the Dead Sea, between Israel and Jordan, at 1319 feet below sea level. Find the difference in elevations.

Insert parentheses so that each expression simplifies to the given number.

105. $2 + 7 \cdot 1 + 3$; 36

106. $6 - 5 \cdot 2 + 2$; -6

107. Explain why -3^2 and $(-3)^2$ simplify to different numbers.

108. Explain why -3^3 and $(-3)^3$ simplify to the same number.

Use a calculator to approximate each square root. For Exercises 113 and 114, simplify the expression. Round answers to four decimal places.

109. $\sqrt{10}$

110. $\sqrt{273}$

111. $\sqrt{7.9}$

112. $\sqrt{19.6}$

113. $\dfrac{-1.682 - 17.895}{(-7.102)(-4.691)}$

114. $\dfrac{(-5.161)(3.222)}{7.955 - 19.676}$

Investment firms often advertise their gains and losses in the form of bar graphs such as the one that follows. This graph shows investment risk over time for the S&P 500 Index by showing average annual compound returns for 1 year, 5 years, 15 years, and 25 years. For example, after one year, the annual compound return in percent for an investor is anywhere from a gain of 181.5% to a loss of 64%. Use this graph to answer the questions below.

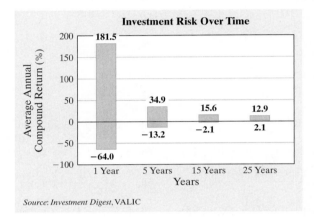

Source: Investment Digest, VALIC

115. A person investing in the S&P 500 Index may expect at most an average annual gain of what percent after 15 years?

116. A person investing in the S&P 500 Index may expect to lose at most an average per year of what percent after 5 years?

117. Find the difference in percent of the highest average annual return and the lowest average annual return after 15 years.

118. Find the difference in percent of the highest average annual return and the lowest average annual return after 25 years.

119. Do you think that the type of investment shown in the figure is recommended for short-term investments or long-term investments? Explain your answer.

INTEGRATED REVIEW ALGEBRAIC EXPRESSIONS AND OPERATIONS ON WHOLE NUMBERS

Sections 1.2–1.3

Find the value of each expression when $x = -1$, $y = 3$, *and* $z = -4$.

1. z^2

2. $-z^2$

3. $\dfrac{4x - z}{2y}$

4. $x(y - 2z)$

Perform indicated operations.

5. $-7 - (-2)$

6. $\dfrac{9}{10} - \dfrac{11}{12}$

7. $\dfrac{-13}{2 - 2}$

8. $(1.2)^2 - (2.1)^2$

9. $\sqrt{64} - \sqrt[3]{64}$

10. $-5^2 - (-5)^2$

11. $9 + 2[(8 - 10)^2 + (-3)^2]$

12. $8 - 6[\sqrt[3]{8}\,(-2) + \sqrt{4}(-5)]$

For Exercises 13 and 14, write each phrase as an algebraic expression. Use x to represent each unknown number.

13. Subtract twice a number from -15.

14. Five more than three times a number.

15. Name the whole number that is not a natural number.

16. True or false: A real number is either a rational number or an irrational number, but never both.

1.4 PROPERTIES OF REAL NUMBERS

OBJECTIVES

1 Use operation and order symbols to write mathematical sentences.

2 Identify identity numbers and inverses.

3 Identify and use the commutative, associative, and distributive properties.

4 Write algebraic expressions.

5 Simplify algebraic expressions.

OBJECTIVE 1 ▶ Using symbols to write mathematical sentences. In Section 1.2, we used the symbol = to mean "is equal to." All of the following key words and phrases also imply equality.

Equality

| equals | is/was | represents | is the same as |
| gives | yields | amounts to | is equal to |

EXAMPLES   Write each sentence as an equation.

1. The sum of x and 5 is 20.

$$x + 5 = 20$$

2. Two times the sum of 3 and y amounts to 4.

$$2 \quad (3 + y) \quad = \quad 4$$

3. The difference of 8 and x is the same as the product of 2 and x.

$$8 - x \quad = \quad 2 \cdot x$$

4. The quotient of z and 9 amounts to 9 plus z.

$$z \div 9 \quad = \quad 9 + z$$

or $$\frac{z}{9} \quad = \quad 9 + z$$

PRACTICES

1–4   Write each sentence using mathematical symbols.

1. The product of -4 and x is 20.

2. Three times the difference of z and 3 equals 9.

3. The sum of x and 5 is the same as 3 less than twice x.

4. The sum of y and 2 is 4 more than the quotient of z and 8.

If we want to write in symbols that two numbers are not equal, we can use the symbol $\neq$, which means "**is not equal to.**" For example,

$$3 \neq 2$$

Graphing two numbers on a number line gives us a way to compare two numbers. For two real numbers a and b, we say ***a* is less than *b*** if on the number line a lies to the left of b. Also, if b is to the right of a on the number line, then ***b* is greater than *a*.** The symbol $<$ means "**is less than.**" Since a is less than b, we write

$$a < b$$

The symbol $>$ means "**is greater than.**" Since b is greater than a, we write

$$b > a$$

▶ **Helpful Hint**

Notice that if $a < b$, then $b > a$. For example, since $-1 < 7$, then $7 > -1$.

EXAMPLE 5 Insert $<$, $>$, or $=$ between each pair of numbers to form a true statement.

a. $-1 \quad -2$ **b.** $\dfrac{12}{4} \quad 3$ **c.** $-5 \quad 0$ **d.** $-3.5 \quad -3.05$

Solution

a. $-1 > -2$ since -1 lies to the right of -2 on the number line.

b. $\dfrac{12}{4} = 3$.

c. $-5 < 0$ since -5 lies to the left of 0 on the number line.

d. $-3.5 < -3.05$ since -3.5 lies to the left of -3.05 on the number line.

PRACTICE
5 Insert $<$, $>$, or $=$ between each pair of numbers to form a true statement.

a. $-6 \quad -5$ **b.** $\dfrac{24}{3} \quad 8$ **c.** $0 \quad -7$ **d.** $2.76 \quad 2.67$

▶ **Helpful Hint**

When inserting the $>$ or $<$ symbol, think of the symbols as arrowheads that "point" toward the smaller number when the statement is true.

In addition to $<$ and $>$, there are the inequality symbols $\leq$ and $\geq$. The symbol

$$\leq \text{ means "is less than or equal to"}$$

and the symbol

$$\geq \text{ means "is greater than or equal to"}$$

For example, the following are true statements.

$$10 \leq 10 \quad \text{since} \quad 10 = 10$$
$$-8 \leq 13 \quad \text{since} \quad -8 < 13$$
$$-5 \geq -5 \quad \text{since} \quad -5 = -5$$
$$-7 \geq -9 \quad \text{since} \quad -7 > -9$$

EXAMPLE 6   Write each sentence using mathematical symbols.

a. The sum of 5 and y is greater than or equal to 7.

b. 11 is not equal to z.

c. 20 is less than the difference of 5 and twice x.

Solution

a. $5 + y \geq 7$ **b.** $11 \neq z$ **c.** $20 < 5 - 2x$ □

PRACTICE
6   Write each sentence using mathematical symbols.

a. The difference of x and 3 is less than or equal to 5.

b. y is not equal to -4.

c. Two is less than the sum of 4 and one-half z.

OBJECTIVE 2 ▶ Identifying identities and inverses. Of all the real numbers, two of them stand out as extraordinary: 0 and 1. Zero is the only number that when *added* to any real number, the result is the same real number. Zero is thus called the **additive identity.** Also, one is the only number that when *multiplied* by any real number, the result is the same real number. One is thus called the **multiplicative identity.**

	Addition	Multiplication
Identity Properties	The additive identity is 0. $a + 0 = 0 + a = a$	The multiplicative identity is 1. $a \cdot 1 = 1 \cdot a = a$

In Section 1.2, we learned that a and $-a$ are opposites.

Another name for opposite is **additive inverse.** For example, the additive inverse of 3 is -3. Notice that the sum of a number and its opposite is always 0.

In Section 1.3, we learned that, for a nonzero number, b and $\dfrac{1}{b}$ are reciprocals.

Another name for reciprocal is **multiplicative inverse.** For example, the multiplicative inverse of $-\dfrac{2}{3}$ is $-\dfrac{3}{2}$. Notice that the product of a number and its reciprocal is always 1.

	Opposite or Additive Inverse	*Reciprocal or Multiplicative Inverse*
Inverse Properties	For each number a, there is a unique number $-a$ called the **additive inverse** or **opposite** of a such that $a + (-a) = (-a) + a = 0$	For each nonzero a, there is a unique number $\dfrac{1}{a}$ called the **multiplicative inverse** or **reciprocal** of a such that $a \cdot \dfrac{1}{a} = \dfrac{1}{a} \cdot a = 1$

EXAMPLE 7   Write the additive inverse, or opposite, of each.

a. 4   **b.** $\dfrac{3}{7}$ **c.** -11.2

Solution

a. The opposite of 4 is -4.

b. The opposite of $\dfrac{3}{7}$ is $-\dfrac{3}{7}$.

c. The opposite of -11.2 is $-(-11.2) = 11.2$.   □

PRACTICE
7   Write the additive inverse, or opposite of each.

a. -7 **b.** 4.7   **c.** $-\dfrac{3}{8}$

EXAMPLE 8 Write the multiplicative inverse, or reciprocal, of each.

a. 11 **b.** -9 **c.** $\dfrac{7}{4}$

Solution

a. The reciprocal of 11 is $\dfrac{1}{11}$.

b. The reciprocal of -9 is $-\dfrac{1}{9}$.

c. The reciprocal of $\dfrac{7}{4}$ is $\dfrac{4}{7}$ because $\dfrac{7}{4} \cdot \dfrac{4}{7} = 1$.

PRACTICE
8 Write the multiplicative inverse, or reciprocal, of each.

a. $-\dfrac{5}{3}$ **b.** 14 **c.** -2

▶ **Helpful Hint**

The number 0 has no reciprocal. Why? There is no number that when multiplied by 0 gives a product of 1.

Concept Check ☑

Can a number's additive inverse and multiplicative inverse ever be the same? Explain.

OBJECTIVE 3 ▶ **Using the commutative, associative, and distributive properties.** In addition to these special real numbers, all real numbers have certain properties that allow us to write equivalent expressions—that is, expressions that have the same value. These properties will be especially useful in Chapter 2 when we solve equations.

The **commutative properties** state that the order in which two real numbers are added or multiplied does not affect their sum or product.

Commutative Properties

For real numbers a and b,

$$\text{Addition:} \quad a + b = b + a$$
$$\text{Multiplication:} \quad a \cdot b = b \cdot a$$

The **associative properties** state that regrouping numbers that are added or multiplied does not affect their sum or product.

Associative Properties

For real numbers a, b, and c,

$$\text{Addition:} \quad (a + b) + c = a + (b + c)$$
$$\text{Multiplication:} \quad (a \cdot b) \cdot c = a \cdot (b \cdot c)$$

EXAMPLE 9 Use the commutative property of addition to write an expression equivalent to $7x + 5$.

Solution $\qquad\qquad 7x + 5 = 5 + 7x.$

PRACTICE
9 Use the commutative property of addition to write an expression equivalent to $8 + 13x$.

Answer to Concept Check:

no; answers may vary

EXAMPLE 10   Use the associative property of multiplication to write an expression equivalent to $4 \cdot (9y)$. Then simplify this equivalent expression.

Solution $4 \cdot (9y) = (4 \cdot 9)y = 36y.$ ◻

PRACTICE
10   Use the associative property of multiplication to write an expression equivalent to $3 \cdot (11b)$. Then simplify the equivalent expression.

The **distributive property** states that multiplication distributes over addition.

> **Distributive Property**
> For real numbers a, b, and c,
> $$a(b + c) = ab + ac$$

EXAMPLE 11   Use the distributive property to multiply.

a. $3(2x + y)$ **b.** $-(3x - 1)$ **c.** $0.7a(b - 2)$

Solution

a. $3(2x + y) = 3 \cdot 2x + 3 \cdot y$ Apply the distributive property.
$= 6x + 3y$ Apply the associative property of multiplication.

b. Recall that $-(3x - 1)$ means $-1(3x - 1)$.

$$-1(3x - 1) = -1(3x) + (-1)(-1)$$
$$= -3x + 1$$

c. $0.7a(b - 2) = 0.7a \cdot b - 0.7a \cdot 2 = 0.7ab - 1.4a$ ◻

PRACTICE
11   Use the distributive property to multiply.

a. $4(x + 5y)$ **b.** $-(3 - 2z)$ **c.** $0.3x(y - 3)$

Concept Check ☑
Is the statement below true? Why or why not?
$$6(2a)(3b) = 6(2a) \cdot 6(3b)$$

OBJECTIVE 4 ▶ Writing algebraic expressions. As mentioned earlier, an important step in problem solving is to be able to write algebraic expressions from word phrases. Sometimes this involves a direct translation, but often an indicated operation is not directly stated but rather implied.

EXAMPLE 12   Write each as an algebraic expression.

a. A vending machine contains x quarters. Write an expression for the *value* of the quarters.

b. The number of grams of fat in x pieces of bread if each piece of bread contains 2 grams of fat.

c. The cost of x desks if each desk costs $156.

d. Sales tax on a purchase of x dollars if the tax rate is 9%.

Answer to Concept Check:

no; $6(2a)(3b) = 12a(3b) = 36ab$

Each of these examples implies finding a product.

Solution

a. The value of the quarters is found by multiplying the value of a quarter (0.25 dollar) by the number of quarters.

In words: value of a quarter · number of quarters

Translate: 0.25 · *x*,   or 0.25*x*

b. In words: number of grams of fat in one piece of bread · number of pieces or bread

Translate: 2 · *x*,   or 2*x*

c. In words: cost of a desk · number of desks

Translate: 156 · *x*,   or 156*x*

d. In words: sales tax rate · purchase price

Translate: 0.09 · *x*,   or 0.09*x*

(Here, we wrote 9% as a decimal, 0.09.) □

PRACTICE
12   Write each as an algebraic expression.

a. A parking meter contains *x* dimes. Write an expression for the value of the dimes.

b. The grams of carbohydrates in *y* cookies if each cookie has 26 g of carbohydrates.

c. The cost of *z* birthday cards if each birthday card costs $1.75.

d. The amount of money you save on a new cell phone costing *t* dollars if it has a 15% discount.

Two or more unknown numbers in a problem may sometimes be related. If so, try letting a variable represent one unknown number and then represent the other unknown number or numbers as expressions containing the same variable.

EXAMPLE 13   Write each as an algebraic expression.

a. Two numbers have a sum of 20. If one number is *x*, represent the other number as an expression in *x*.

b. The older sister is 8 years older than her younger sister. If the age of the younger sister is *x*, represent the age of the older sister as an expression in *x*.

△ **c.** Two angles are complementary if the sum of their measures is 90°. If the measure of one angle is *x* degrees, represent the measure of the other angle as an expression in *x*.

d. If *x* is the first of two consecutive integers, represent the second integer as an expression in *x*.

Solution

a. If two numbers have a sum of 20 and one number is *x*, the other number is "the rest of 20."

In words: twenty minus *x*

Translate: 20 − *x*

b. The older sister's age is

In words: | eight years | added to | younger sister's age |

Translate: 8   + x

c. In words: | ninety | minus | x |

Translate: 90   − x

d. The next consecutive integer is always one more than the previous integer.

In words: | the first integer | plus | one |

Translate: x +   1

PRACTICE
13   Write each as an algebraic expression.

a. Two numbers have a sum of 16. If one number is x, represent the other number as an expression in x.

b. Two angles are supplementary if the sum of their measures is 180°. If the measure of one angle is x degrees, represent the measure of the other angle as an expression in x.

c. If x is the first of two consecutive even integers, represent the next even integer as an expression in x.

d. One brother is 9 years younger than another brother. If the age of the younger brother is x, represent the age of the older brother as an expression in x.

OBJECTIVE 5 ▶ Simplifying algebraic expressions. Often, an expression may be **simplified** by removing grouping symbols and combining any like terms. The **terms** of an expression are the addends of the expression. For example, in the expression $3x^2 + 4x$, the terms are $3x^2$ and $4x$.

Expression	*Terms*
$-2x + y$	$-2x,\ y$
$3x^2 - \dfrac{y}{5} + 7$	$3x^2, -\dfrac{y}{5}, 7$

Terms with the same variable(s) raised to the same power are called **like terms.** We can add or subtract like terms by using the distributive property. This process is called **combining like terms.**

EXAMPLE 14   Use the distributive property to simplify each expression.

a. $3x - 5x + 4$ **b.** $7yz + yz$ **c.** $4z + 6.1$

Solution

a. $3x - 5x + 4 = (3 - 5)x + 4$ Apply the distributive property.

              $= -2x + 4$

b. $7yz + yz = (7 + 1)yz = 8yz$

c. $4z + 6.1$ cannot be simplified further since $4z$ and 6.1 are not like terms.

PRACTICE
14   Use the distributive property to simplify.

a. $6ab - ab$ **b.** $4x - 5 + 6x$ **c.** $17p - 9$

Let's continue to use properties of real numbers to simplify expressions. Recall that the distributive property can also be used to multiply. For example,

$$-2(x + 3) = -2(x) + (-2)(3) = -2x - 6$$

The associative and commutative properties may sometimes be needed to rearrange and group like terms when we simplify expressions.

$$-7x^2 + 5 + 3x^2 - 2 = -7x^2 + 3x^2 + 5 - 2$$
$$= (-7 + 3)x^2 + (5 - 2)$$
$$= -4x^2 + 3$$

EXAMPLE 15 Simplify each expression.

a. $3xy - 2xy + 5 - 7 + xy$ **b.** $7x^2 + 3 - 5(x^2 - 4)$

c. $(2.1x - 5.6) - (-x - 5.3)$ **d.** $\frac{1}{2}(4a - 6b) - \frac{1}{3}(9a + 12b - 1) + \frac{1}{4}$

Solution

a. $3xy - 2xy + 5 - 7 + xy = 3xy - 2xy + xy + 5 - 7$ Apply the commutative property.

$$= (3 - 2 + 1)xy + (5 - 7)$$ Apply the distributive property.

$$= 2xy - 2$$ Simplify.

b. $7x^2 + 3 - 5(x^2 - 4) = 7x^2 + 3 - 5x^2 + 20$ Apply the distributive property.

$$= 2x^2 + 23$$ Simplify.

c. Think of $-(-x - 5.3)$ as $-1(-x - 5.3)$ and use the distributive property.

$$(2.1x - 5.6) - 1(-x - 5.3) = 2.1x - 5.6 + 1x + 5.3$$

$$= 3.1x - 0.3$$ Combine like terms.

d. $\frac{1}{2}\left(4a - 6b\right) - \frac{1}{3}\left(9a + 12b - 1\right) + \frac{1}{4}$

$$= 2a - 3b - 3a - 4b + \frac{1}{3} + \frac{1}{4}$$ Use the distributive property.

$$= -a - 7b + \frac{7}{12}$$ Combine like terms. □

PRACTICE
15 Simplify each expression.

a. $5pq - 2pq - 11 - 4pq + 18$ **b.** $3x^2 + 7 - 2(x^2 - 6)$

c. $(3.7x + 2.5) - (-2.1x - 1.3)$

d. $\frac{1}{5}(15c - 25d) - \frac{1}{2}(8c + 6d + 1) + \frac{3}{4}$

Concept Check ☑

Find and correct the error in the following

$$x - 4(x - 5) = x - 4x - 20$$
$$= -3x - 20$$

Answer to Concept Check:

$x - 4(x - 5) = x - 4x + 20$
$$= -3x + 20$$

VOCABULARY & READINESS CHECK

Complete the table by filling in the symbols.

	Symbol	Meaning		Symbol	Meaning
1.		is less than	**2.**		is greater than
3.		is not equal to	**4.**		is equal to
5.		is greater than or equal to	**6.**		is less than or equal to

Use the choices below to fill in each blank. Not all choices will be used.

like   terms   distributive $-a$ commutative

unlike   combining   associative $\dfrac{1}{a}$

7. The opposite of nonzero number a is _____.

8. The reciprocal of nonzero number a is _____.

9. The _____ property has to do with "order."

10. The _____ property has to do with "grouping."

11. $a(b + c) = ab + ac$ illustrates the _____ property.

12. Terms with the same variable(s) raised to the same powers are called _____ terms.

13. The _____ of an expression are the addends of the expression.

14. The process of adding or subtracting like terms is called _____ like terms.

1.4 EXERCISE SET

MIXED PRACTICE

Write each sentence using mathematical symbols. See Examples 1 through 4 and 6 through 8.

1. The sum of 10 and x is -12.

2. The difference of y and 3 amounts to 12.

3. Twice x, plus 5, is the same as -14.

4. Three more than the product of 4 and c is 7.

5. The quotient of n and 5 is 4 times n.

6. The quotient of 8 and y is 3 more than y.

7. The difference of z and one-half is the same as the product of z and one-half.

8. Five added to one-fourth q is the same as 4 more than q.

9. The product of 7 and x is less than or equal to -21.

10. 10 subtracted from the reciprocal of x is greater than 0.

11. Twice the difference of x and 6 is greater than the reciprocal of 11.

12. Four times the sum of 5 and x is not equal to the opposite of 15.

13. Twice the difference of x and 6 is -27.

14. 5 times the sum of 6 and y is -35.

Insert $<$, $>$, or $=$ between each pair of numbers to form a true statement. See Example 5.

15. -16 -17

16. -14 -24

17. 7.4 7.40

18. $\dfrac{7}{2}$ $\dfrac{35}{10}$

19. $\dfrac{7}{11}$ $\dfrac{9}{11}$

20. $\dfrac{9}{20}$ $\dfrac{3}{20}$

21. $\dfrac{1}{2}$ $\dfrac{5}{8}$

22. $\dfrac{3}{4}$ $\dfrac{7}{8}$

23. -7.9 -7.09

24. -13.07 -13.7

Fill in the chart. See Example 7 and 8.

	Number	Opposite	Reciprocal
25.	5		
26.	7		
27.		8	
28.			$-\dfrac{1}{4}$
29.	$-\dfrac{1}{7}$		
30.	$\dfrac{1}{11}$		
31.	0		
32.	1		
33.			$\dfrac{8}{7}$
34.		$\dfrac{23}{5}$	

35. Name the only real number that has no reciprocal, and explain why this is so.

36. Name the only real number that is its own opposite, and explain why this is so.

Use a commutative property to write an equivalent expression. See Example 9.

37. $7x + y$

38. $3a + 2b$

39. $z \cdot w$

40. $r \cdot s$

41. $\frac{1}{3} \cdot \frac{x}{5}$

42. $\frac{x}{2} \cdot \frac{9}{10}$

43. Is subtraction commutative? Explain why or why not.

44. Is division commutative? Explain why or why not.

Use an associative property to write an equivalent expression. See Example 10.

45. $5 \cdot (7x)$

46. $3 \cdot (10z)$

47. $(x + 1.2) + y$

48. $5q + (2r + s)$

49. $(14z) \cdot y$

50. $(9.2x) \cdot y$

51. Evaluate $12 - (5 - 3)$ and $(12 - 5) - 3$. Use these two expressions and discuss whether subtraction is associative.

52. Evaluate $24 \div (6 \div 3)$ and $(24 \div 6) \div 3$. Use these two expressions and discuss whether division is associative.

Use the distributive property to find the product. See Example 11.

53. $3(x + 5)$

54. $7(y + 2)$

55. $-(2a + b)$

56. $-(c + 7d)$

57. $2(6x + 5y + 2z)$

58. $5(3a + b + 9c)$

59. $-4(x - 2y + 7)$

60. $-10(2a - 3b - 4)$

61. $0.5x(6y - 3)$

62. $1.2m(9n - 4)$

Complete the statement to illustrate the given property.

63. $3x + 6 =$ _____ Commutative property of addition

64. $8 + 0 =$ _____ Additive identity property

65. $\frac{2}{3} + \left(-\frac{2}{3}\right) =$ _____ Additive inverse property

66. $4(x + 3) =$ _____ Distributive property

67. $7 \cdot 1 =$ _____ Multiplicative identity property

68. $0 \cdot (-5.4) =$ _____ Multiplication property of zero

69. $10(2y) =$ _____ Associative property

70. $9y + (x + 3z) =$ _____ Associative property

71. To demonstrate the distributive property geometrically, represent the area of the larger rectangle in two ways: First as length a times width $b + c$, and second as the sum of the areas of the smaller rectangles.

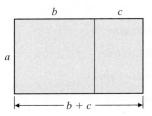

Write each of the following as an algebraic expression. See Examples 12 and 13.

72. Write an expression for the amount of money (in dollars) in n nickels.

73. Write an expression for the amount of money (in dollars) in d dimes.

74. Two numbers have a sum of 25. If one number is x, represent the other number as an expression in x.

75. Two numbers have a sum of 112. If one number is x, represent the other number as an expression in x.

76. Two angles are supplementary if the sum of their measures is $180°$. If the measure of one angle is x degrees, represent the measure of the other angle as an expression in x.

77. If the measure of an angle is $5x$ degrees, represent the measure of its complement as an expression in x.

78. The cost of x compact discs if each compact disc costs $6.49.

79. The cost of y books if each book costs $35.61.

80. If x is an odd integer, represent the next odd integer as an expression in x.

81. If $2x$ is an even integer, represent the next even integer as an expression in x.

MIXED PRACTICE

Simplify each expression. See Examples 11, 14, and 15.

82. $-9 + 4x + 18 - 10x$

83. $5y - 14 + 7y - 20y$

84. $5k - (3k - 10)$

85. $-11c - (4 - 2c)$

86. $(3x + 4) - (6x - 1)$

87. $(8 - 5y) - (4 + 3y)$

88. $3(xy - 2) + xy + 15 - x^2$

89. $-4(yz + 3) - 7yz + 1 + y^2$

90. $-(n + 5) + (5n - 3)$

91. $-(8 - t) + (2t - 6)$

92. $4(6n^2 - 3) - 3(8n^2 + 4)$

93. $5(2z^3 - 6) + 10(3 - z^3)$

94. $3x - 2(x - 5) + x$

95. $7n + 3(2n - 6) - 2$

96. $1.5x + 2.3 - 0.7x - 5.9$

97. $6.3y - 9.7 + 2.2y - 11.1$

98. $\frac{3}{4}b - \frac{1}{2} + \frac{1}{6}b - \frac{2}{3}$

99. $\frac{7}{8}a - \frac{11}{12} - \frac{1}{2}a + \frac{5}{6}$

100. $2(3x + 7)$

101. $4(5y + 12)$

102. $\frac{1}{4}(8x - 4) - \frac{1}{5}(20x - 6y)$

103. $\frac{1}{2}(10x - 2) - \frac{1}{6}(60x - 5y)$

104. $\frac{1}{6}(24a - 18b) - \frac{1}{7}(7a - 21b - 2) - \frac{1}{5}$

105. $\frac{1}{3}(6x - 33y) - \frac{1}{8}(24x - 40y + 1) - \frac{1}{3}$

CONCEPT EXTENSIONS

In each statement, a property of real numbers has been incorrectly applied. Correct the right-hand side of each statement. See the second Concept Check in this section.

106. $3(x + 4) = 3x + 4$

107. $5(7y) = (5 \cdot 7)(5 \cdot y)$

Simplify each expression.

108. $8.1z + 7.3(z + 5.2) - 6.85$

109. $6.5y - 4.4(1.8x - 3.3) + 10.95$

110. Do figures with the same surface area always have the same volume? To see, take two $8\frac{1}{2}$-by-11-inch sheets of paper and construct two cylinders using the following figures as a guide. Working with a partner, measure the height and the radius of each resulting cylinder and use the expression $\pi r^2 h$ to approximate each volume to the nearest tenth of a cubic inch. Explain your results.

Cylinder 1   Cylinder 2

111. Use the same idea as in Exercise 110, work with a partner, and discover whether two rectangles with the same perimeter always have the same area. Explain your results.

The following graph is called a broken-line graph, or simply a line graph. This particular graph shows the past, present, and future predicted U.S. population over 65. Just as with a bar graph, to find the population over 65 for a particular year, read the height of the corresponding point. To read the height, follow the point horizontally to the left until you reach the vertical axis. Use this graph to answer Exercises 112 through 117.

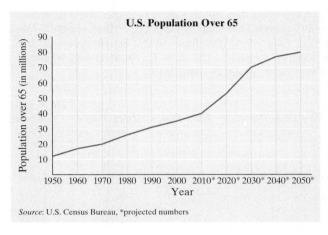

Source: U.S. Census Bureau, *projected numbers

112. Estimate the population over 65 in the year 1970.

113. Estimate the predicted population over 65 in the year 2050.

114. Estimate the predicted population over 65 in the year 2030.

115. Estimate the population over 65 in the year 2000.

116. Is the population over 65 increasing as time passes or decreasing? Explain how you arrived at your answer.

117. The percent of Americans over 65 in 1950 was 8.1%. The percent of Americans over 65 in 2050 is expected to be 2.5 times the percent over 65 in 1950. Estimate the percent of Americans expected to be over age 65 in 2050.

📖 STUDY SKILLS BUILDER

Are You Preparing for a Test on Chapter 1?

Below I have listed some common trouble areas for students in Chapter 1. After studying for your test—but before taking your test—read these.

- Don't forget the order of operations and the distributive property.

$$7 - 3(2x - 6y) + 5 = 7 - 6x + 18y + 5 \quad \text{Use the distributive property.}$$
$$\text{Notice the sign.}$$
$$= -6x + 18y + 12 \quad \text{Combine like terms.}$$

- Don't forget the difference between $(-3)^2$ and -3^2.

$$(-3)^2 = (-3)(-3) = 9$$
$$-3^2 = -1 \cdot 3^2 = -1 \cdot (3 \cdot 3) = -9$$

- Remember that

$$\frac{0}{8} = 0 \text{ while } \frac{8}{0} \text{ is undefined.}$$

- Don't forget the difference between reciprocal and opposite.

$$\text{The opposite of } -\frac{3}{5} \text{ is } \frac{3}{5}.$$

$$\text{The reciprocal of } -\frac{3}{5} \text{ is } -\frac{5}{3}.$$

Remember: This is simply a checklist of common trouble areas. For a review of Chapter 1, see the Highlights and Chapter Review at the end of Chapter 1.

CHAPTER 1 GROUP ACTIVITY

Analyzing Newspaper Circulation

The number of daily newspapers in business in the United States has declined steadily recently, continuing a trend that started in the mid-1970s. In 1900, there were roughly 2300 daily newspapers in operation. However, by 2003, that number had dropped to only 1456 newspapers in existence. Average overall daily newspaper circulation also continues to decline, from 60.2 million in 1992 to 55.2 million in 2003.

The table gives data about daily newspaper circulation for New York City–based newspapers for the years 2005 and 2006. (*Source: Burrels Luce Media Database*) In this activity you will have the opportunity to analyze this data. This activity may be completed by working in groups or individually.

New York–Based Newspaper	2005 Daily Circulation	2006 Daily Circulation	Daily Edition Newsstand Price
Wall Street Journal	2,070,498	2,049,786	$1.00
New York Times	1,121,623	1,142,464	$1.00
New York Daily News	708,773	708,477	$0.50
New York Post	643,056	673,379	$0.35

1. Find the change in circulation from 2005 to 2006 for each newspaper. Did any newspaper gain circulation? If so, which one(s) and by how much?

2. Construct a bar graph showing the change in circulation from 2005 to 2006 for each newspaper. Which newspaper experienced the greatest change in circulation?

3. What was the total daily circulation of these New York City–based newspapers in 2005? 2006? Did total circulation increase or decrease from 2005 to 2006? By how much?

4. Discuss factors that may have contributed to the overall change in daily newspaper circulation.

5. The population of New York City is approximately 8,160,000. Find the number of New York City–based newspapers sold per person in 2006 for New York City. (*Source: CIA Fact Book*)

6. The population of the New York City metropolitan area is approximately 18,700,000. Find the number of New York City–based newspapers sold per person in 2006 for the New York City metropolitan area. (*Source: CIA Fact Book*)

7. Which of the figures found in Questions 5 and 6 do you think is more meaningful? Why might neither of these figures be capable of describing the full circulation situation?

8. Assuming that each copy was sold from a newsstand in the New York City metropolitan area, use the daily edition prices given in the table to approximate the total amount spent each day on these New York City–based newspapers in 2006. Find the total amount spent annually on these daily newspapers in 2006.

9. How accurate do you think the figures you found in Question 8 are? Explain your reasoning.

CHAPTER 1 VOCABULARY CHECK

Fill in each blank with one of the words or phrases listed below.

distributive   real   reciprocals   absolute value   opposite   associative
inequality   commutative   whole   algebraic expression   exponent   variable

1. A(n) _____ is formed by numbers and variables connected by the operations of addition, subtraction, multiplication, division, raising to powers, and/or taking roots.

2. The _____ of a number a is $-a$.

3. $3(x - 6) = 3x - 18$ by the _____ property.

4. The _____ of a number is the distance between that number and 0 on the number line.

5. A(n) _____ is a shorthand notation for repeated multiplication of the same factor.

6. A letter that represents a number is called a _____.

7. The symbols $<$ and $>$ are called _____ symbols.

8. If a is not 0, then a and $\frac{1}{a}$ are called _____.

9. $A + B = B + A$ by the _____ property.

10. $(A + B) + C = A + (B + C)$ by the _____ property.

11. The numbers $0, 1, 2, 3, \ldots$ are called _____ numbers.

12. If a number corresponds to a point on the number line, we know that number is a _____ number.

▶ Helpful Hint

Are you preparing for your test? Don't forget to take the Chapter 1 Test on page 45. Then check your answers at the back of the text and use the Chapter Test Prep Video CD to see the fully worked-out solutions to any of the exercises you want to review.

CHAPTER 1 HIGHLIGHTS

DEFINITIONS AND CONCEPTS	EXAMPLES

SECTION 1.2 ALGEBRAIC EXPRESSIONS AND SETS OF NUMBERS

Letters that represent numbers are called **variables.**

An **algebraic expression** is formed by numbers and variables connected by the operations of addition, subtraction, multiplication, division, raising to powers, and/or taking roots.

To **evaluate** an algebraic expression containing variables, substitute the given numbers for the variables and simplify. The result is called the **value** of the expression.

Natural numbers: $\{1, 2, 3, \dots\}$
Whole numbers: $\{0, 1, 2, 3, \dots\}$
Integers: $\{\dots, -3, -2, -1, 0, 1, 2, 3, \dots\}$
Each listing of three dots above is called an **ellipsis,** which means the pattern continues.
The members of a set are called its **elements.**
Set builder notation describes the elements of a set but does not list them.
Real numbers: $\{x \mid x$ corresponds to a point on the number line.$\}$
Rational numbers: $\left\{ \dfrac{a}{b} \,\middle|\, a \text{ and } b \text{ are integers and } b \neq 0 \right\}.$

Irrational numbers: $\{x \mid x$ is a real number and x is not a rational number$\}$.
If 3 is an element of set A, we write $3 \in A$.
If all the elements of set A are also in set B, we say that set A is a **subset** of set B, and we write $A \subseteq B$.
Absolute value:
$$|a| = \begin{cases} a \text{ if } a \text{ is 0 or a positive number} \\ -a \text{ if } a \text{ is a negative number} \end{cases}$$
The opposite of a number a is the number $-a$.

Examples of variables are
$$x, a, m, y$$
Examples of algebraic expressions are
$$7y, -3, \frac{x^2 - 9}{-2} + 14x, \sqrt{3} + \sqrt{m}$$

Evaluate $2.7x$ if $x = 3$.
$$2.7x = 2.7(3)$$
$$= 8.1$$

Given the set $\left\{ -9.6, -5, -\sqrt{2}, 0, \dfrac{2}{5}, 101 \right\}$ list the elements that belong to the set of

Natural numbers 101
Whole numbers 0, 101
Integers $-5, 0, 101$
Real numbers $-9.6, -5, -\sqrt{2}, 0, \dfrac{2}{5}, 101$

Rational numbers $-9.6, -5, 0, \dfrac{2}{5}, 101$

Irrational numbers $-\sqrt{2}$

List the elements in the set
$\{x \mid x$ is an integer between -2 and $5\}$.
$$\{-1, 0, 1, 2, 3, 4\}$$
$$\{1, 2, 4\} \subseteq \{1, 2, 3, 4\}.$$
$$|3| = 3, |0| = 0, |-7.2| = 7.2$$

The opposite of 5 is -5. The opposite of -11 is 11.

SECTION 1.3 OPERATIONS ON REAL NUMBERS

Adding real numbers
1. To add two numbers with the same sign, add their absolute values and attach their common sign.
2. To add two numbers with different signs, subtract the smaller absolute value from the larger absolute value and attach the sign of the number with the larger absolute value.

Subtracting real numbers:
$$a - b = a + (-b)$$

Multiplying and dividing real numbers:

The product or quotient of two numbers with the same sign is positive.
The product or quotient of two numbers with different signs is negative.

$$\frac{2}{7} + \frac{1}{7} = \frac{3}{7}$$
$$-5 + (-2.6) = -7.6$$
$$-18 + 6 = -12$$
$$20.8 + (-10.2) = 10.6$$
$$18 - 21 = 18 + (-21) = -3$$
$$(-8)(-4) = 32 \qquad \frac{-8}{-4} = 2$$
$$8 \cdot 4 = 32 \qquad \frac{8}{4} = 2$$
$$-17 \cdot 2 = -34 \qquad \frac{-14}{2} = -7$$
$$4(-1.6) = -6.4 \qquad \frac{22}{-2} = -11$$

(continued)

DEFINITIONS AND CONCEPTS	**EXAMPLES**

SECTION 1.3 OPERATIONS ON REAL NUMBERS (continued)

A natural number **exponent** is a shorthand notation for repeated multiplication of the same factor.

$$3^4 = 3 \cdot 3 \cdot 3 \cdot 3 = 81$$

The notation $\sqrt{a}$ is used to denote the **positive,** or **principal, square root** of a nonnegative number a.

$$\sqrt{a} = b \text{ if } b^2 = a \text{ and } b \text{ is positive}.$$

Also,

$$\sqrt[3]{a} = b \text{ if } b^3 = a$$

$$\sqrt[4]{a} = b \text{ if } b^4 = a \text{ and } b \text{ is positive}$$

$$\sqrt{49} = 7$$
$$\sqrt[3]{64} = 4$$
$$\sqrt[4]{16} = 2$$

Order of Operations

Simplify expressions using the order that follows. If grouping symbols such as parentheses are present, simplify expressions within those first, starting with the innermost set. If fraction bars are present, simplify the numerator and denominator separately.

1. Raise to powers or take roots in order from left to right.
2. Multiply or divide in order from left to right.
3. Add or subtract in order from left to right.

Simplify $\dfrac{42 - 2(3^2 - \sqrt{16})}{-8}$.

$$\frac{42 - 2(3^2 - \sqrt{16})}{-8} = \frac{42 - 2(9 - 4)}{-8}$$
$$= \frac{42 - 2(5)}{-8}$$
$$= \frac{42 - 10}{-8}$$
$$= \frac{32}{-8} = -4$$

SECTION 1.4 PROPERTIES OF REAL NUMBERS

Symbols: $=$ is equal to

$\neq$ is not equal to

$>$ is greater than

$<$ is less than

$\geq$ is greater than or equal to

$\leq$ is less than or equal to

$$-5 = -5$$
$$-5 \neq -3$$
$$1.7 > 1.2$$
$$-1.7 < -1.2$$
$$\frac{5}{3} \geq \frac{5}{3}$$
$$-\frac{1}{2} \leq \frac{1}{2}$$

Identity:

$$a + 0 = a \qquad 0 + a = a$$
$$a \cdot 1 = a \qquad 1 \cdot a = a$$

$$3 + 0 = 3 \qquad 0 + 3 = 3$$
$$-1.8 \cdot 1 = -1.8 \qquad 1 \cdot -1.8 = -1.8$$

Inverse:

$$a + (-a) = 0 \qquad -a + a = 0$$
$$a \cdot \frac{1}{a} = 1 \qquad \frac{1}{a} \cdot a = 1, a \neq 0$$

$$7 + (-7) = 0 \qquad -7 + 7 = 0$$
$$5 \cdot \frac{1}{5} = 1 \qquad \frac{1}{5} \cdot 5 = 1$$

Commutative:

$$a + b = b + a$$
$$a \cdot b = b \cdot a$$

$$x + 7 = 7 + x$$
$$9 \cdot y = y \cdot 9$$

Associative:

$$(a + b) + c = a + (b + c)$$
$$(a \cdot b) \cdot c = a \cdot (b \cdot c)$$

$$(3 + 1) + 10 = 3 + (1 + 10)$$
$$(3 \cdot 1) \cdot 10 = 3(1 \cdot 10)$$

Distributive:

$$a(b + c) = ab + ac$$

$$6(x + 5) = 6 \cdot x + 6 \cdot 5$$
$$= 6x + 30$$

CHAPTER 1 REVIEW

(1.2) Find the value of each algebraic expression at the given replacement values.

1. $7x$ when $x = 3$

2. st when $s = 1.6$ and $t = 5$

3. The hummingbird has an average wing speed of 90 beats per second. The expression $90t$ gives the number of wing beats in t seconds. Calculate the number of wing beats in *1 hour* for the hummingbird.

List the elements in each set.

4. $\{x | x$ is an odd integer between -2 and $4\}$

5. $\{x | x$ is an even integer between -3 and $7\}$

6. $\{x | x$ is a negative whole number$\}$

7. $\{x | x$ is a natural number that is not a rational number$\}$

8. $\{x | x$ is a whole number greater than $5\}$

9. $\{x | x$ is an integer less than $3\}$

Determine whether each statement is true or false if $A = \{6, 10, 12\}$, $B = \{5, 9, 11\}$, $C = \{\ldots, -3, -2, -1, 0, 1, 2, 3, \ldots\}$, $D = \{2, 4, 6, \ldots, 16\}$ $E = \{x | x$ is a rational number$\}$, $F = \{\ \}$, $G = \{x | x$ is an irrational number$\}$, and $H = \{x | x$ is a real number$\}$.

10. $10 \in D$

11. $B \in 9$

12. $\sqrt{169} \notin G$

13. $0 \notin F$

14. $\pi \in E$

15. $\pi \in H$

16. $\sqrt{4} \in G$

17. $-9 \in E$

18. $A \subseteq D$

19. $C \nsubseteq B$

20. $C \nsubseteq E$

21. $F \subseteq H$

22. $B \subseteq B$

23. $D \subseteq C$

24. $C \subseteq H$

25. $G \subseteq H$

26. $\{5\} \in B$

27. $\{5\} \subseteq B$

List the elements of the set $\left\{5, -\dfrac{2}{3}, \dfrac{8}{2}, \sqrt{9}, 0.3, \sqrt{7}, 1\dfrac{5}{8}, -1, \pi\right\}$ that are also elements of each given set.

28. Whole numbers

29. Natural numbers

30. Rational numbers

31. Irrational numbers

32. Real numbers

33. Integers

Find the opposite.

34. $-\dfrac{3}{4}$

35. 0.6

36. 0

37. 1

Find the reciprocal.

38. $-\dfrac{3}{4}$

39. 0.6

40. 0

41. 1

(1.3) Simplify.

42. $-7 + 3$

43. $-10 + (-25)$

44. $5(-0.4)$

45. $(-3.1)(-0.1)$

46. $-7 - (-15)$

47. $9 - (-4.3)$

48. $(-6)(-4)(0)(-3)$

49. $(-12)(0)(-1)(-5)$

50. $(-24) \div 0$

51. $0 \div (-45)$

52. $(-36) \div (-9)$

53. $60 \div (-12)$

54. $\left(-\dfrac{4}{5}\right) - \left(-\dfrac{2}{3}\right)$

55. $\left(\dfrac{5}{4}\right) - \left(-2\dfrac{3}{4}\right)$

56. Determine the unknown fractional part.

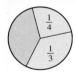

Simplify.

57. $-5 + 7 - 3 - (-10)$

58. $8 - (-3) + (-4) + 6$

59. $3(4 - 5)^4$

60. $6(7 - 10)^2$

61. $\left(-\dfrac{8}{15}\right) \cdot \left(-\dfrac{2}{3}\right)^2$

62. $\left(-\dfrac{3}{4}\right)^2 \cdot \left(-\dfrac{10}{21}\right)$

63. $\dfrac{-\dfrac{6}{15}}{\dfrac{8}{25}}$

64. $\dfrac{\dfrac{4}{9}}{-\dfrac{8}{45}}$

65. $-\dfrac{3}{8} + 3(2) \div 6$

66. $5(-2) - (-3) - \dfrac{1}{6} + \dfrac{2}{3}$

67. $|2^3 - 3^2| - |5 - 7|$

68. $|5^2 - 2^2| + |9 \div (-3)|$

69. $(2^3 - 3^2) - (5 - 7)$

70. $(5^2 - 2^4) + [9 \div (-3)]$

71. $\dfrac{(8 - 10)^3 - (-4)^2}{2 + 8(2) \div 4}$

72. $\dfrac{(2 + 4)^2 + (-1)^5}{12 \div 2 \cdot 3 - 3}$

73. $\dfrac{(4-9)+4-9}{10-12 \div 4 \cdot 8}$

74. $\dfrac{3-7-(7-3)}{15+30 \div 6 \cdot 2}$

75. $\dfrac{\sqrt{25}}{4+3 \cdot 7}$

76. $\dfrac{\sqrt{64}}{24-8 \cdot 2}$

Find the value of each expression when $x = 0$, $y = 3$, and $z = -2$.

77. $x^2 - y^2 + z^2$

78. $\dfrac{5x + z}{2y}$

79. $\dfrac{-7y - 3z}{-3}$

80. $(x - y + z)^2$

△ **81.** The algebraic expression $2\pi r$ represents the circumference of (distance around) a circle of radius r.

    a. Complete the table below by evaluating the expression at given values of r. (Use 3.14 for π)

Radius	r	1	10	100
Circumference	$2\pi r$			

    b. As the radius of a circle increases, does the circumference of the circle increase or decrease?

***(1.4)** Simplify each expression.*

82. $5xy - 7xy + 3 - 2 + xy$

83. $4x + 10x - 19x + 10 - 19$

84. $6x^2 + 2 - 4(x^2 + 1)$

85. $-7(2x^2 - 1) - x^2 - 1$

86. $(3.2x - 1.5) - (4.3x - 1.2)$

87. $(7.6x + 4.7) - (1.9x + 3.6)$

Write each statement using mathematical symbols.

88. Twelve is the product of x and negative 4.

89. The sum of n and twice n is negative fifteen.

90. Four times the sum of y and three is -1.

91. The difference of t and five, multiplied by six is four.

92. Seven subtracted from z is six.

93. Ten less than the product of x and nine is five.

94. The difference of x and 5 is at least 12.

95. The opposite of four is less than the product of y and seven.

96. Two-thirds is not equal to twice the sum of n and one-fourth.

97. The sum of t and six is not more than negative twelve.

Name the property illustrated.

98. $(M + 5) + P = M + (5 + P)$

99. $5(3x - 4) = 15x - 20$

100. $(-4) + 4 = 0$

101. $(3 + x) + 7 = 7 + (3 + x)$

102. $(XY)Z = (YZ)X$

103. $\left(-\dfrac{3}{5}\right) \cdot \left(-\dfrac{5}{3}\right) = 1$

104. $T \cdot 0 = 0$

105. $(ab)c = a(bc)$

106. $A + 0 = A$

107. $8 \cdot 1 = 8$

Complete the equation using the given property.

108. $5x - 15z = $ _____ Distributive property

109. $(7 + y) + (3 + x) = $ _____ Commutative property

110. $0 = $ ____ Additive inverse property

111. $1 = $ ____ Multiplicative inverse property

112. $[(3.4)(0.7)]5 = $ _____ Associative property

113. $7 = $ _____ Additive identity property

Insert $<$, $>$, or $=$ to make each statement true.

114. $-9 \quad -12$

115. $0 \quad -6$

116. $-3 \quad -1$

117. $7 \quad |-7|$

118. $-5 \quad -(-5)$

119. $-(-2) \quad -2$

MIXED REVIEW

Complete the table.

	Number	Opposite of Number	Reciprocal of Number
120.	$-\dfrac{3}{4}$		
121.		-5	

Simplify. If necessary, write answers with positive exponents only.

122. $-2\left(5x + \dfrac{1}{2}\right) + 7.1$

123. $\sqrt{36} \div 2 \cdot 3$

124. $-\dfrac{7}{11} - \left(-\dfrac{1}{11}\right)$

125. $10 - (-1) + (-2) + 6$

126. $\left(-\dfrac{2}{3}\right)^3 \div \dfrac{10}{9}$

127. $\dfrac{(3 - 5)^2 + (-1)^3}{1 + 2(3 - (-1))^2}$

128. $\dfrac{1}{3}(9x - 3y) - (4x - 1) + 4y$

129. The following bar graph shows the U.S. life expectancy at birth for females born in the years shown. Use the graph to fill in the table below by calculating the *increase* in life expectancy of each five-year period shown. (*Source:* Centers for Disease Control)

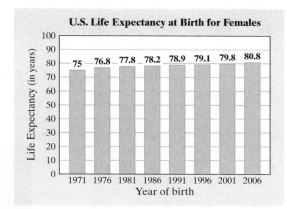

U.S. Life Expectancy at Birth for Females

Year	*Increase in Life Expectancy (in Years) from 5 Years Earlier*
1976	
1981	
1986	
1991	
1996	
2001	
2006	

CHAPTER 1 TEST

Remember to use the Chapter Test Prep Video CD to see the fully worked-out solutions to any of the exercises you want to review.

Determine whether each statement is true or false.

1. $-2.3 > -2.33$ **2.** $-6^2 = (-6)^2$

3. $-5 - 8 = -(5 - 8)$ **4.** $(-2)(-3)(0) = \dfrac{-4}{0}$

5. All natural numbers are integers.

6. All rational numbers are integers.

Simplify.

7. $5 - 12 \div 3(2)$ **8.** $5^2 - 3^4$

9. $(4 - 9)^3 - |-4 - 6|^2$ **10.** $12 + \{6 - [5 - 2(-5)]\}$

11. $\dfrac{6(7 - 9)^3 + (-2)}{(-2)(-5)(-5)}$ **12.** $\dfrac{(4 - \sqrt{16}) - (-7 - 20)}{-2(1 - 4)^2}$

Evaluate each expression when $q = 4$, $r = -2$, and $t = 1$.

13. $q^2 - r^2$ **14.** $\dfrac{5t - 3q}{3r - 1}$

15. The algebraic expression $5.75x$ represents the total cost for x adults to attend the theater.

   a. Complete the table that follows.

   b. As the number of adults increases does the total cost increase or decrease?

Adults	x	1	3	10	20
Total Cost	$5.75x$				

Write each statement using mathematical symbols.

16. Twice the sum of x and five is 30.

17. The square of the difference of six and y, divided by seven, is less than -2.

18. The product of nine and z, divided by the absolute value of -12, is not equal to 10.

19. Three times the quotient of n and five is the opposite of n.

20. Twenty is equal to 6 subtracted from twice x.

21. Negative two is equal to x divided by the sum of x and five.

Name each property illustrated.

22. $6(x - 4) = 6x - 24$

23. $(4 + x) + z = 4 + (x + z)$

24. $(-7) + 7 = 0$

25. $(-18)(0) = 0$

26. Write an expression for the total amount of money (in dollars) in n nickels and d dimes.

Simplify each expression.

27. $-2(3x + 7)$

28. $\dfrac{1}{3}a - \dfrac{3}{8} + \dfrac{1}{6}a - \dfrac{3}{4}$

29. $4y + 10 - 2(y + 10)$

30. $(8.3x - 2.9) - (9.6x - 4.8)$

2

Equations, Inequalities, and Problem Solving

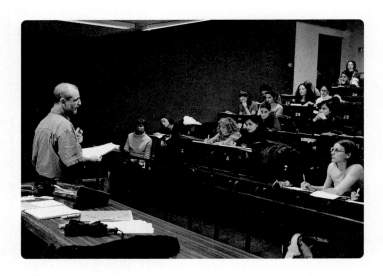

Mathematics is a tool for solving problems in such diverse fields as transportation, engineering, economics, medicine, business, and biology. We solve problems using mathematics by modeling real-world phenomena with mathematical equations or inequalities. Our ability to solve problems using mathematics, then, depends in part on our ability to solve equations and inequalities. In this chapter, we solve linear equations and inequalities in one variable and graph their solutions on number lines.

The federal Bureau of Labor Statistics (BLS) has issued its projections for job growth in the United States between 2000 and 2012. These projections are based on employer surveys distributed and collected by BLS. In Exercise Set 2.2, Exercises 37 and 38, you will find the actual increase in the number of some jobs as well as the percent increase in the number of jobs.

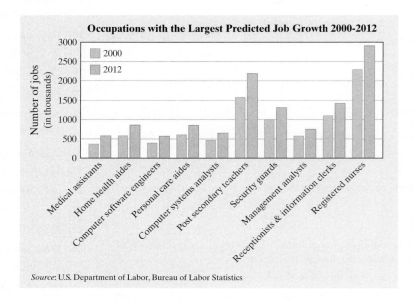

Source: U.S. Department of Labor, Bureau of Labor Statistics

2.1 LINEAR EQUATIONS IN ONE VARIABLE

OBJECTIVES

1 Solve linear equations using properties of equality.

2 Solve linear equations that can be simplified by combining like terms.

3 Solve linear equations containing fractions or decimals.

4 Recognize identities and equations with no solution.

OBJECTIVE 1 ▶ Solving linear equations using properties of equality. Linear equations model many real-life problems. For example, we can use a linear equation to calculate the increase in the percent of households with digital cameras.

With the help of your computer, digital cameras allow you to see your pictures and make copies immediately, send them in e-mail, or use them on a Web page. Current projected percentage of households with these cameras is shown in the graph below.

Percent of Households with a Digital Camera

Source: Lyra Research

To find the increase in percent of households from 2005 to 2006, for example, we can use the equation below:

In words:	increase in percent of households	is	percent of house-holds in 2006	minus	percent of house-holds in 2005
Translate:	x	$=$	64.7	$-$	57

Since our variable x (increase in percent of households) is by itself on one side of the equation, we can find the value of x by simplifying the right side.

$$x = 7.7$$

The increase in the households with digital cameras from 2005 to 2006 is 7.7%.

The **equation** $x = 64.7 - 57$, like every other equation, is a statement that two expressions are equal. Oftentimes, the unknown variable is not by itself on one side of the equation. In these cases, we will use properties of equality to write equivalent equations so that a solution may be found. This is called **solving the equation.** In this section, we concentrate on solving equations such as this one, called **linear equations** in one variable. Linear equations are also called **first-degree equations** since the exponent on the variable is 1.

Linear Equations in One Variable

$$3x = -15 \qquad 7 - y = 3y \qquad 4n - 9n + 6 = 0 \qquad z = -2$$

> **Linear Equations in One Variable**
>
> A linear equation in one variable is an equation that can be written in the form
>
> $$ax + b = c$$
>
> where $a, b,$ and c are real numbers and $a \neq 0$.

When a variable in an equation is replaced by a number and the resulting equation is true, then that number is called a **solution** of the equation. For example, 1 is a solution of the equation $3x + 4 = 7$, since $3(1) + 4 = 7$ is a true statement. But 2 is not a solution of this equation, since $3(2) + 4 = 7$ is not a true statement. The **solution set** of an equation is the set of solutions of the equation. For example, the solution set of $3x + 4 = 7$ is $\{1\}$.

To **solve an equation** is to find the solution set of an equation. Equations with the same solution set are called **equivalent equations.** For example,

$$3x + 4 = 7 \qquad 3x = 3 \qquad x = 1$$

are equivalent equations because they all have the same solution set, namely $\{1\}$. To solve an equation in x, we start with the given equation and write a series of simpler equivalent equations until we obtain an equation of the form

$$x = \text{number}$$

Two important properties are used to write equivalent equations.

The Addition and Multiplication Properties of Equality

If $a, b,$ and $c,$ are real numbers, then

$$a = b \quad \text{and} \quad a + c = b + c \text{ are equivalent equations.}$$
$$\text{Also, } a = b \quad \text{and} \quad ac = bc \text{ are equivalent equations as long as } c \neq 0.$$

The **addition property of equality** guarantees that the same number may be added to both sides of an equation, and the result is an equivalent equation. The **multiplication property of equality** guarantees that both sides of an equation may be multiplied by the same nonzero number, and the result is an equivalent equation. Because we define subtraction in terms of addition $(a - b = a + (-b))$, and division in terms of multiplication $\left(\dfrac{a}{b} = a \cdot \dfrac{1}{b} \right)$, these properties also guarantee that we may *subtract* the same number from both sides of an equation, or *divide* both sides of an equation by the same nonzero number and the result is an equivalent equation.

For example, to solve $2x + 5 = 9$, use the addition and multiplication properties of equality to isolate x—that is, to write an equivalent equation of the form

$$x = \text{number}$$

We will do this in the next example.

EXAMPLE 1   Solve for x: $2x + 5 = 9$.

Solution   First, use the addition property of equality and subtract 5 from both sides. We do this so that our only variable term, $2x$, is by itself on one side of the equation.

$$\begin{aligned}
2x + 5 &= 9 \\
2x + 5 - 5 &= 9 - 5 \qquad \text{Subtract 5 from both sides.} \\
2x &= 4 \qquad\qquad \text{Simplify.}
\end{aligned}$$

Now that the variable term is isolated, we can finish solving for x by using the multiplication property of equality and dividing both sides by 2.

$$\begin{aligned}
\frac{2x}{2} &= \frac{4}{2} \qquad \text{Divide both sides by 2.} \\
x &= 2 \qquad \text{Simplify.}
\end{aligned}$$

Check: To see that 2 is the solution, replace x in the original equation with 2.

$$\begin{aligned}
2x + 5 &= 9 \qquad \text{Original equation} \\
2(2) + 5 &\stackrel{?}{=} 9 \qquad \text{Let } x = 2. \\
4 + 5 &\stackrel{?}{=} 9 \\
9 &= 9 \qquad \text{True}
\end{aligned}$$

Since we arrive at a true statement, 2 is the solution or the solution set is $\{2\}$.

PRACTICE
1   Solve for x: $3x + 7 = 22$.

EXAMPLE 2   Solve: $0.6 = 2 - 3.5c$.

Solution   We use both the addition property and the multiplication property of equality.

$$0.6 = 2 - 3.5c$$

$$0.6 - 2 = 2 - 3.5c - 2 \qquad \text{Subtract 2 from both sides.}$$

$$-1.4 = -3.5c \qquad \text{Simplify. The variable term is now isolated.}$$

$$\frac{-1.4}{-3.5} = \frac{-3.5c}{-3.5} \qquad \text{Divide both sides by } -3.5.$$

$$0.4 = c \qquad \text{Simplify } \frac{-1.4}{-3.5}.$$

> ▶ **Helpful Hint**
>
> Don't forget that
>
> $0.4 = c$ and $c = 0.4$ are equivalent equations.
>
> We may solve an equation so that the variable is alone on either side of the equation.

Check:

$$0.6 = 2 - 3.5c$$

$$0.6 \overset{?}{=} 2 - 3.5(0.4) \qquad \text{Replace } c \text{ with 0.4.}$$

$$0.6 \overset{?}{=} 2 - 1.4 \qquad \text{Multiply.}$$

$$0.6 = 0.6 \qquad \text{True}$$

The solution is 0.4, or the solution set is $\{0.4\}$. ☐

PRACTICE
2   Solve: $2.5 = 3 - 2.5t$.

OBJECTIVE 2 ▶ Solving linear equations that can be simplified by combining like terms.
Often, an equation can be simplified by removing any grouping symbols and combining any like terms.

EXAMPLE 3   Solve: $-4x - 1 + 5x = 9x + 3 - 7x$.

Solution   First we simplify both sides of this equation by combining like terms. Then, let's get variable terms on the same side of the equation by using the addition property of equality to subtract $2x$ from both sides. Next, we use this same property to add 1 to both sides of the equation.

$$-4x - 1 + 5x = 9x + 3 - 7x$$

$$x - 1 = 2x + 3 \qquad \text{Combine like terms.}$$

$$x - 1 - 2x = 2x + 3 - 2x \qquad \text{Subtract } 2x \text{ from both sides.}$$

$$-x - 1 = 3 \qquad \text{Simplify.}$$

$$-x - 1 + 1 = 3 + 1 \qquad \text{Add 1 to both sides.}$$

$$-x = 4 \qquad \text{Simplify.}$$

Notice that this equation is not solved for x since we have $-x$ or $-1x$, not x. To solve for x, we divide both sides by -1.

$$\frac{-x}{-1} = \frac{4}{-1} \qquad \text{Divide both sides by } -1.$$

$$x = -4 \qquad \text{Simplify.}$$

Check to see that the solution is -4, or the solution set is $\{-4\}$. ☐

PRACTICE
3   Solve: $-8x - 4 + 6x = 5x + 11 - 4x$.

If an equation contains parentheses, use the distributive property to remove them.

EXAMPLE 4 Solve: $2(x - 3) = 5x - 9$.

Solution First, use the distributive property.

$$2(x - 3) = 5x - 9$$
$$2x - 6 = 5x - 9 \quad \text{Use the distributive property.}$$

Next, get variable terms on the same side of the equation by subtracting $5x$ from both sides.

$$2x - 6 - 5x = 5x - 9 - 5x \quad \text{Subtract } 5x \text{ from both sides.}$$
$$-3x - 6 = -9 \quad \text{Simplify.}$$
$$-3x - 6 + 6 = -9 + 6 \quad \text{Add 6 to both sides.}$$
$$-3x = -3 \quad \text{Simplify.}$$
$$\frac{-3x}{-3} = \frac{-3}{-3} \quad \text{Divide both sides by } -3.$$
$$x = 1$$

Let $x = 1$ in the original equation to see that 1 is the solution. □

PRACTICE
4 Solve: $3(x - 5) = 6x - 3$.

OBJECTIVE 3 ▶ Solving linear equations containing fractions or decimals. If an equation contains fractions, we first clear the equation of fractions by multiplying both sides of the equation by the _least common denominator_ (LCD) of all fractions in the equation.

EXAMPLE 5 Solve for y: $\frac{y}{3} - \frac{y}{4} = \frac{1}{6}$.

Solution First, clear the equation of fractions by multiplying both sides of the equation by 12, the LCD of denominators 3, 4, and 6.

$$\frac{y}{3} - \frac{y}{4} = \frac{1}{6}$$

$$12\left(\frac{y}{3} - \frac{y}{4}\right) = 12\left(\frac{1}{6}\right) \quad \text{Multiply both sides by the LCD 12.}$$

$$12\left(\frac{y}{3}\right) - 12\left(\frac{y}{4}\right) = 2 \quad \text{Apply the distributive property.}$$

$$4y - 3y = 2 \quad \text{Simplify.}$$

$$y = 2 \quad \text{Simplify.}$$

Check: To check, let $y = 2$ in the original equation.

$$\frac{y}{3} - \frac{y}{4} = \frac{1}{6} \quad \text{Original equation.}$$

$$\frac{2}{3} - \frac{2}{4} \stackrel{?}{=} \frac{1}{6} \quad \text{Let } y = 2.$$

$$\frac{8}{12} - \frac{6}{12} \stackrel{?}{=} \frac{1}{6} \quad \text{Write fractions with the LCD.}$$

$$\frac{2}{12} \stackrel{?}{=} \frac{1}{6} \quad \text{Subtract.}$$

$$\frac{1}{6} = \frac{1}{6} \quad \text{Simplify.}$$

This is a true statement, so the solution is 2. □

PRACTICE
5 Solve for y: $\frac{y}{2} - \frac{y}{5} = \frac{1}{4}$.

As a general guideline, the following steps may be used to solve a linear equation in one variable.

Solving A Linear Equation in One Variable

STEP 1. Clear the equation of fractions by multiplying both sides of the equation by the least common denominator (LCD) of all denominators in the equation.

STEP 2. Use the distributive property to remove grouping symbols such as parentheses.

STEP 3. Combine like terms on each side of the equation.

STEP 4. Use the addition property of equality to rewrite the equation as an equivalent equation with variable terms on one side and numbers on the other side.

STEP 5. Use the multiplication property of equality to isolate the variable.

STEP 6. Check the proposed solution in the original equation.

EXAMPLE 6   Solve for x: $\dfrac{x + 5}{2} + \dfrac{1}{2} = 2x - \dfrac{x - 3}{8}$.

Solution   Multiply both sides of the equation by 8, the LCD of 2 and 8.

> **▶ Helpful Hint**
>
> When we multiply both sides of an equation by a number, the distributive property tells us that each term of the equation is multiplied by the number.

$$8\left(\frac{x + 5}{2} + \frac{1}{2}\right) = 8\left(2x - \frac{x - 3}{8}\right) \qquad \text{Multiply both sides by 8.}$$

$$8\left(\frac{x + 5}{2}\right) + 8 \cdot \frac{1}{2} = 8 \cdot 2x - 8\left(\frac{x - 3}{8}\right) \qquad \text{Apply the distributive property.}$$

$$4(x + 5) + 4 = 16x - (x - 3) \qquad \text{Simplify.}$$

$$4x + 20 + 4 = 16x - x + 3 \qquad \text{Use the distributive property to remove parentheses.}$$

$$4x + 24 = 15x + 3 \qquad \text{Combine like terms.}$$

$$-11x + 24 = 3 \qquad \text{Subtract } 15x \text{ from both sides.}$$

$$-11x = -21 \qquad \text{Subtract 24 from both sides.}$$

$$\frac{-11x}{-11} = \frac{-21}{-11} \qquad \text{Divide both sides by } -11.$$

$$x = \frac{21}{11} \qquad \text{Simplify.}$$

Check: To check, verify that replacing x with $\dfrac{21}{11}$ makes the original equation true. The solution is $\dfrac{21}{11}$. ☐

PRACTICE
6   Solve for x: $x - \dfrac{x - 2}{12} = \dfrac{x + 3}{4} + \dfrac{1}{4}$.

If an equation contains decimals, you may want to first clear the equation of decimals.

EXAMPLE 7   Solve: $0.3x + 0.1 = 0.27x - 0.02$.

Solution   To clear this equation of decimals, we multiply both sides of the equation by 100. Recall that multiplying a number by 100 moves its decimal point two places to the right.

$$100(0.3x + 0.1) = 100(0.27x - 0.02)$$

$$100(0.3x) + 100(0.1) = 100(0.27x) - 100(0.02) \qquad \text{Use the distributive property.}$$

$$30x + 10 = 27x - 2 \qquad \text{Multiply.}$$
$$30x - 27x = -2 - 10 \qquad \text{Subtract } 27x \text{ and } 10 \text{ from both sides.}$$
$$3x = -12 \qquad \text{Simplify.}$$
$$\frac{3x}{3} = \frac{-12}{3} \qquad \text{Divide both sides by 3.}$$
$$x = -4 \qquad \text{Simplify.}$$

Check to see that the solution is -4.

PRACTICE
7   Solve: $0.15x - 0.03 = 0.2x + 0.12$.

Concept Check ☑

Explain what is wrong with the following:

$$3x - 5 = 16$$
$$3x = 11$$
$$\frac{3x}{3} = \frac{11}{3}$$
$$x = \frac{11}{3}$$

OBJECTIVE 4 ▶ Recognizing identities and equations with no solution. So far, each linear equation that we have solved has had a single solution. A linear equation in one variable that has exactly one solution is called a **conditional equation.** We will now look at two other types of equations: contradictions and identities.

An equation in one variable that has no solution is called a **contradiction,** and an equation in one variable that has every number (for which the equation is defined) as a solution is called an **identity.** For review: A linear equation in one variable with

No solution	Is a	Contradiction
Every real number as a solution (as long as the equation is defined)	Is an	Identity

The next examples show how to recognize contradictions and identities.

EXAMPLE 8   Solve for x: $3x + 5 = 3(x + 2)$.

Solution   First, use the distributive property and remove parentheses.

$$3x + 5 = 3(x + 2)$$
$$3x + 5 = 3x + 6 \qquad \text{Apply the distributive property.}$$
$$3x + 5 - 3x = 3x + 6 - 3x \qquad \text{Subtract } 3x \text{ from both sides.}$$
$$5 = 6$$

The equation $5 = 6$ is a false statement no matter what value the variable x might have. Thus, the original equation has no solution. Its solution set is written either as $\{\ \}$ or $\varnothing$. This equation is a contradiction.

PRACTICE
8   Solve for x: $4x - 3 = 4(x + 5)$.

▶ **Helpful Hint**

A solution set of $\{0\}$ and a solution set of $\{\ \}$ are not the same. The solution set $\{0\}$ means 1 solution, 0. The solution set $\{\ \}$ means *no* solution.

Answer to Concept Check:

$$3x - 5 = 16$$
$$3x = 21$$
$$x = 7$$

Therefore, the correct solution set is $\{7\}$.

EXAMPLE 9   Solve for x: $6x - 4 = 2 + 6(x - 1)$.

Solution   First, use the distributive property and remove parentheses.

$$6x - 4 = 2 + 6(x - 1)$$

$$6x - 4 = 2 + 6x - 6 \quad \text{Apply the distributive property.}$$

$$6x - 4 = 6x - 4 \quad \text{Combine like terms.}$$

At this point we might notice that both sides of the equation are the same, so replacing x by any real number gives a true statement. Thus the solution set of this equation is the set of real numbers, and the equation is an identity. Continuing to "solve" $6x - 4 = 6x - 4$, we eventually arrive at the same conclusion.

$$6x - 4 + 4 = 6x - 4 + 4 \quad \text{Add 4 to both sides.}$$

$$6x = 6x \quad \text{Simplify.}$$

$$6x - 6x = 6x - 6x \quad \text{Subtract } 6x \text{ from both sides.}$$

$$0 = 0 \quad \text{Simplify.}$$

Since $0 = 0$ is a true statement for every value of x, all real numbers are solutions. The solution set is the set of all real numbers or, $\mathbb{R}$, $\{x \mid x$ is a real number$\}$, and the equation is called an identity.   □

PRACTICE
9   Solve for x: $5x - 2 = 3 + 5(x - 1)$.

▶ **Helpful Hint**

For linear equations, *any* false statement such as $5 = 6$, $0 = 1$, or $-2 = 2$ informs us that the original equation has no solution. Also, *any* true statement such as $0 = 0$, $2 = 2$, or $-5 = -5$ informs us that the original equation is an identity.

VOCABULARY & READINESS CHECK

Use the choices below to fill in the blanks. Not all choices will be used.

multiplication	value	like
addition	solution	equivalent

1. Equations with the same solution set are called _____ equations.

2. A value for the variable in an equation that makes the equation a true statement is called a _____ of the equation.

3. By the _____ property of equality, $y = -3$ and $y - 7 = -3 - 7$ are equivalent equations.

4. By the _____ property of equality, $2y = -3$ and $\dfrac{2y}{2} = \dfrac{-3}{2}$ are equivalent equations.

Identify each as an equation or an expression.

5. $\dfrac{1}{3}x - 5$ _____

6. $2(x - 3) = 7$ _____

7. $\dfrac{5}{9}x + \dfrac{1}{3} = \dfrac{2}{9} - x$ _____

8. $\dfrac{5}{9}x + \dfrac{1}{3} - \dfrac{2}{9} - x$ _____

By inspection, decide which equations have no solution and which equations have all real numbers as solutions.

9. $2x + 3 = 2x + 3$ **10.** $2x + 1 = 2x + 3$ **11.** $5x - 2 = 5x - 7$ **12.** $5x - 3 = 5x - 3$

2.1 EXERCISE SET

Solve each equation and check. See Examples 1 and 2.

1. $-5x = -30$

2. $-2x = 18$

3. $-10 = x + 12$

4. $-25 = y + 30$

5. $x - 2.8 = 1.9$

6. $y - 8.6 = -6.3$

7. $5x - 4 = 26 + 2x$

8. $5y - 3 = 11 + 3y$

9. $-4.1 - 7z = 3.6$

10. $10.3 - 6x = -2.3$

11. $5y + 12 = 2y - 3$

12. $4x + 14 = 6x + 8$

Solve each equation and check. See Examples 3 and 4.

13. $3x - 4 - 5x = x + 4 + x$

14. $13x - 15x + 8 = 4x + 2 - 24$

15. $8x - 5x + 3 = x - 7 + 10$

16. $6 + 3x + x = -x + 8 - 26 + 24$

17. $5x + 12 = 2(2x + 7)$

18. $2(4x + 3) = 7x + 5$

19. $3(x - 6) = 5x$

20. $6x = 4(x - 5)$

21. $-2(5y - 1) - y = -4(y - 3)$

22. $-4(3n - 2) - n = -11(n - 1)$

Solve each equation and check. See Examples 5 through 7.

23. $\dfrac{x}{2} + \dfrac{x}{3} = \dfrac{3}{4}$

24. $\dfrac{x}{2} + \dfrac{x}{5} = \dfrac{5}{4}$

25. $\dfrac{3t}{4} - \dfrac{t}{2} = 1$

26. $\dfrac{4r}{5} - \dfrac{r}{10} = 7$

27. $\dfrac{n - 3}{4} + \dfrac{n + 5}{7} = \dfrac{5}{14}$

28. $\dfrac{2 + h}{9} + \dfrac{h - 1}{3} = \dfrac{1}{3}$

29. $0.6x - 10 = 1.4x - 14$

30. $0.3x + 2.4 = 0.1x + 4$

31. $\dfrac{3x - 1}{9} + x = \dfrac{3x + 1}{3} + 4$

32. $\dfrac{2z + 7}{8} - 2 = z + \dfrac{z - 1}{2}$

33. $1.5(4 - x) = 1.3(2 - x)$

34. $2.4(2x + 3) = -0.1(2x + 3)$

Solve each equation. See Examples 8 and 9.

35. $4(n + 3) = 2(6 + 2n)$

36. $6(4n + 4) = 8(3 + 3n)$

37. $3(x + 1) + 5 = 3x + 2$

38. $4(x + 2) + 4 = 4x - 8$

39. $2(x - 8) + x = 3(x - 6) + 2$

40. $5(x - 4) + x = 6(x - 2) - 8$

41. $4(x + 5) = 3(x - 4) + x$

42. $9(x - 2) = 8(x - 3) + x$

MIXED PRACTICE

Solve each equation. See Examples 1 through 9.

43. $\dfrac{3}{8} + \dfrac{b}{3} = \dfrac{5}{12}$

44. $\dfrac{a}{2} + \dfrac{7}{4} = 5$

45. $x - 10 = -6x - 10$

46. $4x - 7 = 2x - 7$

47. $5(x - 2) + 2x = 7(x + 4) - 38$

48. $3x + 2(x + 4) = 5(x + 1) + 3$

49. $y + 0.2 = 0.6(y + 3)$

50. $-(w + 0.2) = 0.3(4 - w)$

51. $\dfrac{1}{4}(a + 2) = \dfrac{1}{6}(5 - a)$

52. $\dfrac{1}{3}(8 + 2c) = \dfrac{1}{5}(3c - 5)$

53. $2y + 5(y - 4) = 4y - 2(y - 10)$

54. $9c - 3(6 - 5c) = c - 2(3c + 9)$

55. $6x - 2(x - 3) = 4(x + 1) + 4$

56. $10x - 2(x + 4) = 8(x - 2) + 6$

57. $\dfrac{m - 4}{3} - \dfrac{3m - 1}{5} = 1$

58. $\dfrac{n + 1}{8} - \dfrac{2 - n}{3} = \dfrac{5}{6}$

59. $8x - 12 - 3x = 9x - 7$

60. $10y - 18 - 4y = 12y - 13$

61. $-(3x - 5) - (2x - 6) + 1 = -5(x - 1) - (3x + 2) + 3$

62. $-4(2x - 3) - (10x + 7) - 2 = -(12x - 5) - (4x + 9) - 1$

63. $\dfrac{1}{3}(y + 4) + 6 = \dfrac{1}{4}(3y - 1) - 2$

64. $\dfrac{1}{5}(2y - 1) - 2 = \dfrac{1}{2}(3y - 5) + 3$

65. $2[7 - 5(1 - n)] + 8n = -16 + 3[6(n + 1) - 3n]$

66. $3[8 - 4(n - 2)] + 5n = -20 + 2[5(1 - n) - 6n]$

REVIEW AND PREVIEW

Translate each phrase into an expression. Use the variable x to represent each unknown number. See Section 1.2.

67. The quotient of 8 and a number

68. The sum of 8 and a number

69. The product of 8 and a number

70. The difference of 8 and a number

71. Five subtracted from twice a number

72. Two more than three times a number

CONCEPT EXTENSIONS

Find the error for each proposed solution. Then correct the proposed solution. See the Concept Check in this section.

73.
$$2x + 19 = 13$$
$$2x = 32$$
$$\dfrac{2x}{2} = \dfrac{32}{2}$$
$$x = 16$$

74.
$$-3(x - 4) = 10$$
$$-3x - 12 = 10$$
$$-3x = 22$$
$$\dfrac{-3x}{-3} = \dfrac{22}{-3}$$
$$x = -\dfrac{22}{3}$$

75. $9x + 1.6 = 4x + 0.4$

$5x = 1.2$

$\dfrac{5x}{5} = \dfrac{1.2}{5}$

$x = 0.24$

76. $\dfrac{x}{3} + 7 = \dfrac{5x}{3}$

$x + 7 = 5x$

$7 = 4x$

$\dfrac{7}{4} = \dfrac{4x}{4}$

$\dfrac{7}{2} = x$

77. a. Simplify the expression $4(x + 1) + 1$.

  b. Solve the equation $4(x + 1) + 1 = -7$.

  c. Explain the difference between solving an equation for a variable and simplifying an expression.

78. Explain why the multiplication property of equality does not include multiplying both sides of an equation by 0. (*Hint:* Write down a false statement and then multiply both sides by 0. Is the result true or false? What does this mean?)

79. In your own words, explain why the equation $x + 7 = x + 6$ has no solution while the solution set of the equation $x + 7 = x + 7$ contains all real numbers.

80. In your own words, explain why the equation $x = -x$ has one solution—namely, 0—while the solution set of the equation $x = x$ is all real numbers.

Find the value of K such that the equations are equivalent.

81. $3.2x + 4 = 5.4x - 7$

$3.2x = 5.4x + K$

82. $-7.6y - 10 = -1.1y + 12$

$-7.6y = -1.1y + K$

83. $\dfrac{7}{11}x + 9 = \dfrac{3}{11}x - 14$

$\dfrac{7}{11}x = \dfrac{3}{11}x + K$

84. $\dfrac{x}{6} + 4 = \dfrac{x}{3}$

$x + K = 2x$

85. Write a linear equation in x whose only solution is 5.

86. Write an equation in x that has no solution.

Solve the following.

87. $x(x - 6) + 7 = x(x + 1)$

88. $7x^2 + 2x - 3 = 6x(x + 4) + x^2$

89. $3x(x + 5) - 12 = 3x^2 + 10x + 3$

90. $x(x + 1) + 16 = x(x + 5)$

Solve and check.

91. $2.569x = -12.48534$

92. $-9.112y = -47.537304$

93. $2.86z - 8.1258 = -3.75$

94. $1.25x - 20.175 = -8.15$

📖 STUDY SKILLS BUILDER

Have You Decided to Complete This Course Successfully?

Ask yourself if one of your current goals is to complete this course successfully.

If it is not a goal of yours, ask yourself why? One common reason is fear of failure. Amazingly enough, fear of failure alone can be strong enough to keep many of us from doing our best in any endeavor.

Another common reason is that you simply haven't taken the time to make successfully completing this course one of your goals. How do you do this? Start by writing this goal in your mathematics notebook. Then list steps you will take to ensure success. A great first step is to read or reread Section 1.1 and make a commitment to try the suggestions in that section.

Good luck, and don't forget that a positive attitude will make a big difference.

Let's see how you are doing.

1. Have you decided to make "successfully completing this course" a goal of yours? If no, please list reasons why this has not happened. Study your list and talk to your instructor about this.

2. If your answer to question 1 is yes, take a moment and list in your notebook further specific goals that will help you achieve this major goal of successfully completing this course. (For example, "My goal this semester is not to miss any of my mathematics classes.")

3. Rate your commitment to this course with a number between 1 and 5. Use the diagram below to help.

High Commitment		Average Commitment		Not Committed at all
5	4	3	2	1

4. If you have rated your personal commitment level (from the exercise above) as a 1, 2, or 3, list the reasons why this is so. Then determine whether it is possible to increase your commitment level to a 4 or 5.

2.2 AN INTRODUCTION TO PROBLEM SOLVING

OBJECTIVES

1 Write algebraic expressions that can be simplified.

2 Apply the steps for problem solving.

OBJECTIVE 1 ▶ Writing and simplifying algebraic expressions. In order to prepare for problem solving, we practice writing algebraic expressions that can be simplified.

Our first example involves consecutive integers and perimeter. Recall that *consecutive integers* are integers that follow one another in order. Study the examples of consecutive, even, and odd integers and their representations.

Consecutive Integers:

Consecutive Even Integers:

Consecutive Odd Integers:

EXAMPLE 1   Write the following as algebraic expressions. Then simplify.

a. The sum of three consecutive integers, if x is the first consecutive integer.

△ **b.** The perimeter of the triangle with sides of length x, $5x$, and $6x - 3$.

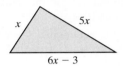

Solution

a. Recall that if x is the first integer, then the next consecutive integer is 1 more, or $x + 1$ and the next consecutive integer is 1 more than $x + 1$, or $x + 2$.

In words:	first integer	plus	next consecutive integer	plus	next consecutive integer
	↓	↓	↓	↓	↓
Translate:	x	$+$	$(x + 1)$	$+$	$(x + 2)$

Then $x + (x + 1) + (x + 2) = x + x + 1 + x + 2$

$= 3x + 3$ Simplify by combining like terms.

b. The perimeter of a triangle is the sum of the lengths of the sides.

In words:	side	$+$	side	$+$	side
	↓		↓		↓
Translate:	x	$+$	$5x$	$+$	$(6x - 3)$

Then $x + 5x + (6x - 3) = x + 5x + 6x - 3$

$= 12x - 3$ Simplify.   □

PRACTICE

1   Write the following algebraic expressions. Then simplify.

a. The sum of three consecutive odd integers, if x is the first consecutive odd integer

b. The perimeter of a trapezoid with bases x and $2x$, and sides of $x + 2$ and $2x - 3$

EXAMPLE 2 The three busiest airports in the United States are in Chicago, Atlanta, and Los Angeles. The airport in Atlanta has 13.3 million more arrivals and departures than the Los Angeles airport. The Chicago airport has 1.3 million more arrivals and departures than the Los Angeles airport. Write the sum of the arrivals and departures from these three cities as a simplified algebraic expression. Let x be the number of arrivals and departures at the Los Angeles airport. (*Source:* U.S. Department of Transportation)

Solution If x = millions of arrivals and departures at the Los Angeles airport, then

$$x + 13.3 = \text{millions of arrivals and departures at the Atlanta airport and}$$
$$x + 1.3 = \text{millions of arrivals and departures at the Chicago airport.}$$

Since we want their sum, we have

In words:	arrivals and departures at Los Angeles	+	arrivals and departures at Atlanta	+	arrivals and departures at Chicago
	↓		↓		↓
Translate:	x	+	$(x + 13.3)$	+	$(x + 1.3)$

$$\text{Then} \quad x + (x + 13.3) + (x + 1.3) = x + x + 13.3 + x + 1.3$$
$$= 3x + 14.6 \quad \text{Combine like terms.}$$

In Exercise 57, we will find the actual number of arrivals and departures at these airports. □

PRACTICE

2 The three busiest airports in Europe are in London, England; Paris, France; and Frankfurt, Germany. The airport in London has 15.7 million more arrivals and departures than the Frankfurt airport. The Paris airport has 1.6 million more arrivals and departures than the Frankfurt airport. Write the sum of the arrivals and departures from these three cities as a simplified algebraic expression. Let x be the number of arrivals and departures at the Frankfurt airport. (*Source:* Association of European Airlines)

▶ **Helpful Hint**
You may want to begin this section by studying key words and phrases and their translations in Sections 1.2 Objective 5 and 1.4 Objective 4.

OBJECTIVE 2 ▶ **Applying steps for problem solving.** Our main purpose for studying algebra is to solve problems. The following problem-solving strategy will be used throughout this text and may also be used to solve real-life problems that occur outside the mathematics classroom.

General Strategy for Problem Solving

1. UNDERSTAND the problem. During this step, become comfortable with the problem. Some ways of doing this are:

   Read and reread the problem.

   Propose a solution and check. Pay careful attention to how you check your proposed solution. This will help when writing an equation to model the problem.

   Construct a drawing.

   Choose a variable to represent the unknown. (Very important part)

2. TRANSLATE the problem into an equation.

3. SOLVE the equation.

4. INTERPRET the results: *Check* the proposed solution in the stated problem and *state* your conclusion.

Let's review this strategy by solving a problem involving unknown numbers.

EXAMPLE 3 **Finding Unknown Numbers**

Find three numbers such that the second number is 3 more than twice the first number, and the third number is four times the first number. The sum of the three numbers is 164.

Solution

▶ Helpful Hint

The purpose of guessing a solution is not to guess correctly but to gain confidence and to help understand the problem and how to model it.

1. UNDERSTAND the problem. First let's read and reread the problem and then propose a solution. For example, if the first number is 25, then the second number is 3 more than twice 25, or 53. The third number is four times 25, or 100. The sum of 25, 53, and 100 is 178, not the required sum, but we have gained some valuable information about the problem. First, we know that the first number is less than 25 since our guess led to a sum greater than the required sum. Also, we have gained some information as to how to model the problem.

   Next let's assign a variable and use this variable to represent any other unknown quantities. If we let

$$x = \text{the first number, then}$$
$$2x + 3 = \text{the second number}$$

3 more than
twice the second number

$$4x = \text{the third number}$$

2. TRANSLATE the problem into an equation. To do so, we use the fact that the sum of the numbers is 164. First let's write this relationship in words and then translate to an equation.

In words:	first number	added to	second number	added to	third number	is	164
	↓	↓	↓	↓	↓	↓	↓
Translate:	x	$+$	$(2x + 3)$	$+$	$4x$	$=$	164

3. SOLVE the equation.

$$x + (2x + 3) + 4x = 164$$
$$x + 2x + 4x + 3 = 164 \quad \text{Remove parentheses.}$$
$$7x + 3 = 164 \quad \text{Combine like terms.}$$
$$7x = 161 \quad \text{Subtract 3 from both sides.}$$
$$x = 23 \quad \text{Divide both sides by 7.}$$

4. INTERPRET. Here, we *check* our work and *state* the solution. Recall that if the first number $x = 23$, then the second number $2x + 3 = 2 \cdot 23 + 3 = 49$ and the third number $4x = 4 \cdot 23 = 92$.

Check: Is the second number 3 more than twice the first number? Yes, since 3 more than twice 23 is $46 + 3$, or 49. Also, their sum, $23 + 49 + 92 = 164$, is the required sum.

State: The three numbers are 23, 49, and 92. □

PRACTICE

3 Find three numbers such that the second number is 8 less than triple the first number, the third number is five times the first number, and the sum of the three numbers is 118.

Many of today's rates and statistics are given as percents. Interest rates, tax rates, nutrition labeling, and percent of households in a given category are just a few examples.

Before we practice solving problems containing percents, let's briefly take a moment and review the meaning of percent and how to find a percent of a number.

The word *percent* means "per hundred," and the symbol % is used to denote percent. This means that 23% is 23 per hundred, or $\frac{23}{100}$. Also,

$$41\% = \frac{41}{100} = 0.41$$

To find a percent of a number, we multiply.

$$16\% \text{ of } 25 = 16\% \cdot 25 = 0.16 \cdot 25 = 4$$

Thus, 16% of 25 is 4.

Study the table below. It will help you become more familiar with finding percents.

Percent	*Meaning/Shortcut*	*Example*
50%	$\frac{1}{2}$ or half of a number	50% of 60 is 30.
25%	$\frac{1}{4}$ or a quarter of a number	25% of 60 is 15.
10%	0.1 or $\frac{1}{10}$ of a number (move the decimal point 1 place to the left)	10% of 60 is 6.0 or 6.
1%	0.01 or $\frac{1}{100}$ of a number (move the decimal point 2 places to the left)	1% of 60 is 0.60 or 0.6.
100%	1 or all of a number	100% of 60 is 60.
200%	2 or double a number	200% of 60 is 120.

Concept Check ☑

Suppose you are finding 112% of a number x. Which of the following is a correct description of the result? Explain.

a. The result is less than x.   **b.** The result is equal to x.   **c.** The result is greater than x.

Next, we solve a problem containing a percent.

EXAMPLE 4   **Finding the Original Price of a Computer**

Suppose that a computer store just announced an 8% decrease in the price of a particular computer model. If this computer sells for $2162 after the decrease, find the original price of this computer.

Solution

1. **UNDERSTAND.** Read and reread the problem. Recall that a percent decrease means a percent of the original price. Let's guess that the original price of the computer is $2500. The amount of decrease is then 8% of $2500, or $(0.08)(\$2500) = \$200$. This means that the new price of the computer is the original price minus the decrease, or $\$2500 - \$200 = \$2300$. Our guess is incorrect, but we now have an idea of how to model this problem. In our model, we will let x = the original price of the computer.

2. **TRANSLATE.**

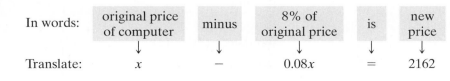

In words:	original price of computer	minus	8% of original price	is	new price
Translate:	x	$-$	$0.08x$	$=$	2162

3. SOLVE the equation.

$$x - 0.08x = 2162$$
$$0.92x = 2162 \qquad \text{Combine like terms.}$$
$$x = \frac{2162}{0.92} = 2350 \qquad \text{Divide both sides by 0.92.}$$

4. INTERPRET.

Check: If the original price of the computer was $2350, the new price is

$$\$2350 - (0.08)(\$2350) = \$2350 - \$188$$
$$= \$2162 \qquad \text{The given new price}$$

State: The original price of the computer was $2350.

PRACTICE
4   At the end of the season, the cost of a snowboard was reduced by 40%. If the snowboard sells for $270 after the decrease, find the original price of the board.

EXAMPLE 5   **Finding the Lengths of a Triangle's Sides**

A pennant in the shape of an isosceles triangle is to be constructed for the Slidell High School Athletic Club and sold at a fund-raiser. The company manufacturing the pennant charges according to perimeter, and the athletic club has determined that a perimeter of 149 centimeters should make a nice profit. If each equal side of the triangle is twice the length of the third side, increased by 12 centimeters, find the lengths of the sides of the triangular pennant.

Solution

1. UNDERSTAND. Read and reread the problem. Recall that the perimeter of a triangle is the distance around. Let's guess that the third side of the triangular pennant is 20 centimeters. This means that each equal side is twice 20 centimeters, increased by 12 centimeters, or $2(20) + 12 = 52$ centimeters.

This gives a perimeter of $20 + 52 + 52 = 124$ centimeters. Our guess is incorrect, but we now have a better understanding of how to model this problem.

Now we let the third side of the triangle $= x$

the first side =	twice	the third side	increased by 12
	↓	↓	↓
=	2	x	+ 12,
	or $2x + 12$		

the second side $= 2x + 12$

2. TRANSLATE.

In words:

first side	+	second side	+	third side	=	149
↓	↓	↓	↓	↓	↓	↓
$(2x + 12)$	+	$(2x + 12)$	+	x	=	149

Translate:

3. SOLVE the equation.

$$(2x + 12) + (2x + 12) + x = 149$$

$$2x + 12 + 2x + 12 + x = 149 \qquad \text{Remove parentheses.}$$

$$5x + 24 = 149 \qquad \text{Combine like terms.}$$

$$5x = 125 \qquad \text{Subtract 24 from both sides.}$$

$$x = 25 \qquad \text{Divide both sides by 5.}$$

4. INTERPRET. If the third side is 25 centimeters, then the first side is $2(25) + 12 = 62$ centimeters and the second side is 62 centimeters also.

Check: The first and second sides are each twice 25 centimeters increased by 12 centimeters or 62 centimeters. Also, the perimeter is $25 + 62 + 62 = 149$ centimeters, the required perimeter.

State: The lengths of the sides of the triangle are 25 centimeters, 62 centimeters, and 62 centimeters. ☐

PRACTICE
5 For its 40th anniversary, North Campus Community College is placing rectangular banners on all the light poles on campus. The perimeter of these banners is 160 inches. If the longer side of each banner is 16″ less than double the width, find the dimensions of the banners.

EXAMPLE 6   **Finding Consecutive Integers**

Kelsey Ohleger was helping her friend Benji Burnstine study for an algebra exam. Kelsey told Benji that her three latest art history quiz scores are three consecutive even integers whose sum is 264. Help Benji find the scores.

Solution

1. UNDERSTAND. Read and reread the problem. Since we are looking for consecutive even integers, let

$$x = \text{the first integer. Then}$$
$$x + 2 = \text{the second consecutive even integer}$$
$$x + 4 = \text{the third consecutive even integer.}$$

2. TRANSLATE.

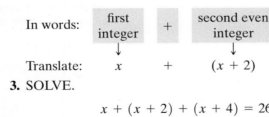

In words:	first integer	+	second even integer	+	third even integer	=	264
Translate:	x	+	$(x + 2)$	+	$(x + 4)$	=	264

3. SOLVE.

$$x + (x + 2) + (x + 4) = 264$$

$$3x + 6 = 264 \qquad \text{Combine like terms.}$$

$$3x = 258 \qquad \text{Subtract 6 from both sides.}$$

$$x = 86 \qquad \text{Divide both sides by 3.}$$

4. INTERPRET. If $x = 86$, then $x + 2 = 86 + 2$ or 88, and $x + 4 = 86 + 4$ or 90.

Check: The numbers 86, 88, and 90 are three consecutive even integers. Their sum is 264, the required sum.

State: Kelsey's art history quiz scores are 86, 88, and 90. ☐

PRACTICE
6 Find three consecutive odd integers whose sum is 81.

VOCABULARY & READINESS CHECK

Fill in each blank with <, >, *or* =. *(Assume that the unknown number is a positive number.)*

1. 130% of a number _____ the number.

2. 70% of a number _____ the number.

3. 100% of a number _____ the number.

4. 200% of a number _____ the number.

Complete the table. The first row has been completed for you.

	First Integer	*All Described Integers*
Three consecutive integers	18	18, 19, 20
5. Four consecutive integers	31	
6. Three consecutive odd integers	31	
7. Three consecutive even integers	18	
8. Four consecutive even integers	92	
9. Three consecutive integers	y	
10. Three consecutive even integers	z (z is even)	
11. Four consecutive integers	p	
12. Three consecutive odd integers	s (s is odd)	

2.2 | EXERCISE SET

Write the following as algebraic expressions. Then simplify. See Examples 1 and 2.

△ **1.** The perimeter of the square with side length y.

△ **2.** The perimeter of the rectangle with length x and width $x - 5$.

▥ **3.** The sum of three consecutive integers if the first is z.

4. The sum of three consecutive odd integers if the first integer is x.

▥ **5.** The total amount of money (in cents) in x nickels, $(x + 3)$ dimes, and $2x$ quarters. (*Hint:* the value of a nickel is 5 cents, the value of a dime is 10 cents, and the value of a quarter is 25 cents)

6. The total amount of money (in cents) in y quarters, $7y$ dimes, and $(2y - 1)$ nickels. (Use the hint for Exercise 5.)

△ **7.** A piece of land along Bayou Liberty is to be fenced and subdivided as shown so that each rectangle has the same dimensions. Express the total amount of fencing needed as an algebraic expression in x.

8. A flooded piece of land near the Mississippi River in New Orleans is to be surveyed and divided into 4 rectangles of equal dimension. Express the total amount of fencing needed as an algebraic expression in x.

△ **9.** Write the perimeter of the floor plan shown as an algebraic expression in x.

10. Write the perimeter of the floor plan shown as an algebraic expression in *x*.

Solve. See Example 3.

11. Four times the difference of a number and 2 is the same as 2 increased by four times the number plus twice the number. Find the number.

12. Twice the sum of a number and 3 is the same as five times the number minus 1 minus four times the number. Find the number.

13. A second number is five times a first number. A third number is 100 more than the first number. If the sum of the three numbers is 415, find the numbers.

14. A second number is 6 less than a first number. A third number is twice the first number. If the sum of the three numbers is 306, find the numbers.

Solve. See Example 4.

15. The United States consists of 2271 million acres of land. Approximately 29% of this land is federally owned. Find the number of acres that are not federally owned. (*Source: U.S. General Services Administration*)

16. The state of Nevada contains the most federally owned acres of land in the United States. If 90% of the state's 70 million acres of land is federally owned, find the number of acres that are not federally owned. (*Source: U.S. General Services Administration*)

17. In 2006, a total of 2748 earthquakes occurred in the United States. Of these, 85.3% were minor tremors with magnitudes of 3.9 or less on the Richter scale. How many minor earthquakes occurred in the United States in 2006? Round to the nearest whole number. (*Source: U.S. Geological Survey National Earthquake Information Center*)

18. Of the 958 tornadoes that occurred in the United States during 2006, 25.5% occurred during the month of April. How many tornadoes occurred during April 2006? Round to the nearest whole. (*Source: Storm Prediction Center*)

19. In a recent survey, 15% of online shoppers in the United States say that they prefer to do business only with large, well-known retailers. In a group of 1500 online shoppers, how many are willing to do business with any size retailers? (*Source: Inc.com*)

20. In 2006, the restaurant and food service industry employed 9.1% of the total employees in the state of California. In 2006, California had approximately 17,029,300 employed workers. How many people worked in the restaurant and food service industry in California? Round to the nearest whole number. (*Source: California Employment Development Center.*)

The following graph is called a circle graph or a pie chart. The circle represents a whole, or in this case, 100%. This particular graph shows the number of minutes per day that people use e-mail at work. Use this graph to answer Exercises 21 through 24.

Time Spent on E-Mail at Work

Source: Pew Internet & American Life Project

21. What percent of e-mail users at work spend less than 15 minutes on e-mail per day?

22. Among e-mail users at work, what is the most common time spent on e-mail per day?

23. If it were estimated that a large company has 5957 employees, how many of these would you expect to be using e-mail more than 3 hours per day? Round to the nearest whole employee.

24. If it were estimated that a medium size company has 278 employees, how many of these would you expect to be using e-mail between 2 and 3 hours per day? Round to the nearest whole employee.

25. In 2006, the population of Canada was 31.6 million. This represented an increase in population of 5.4% since 2001. What was the population of Canada in 2001? (Round to the nearest hundredth of a million.) (*Source: Statistics Canada*)

26. In 2006, the cost of an average hotel room per night was $96.73. This was an increase of 6.8% over the average cost in 2005. Find the average hotel room cost in 2005. (*Source: Smith Travel Research*)

Use the diagrams to find the unknown measures of angles or lengths of sides. Recall that the sum of the angle measures of a triangle is 180°. See Example 5.

27.

28.

29.

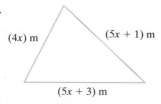

Perimeter is 102 meters.

30.

Perimeter is 75 centimeters.

31.

Perimeter is 99 inches.

32.

Perimeter is 324 feet.

Solve. See Example 6.

33. The sum of three consecutive integers is 228. Find the integers.

34. The sum of three consecutive odd integers is 327. Find the integers.

35. The zip codes of three Nevada locations—Fallon, Fernley, and Gardnerville Ranchos—are three consecutive even integers. If twice the first integer added to the third is 268,222, find each zip code.

36. During a recent year, the average SAT scores in math for the states of Alabama, Louisiana, and Michigan were 3 consecutive integers. If the sum of the first integer, second integer, and three times the third integer is 2637, find each score.

MIXED PRACTICE

Solve. See Examples 1 through 6. Many companies and government agencies predict the growth or decline of occupations. The following data are based on information from the U.S. Department of Labor. Notice that the first table is in increase in number of jobs (in thousands) and the second table is in percent increase in number of jobs.

37. Use the table to find the actual number of jobs for each occupation.

Occupation	Increase in Number of Jobs (in thousands) from 2000 to 2012
Security guards	$2x - 51$
Home health aides	$\frac{3}{2}x + 3$
Computer systems analysts	x
Total	780 thousand

38. Use the table to find the actual percent increase in number of jobs for each occupation.

Occupation	Precent Increase in Number of Jobs from 2000 to 2012
Computer software engineers	$\frac{3}{2}x + 1$
Management analysts	x
Receptionist and information clerks	$x - 1$
Total	105%

39. The occupations of postsecondary teachers, registered nurses, and medical assistants are among the ten with the largest growth from 2000 to 2012. (See the Chapter 2 opener.) The number of postsecondary teacher jobs will grow 173 thousand more than twice the number of medical assistant jobs. The number of registered nurse jobs will grow 22 thousand less than three times the number of medical assistant jobs. If the total growth of these three jobs is predicted to be 1441 thousand, find the predicted growth of each job.

40. The occupations of telephone operators, fishers, and sewing machine operators are among the ten with the largest job decline from 2000 to 2012, according to the U.S. Department of Labor. The number of telephone operators will decline 8 thousand more than twice the number of fishers. The number of sewing machine operators will decline 1 thousand less than

10 times the number of telephone operators. If the total decline of these three jobs is predicted to be 137 thousand, find the predicted decline of each job.

41. America West Airlines has 3 models of Boeing aircraft in their fleet. The 737-300 contains 21 more seats than the 737-200. The 757-200 contains 36 less seats than twice the number of seats in the 737-200. Find the number of seats for each aircraft if the total number of seats for the 3 models is 437. (*Source:* America West Airlines)

42. The new governor of California makes $27,500 more than the governor of New York, and $120,724 more than the governor of Alaska. If the sum of these 3 salaries is $471,276, find the salary of each governor. (*Source:* State Web sites)

43. A new fax machine was recently purchased for an office in Hopedale for $464.40 including tax. If the tax rate in Hopedale is 8%, find the price of the fax machine before tax.

44. A premedical student at a local university was complaining that she had just paid $158.60 for her human anatomy book, including tax. Find the price of the book before taxes if the tax rate at this university is 9%.

45. In 2006, the population of South Africa was 44.2 million people. From 2006 to 2050, South Africa's population is expected to decrease by 5.6%. Find the expected population of South Africa in 2050. Round to the nearest tenth of a million. (*Source:* Population Reference Bureau)

46. In 2006, the population of Morocco was 33.2 million. This represented an increase in population of 1.5% from a year earlier. What was the population of Morocco in 2005? Round to the nearest tenth of a million. (*Source:* Population Reference Bureau)

Recall that two angles are complements of each other if their sum is 90°. Two angles are supplements of each other if their sum is 180°. Find the measure of each angle.

47. One angle is three times its supplement increased by 20°. Find the measures of the two supplementary angles.

48. One angle is twice its complement increased by 30°. Find the measure of the two complementary angles.

Recall that the sum of the angle measures of a triangle is 180°.

49. Find the measures of the angles of a triangle if the measure of one angle is twice the measure of a second angle and the third angle measures 3 times the second angle decreased by 12.

50. Find the angles of an isoceles triangle whose two base angles are equal and whose third angle is 10° less than three times a base angle.

51. Two frames are needed with the same perimeter: one frame in the shape of a square and one in the shape of an equilateral triangle. Each side of the triangle is 6 centimeters longer than each side of the square. Find the dimensions of each frame. (An equilateral triangle has sides that are the same length.)

52. Two frames are needed with the same perimeter: one frame in the shape of a square and one in the shape of a regular pentagon. Each side of the square is 7 inches longer than each side of the pentagon. Find the dimensions of each frame. (A regular polygon has sides that are the same length.)

53. The sum of the first and third of three consecutive even integers is 156. Find the three even integers.

54. The sum of the second and fourth of four consecutive integers is 110. Find the four integers.

△ **55.** The perimeter of the triangle in Example 1b in this section is 483 feet. Find the length of each side.

△ **56.** The perimeter of the trapezoid in Practice 1b in this section is 110 meters. Find the lengths of its sides and bases.

57. The airports in Chicago, Atlanta, and Los Angeles have a total of 197.6 million annual arrivals and departures. Use this information and Example 2 in this section to find the number from each individual airport.

58. The airports in London, Paris, and Frankfurt have a total of 173.9 million annual arrivals and departures. Use this information and Practice 2 in this section to find the number from each airport.

59. Incandescent, fluorescent, and halogen bulbs are lasting longer today than ever before. On average, the number of bulb hours for a fluorescent bulb is 25 times the number of bulb hours for a halogen bulb. The number of bulb hours for an incandescent bulb is 2,500 less than the halogen bulb. If the total number of bulb hours for the three types of bulbs is 105,500, find the number of bulb hours for each type. (*Source: Popular Science Magazine*)

Incandescent   Fluorescent   Halogen
bulb   bulb   bulb

(year: 1870)   (year: 1938)   (year: 1964)

60. The three tallest hospitals in the world are Guy's Tower in London, Queen Mary Hospital in Hong Kong, and Galter Pavilion in Chicago. These buildings have a total height of 1320 feet. Guy's Tower is 67 feet taller than Galter Pavilion and the Queen Mary Hospital is 47 feet taller than Galter Pavilion. Find the heights of the three hospitals.

△ **61.** The official manual for traffic signs is the *Manual on Uniform Traffic Control Devices* published by the Government Printing Office. The rectangular sign below has a length 12 inches more than twice its height. If the perimeter of the sign is 312 inches, find its dimensions.

62. INVESCO Field at Mile High, home to the Denver Broncos, has 11,675 more seats than Heinz Field, home to the Pittsburgh Steelers. Together, these two stadiums can seat a total of 140,575 NFL fans. How many seats does

each stadium have? (*Sources:* Denver Broncos, Pittsburgh Steelers)

63. In 2004, sales in the athletic footwear market in the United States were $4.7 billion. (*Source:* NPD Group)

  a. There was a 5% increase in the athletic footwear sales from 2004 to 2006. Find the total sales for the athletic footwear market in 2006. (Round to the nearest tenth of a billion.)

  b. Twenty-five percent of the sales of footwear were running shoes. Find the amount of money spent on running shoes in 2006. (Round to the nearest hundredth of a billion.)

64. The number of deaths caused by tornadoes decreased 59.2% from the 1950s to the 1990s. There were 579 deaths from tornadoes in the 1990s. (*Source:* National Weather Service)

  a. Find the number of deaths caused by tornadoes in the 1950s. Round to the nearest whole number.

  b. In your own words, explain why you think that the number of tornado-related deaths has decreased so much since the 1950s.

65. China, the United States, and Russia are the countries with the most cellular subscribers in the world. Together, the three countries have 34.8% of the world's cellular subscribers. If the percent of world subscribers in China is 3.1 less than 4 times the percent of world subscribers in Russia, and the percent of world subscribers in the United States is 4.3% more than the percent of world subscribers in Russia, find the percent of world subscribers for each country. (*Source:* Computer Industry of America)

66. In 2006, 74.2 million tax returns were filed electronically (on-line filing, professional electronic filing, and TeleFile). This represents a 108.8% increase over the year 2005. How many income tax returns were filed electronically in 2005? Round to the nearest tenth of a million. (*Source:* IRS)

67. The popularity of the Harry Potter series of books is an unmatched phenomenon among readers of all ages. To satisfy their desires for Harry Potter adventures, author J. K. Rowling increased the number of pages in the later books of the Harry Potter adventures. The final adventure of the series, *Harry Potter and the Deathly Hallows,* boasts 784 pages in its hardcover edition. This is a 154% increase over the number of pages in the first Harry Potter adventure. How many pages are in *Harry Potter and the Sorcerer's Stone*? (Round to the nearest whole page) (*Source:* Amazon.com)

68. During the 2006 Major League Baseball season, the number of home runs hit by Alfonso Soriano of the Washington Nationals, Lance Berkman of the Houston Astros, and Jermaine Dye of the Chicago White Sox were three consecutive integers. Of these three players, Soriano hit the most home runs and Dye hit the least. The total number of home runs hit by these three players over the course of the season was 135. How many home runs did each player hit during the 2006 season? (*Source:* Major League Baseball)

69. During the 2006 Winter Olympic Games in Torino, Italy, the total number of gold medals won by Germany, Canada, and the United States were three consecutive odd integers. Of these three countries, Germany won the most gold medals and Canada won the fewest. If the sum of the first integer, twice the second integer, and four times the third integer is 69, find the number of gold medals won by each country. (*Source: Sports Illustrated Almanac*)

REVIEW AND PREVIEW

Find the value of each expression for the given values. See Section 1.3.

70. $4ab - 3bc$; $a = -5$, $b = -8$, and $c = 2$

71. $ab + 6bc$; $a = 0$, $b = -1$, and $c = 9$

72. $n^2 - m^2$; $n = -3$ and $m = -8$

73. $2n^2 + 3m^2$; $n = -2$ and $m = 7$

74. $P + PRT$; $P = 3000$, $R = 0.0325$, and $T = 2$

75. $\frac{1}{3}lwh$; $l = 37.8$, $w = 5.6$, and $h = 7.9$

CONCEPT EXTENSIONS

76. For Exercise 38, the percents have a sum of 105%. Is this possible? Why or why not?

77. In your own words, explain the differences in the tables for Exercises 37 and 38.

78. Choose five occupations from the chapter opener graph and define these occupations.

79. Find an angle such that its supplement is equal to twice its complement increased by 50°.

Complement

$(90 - x)°$

Supplement

$(180 - x)°$

$x°$

$x°$

80. Newsprint is either discarded or recycled. Americans recycle about 27% of all newsprint, but an amount of newsprint equivalent to 30 million trees is discarded every year. About how many trees' worth of newsprint is *recycled* in the United States each year? (*Source:* The Earth Works Group)

81. The average annual number of cigarettes smoked by an American adult continues to decline. For the years 1997–2006, the equation $y = -49.4x + 1756.8$ approximates this data. Here, x is the number of years since 1997 and y is the average annual number of cigarettes smoked. (*Source:* Centers for Disease Control)

   a. If this trend continues, find the year in which the average annual number of cigarettes smoked is 0. To do this, let $y = 0$ and solve for x.

   b. Predict the average annual number of cigarettes smoked by an American adult in 2012. To do so, let $x = 15$ (since $2012 - 1997 = 15$) and find y.

   c. Use the result of part b to predict the average *daily* number of cigarettes smoked by an American adult in 2012. Round to the nearest whole cigarette. Do you think this number represents the average daily number of cigarettes smoked by an adult smoker? Why or why not?

To break even in a manufacturing business, income or revenue R must equal the cost of production C. Use this information to answer Exercises 82 through 85.

82. The cost C to produce x number of skateboards is $C = 100 + 20x$. The skateboards are sold wholesale for $24 each, so revenue R is given by $R = 24x$. Find how many skateboards the manufacturer needs to produce and sell to break even. (*Hint:* Set the cost expression equal to the revenue expression and solve for x.)

83. The revenue R from selling x number of computer boards is given by $R = 60x$, and the cost C of producing them is given by $C = 50x + 5000$. Find how many boards must be sold to break even. Find how much money is needed to produce the break-even number of boards.

84. In your own words, explain what happens if a company makes and sells fewer products than the break-even number.

85. In your own words, explain what happens if more products than the break-even number are made and sold.

86. In 2006, 74.2 million tax returns were filed electronically. From 2007 to 2011, the average annual increase in electronic filing is projected to be 4.2% of each previous year. If this holds true, what will the number of electronic tax returns be for the next 5 years? Round to the nearest tenth of a million. (*Source:* IRS)

📖 STUDY SKILLS BUILDER

Organizing a Notebook

It's never too late to get organized. If you need ideas about organizing a notebook for your mathematics course, try some of these:

- Use a spiral or ring binder notebook with pockets and use it for mathematics only.

- Start each page by writing the book's section number you are working on at the top.

- When your instructor is lecturing, take notes. ***Always*** include any examples your instructor works for you.

- Place your worked-out homework exercises in your notebook immediately after the lecture notes from that section. This way, a section's worth of material is together.

- Homework exercises: Attempt all assigned homework. For odd-numbered exercises, you are not through until you check your answers against the back of the book.

Correct any exercises with incorrect answers. You may want to place a "?" by any homework exercises or notes that you need to ask questions about. Also, consider placing a "!" by any notes or exercises you feel are important.

- Place graded quizzes in the pockets of your notebook. If you are using a binder, you can place your quizzes in a special section of your binder.

Let's check your notebook organization by answering the following questions.

1. Do you have a spiral or ring binder notebook for your mathematics course only?

2. Have you ever had to flip through several sheets of notes and work in your mathematics notebook to determine what section's work you are in?

3. Are you now writing the textbook's section number at the top of each notebook page?

4. Have you ever lost or had trouble finding a graded quiz or test?

5. Are you now placing all your graded work in a dedicated place in your notebook?

6. Are you attempting all of your homework and placing all of your work in your notebook?

7. Are you checking and correcting your homework in your notebook? If not, why not?

8. Are you writing in your notebook the examples your instructor works for you in class?

2.3 FORMULAS AND PROBLEM SOLVING

OBJECTIVES

1 Solve a formula for a specified variable.

2 Use formulas to solve problems.

OBJECTIVE 1 ▶ Solving a formula for a specified variable. Solving problems that we encounter in the real world sometimes requires us to express relationships among measured quantities. An equation that describes a known relationship among quantities, such as distance, time, volume, weight, money, and gravity is called a **formula.** Some examples of formulas are

Formula	*Meaning*
$I = PRT$	Interest = principal · rate · time
$A = lw$	Area of a rectangle = length · width
$d = rt$	Distance = rate · time
$C = 2\pi r$	Circumference of a circle = $2 \cdot \pi \cdot$ radius
$V = lwh$	Volume of a rectangular solid = length · width · height

Other formulas are listed in the front cover of this text. Notice that the formula for the volume of a rectangular solid $V = lwh$ is solved for V since V is by itself on one side of the equation with no V's on the other side of the equation. Suppose that the volume of a rectangular solid is known as well as its width and its length, and we wish to find its height. One way to find its height is to begin by solving the **formula** $V = lwh$ for h.

 EXAMPLE 1 Solve: $V = lwh$ for h.

Solution To solve $V = lwh$ for h, isolate h on one side of the equation. To do so, divide both sides of the equation by lw.

$$V = lwh$$
$$\frac{V}{lw} = \frac{lwh}{lw} \quad \text{Divide both sides by } lw.$$
$$\frac{V}{lw} = h \quad \text{Simplify.}$$

Then to find the height of a rectangular solid, divide the volume by the product of its length and its width. □

PRACTICE
1 Solve: $I = Prt$ for t.

The following steps may be used to solve formulas and equations in general for a specified variable.

> **Solving Equations for a Specified Variable**
>
> **STEP 1.** Clear the equation of fractions by multiplying each side of the equation by the least common denominator.
>
> **STEP 2.** Use the distributive property to remove grouping symbols such as parentheses.
>
> **STEP 3.** Combine like terms on each side of the equation.
>
> **STEP 4.** Use the addition property of equality to rewrite the equation as an equivalent equation with terms containing the specified variable on one side and all other terms on the other side.
>
> **STEP 5.** Use the distributive property and the multiplication property of equality to isolate the specified variable.

EXAMPLE 2   Solve: $3y - 2x = 7$ for y.

Solution   This is a linear equation in two variables. Often an equation such as this is solved for y in order to reveal some properties about the graph of this equation, which we will learn more about in Chapter 3. Since there are no fractions or grouping symbols, we begin with Step 4 and isolate the term containing the specified variable y by adding $2x$ to both sides of the equation.

$$3y - 2x = 7$$
$$3y - 2x + 2x = 7 + 2x \quad \text{Add } 2x \text{ to both sides.}$$
$$3y = 7 + 2x$$

To solve for y, divide both sides by 3.

$$\frac{3y}{3} = \frac{7 + 2x}{3} \quad \text{Divide both sides by 3.}$$

$$y = \frac{2x + 7}{3} \quad \text{or} \quad y = \frac{2x}{3} + \frac{7}{3} \qquad \square$$

PRACTICE
2   Solve: $7x - 2y = 5$ for y.

△ **EXAMPLE 3**   Solve: $A = \frac{1}{2}(B + b)h$ for b.

Solution   Since this formula for finding the area of a trapezoid contains fractions, we begin by multiplying both sides of the equation by the LCD 2.

$$A = \frac{1}{2}(B + b)h$$

$$2 \cdot A = 2 \cdot \frac{1}{2}(B + b)h \quad \text{Multiply both sides by 2.}$$

$$2A = (B + b)h \qquad \text{Simplify.}$$

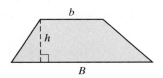

Next, use the distributive property and remove parentheses.

$$2A = (B + b)h$$
$$2A = Bh + bh \qquad \text{Apply the distributive property.}$$
$$2A - Bh = bh \qquad \text{Isolate the term containing } b \text{ by subtracting } Bh \text{ from both sides.}$$
$$\frac{2A - Bh}{h} = \frac{bh}{h} \qquad \text{Divide both sides by } h.$$
$$\frac{2A - Bh}{h} = b, \quad \text{or} \quad b = \frac{2A - Bh}{h}$$

☐

PRACTICE

3 Solve: $A = P + Prt$ for r.

OBJECTIVE 2 ▶ Using formulas to solve problems. In this section, we also solve problems that can be modeled by known formulas. We use the same problem-solving steps that were introduced in the previous section.

Formulas are very useful in problem solving. For example, the compound interest formula

$$A = P\left(1 + \frac{r}{n}\right)^{nt}$$

is used by banks to compute the amount A in an account that pays compound interest. The variable P represents the principal or amount invested in the account, r is the annual rate of interest, t is the time in years, and n is the number of times compounded per year.

EXAMPLE 4   **Finding the Amount in a Savings Account**

Karen Estes just received an inheritance of $10,000 and plans to place all the money in a savings account that pays 5% compounded quarterly to help her son go to college in 3 years. How much money will be in the account in 3 years?

Solution

1. UNDERSTAND. Read and reread the problem. The appropriate formula needed to solve this problem is the compound interest formula

$$A = P\left(1 + \frac{r}{n}\right)^{nt}$$

   Make sure that you understand the meaning of all the variables in this formula.

$$A = \text{amount in the account after } t \text{ years}$$
$$P = \text{principal or amount invested}$$
$$t = \text{time in years}$$
$$r = \text{annual rate of interest}$$
$$n = \text{number of times compounded per year}$$

2. TRANSLATE. Use the compound interest formula and let $P = \$10,000$, $r = 5\% = 0.05$, $t = 3$ years, and $n = 4$ since the account is compounded quarterly, or 4 times a year.

   Formula: $A = P\left(1 + \frac{r}{n}\right)^{nt}$

   Substitute: $A = 10{,}000\left(1 + \frac{0.05}{4}\right)^{4 \cdot 3}$

3. SOLVE. We simplify the right side of the equation.

$$A = 10,000\left(1 + \frac{0.05}{4}\right)^{4\cdot3}$$

$A = 10,000(1.0125)^{12}$ Simplify $1 + \frac{0.05}{4}$ and write $4\cdot3$ as 12.

$A \approx 10,000(1.160754518)$ Approximate $(1.0125)^{12}$.

$A \approx 11,607.55$ Multiply and round to two decimal places.

4. INTERPRET.

Check: Repeat your calculations to make sure that no error was made. Notice that $11,607.55 is a reasonable amount to have in the account after 3 years.

State: In 3 years, the account will contain $11,607.55.

PRACTICE

4   Russ placed $8000 into his credit union account paying 6% compounded semi-annually (twice a year). How much will be in Russ's account in 4 years?

Graphing Calculator Explorations

To solve Example 4, we approximated the expression

$$10,000\left(1 + \frac{0.05}{4}\right)^{4\cdot3}.$$

Use the keystrokes shown in the accompanying calculator screen to evaluate this expression using a graphing calculator. Notice the use of parentheses.

```
10000(1+(.05/4))
^(4*3)
        11607.54518
```

EXAMPLE 5   **Finding Cycling Time**

The fastest average speed by a cyclist across the continental United States is 15.4 mph, by Pete Penseyres. If he traveled a total distance of about 3107.5 miles at this speed, find his time cycling. Write the time in days, hours, and minutes. (*Source: The Guinness Book of World Records*)

Solution

1. UNDERSTAND. Read and reread the problem. The appropriate formula needed is the distance formula

$$d = rt \quad \text{where}$$
$$d = \text{distance traveled} \quad r = \text{rate} \quad \text{and} \quad t = \text{time}$$

2. TRANSLATE. Use the distance formula and let $d = 3107.5$ miles and $r = 15.4$ mph.

Check: $d = rt$

State: $3107.5 = 15.4t$

3. SOLVE.

$$\frac{3107.5}{15.4} = \frac{15.4t}{15.4} \quad \text{Divide both sides by 15.4.}$$

$$201.79 \approx t$$

The time is approximately 201.79 hours. Since there are 24 hours in a day, we divide 201.79 by 24 and find that the time is approximately 8.41 days. Now, let's convert the decimal part of 8.41 days back to hours. To do this, multiply 0.41 by 24 and the result is 9.84 hours. Next, we convert the decimal part of 9.84 hours to minutes by multiplying by 60 since there are 60 minutes in an hour. We have $0.84 \cdot 60 \approx 50$ minutes rounded to the nearest whole. The time is then approximately

8 days, 9 hours, 50 minutes.

4. INTERPRET.

Check: Repeat your calculations to make sure that an error was not made.

State: Pete Penseyres's cycling time was approximately 8 days, 9 hours, 50 minutes. □

PRACTICE

5 Nearly 4800 cyclists from 36 U.S. states and 6 countries recently rode in the Pan-Massachusetts Challenge recently to raise money for cancer research and treatment. If the riders of a certain team traveled their 192-mile route at an average speed of 7.5 miles per hour, find the time they spent cycling. Write the answer in hours and minutes.

2.3 EXERCISE SET

 MyMathLab Powered by CourseCompass™ and MathXL® Math XL PRACTICE   WATCH   DOWNLOAD READ   REVIEW

Solve each equation for the specified variable. See Examples 1–3.

1. $D = rt$; for t

2. $W = gh$; for g

3. $I = PRT$; for R

△ **4.** $V = lwh$; for l

▣ **5.** $9x - 4y = 16$; for y

6. $2x + 3y = 17$; for y

△ **7.** $P = 2L + 2W$; for W

8. $A = 3M - 2N$; for N

9. $J = AC - 3$; for A

10. $y = mx + b$; for x

11. $W = gh - 3gt^2$; for g

12. $A = Prt + P$; for P

13. $T = C(2 + AB)$; for B

14. $A = 5H(b + B)$; for b

△ **15.** $C = 2\pi r$; for r

△ **16.** $S = 2\pi r^2 + 2\pi rh$; for h

17. $E = I(r + R)$; for r

18. $A = P(1 + rt)$; for t

▣ **19.** $s = \dfrac{n}{2}(a + L)$; for L

20. $C = \dfrac{5}{9}(F - 32)$; for F

21. $N = 3st^4 - 5sv$; for v

22. $L = a + (n - 1)d$; for d

△ **23.** $S = 2LW + 2LH + 2WH$; for H

24. $T = 3vs - 4ws + 5vw$; for v

In this exercise set, round all dollar amounts to two decimal places. Solve. See Example 4.

25. Complete the table and find the balance A if $3500 is invested at an annual percentage rate of 3% for 10 years and compounded n times a year.

n	1	2	4	12	365
A					

26. Complete the table and find the balance A if $5000 is invested at an annual percentage rate of 6% for 15 years and compounded n times a year.

n	1	2	4	12	365
A					

27. A principal of $6000 is invested in an account paying an annual percentage rate of 4%. Find the amount in the account after 5 years if the account is compounded

    a. semiannually   **b.** quarterly

    c. monthly

28. A principal of $25,000 is invested in an account paying an annual percentage rate of 5%. Find the amount in the account after 2 years if the account is compounded

    a. semiannually   **b.** quarterly

    c. monthly

MIXED PRACTICE

Solve. See Examples 4 and 5.

29. The day's high temperature in Phoenix, Arizona, was recorded as 104°F. Write 104°F as degrees Celsius. [Use the formula $C = \dfrac{5}{9}(F - 32)$]

30. The annual low temperature in Nome, Alaska, was recorded as −15°C. Write −15°C as degrees Fahrenheit. [Use the formula $F = \dfrac{9}{5}C + 32$]

31. Omaha, Nebraska, is about 90 miles from Lincoln, Nebraska. Irania must go to the law library in Lincoln to get a document for the law firm she works for. Find how long it takes her to drive round-trip if she averages 50 mph.

32. It took the Selby family $5\frac{1}{2}$ hours round-trip to drive from their house to their beach house 154 miles away. Find their average speed.

△ **33.** A package of floor tiles contains 24 one-foot-square tiles. Find how many packages should be bought to cover a square ballroom floor whose side measures 64 feet.

64 ft

64 ft

△ **34.** One-foot-square ceiling tiles are sold in packages of 50. Find how many packages must be bought for a rectangular ceiling 18 feet by 12 feet.

▣ **35.** If the area of a triangular kite is 18 square feet and its base is
△   4 feet, find the height of the kite.

4 ft

height

36. Bryan, Eric, Mandy, and Melissa would like to go to Disneyland in 3 years. Their total cost should be $4500. If each invests $1000 in a savings account paying 5.5% interest, compounded semiannually, will they have enough in 3 years?

△ **37.** A gallon of latex paint can cover 500 square feet. Find how many gallon containers of paint should be bought to paint two coats on each wall of a rectangular room whose dimensions are 14 feet by 16 feet (assume 8-foot ceilings).

△ **38.** A gallon of enamel paint can cover 300 square feet. Find how many gallon containers of paint should be bought to paint three coats on a wall measuring 21 feet by 8 feet.

△ **39.** A portion of the external tank of the Space Shuttle *Endeavour* is a liquid hydrogen tank. If the ends of the tank are hemispheres, find the volume of the tank. To do so, answer parts **a** through **c**.

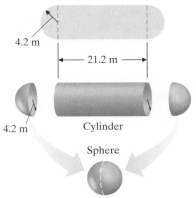

4.2 m

21.2 m

4.2 m   Cylinder

Sphere

a. Find the volume of the cylinder shown. Round to 2 decimal places.

b. Find the volume of the sphere shown. Round to 2 decimal places.

c. Add the results of parts **a** and **b**. This sum is the approximate volume of the tank.

△ **40.** In 1945, Arthur C. Clarke, a scientist and science-fiction writer, predicted that an artificial satellite placed at a height of 22,248 miles directly above the equator would orbit the globe at the same speed with which the Earth was rotating. This belt along the equator is known as the Clarke belt. Use the formula for circumference of a circle and find the "length" of the Clarke belt. (*Hint:* Recall that the radius of the Earth is approximately 4000 miles. Round to the nearest whole mile.)

22,248 mi

41. Amelia Earhart was the first woman to fly solo nonstop coast to coast, setting the women's nonstop transcontinental speed record. She traveled 2447.8 miles in 19 hours 5 minutes. Find the average speed of her flight in miles per hour. (Change 19 hours 5 minutes into hours and use the formula $d = rt$.) Round to the nearest tenth of a mile per hour.

△ **42.** The Space Shuttle *Endeavour* has a cargo bay that is in the shape of a cylinder whose length is 18.3 meters and whose diameter is 4.6 meters. Find its volume.

△ **43.** The deepest hole in the ocean floor is beneath the Pacific Ocean and is called Hole 504B. It is located off the coast of Ecuador. Scientists are drilling it to learn more about the Earth's history. Currently, the hole is in the shape of a cylinder whose volume is approximately 3800 cubic feet and whose length is 1.3 miles. Find the radius of the hole to the nearest hundredth of a foot. (*Hint:* Make sure the same units of measurement are used.)

44. The deepest man-made hole is called the Kola Superdeep Borehole. It is approximately 8 miles deep and is located near a small Russian town in the Arctic Circle. If it takes 7.5 hours to remove the drill from the bottom of the hole, find the rate that the drill can be retrieved in feet per second. Round to the nearest tenth. (*Hint:* Write 8 miles as feet, 7.5 hours as seconds, then use the formula $d = rt$.)

△ **45.** Eartha is the world's largest globe. It is located at the headquarters of DeLorme, a mapmaking company in Yarmouth, Maine. Eartha is 41.125 feet in diameter. Find its exact circumference (distance around) and then approximate its circumference using 3.14 for π. (*Source:* DeLorme)

△ **46.** Eartha is in the shape of a sphere. Its radius is about 20.6 feet. Approximate its volume to the nearest cubic foot. (*Source:* DeLorme)

47. Find *how much interest* $10,000 earns in 2 years in a certificate of deposit paying 8.5% interest compounded quarterly.

48. Find how long it takes Mark to drive 135 miles on I-10 if he merges onto I-10 at 10 a.m. and drives nonstop with his cruise control set on 60 mph.

The calorie count of a serving of food can be computed based on its composition of carbohydrate, fat, and protein. The calorie count C for a serving of food can be computed using the formula $C = 4h + 9f + 4p$, where h is the number of grams of carbohydrate contained in the serving, f is the number of grams of fat contained in the serving, and p is the number of grams of protein contained in the serving.

49. Solve this formula for *f*, the number of grams of fat contained in a serving of food.

50. Solve this formula for *h*, the number of grams of carbohydrate contained in a serving of food.

51. A serving of cashews contains 14 grams of fat, 7 grams of carbohydrate, and 6 grams of protein. How many calories are in this serving of cashews?

52. A serving of chocolate candies contains 9 grams of fat, 30 grams of carbohydrate, and 2 grams of protein. How many calories are in this serving of chocolate candies?

53. A serving of raisins contains 130 calories and 31 grams of carbohydrate. If raisins are a fat-free food, how much protein is provided by this serving of raisins?

54. A serving of yogurt contains 120 calories, 21 grams of carbohydrate, and 5 grams of protein. How much fat is provided by this serving of yogurt? Round to the nearest tenth of a gram.

REVIEW AND PREVIEW

Determine which numbers in the set $\{-3, -2, -1, 0, 1, 2, 3\}$ are solutions of each inequality. See Sections 1.3 and 2.1.

55. $x < 0$

56. $x > 1$

57. $x + 5 \leq 6$

58. $x - 3 \geq -7$

59. In your own words, explain what real numbers are solutions of $x < 0$.

60. In your own words, explain what real numbers are solutions of $x > 1$.

CONCEPT EXTENSIONS

61. Solar system distances are so great that units other than miles or kilometers are often used. For example, the astronomical unit (AU) is the average distance between Earth and the Sun, or 92,900,000 miles. Use this information to convert each planet's distance in miles from the Sun to astronomical units. Round to three decimal places. (*Source:* National Space Science Data Center)

Planet	Miles from the Sun	AU from the Sun	Planet	Miles from the Sun	AU from the Sun
Mercury	36 million		Saturn	886.1 million	
Venus	67.2 million		Uranus	1783 million	
Earth	92.9 million		Neptune	2793 million	
Mars	141.5 million		Pluto	3670 million	
Jupiter	483.3 million				

62. An orbit such as Clarke's belt in Exercise 40 is called a geostationary orbit. In your own words, why do you think that communications satellites are placed in geostationary orbits?

63. How much do you think it costs each American to build a space shuttle? Write down your estimate. The space shuttle *Endeavour* was completed in 1992 and cost approximately $1.7 billion. If the population of the United States in 1992 was 250 million, find the cost per person to build the *Endeavour*. How close was your estimate?

64. If you are investing money in a savings account paying a rate of *r*, which account should you choose—an account compounded 4 times a year or 12 times a year? Explain your choice.

65. To borrow money at a rate of *r*, which loan plan should you choose—one compounding 4 times a year or 12 times a year? Explain your choice.

66. The Drake Equation is a formula used to estimate the number of technological civilizations that might exist in our own Milky Way Galaxy. The Drake Equation is given as $N = R^* \times f_p \times n_e \times f_l \times f_i \times f_c \times L$. Solve the Drake Equation for the variable n_e. (*Note:* Descriptions of the meaning of each variable in this equation, as well as Drake Equation calculators, exist online. For more information, try doing a Web search on "Drake Equation.")

67. On April 1, 1985, *Sports Illustrated* published an April Fool's story by writer George Plimpton. He wrote that the New York Mets had discovered a man who could throw a

168-miles-per-hour fast ball. If the distance from the pitcher's mound to the plate is 60.5 feet, how long would it take for a ball thrown at that rate to travel that distance? (*Hint:* Write the rate 168 miles per hour in feet per second. Then use the formula $d = r \cdot t$.)

$$168 \text{ miles per hour} = \frac{168 \text{ miles}}{1 \text{ hour}}$$

$$= \frac{\_\_\text{feet}}{\_\_\text{seconds}}$$

$$= \frac{\_\_\text{feet}}{1 \text{ second}}$$

$$= \_\_\text{feet per second}$$

*The measure of the chance or likelihood of an event occurring is its **probability**. A formula basic to the study of probability is the formula for the probability of an event when all the outcomes are equally likely. This formula is*

$$Probability \ of \ an \ event = \frac{\textit{number of ways that the event can occur}}{\textit{number of possible outcomes}}$$

For example, to find the probability that a single spin on the spinner will result in red, notice first that the spinner is divided into 8 parts, so there are 8 possible outcomes. Next, notice that there is only one sector of the spinner colored red, so the number of ways that the spinner can land on red is 1. Then this probability denoted by P(red) is

$$P(\text{red}) = \tfrac{1}{8}$$

Find each probability in simplest form.

68. $P(\text{green})$

69. $P(\text{yellow})$

70. $P(\text{black})$

71. $P(\text{blue})$

72. $P(\text{green or blue})$

73. $P(\text{black or yellow})$

74. $P(\text{red, green, or black})$

75. $P(\text{yellow, blue, or black})$

76. $P(\text{white})$

77. $P(\text{red, yellow, green, blue, or black})$

78. From the previous probability formula, what do you think is always the probability of an event that is impossible occuring?

79. What do you think is always the probability of an event that is sure to occur?

 STUDY SKILLS BUILDER

How Are Your Homework Assignments Going?

It is very important in mathematics to keep up with homework. Why? Many concepts build on each other. Often your understanding of a day's concepts depends on an understanding of the previous day's material.

Remember that completing your homework assignment involves a lot more than attempting a few of the problems assigned.

To complete a homework assignment, remember these four things:

- Attempt all of it.
- Check it.
- Correct it.
- If needed, ask questions about it.

Take a moment and review your completed homework assignments. Answer the questions below based on this review.

1. Approximate the fraction of your homework you have attempted.

2. Approximate the fraction of your homework you have checked (if possible).

3. If you are able to check your homework, have you corrected it when errors have been found?

4. When working homework, if you do not understand a concept, what do you do?

2.4 LINEAR INEQUALITIES AND PROBLEM SOLVING

Relationships among measurable quantities are not always described by equations. For example, suppose that a salesperson earns a base of $600 per month plus a commission of 20% of sales. Suppose we want to find the minimum amount of sales needed to receive a total income of *at least* $1500 per month. Here, the phrase "at least" implies that an income of $1500 *or more* is acceptable. In symbols, we can write

$$\text{income} \geq 1500$$

This is an example of an inequality, and we will solve this problem in Example 8.

A **linear inequality** is similar to a linear equation except that the equality symbol is replaced with an inequality symbol, such as $<$, $>$, $\leq$, or $\geq$.

Linear Inequalities in One Variable

$3x + 5 \geq 4$	$2y < 0$	$3(x - 4) > 5x$	$\dfrac{x}{3} \leq 5$
↑	↑	↑	↑
is greater than or equal to	is less than	is greater than	is less than or equal to

> **Linear Inequality in One Variable**
>
> A linear inequality in one variable is an inequality that can be written in the form
>
> $$ax + b < c$$
>
> where a, b, and c are real numbers and $a \neq 0$.

In this section, when we make definitions, state properties, or list steps about an inequality containing the symbol $<$, we mean that the definition, property, or steps apply to inequalities containing the symbols $>$, $\leq$ and $\geq$ also.

OBJECTIVE 1 ▶ Using interval notation. A **solution** of an inequality is a value of the variable that makes the inequality a true statement. The **solution set** of an inequality is the set of all solutions. Notice that the solution set of the inequality $x > 2$, for example, contains all numbers greater than 2. Its graph is an interval on the number line since an infinite number of values satisfy the variable. If we use open/closed-circle notation, the graph of $\{x \mid x > 2\}$ looks like the following.

In this text **interval notation** will be used to write solution sets of inequalities. To help us understand this notation, a different graphing notation will be used. Instead of an open circle, we use a parenthesis. With this new notation, the graph of $\{x \mid x > 2\}$ now looks like

and can be represented in interval notation as $(2, \infty)$. The symbol ∞ is read "infinity" and indicates that the interval includes *all* numbers greater than 2. The left parenthesis indicates that 2 *is not* included in the interval.

In the case where 2 *is* included in the interval, we use a bracket. The graph of $\{x \mid x \geq 2\}$ is below

and can be represented as $[2, \infty)$.

The following table shows three equivalent ways to describe an interval: in set notation, as a graph, and in interval notation.

Set Notation	Graph	Interval Notation
$\{x \mid x < a\}$		$(-\infty, a)$
$\{x \mid x > a\}$		(a, ∞)
$\{x \mid x \leq a\}$		$(-\infty, a]$
$\{x \mid x \geq a\}$		$[a, \infty)$
$\{x \mid a < x < b\}$		(a, b)
$\{x \mid a \leq x \leq b\}$		$[a, b]$
$\{x \mid a < x \leq b\}$		$(a, b]$
$\{x \mid a \leq x < b\}$		$[a, b)$

▶ **Helpful Hint**

Notice that a parenthesis is always used to enclose ∞ and $-\infty$.

Concept Check ✓

Explain what is wrong with writing the interval $(5, \infty]$.

EXAMPLE 1   Graph each set on a number line and then write in interval notation.

a. $\{x \mid x \geq 2\}$ **b.** $\{x \mid x < -1\}$ **c.** $\{x \mid 0.5 < x \leq 3\}$

Solution

a. $[2, \infty)$

b. $(-\infty, -1)$

c. $(0.5, 3]$

PRACTICE

1   Graph each set on a number line and then write in interval notation.

a. $\{x \mid x < 3.5\}$
b. $\{x \mid x \geq -3\}$
c. $\{x \mid -1 \leq x < 4\}$

OBJECTIVE 2 ▶ Solving linear inequalities using the addition property. We will use interval notation to write solutions of linear inequalities. To solve a linear inequality, we use a process similar to the one used to solve a linear equation. We use properties of inequalities to write equivalent inequalities until the variable is isolated.

> **Addition Property of Inequality**
> If a, b, and c are real numbers, then
> $$a < b \quad \text{and} \quad a + c < b + c$$
> are equivalent inequalities.

In other words, we may add the same real number to both sides of an inequality and the resulting inequality will have the same solution set. This property also allows us to subtract the same real number from both sides.

EXAMPLE 2   Solve: $x - 2 < 5$. Graph the solution set and write it in interval notation.

Solution
$$x - 2 < 5$$
$$x - 2 + 2 < 5 + 2 \quad \text{Add 2 to both sides.}$$
$$x < 7 \quad \text{Simplify.}$$

The solution set is $\{x \mid x < 7\}$, which in interval notation is $(-\infty, 7)$. The graph of the solution set is

PRACTICE

2   Solve: $x + 5 > 9$. Graph the solution set and write it in interval notation.

> ▶ **Helpful Hint**
> In Example 2, the solution set is $\{x \mid x < 7\}$. This means that *all* numbers less than 7 are solutions. For example, 6.9, 0, $-\pi$, 1, and -56.7 are solutions, just to name a few. To see this, replace x in $x - 2 < 5$ with each of these numbers and see that the result is a true inequality.

EXAMPLE 3   Solve: $3x + 4 \geq 2x - 6$. Graph the solution set and write it in interval notation.

Solution
$$3x + 4 \geq 2x - 6$$
$$3x + 4 - 2x \geq 2x - 6 - 2x \quad \text{Subtract } 2x \text{ from both sides.}$$
$$x + 4 \geq -6 \quad \text{Combine like terms.}$$
$$x + 4 - 4 \geq -6 - 4 \quad \text{Subtract 4 from both sides.}$$
$$x \geq -10 \quad \text{Simplify.}$$

The solution set is $\{x \mid x \geq -10\}$, which in interval notation is $[-10, \infty)$. The graph of the solution set is

PRACTICE

3   Solve: $8x + 21 \leq 2x - 3$. Graph the solution set and write it in interval notation.

OBJECTIVE 3 ▶ **Solving linear inequalities using the multiplication and addition properties.** Next, we introduce and use the multiplication property of inequality to solve linear inequalities. To understand this property, let's start with the true statement $-3 < 7$ and multiply both sides by 2.

$$-3 < 7$$
$$-3(2) < 7(2) \quad \text{Multiply by 2.}$$
$$-6 < 14 \quad \text{True}$$

The statement remains true.

Notice what happens if both sides of $-3 < 7$ are multiplied by -2.

$$-3 < 7$$
$$-3(-2) < 7(-2) \quad \text{Multiply by } -2.$$
$$6 < -14 \quad \text{False}$$

The inequality $6 < -14$ is a false statement. However, **if the direction of the inequality sign is reversed,** the result is true.

$$6 > -14 \quad \text{True}$$

These examples suggest the following property.

Multiplication Property of Inequality

If $a, b,$ and c are real numbers and c is **positive**, then

$$a < b \quad \text{and} \quad ac < bc$$

are equivalent inequalities.

If $a, b,$ and c are real numbers and c is **negative**, then

$$a < b \quad \text{and} \quad ac > bc$$

are equivalent inequalities.

In other words, we may multiply both sides of an inequality by the same positive real number and the result is an equivalent inequality.

We may also multiply both sides of an inequality by the same **negative number** and **reverse the direction of the inequality symbol**, and the result is an equivalent inequality. The multiplication property holds for division also, since division is defined in terms of multiplication.

▶ **Helpful Hint**

Whenever both sides of an inequality are multiplied or divided by a negative number, the direction of the inequality symbol **must be** reversed to form an equivalent inequality.

EXAMPLE 4 Solve and graph the solution set. Write the solution set in interval notation.

a. $\dfrac{1}{4}x \le \dfrac{3}{8}$ **b.** $-2.3x < 6.9$

Solution

a.
$$\frac{1}{4}x \le \frac{3}{8}$$

$$4 \cdot \frac{1}{4}x \le 4 \cdot \frac{3}{8} \quad \text{Multiply both sides by 4.}$$

$$x \le \frac{3}{2} \quad \text{Simplify.}$$

▶ **Helpful Hint**

The inequality symbol is the same since we are multiplying by a *positive* number.

The solution set is $\left\{ x | x \leq \dfrac{3}{2} \right\}$, which in interval notation is $\left(-\infty, \dfrac{3}{2} \right]$. The graph of the solution set is

$$\overset{\longleftarrow}{\underset{-3\ -2\ -1\ \ \ 0\ \ \ 1\ \underset{\frac{3}{2}}{3}\ 2\ \ \ 3}{\rule{0pt}{0pt}}}$$

b. $\qquad\qquad -2.3x < 6.9$

> **Helpful Hint**
> The inequality symbol is *reversed* since we divided by a *negative* number.

$$\dfrac{-2.3x}{-2.3} > \dfrac{6.9}{-2.3} \qquad \text{Divide both sides by } -2.3 \text{ and reverse the inequality symbol.}$$

$$x > -3 \qquad \text{Simplify.}$$

The solution set is $\{x | x > -3\}$, which is $(-3, \infty)$ in interval notation. The graph of the solution set is

$$\overset{\longleftarrow}{\underset{-5\ -4\ -3\ -2\ -1\ \ 0\ \ 1\ \ 2\ \ 3}{\rule{0pt}{0pt}}}$$ $\square$

PRACTICE

4 Solve and graph the solution set. Write the solution set in interval notation.

a. $\dfrac{2}{5}x \geq \dfrac{4}{15}$

b. $-2.4x < 9.6$

Concept Check

In which of the following inequalities must the inequality symbol be reversed during the solution process?

a. $-2x > 7$ **c.** $-x + 4 + 3x < 7$

b. $2x - 3 > 10$ **d.** $-x + 4 < 5$

  To solve linear inequalities in general, we follow steps similar to those for solving linear equations.

Solving a Linear Inequality in One Variable

STEP 1. Clear the inequality of fractions by multiplying both sides of the inequality by the least common denominator (LCD) of all fractions in the inequality.

STEP 2. Use the distributive property to remove grouping symbols such as parentheses.

STEP 3. Combine like terms on each side of the inequality.

STEP 4. Use the addition property of inequality to write the inequality as an equivalent inequality with variable terms on one side and numbers on the other side.

STEP 5. Use the multiplication property of inequality to isolate the variable.

EXAMPLE 5   Solve: $-(x - 3) + 2 \leq 3(2x - 5) + x$.

Solution $-(x - 3) + 2 \leq 3(2x - 5) + x$

$\qquad\qquad -x + 3 + 2 \leq 6x - 15 + x \qquad$ Apply the distributive property.

$\qquad\qquad\qquad 5 - x \leq 7x - 15 \qquad$ Combine like terms.

$\qquad\qquad 5 - x + x \leq 7x - 15 + x \qquad$ Add x to both sides.

$\qquad\qquad\qquad\quad 5 \leq 8x - 15 \qquad$ Combine like terms.

Answer to Concept Check:
a, d

> ▶ **Helpful Hint**
>
> Don't forget that $\frac{5}{2} \le x$ means
>
> the same as $x \ge \frac{5}{2}$.

$$5 + 15 \le 8x - 15 + 15 \quad \text{Add 15 to both sides.}$$
$$20 \le 8x \quad \text{Combine like terms.}$$
$$\frac{20}{8} \le \frac{8x}{8} \quad \text{Divide both sides by 8.}$$
$$\frac{5}{2} \le x, \quad \text{or} \quad x \ge \frac{5}{2} \quad \text{Simplify.}$$

The solution set written in interval notation is $\left[\dfrac{5}{2}, \infty \right)$ and its graph is

PRACTICE

5   Solve: $-(4x + 6) \le 2(5x + 9) + 2x$. Graph and write the solution set in interval notation.

EXAMPLE 6   Solve: $\dfrac{2}{5}(x - 6) \ge x - 1$.

Solution

$$\frac{2}{5}(x - 6) \ge x - 1$$

$$5\left[\frac{2}{5}(x - 6)\right] \ge 5(x - 1) \quad \text{Multiply both sides by 5 to eliminate fractions.}$$

$$2(x - 6) \ge 5(x - 1)$$
$$2x - 12 \ge 5x - 5 \quad \text{Apply the distributive property.}$$
$$-3x - 12 \ge -5 \quad \text{Subtract } 5x \text{ from both sides.}$$
$$-3x \ge 7 \quad \text{Add 12 to both sides.}$$
$$\frac{-3x}{-3} \le \frac{7}{-3} \quad \text{Divide both sides by } -3 \text{ and reverse the inequality symbol.}$$
$$x \le -\frac{7}{3} \quad \text{Simplify.}$$

The solution set written in interval notation is $\left(-\infty, -\dfrac{7}{3} \right]$ and its graph is

PRACTICE

6   Solve: $\dfrac{3}{5}(x - 3) \ge x - 7$. Graph and write the solution set in interval notation.

EXAMPLE 7   Solve: $2(x + 3) > 2x + 1$.

Solution

$$2(x + 3) > 2x + 1$$
$$2x + 6 > 2x + 1 \quad \text{Distribute on the left side.}$$
$$2x + 6 - 2x > 2x + 1 - 2x \quad \text{Subtract } 2x \text{ from both sides.}$$
$$6 > 1 \quad \text{Simplify.}$$

$6 > 1$ is a true statement for all values of x, so this inequality and the original inequality are true for all numbers. The solution set is $\{x \mid x \text{ is a real number}\}$, or $(-\infty, \infty)$ in interval notation, and its graph is

PRACTICE

7 Solve: $4(x - 2) < 4x + 5$. Graph and write the solution set in interval notation.

OBJECTIVE 4 ▶ Solving problems modeled by linear inequalities. Application problems containing words such as "at least," "at most," "between," "no more than," and "no less than" usually indicate that an inequality be solved instead of an equation. In solving applications involving linear inequalities, we use the same procedure as when we solved applications involving linear equations.

EXAMPLE 8 **Calculating Income with Commission**

A salesperson earns $600 per month plus a commission of 20% of sales. Find the minimum amount of sales needed to receive a total income of at least $1500 per month.

Solution

1. UNDERSTAND. Read and reread the problem. Let x = amount of sales
2. TRANSLATE. As stated in the beginning of this section, we want the income to be greater than or equal to $1500. To write an inequality, notice that the salesperson's income consists of $600 plus a commission (20% of sales).

In words:	600	+	commission (20% of sales)	$\geq$	1500
	$\downarrow$		$\downarrow$		$\downarrow$
Translate:	600	+	$0.20x$	$\geq$	1500

3. SOLVE the inequality for x.

$$600 + 0.20x \geq 1500$$
$$600 + 0.20x - 600 \geq 1500 - 600$$
$$0.20x \geq 900$$
$$x \geq 4500$$

4. INTERPRET.

Check: The income for sales of $4500 is

$$600 + 0.20(4500), \text{ or } 1500.$$

Thus, if sales are greater than or equal to $4500, income is greater than or equal to $1500.

State: The minimum amount of sales needed for the salesperson to earn at least $1500 per month is $4500 per month.

PRACTICE

8 A salesperson earns $900 a month plus a commission of 15% of sales. Find the minimum amount of sales needed to receive a total income of at least $2400 per month.

EXAMPLE 9 **Finding the Annual Consumption**

In the United States, the annual consumption of cigarettes is declining. The consumption c in billions of cigarettes per year since the year 1990 can be approximated by the formula

$$c = -9.2t + 527.33$$

where t is the number of years after 1990. Use this formula to predict the years that the consumption of cigarettes will be less than 200 billion per year.

Solution

1. **UNDERSTAND.** Read and reread the problem. To become familiar with the given formula, let's find the cigarette consumption after 20 years, which would be the year $1990 + 20$, or 2010. To do so, we substitute 20 for t in the given formula.

$$c = -9.2(20) + 527.33 = 343.33$$

Thus, in 2010, we predict cigarette consumption to be about 343.3 billion.

Variables have already been assigned in the given formula. For review, they are c = the annual consumption of cigarettes in the United States in billions of cigarettes

$$t = \text{the number of years after 1990}$$

2. **TRANSLATE.** We are looking for the years that the consumption of cigarettes c is less than 200. Since we are finding years t, we substitute the expression in the formula given for c, or

$$-9.2t + 527.33 < 200$$

3. **SOLVE** the inequality.

$$-9.2t + 527.33 < 200$$
$$-9.2t < -327.33$$
$$t > \text{approximately } 35.58$$

4. **INTERPRET.**

Check: Substitute a number greater than 35.58 and see that c is less than 200.

State: The annual consumption of cigarettes will be less than 200 billion more than 35.58 years after 1990, or in approximately $36 + 1990 = 2026$.   ☐

PRACTICE
9   Use the formula given in Example 9 to predict when the consumption of cigarettes will be less than 250 billion per year.

VOCABULARY & READINESS CHECK

Match each graph with the interval notation that describes it.

1.

   a. $(-5, \infty)$ **b.** $(-5, -\infty)$
   c. $(\infty, -5)$ **d.** $(-\infty, -5)$

2.
   a. $(-\infty, -11]$ **b.** $(-11, \infty)$
   c. $[-11, \infty)$ **d.** $(-\infty, -11)$

3.
   a. $\left[\dfrac{7}{4}, -2.5\right)$ **b.** $\left(-2.5, \dfrac{7}{4}\right]$
   c. $\left[-2.5, \dfrac{7}{4}\right)$ **d.** $\left(\dfrac{7}{4}, -2.5\right)$

4.
   a. $\left[-\dfrac{10}{3}, 0.2\right)$ **b.** $\left(0.2, -\dfrac{10}{3}\right]$
   c. $\left(-\dfrac{10}{3}, 0.2\right]$ **d.** $\left[0.2, -\dfrac{10}{3}\right)$

Use the choices below to fill in each blank.

$(-\infty, -0.4)$ $\qquad$ $(-\infty, -0.4]$ $\qquad$ $[-0.4, \infty)$ $\qquad$ $(-0.4, \infty)$ $\qquad$ $(\infty, -0.4]$

5. The set $\{x \mid x \geq -0.4\}$ written in interval notation is _____.

6. The set $\{x \mid x < -0.4\}$ written in interval notation is _____.

7. The set $\{x \mid x \leq -0.4\}$ written in interval notation is _____.

8. The set $\{x \mid x > -0.4\}$ written in interval notation is _____.

Each inequality below is solved by dividing both sides by the coefficient of x. In which inequality will the inequality symbol be reversed during this solution process?

9. $3x > -14$ $\qquad$ **10.** $-3x \leq 14$ $\qquad$ **11.** $-3x < -14$ $\qquad$ **12.** $-x \geq 23$

2.4 | EXERCISE SET

PRACTICE $\quad$ WATCH $\quad$ DOWNLOAD $\quad$ READ $\quad$ REVIEW

Graph the solution set of each inequality and write it in interval notation. See Example 1.

1. $\{x \mid x < -3\}$ $\qquad$ **2.** $\{x \mid x > 5\}$

3. $\{x \mid x \geq 0.3\}$ $\qquad$ **4.** $\{x \mid x < -0.2\}$

5. $\{x \mid -7 \leq x\}$ $\qquad$ **6.** $\{x \mid -7 \geq x\}$

7. $\{x \mid -2 < x < 5\}$ $\qquad$ **8.** $\{x \mid -5 \leq x \leq -1\}$

9. $\{x \mid 5 \geq x > -1\}$ $\qquad$ **10.** $\{x \mid -3 > x \geq -7\}$

Solve. Graph the solution set and write it in interval notation. See Examples 2 through 4.

11. $x - 7 \geq -9$ $\qquad$ **12.** $x + 2 \leq -1$

13. $7x < 6x + 1$ $\qquad$ **14.** $11x < 10x + 5$

15. $8x - 7 \leq 7x - 5$ $\qquad$ **16.** $7x - 1 \geq 6x - 1$

17. $\dfrac{3}{4}x \geq 6$ $\qquad$ **18.** $\dfrac{5}{6}x \geq 5$

19. $5x < -23.5$ $\qquad$ **20.** $4x > -11.2$

21. $-3x \geq 9$ $\qquad$ **22.** $-4x \geq 8$

Solve. Write the solution set using interval notation. See Examples 5 through 7.

23. $-2x + 7 \geq 9$

24. $8 - 5x \leq 23$

25. $15 + 2x \geq 4x - 7$

26. $20 + x < 6x - 15$

27. $4(2x + 1) > 4$

28. $6(2 - 3x) \geq 12$

29. $3(x - 5) < 2(2x - 1)$

30. $5(x + 4) \leq 4(2x + 3)$

31. $\dfrac{5x + 1}{7} - \dfrac{2x - 6}{4} \geq -4$

32. $\dfrac{1 - 2x}{3} + \dfrac{3x + 7}{7} > 1$

33. $-3(2x - 1) < -4[2 + 3(x + 2)]$

34. $-2(4x + 2) > -5[1 + 2(x - 1)]$

MIXED PRACTICE

Solve. Write the solution set using interval notation. See Examples 1 through 7.

35. $x + 9 < 3$ $\qquad$ **36.** $x - 9 < -12$

37. $-x < -4$ $\qquad$ **38.** $-x > -2$

39. $-7x \leq 3.5$ $\qquad$ **40.** $-6x \leq 4.2$

41. $\dfrac{1}{2} + \dfrac{2}{3} \geq \dfrac{x}{6}$

42. $\dfrac{3}{4} - \dfrac{2}{3} \geq \dfrac{x}{6}$

43. $-5x + 4 \leq -4(x - 1)$

44. $-6x + 2 < -3(x + 4)$

45. $\dfrac{3}{4}(x - 7) \geq x + 2$

46. $\dfrac{4}{5}(x + 1) \leq x + 1$

47. $0.8x + 0.6x \geq 4.2$

48. $0.7x - x > 0.45$

49. $4(x - 6) + 2x - 4 \geq 3(x - 7) + 10x$

50. $7(2x + 3) + 4x \leq 7 + 5(3x - 4) + x$

51. $14 - (5x - 6) \geq -6(x + 1) - 5$

52. $13y - (9y + 2) \leq 5(y - 6) + 10$

53. $\dfrac{1}{2}(3x - 4) \leq \dfrac{3}{4}(x - 6) + 1$

54. $\dfrac{2}{3}(x + 3) < \dfrac{1}{6}(2x - 8) + 2$

55. $\dfrac{-x + 2}{2} - \dfrac{1 - 5x}{8} < -1$

56. $\dfrac{3 - 4x}{6} - \dfrac{1 - 2x}{12} \leq -2$

57.

$\dfrac{x + 5}{5} - \dfrac{3 + x}{8} \geq -\dfrac{3}{10}$

58. $\dfrac{x - 4}{2} - \dfrac{x - 2}{3} > \dfrac{5}{6}$

59. $\dfrac{x + 3}{12} + \dfrac{x - 5}{15} < \dfrac{2}{3}$

60. $\dfrac{3x + 2}{18} - \dfrac{1 + 2x}{6} \leq -\dfrac{1}{2}$

61. $0.4(4x - 3) < 1.2(x + 2)$

62. $0.2(8x - 2) < 1.2(x - 3)$

63. $\dfrac{2}{5}x - \dfrac{1}{4} \leq \dfrac{3}{10}x - \dfrac{4}{5}$

64. $\dfrac{7}{12}x - \dfrac{1}{3} \leq \dfrac{3}{8}x - \dfrac{5}{6}$

65. $4(x - 1) \geq 4x - 8$

66. $3x + 1 < 3(x - 2)$

67. $7x < 7(x - 2)$

68. $8(x + 3) \leq 7(x + 5) + x$

Solve. See Examples 8 and 9. For Exercises 69 through 76,
a. *answer with an inequality, and* *b.* *in your own words, explain*
the meaning of your answer to part a.

69. Shureka Washburn has scores of 72, 67, 82, and 79 on her
algebra tests.

   a. Use an inequality to find the scores she must make on the
final exam to pass the course with an average of 77 or
higher, given that the final exam counts as two tests.

   b. In your own words explain the meaning of your answer to
part a.

70. In a Winter Olympics 5000-meter speed-skating event, Hans
Holden scored times of 6.85, 7.04, and 6.92 minutes on his
first three trials.

   a. Use an inequality to find the times he can score on his last
trial so that his average time is under 7.0 minutes.

   b. In your own words, explain the meaning of your answer to
part a.

71. A small plane's maximum takeoff weight is 2000 pounds or
less. Six passengers weigh an average of 160 pounds each.
Use an inequality to find the luggage and cargo weights the
plane can carry.

72. A shopping mall parking garage charges $1 for the first half-
hour and 60 cents for each additional half-hour. Use an inequality to find how long you can park if you have only $4.00
in cash.

73. A clerk must use the elevator to move boxes of paper. The
elevator's maximum weight limit is 1500 pounds. If each box
of paper weighs 66 pounds and the clerk weighs 147 pounds,
use an inequality to find the number of whole boxes she can
move on the elevator at one time.

74. To mail an envelope first class, the U.S. Post Office
charges 41 cents for the first ounce and 17 cents per ounce
for each additional ounce. Use an inequality to find the
number of whole ounces that can be mailed for no more
than $2.50.

75. Northeast Telephone Company offers two billing plans for
local calls.

Plan 1: $25 per month for unlimited calls
Plan 2: $13 per month plus $0.06 per call

Use an inequality to find the number of monthly calls for
which plan 1 is more economical than plan 2.

76. A car rental company offers two subcompact rental plans.

Plan A: $36 per day and unlimited mileage
Plan B: $24 per day plus $0.15 per mile

Use an inequality to find the number of daily miles for which
plan A is more economical than plan B.

77. At room temperature, glass used in windows actually has
some properties of a liquid. It has a very slow, viscous flow.
(Viscosity is the property of a fluid that resists internal flow.
For example, lemonade flows more easily than fudge syrup.
Fudge syrup has a higher viscosity than lemonade.) Glass
does not become a true liquid until temperatures are
greater than or equal to 500°C. Find the Fahrenheit temperatures for which glass is a liquid. (Use the formula
$F = \dfrac{9}{5}C + 32$.)

78. Stibnite is a silvery white mineral with a metallic luster. It is
one of the few minerals that melts easily in a match flame
or at temperatures of approximately 977°F or greater. Find
the Celsius temperatures for which stibnite melts. [Use the
formula $C = \dfrac{5}{9}(F - 32)$.]

79. Although beginning salaries vary greatly according to your
field of study, the equation

$$s = 651.2t + 28,472$$

can be used to approximate and to predict average beginning salaries for candidates with bachelor's degrees. The
variable s is the starting salary and t is the number of years
after 1990.

   a. Approximate when beginning salaries for candidates will
be greater than $42,000.

   b. Determine the year you plan to graduate from college.
Use this year to find the corresponding value of t and
approximate your beginning salary.

80. a. Use the formula in Example 9 to estimate the years that
the consumption of cigarettes will be less than 50 billion
per year.

   b. Use your answer to part a to describe the limitations of
your answer.

The average consumption per person per year of whole milk w in gallons can be approximated by the equation

$$y = -0.19t + 7.6$$

where t is the number of years after 2000. The average consumption of nonfat milk s per person per year can be approximated by the equation

$$y = -0.07t + 3.5$$

where t is the number of years after 2000. The consumption of whole milk is shown on the graph in red and the consumption of nonfat milk is shown on the graph in blue. Use this information to answer Exercises 81–88.

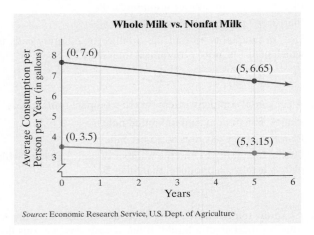

Whole Milk vs. Nonfat Milk

Source: Economic Research Service, U.S. Dept. of Agriculture

81. Is the consumption of whole milk increasing or decreasing over time? Explain how you arrived at your answer.

82. Is the consumption of nonfat milk increasing or decreasing over time? Explain how you arrived at your answer.

83. Predict the consumption of whole milk in the year 2010. (*Hint:* Find the value of t that corresponds to the year 2010.)

84. Predict the consumption of nonfat milk in the year 2010. (*Hint:* Find the value of t that corresponds to the year 2010.)

85. Determine when the consumption of whole milk will be less than 6 gallons per person per year.

86. Determine when the consumption of nonfat milk will be less than 3 gallons per person per year.

87. For 2000 through 2005 the consumption of whole milk was greater than the consumption of nonfat milk. Explain how this can be determined from the graph.

88. How will the two lines in the graph appear if the consumption of whole milk is the same as the consumption of nonfat milk?

REVIEW AND PREVIEW

List or describe the integers that make both inequalities true. See Section 1.4.

89. $x < 5$ and $x > 1$

90. $x \geq 0$ and $x \leq 7$

91. $x \geq -2$ and $x \geq 2$

92. $x < 6$ and $x < -5$

Solve each equation for x. See Section 2.1.

93. $2x - 6 = 4$

94. $3x - 12 = 3$

95. $-x + 7 = 5x - 6$

96. $-5x - 4 = -x - 4$

CONCEPT EXTENSIONS

Each row of the table shows three equivalent ways of describing an interval. Complete this table by filling in the equivalent descriptions. The first row has been completed for you.

	Set Notation	Graph	Interval Notation
	$\{x \mid x < -3\}$	⟵─────)───⟶ -3	$(-\infty, -3)$
97.		⟵───┼───⟶ 2	
98.		⟵───┼───⟶ -4	
99.	$\{x \mid x < 0\}$		
100.	$\{x \mid x \leq 5\}$		
101.			$(-2, 1.5]$
102.			$[-3.7, 4)$

103. Solve: $2x - 3 = 5$.

104. Solve: $2x - 3 < 5$.

105. Solve: $2x - 3 > 5$.

106. Read the equations and inequalities for Exercises 103, 104, and 105 and their solutions. In your own words, write down your thoughts.

107. When graphing the solution set of an inequality, explain how you know whether to use a parenthesis or a bracket.

108. Explain what is wrong with the interval notation $(-6, -\infty)$.

109. Explain how solving a linear inequality is similar to solving a linear equation.

110. Explain how solving a linear inequality is different from solving a linear equation.

111. Write an inequality whose solution set is $\{x \mid x \leq 2\}$.

THE BIGGER PICTURE SOLVING EQUATIONS AND INEQUALITIES

This is a special feature that will be repeated and expanded throughout this text. It is very important for you to be able to recognize and solve different types of equations and inequalities. To help you do this, we will begin an outline below and continually expand this outline as different equations and inequalities are introduced. Although suggestions will be given, this outline should be in your own words and you should include at least "how to recognize" and "how to begin to solve" under each letter heading.

For example:

Solving Equations and Inequalities

I. Equations

A. Linear equations: Power on variable is 1 and there are no variables in denominator. (Section 2.1)

$$5(x - 2) = \frac{4(2x + 1)}{3}$$

$$3 \cdot 5(x - 2) = \cancel{3} \cdot \frac{4(2x + 1)}{\cancel{3}} \quad \text{Multiply both sides by the LCD, 3.}$$

$$15(x - 2) = 4(2x + 1) \quad \text{Simplify.}$$

$$15x - 30 = 8x + 4 \quad \text{Multiply.}$$

$$7x = 34 \quad \text{Add 30 and subtract } 8x \text{ from both sides.}$$

$$x = \frac{34}{7} \quad \text{Divide both sides by 7.}$$

II. Inequalities

A. Linear Inequalities: Inequality sign and power on x is 1 and there are no variables in denominator. (Section 2.4)

$$-3(x + 2) \geq 6 \quad \text{Linear inequality}$$

$$-3x - 6 \geq 6 \quad \text{Multiply.}$$

$$-3x \geq 12 \quad \text{Add 6 to both sides.}$$

$$\frac{-3x}{-3} \leq \frac{12}{-3} \quad \text{Divide both sides by } -3, \text{ and } change \text{ the direction of the inequality sign.}$$

$$x \leq -4 \text{ or } (-\infty, -4]$$

Solve. Write inequality solutions in interval notation.

1. $3x - 4 = 3(2x - 1) + 7$

2. $5 + 2x = 5(x + 1)$

3. $\dfrac{x + 3}{2} > 1$

4. $\dfrac{x - 2}{2} - \dfrac{x - 4}{3} = \dfrac{5}{6}$

5. $\dfrac{7}{5} + \dfrac{y}{10} = 2$

6. $5 + 2x = 2(x + 1)$

7. $4(x - 2) + 3x \geq 9(x - 1) - 2$

8. $6(x + 1) - 2 = 6x + 4$

INTEGRATED REVIEW LINEAR EQUATIONS AND INEQUALITIES

Sections 2.1– 2.4

Solve each equation or inequality. For inequalities, write the solution set in interval notation.

1. $-4x = 20$

2. $-4x < 20$

3. $\dfrac{3x}{4} \geq 2$

4. $5x + 3 \geq 2 + 4x$

5. $6(y - 4) = 3(y - 8)$

6. $-4x \leq \dfrac{2}{5}$

7. $-3x \geq \dfrac{1}{2}$

8. $5(y + 4) = 4(y + 5)$

9. $7x < 7(x - 2)$

10. $\dfrac{-5x + 11}{2} \leq 7$

11. $-5x + 1.5 = -19.5$

12. $-5x + 4 = -26$

13. $5 + 2x - x = -x + 3 - 14$

14. $12x + 14 < 11x - 2$

15. $\dfrac{x}{5} - \dfrac{x}{4} = \dfrac{x - 2}{2}$

16. $12x - 12 = 8(x - 1)$

17. $2(x - 3) > 70$

18. $-3x - 4.7 = 11.8$

19. $-2(b - 4) - (3b - 1) = 5b + 3$

20. $8(x + 3) < 7(x + 5) + x$

21. $\dfrac{3t + 1}{8} = \dfrac{5 + 2t}{7} + 2$

22. $4(x - 6) - x = 8(x - 3) - 5x$

23. $\dfrac{x}{6} + \dfrac{3x - 2}{2} < \dfrac{2}{3}$

24. $\dfrac{y}{3} + \dfrac{y}{5} = \dfrac{y + 3}{10}$

25. $5(x - 6) + 2x > 3(2x - 1) - 4$

26. $14(x - 1) - 7x \leq 2(3x - 6) + 4$

27. $\dfrac{1}{4}(3x + 2) - x \geq \dfrac{3}{8}(x - 5) + 2$

28. $\dfrac{1}{3}(x - 10) - 4x > \dfrac{5}{6}(2x + 1) - 1$

Example 5 shows that some compound inequalities have no solution. Also, some have all real numbers as solutions.

90 CHAPTER 2 Equations, Inequalities, and Problem Solving

To solve a compound inequality written in a compact form, such as $2 < 4 - x < 7$, we get x alone in the "middle part." Since a compound inequality is really two inequalities in one statement, we must perform the same operations on all three parts of the inequality.

EXAMPLE 4 Solve: $2 < 4 - x < 7$

Solution To get x alone, we first subtract 4 from all three parts.

$$2 < 4 - x < 7$$
$$2 - 4 < 4 - x - 4 < 7 - 4 \quad \text{Subtract 4 from all three parts.}$$
$$-2 < -x < 3 \quad \text{Simplify.}$$
$$\frac{-2}{-1} > \frac{-x}{-1} > \frac{3}{-1} \quad \begin{array}{l}\text{Divide all three parts by } -1 \text{ and} \\ \text{reverse the inequality symbols.}\end{array}$$
$$2 > x > -3$$

> ▶ **Helpful Hint**
> Don't forget to reverse both inequality symbols.

This is equivalent to $-3 < x < 2$.

The solution set in interval notation is $(-3, 2)$, and its graph is shown.

PRACTICE
4 Solve: $3 < 5 - x < 9$. Write the solution set in interval notation.

EXAMPLE 5 Solve: $-1 \le \dfrac{2x}{3} + 5 \le 2$.

Solution First, clear the inequality of fractions by multiplying all three parts by the LCD of 3.

$$-1 \le \frac{2x}{3} + 5 \le 2$$
$$3(-1) \le 3\left(\frac{2x}{3} + 5\right) \le 3(2) \quad \text{Multiply all three parts by the LCD of 3.}$$
$$-3 \le 2x + 15 \le 6 \quad \text{Use the distributive property and multiply.}$$
$$-3 - 15 \le 2x + 15 - 15 \le 6 - 15 \quad \text{Subtract 15 from all three parts.}$$
$$-18 \le 2x \le -9 \quad \text{Simplify.}$$
$$\frac{-18}{2} \le \frac{2x}{2} \le \frac{-9}{2} \quad \text{Divide all three parts by 2.}$$
$$-9 \le x \le -\frac{9}{2} \quad \text{Simplify.}$$

The graph of the solution is shown.

The solution set in interval notation is $\left[-9, -\dfrac{9}{2}\right]$.

PRACTICE
5 Solve: $-4 \le \dfrac{x}{2} - 1 \le 3$. Write the solution set in interval notation.

OBJECTIVE 3 ▶ **Finding the union of two sets.** The solution set of a compound inequality formed by the word **or** is the **union** of the solution sets of the two inequalities. We use the symbol $\cup$ to denote "union."

Union of Two Sets

The **union** of two sets, A and B, is the set of elements that belong to *either* of the sets.
A union B is denoted by

$$A \qquad B$$
$$A \cup B$$

EXAMPLE 6   If $A = \{x | x \text{ is an even number greater than 0 and less than 10}\}$
and $B = \{3, 4, 5, 6\}$. Find $A \cup B$.

Solution   Recall from Example 1 that $A = \{2, 4, 6, 8\}$. The numbers that are in either
set or both sets are $\{2, 3, 4, 5, 6, 8\}$. This set is the union. □

PRACTICE
6   If $A = \{x | x \text{ is an odd number greater than 0 and less than 10}\}$ and
$B = \{2, 3, 4, 5, 6\}$. Find $A \cup B$.

OBJECTIVE 4 ▶ **Solving compound inequalities containing "or."** A value is a solution
of a compound inequality formed by the word **or** if it is a solution of **either** inequality.
For example, the solution set of the compound inequality $x \leq 1$ **or** $x \geq 3$ contains all
numbers that make the inequality $x \leq 1$ a true statement **or** the inequality $x \geq 3$ a
true statement.

$\{x | x \leq 1\}$ $(-\infty, 1]$

$\{x | x \geq 3\}$ $[3, \infty)$

$\{x | x \leq 1 \text{ or } x \geq 3\}$ $(-\infty, 1] \cup [3, \infty)$

In interval notation, the set $\{x | x \leq 1 \text{ or } x \geq 3\}$ is written as $(-\infty, 1] \cup [3, \infty)$.

EXAMPLE 7   Solve: $5x - 3 \leq 10 \text{ or } x + 1 \geq 5$.

Solution   First we solve each inequality separately.

$$5x - 3 \leq 10 \quad or \quad x + 1 \geq 5$$
$$5x \leq 13 \quad or \quad x \geq 4$$
$$x \leq \frac{13}{5} \quad or \quad x \geq 4$$

Now we can graph each interval and find their union.

$\left\{x | x \leq \dfrac{13}{5}\right\}$ $\left(-\infty, \dfrac{13}{5}\right]$

$\{x | x \geq 4\}$ $[4, \infty)$

$\left\{x | x \leq \dfrac{13}{5} \text{ or } x \geq 4\right\}$ $\left(-\infty, \dfrac{13}{5}\right] \cup [4, \infty)$

The solution set is $\left(-\infty, \dfrac{13}{5}\right] \cup [4, \infty)$. □

PRACTICE
7   Solve: $8x + 5 \leq 8 \text{ or } x - 1 \geq 2$. Write the solution set in interval notation.

EXAMPLE 8 Solve: $-2x - 5 < -3$ or $6x < 0$.

Solution First we solve each inequality separately.

$$-2x - 5 < -3 \quad or \quad 6x < 0$$
$$-2x < 2 \quad or \quad x < 0$$
$$x > -1 \quad or \quad x < 0$$

Now we can graph each interval and find their union.

$\{x | x > -1\}$ $(-1, \infty)$

$\{x | x < 0\}$ $(-\infty, 0)$

$\{x | x > -1 \ or \ x < 0\}$ $(-\infty, \infty)$
= all real numbers

The solution set is $(-\infty, \infty)$.

PRACTICE
8 Solve: $-3x - 2 > -8$ or $5x > 0$. Write the solution set in interval notation.

Concept Check ☑

Which of the following is *not* a correct way to represent the set of all numbers between -3 and 5?

a. $\{x | {}^{-}3 < x < 5\}$ **b.** $-3 < x$ or $x < 5$

c. $(-3, 5)$ **d.** $x > -3$ and $x < 5$

Answer to Concept Check:
b is not correct

VOCABULARY & READINESS CHECK

Use the choices below to fill in each blank. Some choices may be used more than once.

or	$\cup$	$\varnothing$
and	$\cap$	compound

1. Two inequalities joined by the words "and" or "or" are called _____ inequalities.
2. The word _____ means intersection.
3. The word _____ means union.
4. The symbol _____ represents intersection.
5. The symbol _____ represents union.
6. The symbol _____ is the empty set.
7. The inequality $-2 \leq x < 1$ means $-2 \leq x$ _____ $x < 1$.
8. $\{x | x < 0 \text{ and } x > 0\} =$ _____

2.5 EXERCISE SET

MIXED PRACTICE

If $A = \{x | x \text{ is an even integer}\}$, $B = \{x | x \text{ is an odd integer}\}$, $C = \{2, 3, 4, 5\}$, and $D = \{4, 5, 6, 7\}$, list the elements of each set. See Examples 1 and 6.

1. $C \cup D$
2. $C \cap D$
3. $A \cap D$
4. $A \cup D$
5. $A \cup B$
6. $A \cap B$
7. $B \cap D$
8. $B \cup D$
9. $B \cup C$
10. $B \cap C$
11. $A \cap C$
12. $A \cup C$

Solve each compound inequality. Graph the solution set and write it in interval notation. See Examples 2 and 3.

13. $x < 1$ and $x > -3$
14. $x \leq 0$ and $x \geq -2$
15. $x \leq -3$ and $x \geq -2$
16. $x < 2$ and $x > 4$

17. $x < -1$ and $x < 1$

18. $x \geq -4$ and $x > 1$

Solve each compound inequality. Write solutions in interval notation. See Examples 2 and 3.

19. $x + 1 \geq 7$ and $3x - 1 \geq 5$

20. $x + 2 \geq 3$ and $5x - 1 \geq 9$

21. $4x + 2 \leq -10$ and $2x \leq 0$

22. $2x + 4 > 0$ and $4x > 0$

23. $-2x < -8$ and $x - 5 < 5$

24. $-7x \leq -21$ and $x - 20 \leq -15$

Solve each compound inequality. See Examples 4 and 5.

25. $5 < x - 6 < 11$

26. $-2 \leq x + 3 \leq 0$

27. $-2 \leq 3x - 5 \leq 7$

28. $1 < 4 + 2x < 7$

29. $1 \leq \dfrac{2}{3}x + 3 \leq 4$

30. $-2 < \dfrac{1}{2}x - 5 < 1$

31. $-5 \leq \dfrac{-3x + 1}{4} \leq 2$

32. $-4 \leq \dfrac{-2x + 5}{3} \leq 1$

Solve each compound inequality. Graph the solution set and write it in interval notation. See Examples 7 and 8.

33. $x < 4$ or $x < 5$

34. $x \geq -2$ or $x \leq 2$

35. $x \leq -4$ or $x \geq 1$

36. $x < 0$ or $x < 1$

37. $x > 0$ or $x < 3$

38. $x \geq -3$ or $x \leq -4$

Solve each compound inequality. Write solutions in interval notation. See Examples 7 and 8.

39. $-2x \leq -4$ or $5x - 20 \geq 5$

40. $-5x \leq 10$ or $3x - 5 \geq 1$

41. $x + 4 < 0$ or $6x > -12$

42. $x + 9 < 0$ or $4x > -12$

43. $3(x - 1) < 12$ or $x + 7 > 10$

44. $5(x - 1) \geq -5$ or $5 - x \leq 11$

MIXED PRACTICE

Solve each compound inequality. Write solutions in interval notation. See Examples 1 through 8.

45. $x < \dfrac{2}{3}$ and $x > -\dfrac{1}{2}$

46. $x < \dfrac{5}{7}$ and $x < 1$

47. $x < \dfrac{2}{3}$ or $x > -\dfrac{1}{2}$

48. $x < \dfrac{5}{7}$ or $x < 1$

49. $0 \leq 2x - 3 \leq 9$

50. $3 < 5x + 1 < 11$

51. $\dfrac{1}{2} < x - \dfrac{3}{4} < 2$

52. $\dfrac{2}{3} < x + \dfrac{1}{2} < 4$

53. $x + 3 \geq 3$ and $x + 3 \leq 2$

54. $2x - 1 \geq 3$ and $-x > 2$

55. $3x \geq 5$ or $-\dfrac{5}{8}x - 6 > 1$

56. $\dfrac{3}{8}x + 1 \leq 0$ or $-2x < -4$

57. $0 < \dfrac{5 - 2x}{3} < 5$

58. $-2 < \dfrac{-2x - 1}{3} < 2$

59. $-6 < 3(x - 2) \leq 8$

60. $-5 < 2(x + 4) < 8$

61. $-x + 5 > 6$ and $1 + 2x \leq -5$

62. $5x \leq 0$ and $-x + 5 < 8$

63. $3x + 2 \leq 5$ or $7x > 29$

64. $-x < 7$ or $3x + 1 < -20$

65. $5 - x > 7$ and $2x + 3 \geq 13$

66. $-2x < -6$ or $1 - x > -2$

67. $-\dfrac{1}{2} \leq \dfrac{4x - 1}{6} < \dfrac{5}{6}$

68. $-\dfrac{1}{2} \leq \dfrac{3x - 1}{10} < \dfrac{1}{2}$

69. $\dfrac{1}{15} < \dfrac{8 - 3x}{15} < \dfrac{4}{5}$

70. $-\dfrac{1}{4} < \dfrac{6 - x}{12} < -\dfrac{1}{6}$

71. $0.3 < 0.2x - 0.9 < 1.5$

72. $-0.7 \leq 0.4x + 0.8 < 0.5$

REVIEW AND PREVIEW

Evaluate the following. See Sections 1.2 and 1.3.

73. $|-7| - |19|$

74. $|-7 - 19|$

75. $-(-6) - |-10|$

76. $|-4| - (-4) + |-20|$

Find by inspection all values for x that make each equation true.

77. $|x| = 7$

78. $|x| = 5$

79. $|x| = 0$

80. $|x| = -2$

CONCEPT EXTENSIONS

Use the graph to answer Exercises 81 and 82.

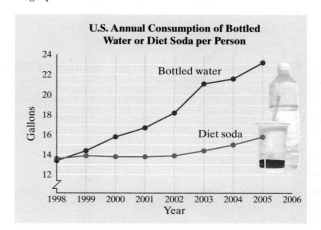

U.S. Annual Consumption of Bottled Water or Diet Soda per Person

81. For what years was the consumption of bottled water greater than 20 gallons per person *and* the consumption of diet soda greater than 14 gallons per person?

82. For what years was the consumption of bottled water less than 15 gallons per person *or* the consumption of diet soda greater than 14 gallons per person?

The formula for converting Fahrenheit temperatures to Celsius temperatures is $C = \frac{5}{9}(F - 32)$. Use this formula for Exercises 83 and 84.

83. During a recent year, the temperatures in Chicago ranged from $-29°$ to $35°C$. Use a compound inequality to convert these temperatures to Fahrenheit temperatures.

84. In Oslo, the average temperature ranges from $-10°$ to $18°$ Celsius. Use a compound inequality to convert these temperatures to the Fahrenheit scale.

Solve.

85. Christian D'Angelo has scores of 68, 65, 75, and 78 on his algebra tests. Use a compound inequality to find the scores he can make on his final exam to receive a C in the course. The final exam counts as two tests, and a C is received if the final course average is from 70 to 79.

86. Wendy Wood has scores of 80, 90, 82, and 75 on her chemistry tests. Use a compound inequality to find the range of scores she can make on her final exam to receive a B in the course. The final exam counts as two tests, and a B is received if the final course average is from 80 to 89.

*Solve each compound inequality for x. See the example below. To solve $x - 6 < 3x < 2x + 5$, notice that this inequality contains a variable not only in the middle, but also on the left and the right. When this occurs, we solve by rewriting the inequality using the word **and**.*

$$x - 6 < 3x \quad \text{and} \quad 3x < 2x + 5$$
$$-6 < 2x \quad \text{and} \quad x < 5$$
$$-3 < x$$
$$x > -3 \quad \text{and} \quad x < 5$$

$$x > -3$$

$$x < 5$$

$$-3 < x < 5, \text{ or } (-3, 5)$$

87. $2x - 3 < 3x + 1 < 4x - 5$

88. $x + 3 < 2x + 1 < 4x + 6$

89. $-3(x - 2) \le 3 - 2x \le 10 - 3x$

90. $7x - 1 \le 7 + 5x \le 3(1 + 2x)$

91. $5x - 8 < 2(2 + x) < -2(1 + 2x)$

92. $1 + 2x < 3(2 + x) < 1 + 4x$

THE BIGGER PICTURE   SOLVING EQUATIONS AND INEQUALITIES

We now continue the outline started in Section 2.4. Although suggestions will be given, this outline should be in your own words. Once you complete this new portion, try the exercises below.

Solving Equations and Inequalities

I. Equations

  A. Linear equations (Section 2.1)

II. Inequalities

  A. Linear Inequalities (Section 2.4)

  B. Compound Inequalities: Two inequality signs or 2 inequalities separated by "and" or "or." *Or* means *union* and *and* means *intersection.* (Section 2.5)

Solve. Write inequality solutions in interval notation.

1. $x - 2 \le 1$ and $3x - 1 \ge -4$

2. $-2 < x - 1 < 5$

3. $-2x + 2.5 = -7.7$

4. $-5x > 20$

5. $x \le -3$ or $x \le -5$

6. $5x < -10$ or $3x - 4 > 2$

7. $\dfrac{5t}{2} - \dfrac{3t}{4} = 7$

8. $5(x - 3) + x + 2 \ge 3(x + 2) + 2x$

$x \le 3$ *and* $x < -7$

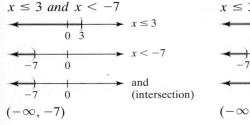

$(-\infty, -7)$

$x \le 3$ *or* $x < -7$

$(-\infty, 3]$

2.6 | ABSOLUTE VALUE EQUATIONS

OBJECTIVE

1 Solve absolute value equations.

OBJECTIVE 1 ▶ Solving absolute equations. In Chapter 1, we defined the absolute value of a number as its distance from 0 on a number line.

$$|-2| = 2 \text{ and } |3| = 3$$

In this section, we concentrate on solving equations containing the absolute value of a variable or a variable expression. Examples of absolute value equations are

$$|x| = 3 \qquad -5 = |2y + 7| \qquad |z - 6.7| = |3z + 1.2|$$

Since distance and absolute value are so closely related, absolute value equations and inequalities (see Section 2.7) are extremely useful in solving distance-type problems, such as calculating the possible error in a measurement.

For the absolute value equation $|x| = 3$, its solution set will contain all numbers whose distance from 0 is 3 units. Two numbers are 3 units away from 0 on the number line: 3 and -3.

Thus, the solution set of the equation $|x| = 3$ is $\{3, -3\}$. This suggests the following:

Solving Equations of the Form $|X| = a$

If a is a positive number, then $|X| = a$ is equivalent to $X = a$ or $X = -a$.

EXAMPLE 1   Solve: $|p| = 2$.

Solution   Since 2 is positive, $|p| = 2$ is equivalent to $p = 2$ or $p = -2$.

To check, let $p = 2$ and then $p = -2$ in the original equation.

$|p| = 2$	Original equation	$|p| = 2$	Original equation
$|2| = 2$	Let $p = 2$.	$|-2| = 2$	Let $p = -2$.
$2 = 2$	True	$2 = 2$	True

The solutions are 2 and -2 or the solution set is $\{2, -2\}$.   □

PRACTICE

1   Solve: $|q| = 7$.

If the expression inside the absolute value bars is more complicated than a single variable, we can still apply the absolute value property.

▶ **Helpful Hint**

For the equation $|X| = a$ in the box above, X can be a single variable or a variable expression.

EXAMPLE 2 Solve: $|5w + 3| = 7$.

Solution   Here the expression inside the absolute value bars is $5w + 3$. If we think of the expression $5w + 3$ as X in the absolute value property, we see that $|X| = 7$ is equivalent to

$$X = 7 \quad \text{or} \quad X = -7$$

Then substitute $5w + 3$ for X, and we have

$$5w + 3 = 7 \quad \text{or} \quad 5w + 3 = -7$$

Solve these two equations for w.

$$5w + 3 = 7 \quad \text{or} \quad 5w + 3 = -7$$
$$5w = 4 \quad \text{or} \quad 5w = -10$$
$$w = \frac{4}{5} \quad \text{or} \quad w = -2$$

Check: To check, let $w = -2$ and then $w = \frac{4}{5}$ in the original equation.

$$\text{Let } w = -2 \qquad\qquad \text{Let } w = \frac{4}{5}$$

$$|5(-2) + 3| = 7 \qquad\qquad \left|5\left(\frac{4}{5}\right) + 3\right| = 7$$

$$|-10 + 3| = 7 \qquad\qquad |4 + 3| = 7$$

$$|-7| = 7 \qquad\qquad |7| = 7$$

$$7 = 7 \quad \text{True} \qquad\qquad 7 = 7 \quad \text{True}$$

Both solutions check, and the solutions are -2 and $\frac{4}{5}$ or the solution set is $\left\{-2, \frac{4}{5}\right\}$.   □

PRACTICE
2   Solve: $|2x - 3| = 5$.

EXAMPLE 3   Solve: $\left|\dfrac{x}{2} - 1\right| = 11$.

Solution $\left|\dfrac{x}{2} - 1\right| = 11$ is equivalent to

$$\frac{x}{2} - 1 = 11 \qquad \text{or} \qquad \frac{x}{2} - 1 = -11$$
$$2\left(\frac{x}{2} - 1\right) = 2(11) \quad \text{or} \quad 2\left(\frac{x}{2} - 1\right) = 2(-11) \quad \text{Clear fractions.}$$
$$x - 2 = 22 \qquad \text{or} \qquad x - 2 = -22 \qquad \text{Apply the distributive property.}$$
$$x = 24 \qquad \text{or} \qquad x = -20$$

The solutions are 24 and -20.   □

PRACTICE
3   Solve: $\left|\dfrac{x}{5} + 1\right| = 15$.

To apply the absolute value rule, first make sure that the absolute value expression is isolated.

▶ **Helpful Hint**

If the equation has a single absolute value expression containing variables, isolate the absolute value expression first.

EXAMPLE 4   Solve: $|2x| + 5 = 7$.

Solution   We want the absolute value expression alone on one side of the equation, so begin by subtracting 5 from both sides. Then apply the absolute value property.

$$|2x| + 5 = 7$$
$$|2x| = 2 \qquad \text{Subtract 5 from both sides.}$$
$$2x = 2 \quad \text{or} \quad 2x = -2$$
$$x = 1 \quad \text{or} \quad x = -1$$

The solutions are -1 and 1. ☐

PRACTICE
4   Solve: $|3x| + 8 = 14$.

EXAMPLE 5   Solve: $|y| = 0$.

Solution   We are looking for all numbers whose distance from 0 is zero units. The only number is 0. The solution is 0. ☐

PRACTICE
5   Solve: $|z| = 0$.

The next two examples illustrate a special case for absolute value equations. This special case occurs when an isolated absolute value is equal to a negative number.

EXAMPLE 6   Solve: $2|x| + 25 = 23$.

Solution   First, isolate the absolute value.

$$2|x| + 25 = 23$$
$$2|x| = -2 \qquad \text{Subtract 25 from both sides.}$$
$$|x| = -1 \qquad \text{Divide both sides by 2.}$$

The absolute value of a number is never negative, so this equation has no solution. The solution set is $\{ \ \}$ or $\varnothing$. ☐

PRACTICE
6   Solve: $3|z| + 9 = 7$.

EXAMPLE 7   Solve: $\left| \dfrac{3x + 1}{2} \right| = -2$.

Solution   Again, the absolute value of any expression is never negative, so no solution exists. The solution set is $\{ \ \}$ or $\varnothing$. ☐

PRACTICE
7   Solve: $\left| \dfrac{5x + 3}{4} \right| = -8$.

Given two absolute value expressions, we might ask, when are the absolute values of two expressions equal? To see the answer, notice that

$$|2| = |2|, \quad |-2| = |-2|, \quad |-2| = |2|, \quad \text{and} \quad |2| = |-2|$$

$$\text{same} \qquad \text{same} \qquad \text{opposites} \qquad \text{opposites}$$

Two absolute value expressions are equal when the expressions inside the absolute value bars are equal to or are opposites of each other.

EXAMPLE 8   Solve: $|3x + 2| = |5x - 8|$.

Solution   This equation is true if the expressions inside the absolute value bars are equal to or are opposites of each other.

$$3x + 2 = 5x - 8 \quad \text{or} \quad 3x + 2 = -(5x - 8)$$

Next, solve each equation.

$$3x + 2 = 5x - 8 \quad \text{or} \quad 3x + 2 = -5x + 8$$
$$-2x + 2 = -8 \qquad \text{or} \quad 8x + 2 = 8$$
$$-2x = -10 \qquad \text{or} \qquad 8x = 6$$
$$x = 5 \qquad \text{or} \qquad x = \frac{3}{4}$$

The solutions are $\frac{3}{4}$ and 5.   □

PRACTICE
8   Solve: $|2x + 4| = |3x - 1|$.

EXAMPLE 9   Solve: $|x - 3| = |5 - x|$.

Solution
$$x - 3 = 5 - x \quad \text{or} \qquad x - 3 = -(5 - x)$$
$$2x - 3 = 5 \qquad \text{or} \qquad x - 3 = -5 + x$$
$$2x = 8 \qquad \text{or} \quad x - 3 - x = -5 + x - x$$
$$x = 4 \qquad \text{or} \qquad -3 = -5 \qquad \text{False}$$

Recall from Section 2.1 that when an equation simplifies to a false statement, the equation has no solution. Thus, the only solution for the original absolute value equation is 4.   □

PRACTICE
9   Solve: $|x - 2| = |8 - x|$.

Concept Check ☑

True or false? Absolute value equations always have two solutions. Explain your answer.

The following box summarizes the methods shown for solving absolute value equations.

> **Absolute Value Equations**
>
> $|X| = a$ $\begin{cases} \text{If } a \text{ is positive, then solve } X = a \text{ or } X = -a. \\ \text{If } a \text{ is 0, solve } X = 0. \\ \text{If } a \text{ is negative, the equation } |X| = a \text{ has no solution.} \end{cases}$
>
> $|X| = |Y|$ Solve $X = Y$ or $X = -Y$.

Answer to Concept Check:
false; answers may vary

VOCABULARY & READINESS CHECK

Match each absolute value equation with an equivalent statement.

1. $|x - 2| = 5$
2. $|x - 2| = 0$
3. $|x - 2| = |x + 3|$
4. $|x + 3| = 5$
5. $|x + 3| = -5$

A. $x - 2 = 0$
B. $x - 2 = x + 3$ or $x - 2 = -(x + 3)$
C. $x - 2 = 5$ or $x - 2 = -5$
D. $\emptyset$
E. $x + 3 = 5$ or $x + 3 = -5$

2.6 EXERCISE SET

Solve each absolute value equation. See Examples 1 through 7.

1. $|x| = 7$

2. $|y| = 15$

3. $|3x| = 12.6$

4. $|6n| = 12.6$

5. $|2x - 5| = 9$

6. $|6 + 2n| = 4$

7. $\left|\dfrac{x}{2} - 3\right| = 1$

8. $\left|\dfrac{n}{3} + 2\right| = 4$

9. $|z| + 4 = 9$

10. $|x| + 1 = 3$

11. $|3x| + 5 = 14$

12. $|2x| - 6 = 4$

13. $|2x| = 0$

14. $|7z| = 0$

15. $|4n + 1| + 10 = 4$

16. $|3z - 2| + 8 = 1$

17. $|5x - 1| = 0$

18. $|3y + 2| = 0$

19. Write an absolute value equation representing all numbers x whose distance from 0 is 5 units.

20. Write an absolute value equation representing all numbers x whose distance from 0 is 2 units.

Solve. See Examples 8 and 9.

21. $|5x - 7| = |3x + 11|$

22. $|9y + 1| = |6y + 4|$

23. $|z + 8| = |z - 3|$

24. $|2x - 5| = |2x + 5|$

25. Describe how solving an absolute value equation such as $|2x - 1| = 3$ is similar to solving an absolute value equation such as $|2x - 1| = |x - 5|$.

26. Describe how solving an absolute value equation such as $|2x - 1| = 3$ is different from solving an absolute value equation such as $|2x - 1| = |x - 5|$.

MIXED PRACTICE

Solve each absolute value equation. See Examples 1 through 9.

27. $|x| = 4$

28. $|x| = 1$

29. $|y| = 0$

30. $|y| = 8$

31. $|z| = -2$

32. $|y| = -9$

33. $|7 - 3x| = 7$

34. $|4m + 5| = 5$

35. $|6x| - 1 = 11$

36. $|7z| + 1 = 22$

37. $|4p| = -8$

38. $|5m| = -10$

39. $|x - 3| + 3 = 7$

40. $|x + 4| - 4 = 1$

41. $\left|\dfrac{z}{4} + 5\right| = -7$

42. $\left|\dfrac{c}{5} - 1\right| = -2$

43. $|9v - 3| = -8$

44. $|1 - 3b| = -7$

45. $|8n + 1| = 0$

46. $|5x - 2| = 0$

47. $|1 + 6c| - 7 = -3$

48. $|2 + 3m| - 9 = -7$

49. $|5x + 1| = 11$

50. $|8 - 6c| = 1$

51. $|4x - 2| = |-10|$

52. $|3x + 5| = |-4|$

53. $|5x + 1| = |4x - 7|$

54. $|3 + 6n| = |4n + 11|$

55. $|6 + 2x| = -|-7|$

56. $|4 - 5y| = -|-3|$

57. $|2x - 6| = |10 - 2x|$

58. $|4n + 5| = |4n + 3|$

59. $\left|\dfrac{2x - 5}{3}\right| = 7$

60. $\left|\dfrac{1 + 3n}{4}\right| = 4$

61. $2 + |5n| = 17$

62. $8 + |4m| = 24$

63. $\left|\dfrac{2x - 1}{3}\right| = |-5|$

64. $\left|\dfrac{5x + 2}{2}\right| = |-6|$

65. $|2y - 3| = |9 - 4y|$

66. $|5z - 1| = |7 - z|$

67. $\left|\dfrac{3n + 2}{8}\right| = |-1|$

68. $\left|\dfrac{2r - 6}{5}\right| = |-2|$

69. $|x + 4| = |7 - x|$

70. $|8 - y| = |y + 2|$

71. $\left|\dfrac{8c - 7}{3}\right| = -|-5|$

72. $\left|\dfrac{5d + 1}{6}\right| = -|-9|$

73. Explain why some absolute value equations have two solutions.

74. Explain why some absolute value equations have one solution.

REVIEW AND PREVIEW

The circle graph shows the U.S. Cheese consumption for 2005. Use this graph to answer Exercises 75–77. See Section 2.2. (Source: National Agriculture Statistics Service, USDA)

U.S. Cheese Consumption

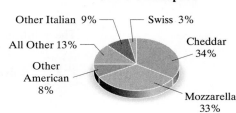

75. What percent of cheese consumption came from chedder cheese?

76. A circle contains 360°. Find the number of degrees in the 3% sector for swiss cheese.

77. If a family consumed 120 pounds of cheese in 2005, find the amount of mozzarella we might expect they consumed.

List five integer solutions of each inequality. See Sections 1.2 through 1.4.

78. $|x| \le 3$

79. $|x| \ge -2$

80. $|y| > -10$

81. $|y| < 0$

CONCEPT EXTENSIONS

82. Write an absolute value equation representing all numbers x whose distance from 1 is 5 units.

83. Write an absolute value equation representing all numbers x whose distance from 7 is 2 units.

Write each as an equivalent absolute value.

84. $x = 6$ or $x = -6$

85. $2x - 1 = 4$ or $2x - 1 = -4$

86. $x - 2 = 3x - 4$ or $x - 2 = -(3x - 4)$

87. For what value(s) of c will an absolute value equation of the form $|ax + b| = c$ have
   a. one solution?
   b. no solution?
   c. two solutions?

2.7 ABSOLUTE VALUE INEQUALITIES

OBJECTIVES

1 Solve absolute value inequalities of the form $|x| < a$.

2 Solve absolute value inequalities of the form $|x| > a$.

OBJECTIVE 1 ▶ Solving absolute value inequalities of the form $|x| < a$. The solution set of an absolute value inequality such as $|x| < 2$ contains all numbers whose distance from 0 is less than 2 units, as shown below.

The solution set is $\{x | -2 < x < 2\}$, or $(-2, 2)$ in interval notation.

EXAMPLE 1 Solve: $|x| \leq 3$.

Solution The solution set of this inequality contains all numbers whose distance from 0 is less than or equal to 3. Thus 3, -3, and all numbers between 3 and -3 are in the solution set.

The solution set is $[-3, 3]$. ☐

PRACTICE
1 Solve: $|x| < 2$ and graph the solution set.

In general, we have the following.

Solving Absolute Value Inequalities of the Form $|X| < a$

If a is a positive number, then $|X| < a$ is equivalent to $-a < X < a$.

This property also holds true for the inequality symbol $\leq$.

EXAMPLE 2 Solve for m: $|m - 6| < 2$.

Solution Replace X with $m - 6$ and a with 2 in the preceding property, and we see that

$$|m - 6| < 2 \quad \text{is equivalent to} \quad -2 < m - 6 < 2$$

Solve this compound inequality for m by adding 6 to all three parts.

$$-2 < m - 6 < 2$$
$$-2 + 6 < m - 6 + 6 < 2 + 6 \quad \text{Add 6 to all three parts.}$$
$$4 < m < 8 \quad \text{Simplify.}$$

The solution set is $(4, 8)$, and its graph is shown.

☐

PRACTICE
2 Solve for b: $|b + 1| < 3$. Graph the solution set.

▶ **Helpful Hint**

Before using an absolute value inequality property, isolate the absolute value expression on one side of the inequality.

EXAMPLE 3   Solve for x: $|5x + 1| + 1 \leq 10$.

Solution   First, isolate the absolute value expression by subtracting 1 from both sides.

$$|5x + 1| + 1 \leq 10$$
$$|5x + 1| \leq 10 - 1 \quad \text{Subtract 1 from both sides.}$$
$$|5x + 1| \leq 9 \quad \text{Simplify.}$$

Since 9 is positive, we apply the absolute value property for $|X| \leq a$.

$$-9 \leq 5x + 1 \leq 9$$
$$-9 - 1 \leq 5x + 1 - 1 \leq 9 - 1 \quad \text{Subtract 1 from all three parts.}$$
$$-10 \leq 5x \leq 8 \quad \text{Simplify.}$$
$$-2 \leq x \leq \frac{8}{5} \quad \text{Divide all three parts by 5.}$$

The solution set is $\left[-2, \dfrac{8}{5}\right]$, and the graph is shown above.   □

PRACTICE
3   Solve for x: $|3x - 2| + 5 \leq 9$. Graph the solution set.

EXAMPLE 4   Solve for x: $\left|2x - \dfrac{1}{10}\right| < -13$.

Solution   The absolute value of a number is always nonnegative and can never be less than -13. Thus this absolute value inequality has no solution. The solution set is $\{\ \}$ or $\varnothing$.   □

PRACTICE
4   Solve for x: $\left|3x + \dfrac{5}{8}\right| < -4$.

OBJECTIVE 2 ▶ **Solving absolute value inequalities of the form** $|x| > a$. Let us now solve an absolute value inequality of the form $|X| > a$, such as $|x| \geq 3$. The solution set contains all numbers whose distance from 0 is 3 or more units. Thus the graph of the solution set contains 3 and all points to the right of 3 on the number line or -3 and all points to the left of -3 on the number line.

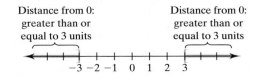

This solution set is written as $\{x \mid x \leq -3 \text{ or } x \geq 3\}$. In interval notation, the solution is $(-\infty, -3] \cup [3, \infty)$, since "or" means "union." In general, we have the following.

> **Solving Absolute Value Inequalities of the Form $|X| > a$**
> If a is a positive number, then $|X| > a$ is equivalent to $X < -a$ or $X > a$.

This property also holds true for the inequality symbol $\geq$.

EXAMPLE 5 Solve for y: $|y - 3| > 7$.

Solution Since 7 is positive, we apply the property for $|X| > a$.

$$|y - 3| > 7 \text{ is equivalent to } y - 3 < -7 \text{ or } y - 3 > 7$$

Next, solve the compound inequality.

$$
\begin{array}{lcl}
y - 3 < -7 & \text{or} & y - 3 > 7 \\
y - 3 + 3 < -7 + 3 & \text{or} & y - 3 + 3 > 7 + 3 \quad \text{Add 3 to both sides.} \\
y < -4 & \text{or} & y > 10 \quad\quad\quad \text{Simplify.}
\end{array}
$$

The solution set is $(-\infty, -4) \cup (10, \infty)$, and its graph is shown.

PRACTICE
5 Solve for y: $|y + 4| \geq 6$.

Examples 6 and 8 illustrate special cases of absolute value inequalities. These special cases occur when an isolated absolute value expression is less than, less than or equal to, greater than, or greater than or equal to a negative number or 0.

EXAMPLE 6 Solve: $|2x + 9| + 5 > 3$.

Solution First isolate the absolute value expression by subtracting 5 from both sides.

$$
\begin{array}{ll}
|2x + 9| + 5 > 3 & \\
|2x + 9| + 5 - 5 > 3 - 5 & \text{Subtract 5 from both sides.} \\
|2x + 9| > -2 & \text{Simplify.}
\end{array}
$$

The absolute value of any number is always nonnegative and thus is always greater than -2. This inequality and the original inequality are true for all values of x. The solution set is $\{x \mid x \text{ is a real number}\}$ or $(-\infty, \infty)$ and its graph is shown.

PRACTICE
6 Solve: $|4x + 3| + 5 > 3$. Graph the solution set.

Answer to Concept Check:
$(-\infty, \infty)$ since the absolute value is always nonnegative

Concept Check ☑

Without taking any solution steps, how do you know that the absolute value inequality $|3x - 2| > -9$ has a solution? What is its solution?

EXAMPLE 7   Solve: $\left|\dfrac{x}{3} - 1\right| - 7 \geq -5$.

Solution   First, isolate the absolute value expression by adding 7 to both sides.

$$\left|\frac{x}{3} - 1\right| - 7 \geq -5$$

$$\left|\frac{x}{3} - 1\right| - 7 + 7 \geq -5 + 7 \quad \text{Add 7 to both sides.}$$

$$\left|\frac{x}{3} - 1\right| \geq 2 \qquad\qquad \text{Simplify.}$$

Next, write the absolute value inequality as an equivalent compound inequality and solve.

$$\frac{x}{3} - 1 \leq -2 \qquad \text{or} \qquad \frac{x}{3} - 1 \geq 2$$

$$3\left(\frac{x}{3} - 1\right) \leq 3(-2) \quad \text{or} \quad 3\left(\frac{x}{3} - 1\right) \geq 3(2) \quad \text{Clear the inequalities of fractions.}$$

$$x - 3 \leq -6 \qquad \text{or} \qquad x - 3 \geq 6 \qquad \text{Apply the distributive property.}$$

$$x \leq -3 \qquad \text{or} \qquad x \geq 9 \qquad \text{Add 3 to both sides.}$$

The solution set is $(-\infty, -3] \cup [9, \infty)$, and its graph is shown.

PRACTICE
7   Solve: $\left|\dfrac{x}{2} - 3\right| - 5 > -2$. Graph the solution set.

EXAMPLE 8   Solve for x: $\left|\dfrac{2(x + 1)}{3}\right| \leq 0$.

Solution   Recall that "$\leq$" means "less than or equal to." The absolute value of any expression will never be less than 0, but it may be equal to 0. Thus, to solve $\left|\dfrac{2(x + 1)}{3}\right| \leq 0$ we solve $\left|\dfrac{2(x + 1)}{3}\right| = 0$

$$\frac{2(x + 1)}{3} = 0$$

$$3\left[\frac{2(x + 1)}{3}\right] = 3(0) \quad \text{Clear the equation of fractions.}$$

$$2x + 2 = 0 \qquad \text{Apply the distributive property.}$$

$$2x = -2 \qquad \text{Subtract 2 from both sides.}$$

$$x = -1 \qquad \text{Divide both sides by 2.}$$

The solution set is $\{-1\}$.

PRACTICE
8   Solve for x: $\left|\dfrac{3(x - 2)}{5}\right| \leq 0$.

The following box summarizes the types of absolute value equations and inequalities.

Solving Absolute Value Equations and Inequalities with $a > 0$

Algebraic Solution	**Solution Graph**
$|X| = a$ is equivalent to $X = a$ or $X = -a$.	
$|X| < a$ is equivalent to $-a < X < a$.	
$|X| > a$ is equivalent to $X < -a$ or $X > a$.	

VOCABULARY & READINESS CHECK

Match each absolute value statement with an equivalent statement.

1. $|2x + 1| = 3$

2. $|2x + 1| \le 3$

3. $|2x + 1| < 3$

4. $|2x + 1| \ge 3$

5. $|2x + 1| > 3$

A. $2x + 1 > 3$ or $2x + 1 < -3$

B. $2x + 1 \ge 3$ or $2x + 1 \le -3$

C. $-3 < 2x + 1 < 3$

D. $2x + 1 = 3$ or $2x + 1 = -3$

E. $-3 \le 2x + 1 \le 3$

2.7 EXERCISE SET

MyMathLab PRACTICE · WATCH · DOWNLOAD · READ · REVIEW

Solve each inequality. Then graph the solution set and write it in interval notation. See Examples 1 through 4.

1. $|x| \le 4$

2. $|x| < 6$

3. $|x - 3| < 2$

4. $|y - 7| \le 5$

5. $|x + 3| < 2$

6. $|x + 4| < 6$

7. $|2x + 7| \le 13$

8. $|5x - 3| \le 18$

9. $|x| + 7 \le 12$

10. $|x| + 6 \le 7$

11. $|3x - 1| < -5$

12. $|8x - 3| < -2$

13. $|x - 6| - 7 \le -1$

14. $|z + 2| - 7 < -3$

Solve each inequality. Graph the solution set and write it in interval notation. See Examples 5 through 7.

15. $|x| > 3$

16. $|y| \ge 4$

17. $|x + 10| \ge 14$

18. $|x - 9| \ge 2$

19. $|x| + 2 > 6$

20. $|x| - 1 > 3$

21. $|5x| > -4$

22. $|4x - 11| > -1$

23. $|6x - 8| + 3 > 7$

24. $|10 + 3x| + 1 > 2$

Solve each inequality. Graph the solution set and write it in interval notation. See Example 8.

25. $|x| \le 0$

26. $|x| \ge 0$

27. $|8x + 3| > 0$

28. $|5x - 6| < 0$

MIXED PRACTICE

Solve each inequality. Graph the solution set and write it in interval notation. See Examples 1 through 8.

29. $|x| \le 2$

30. $|z| < 8$

31. $|y| > 1$

32. $|x| \ge 10$

33. $|x - 3| < 8$

34. $|-3 + x| \le 10$

35. $|0.6x - 3| > 0.6$

36. $|1 + 0.3x| \ge 0.1$

37. $5 + |x| \le 2$

38. $8 + |x| < 1$

39. $|x| > -4$

40. $|x| \le -7$

41. $|2x - 7| \le 11$

42. $|5x + 2| < 8$

43. $|x + 5| + 2 \ge 8$

44. $|-1 + x| - 6 > 2$

45. $|x| > 0$

46. $|x| < 0$

47. $9 + |x| > 7$

48. $5 + |x| \ge 4$

49. $6 + |4x - 1| \le 9$

50. $-3 + |5x - 2| \le 4$

51. $\left|\dfrac{2}{3}x + 1\right| > 1$

52. $\left|\dfrac{3}{4}x - 1\right| \ge 2$

53. $|5x + 3| < -6$

54. $|4 + 9x| \ge -6$

55. $\left|\dfrac{8x - 3}{4}\right| \le 0$

56. $\left|\dfrac{5x + 6}{2}\right| \le 0$

57. $|1 + 3x| + 4 < 5$

58. $|7x - 3| - 1 \le 10$

59. $\left|\dfrac{x + 6}{3}\right| > 2$

60. $\left|\dfrac{7 + x}{2}\right| \ge 4$

61. $-15 + |2x - 7| \le -6$

62. $-9 + |3 + 4x| < -4$

63. $\left| 2x + \dfrac{3}{4} \right| - 7 \le -2$

64. $\left| \dfrac{3}{5} + 4x \right| - 6 < -1$

MIXED PRACTICE

Solve each equation or inequality for x. (Sections 2.6, 2.7)

65. $|2x - 3| < 7$

66. $|2x - 3| > 7$

67. $|2x - 3| = 7$

68. $|5 - 6x| = 29$

69. $|x - 5| \ge 12$

70. $|x + 4| \ge 20$

71. $|9 + 4x| = 0$

72. $|9 + 4x| \ge 0$

73. $|2x + 1| + 4 < 7$

74. $8 + |5x - 3| \ge 11$

75. $|3x - 5| + 4 = 5$

76. $|5x - 3| + 2 = 4$

77. $|x + 11| = -1$

78. $|4x - 4| = -3$

79. $\left| \dfrac{2x - 1}{3} \right| = 6$

80. $\left| \dfrac{6 - x}{4} \right| = 5$

81. $\left| \dfrac{3x - 5}{6} \right| > 5$

82. $\left| \dfrac{4x - 7}{5} \right| < 2$

REVIEW AND PREVIEW

Recall the formula:

$$\text{Probability of an event} = \frac{\text{number of ways that the event can occur}}{\text{number of possible outcomes}}$$

Find the probability of rolling each number on a single toss of a die. (Recall that a die is a cube with each of its six sides containing 1, 2, 3, 4, 5, and 6 black dots, respectively.) See Section 2.3.

83. $P(\text{rolling a 2})$

84. $P(\text{rolling a 5})$

85. $P(\text{rolling a 7})$

86. $P(\text{rolling a 0})$

87. $P(\text{rolling a 1 or 3})$

88. $P(\text{rolling a 1, 2, 3, 4, 5, or 6})$

Consider the equation $3x - 4y = 12$. For each value of x or y given, find the corresponding value of the other variable that makes the statement true. See Section 2.3.

89. If $x = 2$, find y

90. If $y = -1$, find x

91. If $y = -3$, find x

92. If $x = 4$, find y

CONCEPT EXTENSIONS

93. Write an absolute value inequality representing all numbers x whose distance from 0 is less than 7 units.

94. Write an absolute value inequality representing all numbers x whose distance from 0 is greater than 4 units.

95. Write $-5 \le x \le 5$ as an equivalent inequality containing an absolute value.

96. Write $x > 1$ or $x < -1$ as an equivalent inequality containing an absolute value.

97. Describe how solving $|x - 3| = 5$ is different from solving $|x - 3| < 5$.

98. Describe how solving $|x + 4| = 0$ is similar to solving $|x + 4| \le 0$.

The expression $|x_T - x|$ is defined to be the absolute error in x, where x_T is the true value of a quantity and x is the measured value or value as stored in a computer.

99. If the true value of a quantity is 3.5 and the absolute error must be less than 0.05, find the acceptable measured values.

100. If the true value of a quantity is 0.2 and the approximate value stored in a computer is $\dfrac{51}{256}$, find the absolute error.

THE BIGGER PICTURE   SOLVING EQUATIONS AND INEQUALITIES

We now continue the outline from Sections 2.4 and 2.5. Although suggestions will be given, this outline should be in your own words and you should include at least "how to recognize" and "how to begin to solve" under each letter heading.

    For example:

Solving Equations and Inequalities

I. Equations

    A. Linear equations (Section 2.1)

B. Absolute Value Equations: Equation contains the absolute value of a variable expression. (Section 2.6)

$$|3x - 1| - 12 = -4 \quad \text{Absolute value equation.}$$

$$|3x - 1| = 8 \quad \text{Isolate absolute value.}$$

$$3x - 1 = 8 \quad \text{or} \quad 3x - 1 = -8$$

$$3x = 9 \quad \text{or} \quad 3x = -7$$

$$x = 3 \quad \text{or} \quad x = -\dfrac{7}{3}$$

$$|x - 5| = |x + 1| \quad \text{Absolute value equation.}$$

$$x - 5 = x + 1 \quad \text{or} \quad x - 5 = -(x + 1)$$

$$\underbrace{-5 = 1}_{\text{No solution}} \quad \text{or} \quad x - 5 = -x - 1$$

$$\text{or} \quad 2x = 4$$

$$x = 2$$

II. Inequalities

    A. Linear Inequalities (Section 2.4)

    B. Compound Inequalities (Section 2.5)

    C. Absolute Value Inequalities: Inequality with absolute value bars about variable expression. (Section 2.7)

$\|x - 5\| - 8 < -2$	$\|2x + 1\| \geq 17$
$\|x - 5\| < 6$	$2x + 1 \geq 17 \text{ or } 2x + 1 \leq -17$
$-6 < x - 5 < 6$	$2x \geq 16 \text{ or } \quad 2x \leq -18$
$-1 < x < 11$	$x \geq 8 \text{ or } \quad x \leq -9$
$(-1, 11)$	$(-\infty, -9] \cup [8, \infty)$

Solve. If an inequality, write your solutions in interval notation.

1. $9x - 14 = 11x + 2$
2. $|x - 4| = 17$
3. $x - 1 \leq 5 \text{ or } 3x - 2 \leq 10$
4. $-x < 7 \text{ and } 4x \leq 20$
5. $|x - 2| = |x + 15|$
6. $9y - 6y + 1 = 4y + 10 - y + 3$
7. $1.5x - 3 = 1.2x - 18$
8. $\dfrac{7x + 1}{8} - 3 = x + \dfrac{2x + 1}{4}$
9. $|5x + 2| - 10 \leq -3$
10. $|x + 11| > 2$
11. $|9x + 2| - 1 = 24$
12. $\left|\dfrac{3x - 1}{2}\right| = |2x + 5|$

CHAPTER 2 GROUP ACTIVITY

Analyzing Municipal Budgets

Nearly all cities, towns, and villages operate with an annual budget. Budget items might include expenses for fire and police protection as well as for street maintenance and parks. No matter how big or small the budget, city officials need to know if municipal spending is over or under budget. In this project, you will have the opportunity to analyze a municipal budget and make budgetary recommendations. This project may be completed by working in groups or individually.

Suppose that each year your town creates a municipal budget. The next year's annual municipal budget is submitted for approval by the town's citizens at the annual town meeting. This year's budget was printed in the town newspaper earlier in the year.

You have joined a group of citizens who are concerned about your town's budgeting and spending processes. Your group plans to analyze this year's budget along with what was actually spent by the town this year. You hope to present your findings at the annual town meeting and make some budgetary recommendations for next year's budget. The municipal budget contains many different areas of spending. To help focus your group's analysis, you have decided to research spending habits only for categories in which the actual expenses differ from the budgeted amount by more than 12% of the budgeted amount.

1. For each category in the budget, write a specific absolute value inequality that describes the condition that must be met before your group will research spending habits for that category. In each case, let the variable x represent the actual expense for a budget category.

2. For each category in the budget, write an equivalent compound inequality for the condition described in Question 1. Again, let the variable x represent the actual expense for a budget category.

3. On the next page is a listing of the actual expenditures made this year for each budget category. Use the inequalities from either Question 1 or Question 2 to complete the Budget Worksheet given at the end of this project. (The first category has been filled in.) From the Budget Worksheet, decide which categories must be researched.

4. Can you think of possible reasons why spending in the categories that must be researched were over or under budget?

5. Based on this year's municipal budget and actual expenses, what recommendations would you make for next year's budget? Explain your reasoning.

6. (Optional) Research the annual budget used by your own town or your college or university. Conduct a similar analysis of the budget with respect to actual expenses. What can you conclude?

	Department/Program	Actual Expenditure
I.	**Board of Health**	
	Immunization Programs	$14,800
	Inspections	$41,900
II.	**Fire Department**	
	Equipment	$375,000
	Salaries	$268,500
III.	**Libraries**	
	Book/Periodical Purchases	$107,300
	Equipment	$29,000
	Salaries	$118,400
IV.	**Parks and Recreation**	
	Maintenance	$82,500
	Playground Equipment	$45,000
	Salaries	$118,000
	Summer Programs	$96,200
V.	**Police Department**	
	Equipment	$328,000
	Salaries	$405,000
VI.	**Public Works**	
	Recycling	$48,100
	Sewage	$92,500
	Snow Removal & Road Salt	$268,300
	Street Maintenance	$284,000
	Water Treatment	$94,100
	TOTAL	$2,816,600

THE TOWN CRIER

Annual Budget Set at Town Meeting

ANYTOWN, USA (MG)—This year's annual budget is as follows:

	Amount Budgeted
BOARD OF HEALTH	
Immunization Programs	$15,000
Inspections	$50,000
FIRE DEPARTMENT	
Equipment	$450,000
Salaries	$275,000
LIBRARIES	
Book/Periodical Purchases	$90,000
Equipment	$30,000
Salaries	$120,000
PARKS AND RECREATION	
Maintenance	$70,000
Playground Equipment	$50,000
Salaries	$140,000
Summer Programs	$80,000
POLICE DEPARTMENT	
Equipment	$300,000
Salaries	$400,000
PUBLIC WORKS	
Recycling	$50,000
Sewage	$100,000
Snow Removal & Road Salt	$200,000
Street Maintenance	$250,000
Water Treatment	$100,000
TOTAL	**$2,770,000**

BUDGET WORKSHEET

Budget category	Budgeted amount	Minimum allowed	Actual expense	Maximum allowed	Within budget?	Amt over/ under budget
Immunization Programs	$15,000	$13,200	$14,800	$16,800	Yes	Under $200

CHAPTER 2 VOCABULARY CHECK

Fill in each blank with one of the words or phrases listed below.

contradiction   linear inequality in one variable   compound inequality   solution

absolute value   consecutive integers   identity   union

formula   linear equation in one variable   intersection

1. The statement "$x < 5$ or $x > 7$" is called a(n) _____ .

2. An equation in one variable that has no solution is called a(n) _____ .

3. The _____ of two sets is the set of all elements common to both sets.

4. The _____ of two sets is the set of all elements that belong to either of the sets.

5. An equation in one variable that has every number (for which the equation is defined) as a solution is called a(n) _____ .

6. The equation $d = rt$ is also called a(n) _____ .

7. A number's distance from 0 is called its _____ .

8. When a variable in an equation is replaced by a number and the resulting equation is true, then that number is called a(n) _____ of the equation.

9. The integers 17, 18, 19 are examples of _____ .

10. The statement $5x - 0.2 < 7$ is an example of a(n) _____ .

11. The statement $5x - 0.2 = 7$ is an example of a(n) _____ .

> ▶ **Helpful Hint**
>
> Are you preparing for your test? Don't forget to take the Chapter 2 Test on page 115. Then check your answers at the back of the text and use the Chapter Test Prep Video CD to see the fully worked-out solutions to any of the exercises you want to review.

CHAPTER 2 HIGHLIGHTS

DEFINITIONS AND CONCEPTS	EXAMPLES

SECTION 2.1   LINEAR EQUATIONS IN ONE VARIABLE

An **equation** is a statement that two expressions are equal.

Equations:

$$5 = 5 \qquad 7x + 2 = -14 \qquad 3(x - 1)^2 = 9x^2 - 6$$

A **linear equation in one variable** is an equation that can be written in the form $ax + b = c$, where a, b, and c are real numbers and a is not 0.

Linear equations:

$$7x + 2 = -14 \qquad x = -3$$
$$5(2y - 7) = -2(8y - 1)$$

A **solution** of an equation is a value for the variable that makes the equation a true statement.

Check to see that -1 is a solution of

$3(x - 1) = 4x - 2$.

$$3(-1 - 1) = 4(-1) - 2$$
$$3(-2) = -4 - 2$$
$$-6 = -6 \qquad \text{True}$$

Thus, -1 is a solution.

Equivalent equations have the same solution.

$x - 12 = 14$ and $x = 26$ are equivalent equations.

The **addition property of equality** guarantees that the same number may be added to (or subtracted from) both sides of an equation, and the result is an equivalent equation.

Solve for x: $-3x - 2 = 10$.

$$-3x - 2 + 2 = 10 + 2 \qquad \text{Add 2 to both sides.}$$
$$-3x = 12$$

The **multiplication property of equality** guarantees that both sides of an equation may be multiplied by (or divided by) the same nonzero number, and the result is an equivalent equation.

$$\frac{-3x}{-3} = \frac{12}{-3} \qquad \text{Divide both sides by } -3.$$
$$x = -4$$

To solve linear equations in one variable:

Solve for x:

$$x - \frac{x - 2}{6} = \frac{x - 7}{3} + \frac{2}{3}$$

1. Clear the equation of fractions.

1. $\quad 6\left(x - \dfrac{x - 2}{6}\right) = 6\left(\dfrac{x - 7}{3} + \dfrac{2}{3}\right)$ Multiply both sides by 6.

$$6x - (x - 2) = 2(x - 7) + 2(2)$$

2. Remove grouping symbols such as parentheses.

2. $\quad 6x - x + 2 = 2x - 14 + 4$ Remove grouping symbols.

3. Simplify by combining like terms.

3. $\quad 5x + 2 = 2x - 10$

4. Write variable terms on one side and numbers on the other side using the addition property of equality.

4. $\quad 5x + 2 - 2 = 2x - 10 - 2$ Subtract 2.

$$5x = 2x - 12$$
$$5x - 2x = 2x - 12 - 2x \qquad \text{Subtract } 2x.$$
$$3x = -12$$

DEFINITIONS AND CONCEPTS	**EXAMPLES**

SECTION 2.1 LINEAR EQUATIONS IN ONE VARIABLE

5. Isolate the variable using the multiplication property of equality.

5.
$$\frac{3x}{3} = \frac{-12}{3} \qquad \text{Divide by 3.}$$
$$x = -4$$

6. Check the proposed solution in the original equation.

6. $-4 - \dfrac{-4-2}{6} \overset{?}{=} \dfrac{-4-7}{3} + \dfrac{2}{3}$ Replace x with -4 in the original equation.

$$-4 - \frac{-6}{6} \overset{?}{=} \frac{-11}{3} + \frac{2}{3}$$

$$-4 - (-1) \overset{?}{=} \frac{-9}{3}$$

$$-3 = -3 \qquad \text{True}$$

SECTION 2.2 AN INTRODUCTION TO PROBLEM SOLVING

Problem-Solving Strategy

Colorado is shaped like a rectangle whose length is about 1.3 times its width. If the perimeter of Colorado is 2070 kilometers, find its dimensions.

1. UNDERSTAND the problem.

1. Read and reread the problem. Guess a solution and check your guess.
Let x = width of Colorado in kilometers. Then
$1.3x$ = length of Colorado in kilometers

1.3x

2. TRANSLATE the problem.

2. In words:

twice the length	+	twice the width	=	perimeter
↘		↓		↓
Translate: $2(1.3x)$	+	$2x$	=	2070

3. SOLVE the equation.

3. $2.6x + 2x = 2070$
$4.6x = 2070$
$x = 450$

4. INTERPRET the results.

4. If $x = 450$ kilometers, then $1.3x = 1.3(450) = 585$ kilometers. *Check:* The perimeter of a rectangle whose width is 450 kilometers and length is 585 kilometers is $2(450) + 2(585) = 2070$ kilometers, the required perimeter. *State:* The dimensions of Colorado are 450 kilometers by 585 kilometers

SECTION 2.3 FORMULAS AND PROBLEM SOLVING

An equation that describes a known relationship among quantities is called a **formula**.

Formulas:

$$A = \pi r^2 \text{ (area of a circle)}$$

$$I = PRT \qquad \text{(interest = principal} \cdot \text{rate} \cdot \text{time)}$$

(continued)

DEFINITIONS AND CONCEPTS	**EXAMPLES**

SECTION 2.3 FORMULAS AND PROBLEM SOLVING (continued)

To solve a formula for a specified variable, use the steps for solving an equation. Treat the specified variable as the only variable of the equation.

Solve $A = 2HW + 2LW + 2LH$ for H

$$A - 2LW = 2HW + 2LH \quad \text{Subtract } 2LW.$$
$$A - 2LW = H(2W + 2L) \quad \text{Factor out } H.$$

$$\frac{A - 2LW}{2W + 2L} = \frac{H(2W + 2L)}{2W + 2L} \quad \text{Divide by } 2W + 2L.$$

$$\frac{A - 2LW}{2W + 2L} = H \quad \text{Simplify.}$$

SECTION 2.4 LINEAR INEQUALITIES AND PROBLEM SOLVING

A **linear inequality in one variable** is an inequality that can be written in the form $ax + b < c$, where a, b, and c are real numbers and $a \neq 0$. (The inequality symbols $\leq$, $>$, and $\geq$ also apply here.)

Linear inequalities:

$$5x - 2 \leq -7 \qquad 3y > 1 \qquad \frac{z}{7} < -9(z - 3)$$

$$x - 9 \leq -16$$
$$x - 9 + 9 \leq -16 + 9 \quad \text{Add 9.}$$
$$x \leq -7$$

The **addition property of inequality** guarantees that the same number may be added to (or subtracted from) both sides of an inequality, and the resulting inequality will have the same solution set.

Solve.

$$6x < -66$$
$$\frac{6x}{6} < \frac{-66}{6} \quad \text{Divide by 6. Do not reverse direction}$$
$$\phantom{\frac{6x}{6} < \frac{-66}{6}} \quad \text{of inequality symbol.}$$
$$x < -11$$

The **multiplication property of inequality** guarantees that both sides of an inequality may be multiplied by (or divided by) the same **positive** number, and the resulting inequality will have the same solution set. We may also multiply (or divide) both sides of an inequality by the same **negative** number and **reverse the direction of the inequality symbol,** and the result is an inequality with the same solution set.

Solve.

$$-6x < -66$$
$$\frac{-6x}{-6} > \frac{-66}{-6} \quad \text{Divide by } -6. \text{ Reverse direction}$$
$$\phantom{\frac{-6x}{-6} > \frac{-66}{-6}} \quad \text{of inequality symbol.}$$
$$x > 11$$

To solve a linear inequality in one variable:

Solve for x:

$$\frac{3}{7}(x - 4) \geq x + 2$$

1. Clear the equation of fractions.

1. $7\left[\frac{3}{7}(x - 4)\right] \geq 7(x + 2) \quad \text{Multiply by 7.}$

$$3(x - 4) \geq 7(x + 2)$$

2. Remove grouping symbols such as parentheses.

2. $3x - 12 \geq 7x + 14 \quad \text{Apply the distributive property.}$

3. Simplify by combining like terms.

4. Write variable terms on one side and numbers on the other side using the addition property of inequality.

4. $-4x - 12 \geq 14 \quad \text{Subtract } 7x.$
$$-4x \geq 26 \quad \text{Add 12.}$$
$$\frac{-4x}{-4} \leq \frac{26}{-4} \quad \text{Divide by } -4. \text{ Reverse direction of inequality symbol.}$$

5. Isolate the variable using the multiplication property of inequality.

$$x \leq -\frac{13}{2}$$

DEFINITIONS AND CONCEPTS	**EXAMPLES**

Two inequalities joined by the words **and** or **or** are called **compound inequalities.**

Compound inequalities:
$$x - 7 \leq 4 \quad \text{and} \quad x \geq -21$$
$$2x + 7 > x - 3 \quad \text{or} \quad 5x + 2 > -3$$

The solution set of a compound inequality formed by the word **and** is the **intersection** $\cap$ of the solution sets of the two inequalities.

Solve for x:

$$x < 5 \text{ and } x < 3$$

$\{x | x < 5\}$ $(-\infty, 5)$

$\{x | x < 3\}$ $(-\infty, 3)$

$\{x | x < 3$ and $x < 5\}$ $(-\infty, 3)$

The solution set of a compound inequality formed by the word **or** is the **union**, $\cup$, of the solution sets of the two inequalities.

Solve for x:

$$x - 2 \geq -3 \quad \text{or} \quad 2x \leq -4$$
$$x \geq -1 \quad \text{or} \quad x \leq -2$$

$\{x | x \geq -1\}$ $[-1, \infty)$

$\{x | x \leq -2\}$ $(-\infty, -2]$

$\{x | x \leq -2$ or $x \geq -1\}$ $(-\infty, -2] \cup [-1, \infty)$

If a is a positive number, then $|x| = a$ is equivalent to $x = a$ or $x = -a$.

Solve for y:
$$|5y - 1| - 7 = 4$$
$$|5y - 1| = 11$$
$$5y - 1 = 11 \quad \text{or} \quad 5y - 1 = -11 \quad \text{Add 7.}$$
$$5y = 12 \quad \text{or} \quad 5y = -10 \quad \text{Add 1.}$$
$$y = \frac{12}{5} \quad \text{or} \quad y = -2 \quad \text{Divide by 5.}$$

The solutions are -2 and $\frac{12}{5}$.

If a is negative, then $|x| = a$ has no solution.

Solve for x:
$$\left| \frac{x}{2} - 7 \right| = -1$$

The solution set is $\{ \}$ or $\varnothing$.

If an absolute value equation is of the form $|x| = |y|$, solve $x = y$ or $x = -y$.

Solve for x:
$$|x - 7| = |2x + 1|$$
$$x - 7 = 2x + 1 \quad \text{or} \quad x - 7 = -(2x + 1)$$
$$x = 2x + 8 \quad\quad\quad x - 7 = -2x - 1$$
$$-x = 8 \quad\quad\quad x = -2x + 6$$
$$x = -8 \quad \text{or} \quad 3x = 6$$
$$x = 2$$

The solutions are -8 and 2.

Solve.

55. George Boros can pay his housekeeper $15 per week to do his laundry, or he can have the laundromat do it at a cost of 50 cents per pound for the first 10 pounds and 40 cents for each additional pound. Use an inequality to find the weight at which it is more economical to use the housekeeper than the laundromat.

56. Ceramic firing temperatures usually range from 500° to 1000° Fahrenheit. Use a compound inequality to convert this range to the Celsius scale. Round to the nearest degree.

57. In the Olympic gymnastics competition, Nana must average a score of 9.65 to win the silver medal. Seven of the eight judges have reported scores of 9.5, 9.7, 9.9, 9.7, 9.7, 9.6, and 9.5. Use an inequality to find the minimum score that Nana must receive from the last judge to win the silver medal.

58. Carol would like to pay cash for a car when she graduates from college and estimates that she can afford a car that costs between $4000 and $8000. She has saved $500 so far and plans to earn the rest of the money by working the next two summers. If Carol plans to save the same amount each summer, use a compound inequality to find the range of money she must save each summer to buy the car.

(2.5) Solve each inequality. Write your answers in interval notation.

59. $1 \le 4x - 7 \le 3$

60. $-2 \le 8 + 5x < -1$

61. $-3 < 4(2x - 1) < 12$

62. $-6 < x - (3 - 4x) < -3$

63. $\dfrac{1}{6} < \dfrac{4x - 3}{3} \le \dfrac{4}{5}$

64. $x \le 2$ and $x > -5$

65. $3x - 5 > 6$ or $-x < -5$

(2.6) Solve each absolute value equation.

66. $|x - 7| = 9$ **67.** $|8 - x| = 3$

68. $|2x + 9| = 9$ **69.** $|-3x + 4| = 7$

70. $|3x - 2| + 6 = 10$ **71.** $5 + |6x + 1| = 5$

72. $-5 = |4x - 3|$ **73.** $|5 - 6x| + 8 = 3$

74. $-8 = |x - 3| - 10$ **75.** $\left|\dfrac{3x - 7}{4}\right| = 2$

76. $|6x + 1| = |15 + 4x|$

(2.7) Solve each absolute value inequality. Graph the solution set and write it in interval notation.

77. $|5x - 1| < 9$

78. $|6 + 4x| \ge 10$

79. $|3x| - 8 > 1$

80. $9 + |5x| < 24$

81. $|6x - 5| \le -1$

82. $\left|3x + \dfrac{2}{5}\right| \ge 4$

83. $\left|\dfrac{x}{3} + 6\right| - 8 > -5$

84. $\left|\dfrac{4(x - 1)}{7}\right| + 10 < 2$

MIXED REVIEW

Solve.

85. $\dfrac{x - 2}{5} + \dfrac{x + 2}{2} = \dfrac{x + 4}{3}$

86. $\dfrac{2z - 3}{4} - \dfrac{4 - z}{2} = \dfrac{z + 1}{3}$

87. China, the United States, and France are predicted to be the top tourist destinations by 2020. In this year, the United States is predicted to have 9 million more tourists than France, and China is predicted to have 44 million more tourists than France. If the total number of tourists predicted for these three countries is 332 million, find the number predicted for each country in 2020.

△ **88.** $A = \dfrac{h}{2}(B + b)$ for B

△ **89.** $V = \dfrac{1}{3}\pi r^2 h$ for h

△ **90.** Determine which container holds more ice cream, an 8 inch × 5 inch × 3 inch box or a cylinder with radius of 3 inches and height of 6 inches.

91. Erasmos Gonzalez left Los Angeles at 11 a.m. and drove nonstop to San Diego, 130 miles away. If he arrived at 1:15 p.m., find his average speed, rounded to the nearest mile per hour.

Solve. If an inequality, write your solutions in interval notation.

92. $48 + x \ge 5(2x + 4) - 2x$

93. $\dfrac{3(x - 2)}{5} > \dfrac{-5(x - 2)}{3}$

94. $0 \le \dfrac{2(3x + 4)}{5} \le 3$

95. $x \le 2$ or $x > -5$

96. $-2x \le 6$ and $-2x + 3 < -7$

97. $|7x| - 26 = -5$

98. $\left|\dfrac{9 - 2x}{5}\right| = -3$

99. $|x - 3| = |7 + 2x|$

100. $|6x - 5| \ge -1$

101. $\left|\dfrac{4x - 3}{5}\right| < 1$

CHAPTER 2 TEST

Remember to use the Chapter Test Prep Video CD to see the fully worked-out solutions to any of the exercises you want to review.

Solve each equation.

1. $8x + 14 = 5x + 44$

2. $9(x + 2) = 5[11 - 2(2 - x) + 3]$

3. $3(y - 4) + y = 2(6 + 2y)$

4. $7n - 6 + n = 2(4n - 3)$

5. $\dfrac{7w}{4} + 5 = \dfrac{3w}{10} + 1$

6. $\dfrac{z + 7}{9} + 1 = \dfrac{2z + 1}{6}$

7. $|6x - 5| - 3 = -2$

8. $|8 - 2t| = -6$

9. $|2x - 3| = |4x + 5|$

10. $|x - 5| = |x + 2|$

Solve each equation for the specified variable.

11. $3x - 4y = 8$ for y

12. $S = gt^2 + gvt$ for g

13. $F = \dfrac{9}{5}C + 32$ for C

Solve each inequality. Write your solutions in interval notation.

14. $3(2x - 7) - 4x > -(x + 6)$

15. $\dfrac{3x - 2}{3} - \dfrac{5x + 1}{4} \geq 0$

16. $-3 < 2(x - 3) \leq 4$

17. $|3x + 1| > 5$

18. $|x - 5| - 4 < -2$

19. $x \geq 5$ and $x \geq 4$

20. $x \geq 5$ or $x \geq 4$

21. $-1 \leq \dfrac{2x - 5}{3} < 2$

22. $6x + 1 > 5x + 4$ or $1 - x > -4$

23. Find 12% of 80.

24. In 2014, the number of people employed as network systems and data communications analysts is expected to be 357,000 in the United States. This represents a 55% increase over the number of people employed in these fields in 2004. Find the number of network systems and data communications analysts employed in 2004. (*Source:* Bureau of Labor Statistics)

25. A circular dog pen has a circumference of 78.5 feet. Approximate π by 3.14 and estimate how many hunting dogs could be safely kept in the pen if each dog needs at least 60 square feet of room.

26. The company that makes Photoray sunglasses figures that the cost C to make x number of sunglasses weekly is given by $C = 3910 + 2.8x$, and the weekly revenue R is given by $R = 7.4x$. Use an inequality to find the number of sunglasses that must be made and sold to make a profit. (Revenue must exceed cost in order to make a profit.)

27. Find the amount of money in an account after 10 years if a principal of $2500 is invested at 3.5% interest compounded quarterly. (Round to the nearest cent.)

28. The most populous city in the United States is New York, although it is only the third most populous city in the world. Tokyo is the most populous city in the world. Second place is held by Seoul, Korea. Seoul's population is 1.3 million more than New York's, and Tokyo's is 10.2 million less than twice the population of New York. If the sum of the populations of these three cities is 78.3 million, find the population of each city.

CHAPTER 2 CUMULATIVE REVIEW

List the elements in each set.

1. **a.** $\{x \mid x$ is a natural number greater than 100$\}$

   b. $\{x \mid x$ is a whole number between 1 and 6$\}$

2. **a.** $\{x \mid x$ is an integer between -3 and 5$\}$

   b. $\{x \mid x$ is a whole number between 3 and 5$\}$

3. Find each value.

   a. $|3|$

   b. $\left| -\dfrac{1}{7} \right|$

   c. $-|2.7|$

   d. $-|-8|$

   e. $|0|$

4. Find the opposite of each number.

   a. $\dfrac{2}{3}$

   b. -9

   c. 1.5

5. Add.

   a. $-3 + (-11)$

   b. $3 + (-7)$

   c. $-10 + 15$

   d. $-8.3 + (-1.9)$

   e. $-\dfrac{2}{3} + \dfrac{3}{7}$

6. Subtract.

   a. $-2 - (-10)$

   b. $1.7 - 8.9$

   c. $-\dfrac{1}{2} - \dfrac{1}{4}$

7. Find the square roots.

  a. $\sqrt{9}$ **b.** $\sqrt{25}$

  c. $\sqrt{\dfrac{1}{4}}$ **d.** $-\sqrt{36}$

  e. $\sqrt{-36}$

8. Multiply or divide.

  a. $-3(-2)$ **b.** $-\dfrac{3}{4}\left(-\dfrac{4}{7}\right)$

  c. $\dfrac{0}{-2}$ **d.** $\dfrac{-20}{-2}$

9. Evaluate each algebraic expression when $x = 4$ and $y = -3$.

  a. $3x - 7y$

  b. $-2y^2$

  c. $\dfrac{\sqrt{x}}{y} - \dfrac{y}{x}$

10. Find the roots.

  a. $\sqrt[4]{1}$

  b. $\sqrt[3]{8}$

  c. $\sqrt[4]{81}$

11. Write each sentence using mathematical symbols.

  a. The sum of x and 5 is 20.

  b. Two times the sum of 3 and y amounts to 4.

  c. Subtract 8 from x, and the difference is the same as the product of 2 and x.

  d. The quotient of z and 9 amounts to 9 plus z.

12. Insert $<, >,$ or $=$ between each pair of numbers to form a true statement.

  a. $-3 \quad -5$

  b. $\dfrac{-12}{-4} \quad 3$

  c. $0 \quad -2$

13. Use the commutative property of addition to write an expression equivalent to $7x + 5$.

14. Use the associative property of multiplication to write an expression equivalent to $5 \cdot (7x)$. Then simplify the expression.

Solve for x.

15. $2x + 5 = 9$

16. $11.2 = 1.2 - 5x$

17. $6x - 4 = 2 + 6(x - 1)$

18. $2x + 1.5 = -0.2 + 1.6x$

19. Write the following as algebraic expressions. Then simplify.

  a. The sum of three consecutive integers, if x is the first consecutive integer.

  b. The perimeter of the triangle with sides of length x, $5x$, and $6x - 3$.

20. Write the following as algebraic expressions. Then simplify.

  a. The sum of three consecutive integers if x is the first consecutive integers.

  b. The perimeter of a square with side length $3x + 1$.

21. Find two numbers such that the second number is 3 more than twice the first number and the third number is four times the first number. The sum of the three numbers is 164.

22. Find two numbers such that the second number is 2 more than three times the first number and the difference of the two numbers is 24.

23. Solve $3y - 2x = 7$ for y.

24. Solve $7x - 4y = 10$ for x.

25. Solve $A = \dfrac{1}{2}(B + b)h$ for b.

26. Solve $P = 2l + 2w$ for l.

27. Graph each set on a number line and then write in interval notation.

  a. $\{x \mid x \geq 2\}$

  b. $\{x \mid x < -1\}$

  c. $\{x \mid 0.5 < x \leq 3\}$

28. Graph each set on a number line and then write in interval notation.

  a. $\{x \mid x \leq -3\}$

  b. $\{x \mid -2 \leq x < 0.1\}$

Solve.

29. $-(x - 3) + 2 \leq 3(2x - 5) + x$

30. $2(7x - 1) - 5x > -(-7x) + 4$

31. $2(x + 3) > 2x + 1$

32. $4(x + 1) - 3 < 4x + 1$

33. If $A = \{x \mid x$ is an even number greater than 0 and less than $10\}$ and $B = \{3, 4, 5, 6\}$, find $A \cap B$.

34. Find the union: $\{-2, 0, 2, 4\} \cup \{-1, 1, 3, 5\}$

35. Solve: $x - 7 < 2$ and $2x + 1 < 9$

36. Solve: $x + 3 \leq 1$ or $3x - 1 < 8$

37. If $A = \{x \mid x$ is an even number greater than 0 and less than $10\}$ and $B = \{3, 4, 5, 6\}$, find $A \cup B$.

38. Find the intersection: $\{-2, 0, 2, 4\} \cap \{-1, 1, 3, 5\}$

39. Solve: $-2x - 5 < -3$ or $6x < 0$

40. Solve: $-2x - 5 < -3$ and $6x < 0$

Solve.

41. $|p| = 2$

42. $|x| = 5$

43. $\left|\dfrac{x}{2} - 1\right| = 11$

44. $\left|\dfrac{y}{3} + 2\right| = 10$

45. $|x - 3| = |5 - x|$

46. $|x + 3| = |7 - x|$

47. $|x| \leq 3$

48. $|x| > 1$

49. $|2x + 9| + 5 > 3$

50. $|3x + 1| + 9 < 1$

CHAPTER

3

Graphs and Functions

Over the past few years, diamonds have gained much higher visibility by increased media advertising. Strong consumer demand has caused the industry to increase production and is the basis for the bar graph below. By a method called least squares (Section 3.2), the function $f(x) = 0.42x + 10.5$ approximates the data below where $f(x)$ is world diamond production value (in billions of dollars) and where x is the number of years past 2000. In Section 3.2, Exercises 87 and 88, page 144, we will use this linear equation to predict diamond production.

The linear equations and inequalities we explored in Chapter 2 are statements about a single variable. This chapter examines statements about two variables: linear equations and inequalities in two variables. We focus particularly on graphs of those equations and inequalities which lead to the notion of relation and to the notion of function, perhaps the single most important and useful concept in all of mathematics.

**World Diamond Production
(Forecast at 2005 Prices)**

$f(x) = 0.42x + 10.5$

Source: Diamond Facts 2006

3.1 GRAPHING EQUATIONS

OBJECTIVES

1 Plot ordered pairs.

2 Determine whether an ordered pair of numbers is a solution to an equation in two variables.

3 Graph linear equations.

4 Graph nonlinear equations.

OBJECTIVE 1 ▶ Plotting ordered pairs. Graphs are widely used today in newspapers, magazines, and all forms of newsletters. A few examples of graphs are shown here.

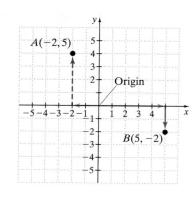

Percent of Sales Completed Using Cards*

Source: The Nilson Report

*These include credit or debit cards, prepaid cards and EBT (electronic benefits transfer) cards.

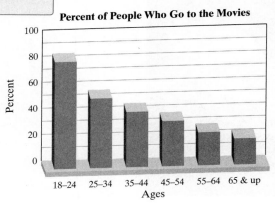

Percent of People Who Go to the Movies

Source: TELENATION/Market Facts, Inc.

To review how to read these graphs, we review their origin—the rectangular coordinate system. One way to locate points on a plane is by using a **rectangular coordinate system,** which is also called a **Cartesian coordinate system** after its inventor, René Descartes (1596–1650).

A rectangular coordinate system consists of two number lines that intersect at right angles at their 0 coordinates. We position these axes on paper such that one number line is horizontal and the other number line is then vertical. The horizontal number line is called the *x*-**axis** (or the axis of the **abscissa**), and the vertical number line is called the *y*-**axis** (or the axis of the **ordinate**). The point of intersection of these axes is named the **origin.**

Notice in the left figure below that the axes divide the plane into four regions. These regions are called **quadrants.** The top-right region is quadrant I. Quadrants II, III, and IV are numbered counterclockwise from the first quadrant as shown. The *x*-axis and the *y*-axis are not in any quadrant.

Each point in the plane can be located, or **plotted,** or graphed by describing its position in terms of distances along each axis from the origin. An **ordered pair,** represented by the notation (x, y), records these distances.

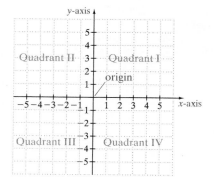

For example, the location of point A in the figure on the right on the previous page is described as 2 units to the left of the origin along the x-axis and 5 units upward parallel to the y-axis. Thus, we identify point A with the ordered pair $(-2, 5)$. Notice that the order of these numbers is *critical*. The x-value -2 is called the **x-coordinate** and is associated with the x-axis. The y-value 5 is called the **y-coordinate** and is associated with the y-axis.

Compare the location of point A with the location of point B, which corresponds to the ordered pair $(5, -2)$. Can you see that the order of the coordinates of an ordered pair matters? Also, two ordered pairs are considered equal and correspond to the same point if and only if their x-coordinates are equal and their y-coordinates are equal.

Keep in mind that **each ordered pair corresponds to exactly one point in the real plane and that each point in the plane corresponds to exactly one ordered pair.** Thus, we may refer to the ordered pair (x, y) as the point (x, y).

EXAMPLE 1   Plot each ordered pair on a Cartesian coordinate system and name the quadrant or axis in which the point is located.

a. $(2, -1)$ **b.** $(0, 5)$ **c.** $(-3, 5)$ **d.** $(-2, 0)$ **e.** $\left(-\dfrac{1}{2}, -4\right)$ **f.** $(1.5, 1.5)$

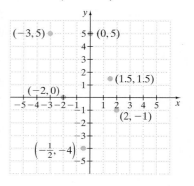

Solution   The six points are graphed as shown.

a. $(2, -1)$ lies in quadrant IV.

b. $(0, 5)$ is on the y-axis.

c. $(-3, 5)$ lies in quadrant II.

d. $(-2, 0)$ is on the x-axis.

e. $\left(-\dfrac{1}{2}, -4\right)$ is in quadrant III.

f. $(1.5, 1.5)$ is in quadrant I.

PRACTICE
1   Plot each ordered pair on a Cartesian coordinate system and name the quadrant or axis in which the point is located.

a. $(3, -4)$ **b.** $(0, -2)$ **c.** $(-2, 4)$ **d.** $(4, 0)$ **e.** $\left(-1\dfrac{1}{2}, -2\right)$ **f.** $(2.5, 3.5)$

Notice that the y-coordinate of any point on the x-axis is 0. For example, the point with coordinates $(-2, 0)$ lies on the x-axis. Also, the x-coordinate of any point on the y-axis is 0. For example, the point with coordinates $(0, 5)$ lies on the y-axis. These points that lie on the axes do not lie in any quadrants.

Concept Check ☑

Which of the following correctly describes the location of the point $(3, -6)$ in a rectangular coordinate system?

a. 3 units to the left of the y-axis and 6 units above the x-axis

b. 3 units above the x-axis and 6 units to the left of the y-axis

c. 3 units to the right of the y-axis and 6 units below the x-axis

d. 3 units below the x-axis and 6 units to the right of the y-axis

Many types of real-world data occur in pairs. The graph below was shown at the beginning of this section. Notice the paired data (2013, 57) and the corresponding plotted point, both in blue.

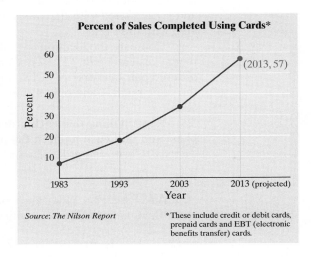

Percent of Sales Completed Using Cards*

Source: The Nilson Report

*These include credit or debit cards, prepaid cards and EBT (electronic benefits transfer) cards.

This paired data point, (2013, 57), means that in the year 2013, it is predicted that 57% of sales will be completed using some type of card (credit, debit, etc.).

OBJECTIVE 2 ▶ Determining whether an ordered pair is a solution. Solutions of equations in two variables consist of two numbers that form a true statement when substituted into the equation. A convenient notation for writing these numbers is as ordered pairs. A solution of an equation containing the variables x and y is written as a pair of numbers in the order (x, y). If the equation contains other variables, we will write ordered pair solutions in alphabetical order.

EXAMPLE 2 Determine whether $(0, -12), (1, 9)$, and $(2, -6)$ are solutions of the equation $3x - y = 12$.

Solution To check each ordered pair, replace x with the x-coordinate and y with the y-coordinate and see whether a true statement results.

Let $x = 0$ and $y = -12$. Let $x = 1$ and $y = 9$. Let $x = 2$ and $y = -6$.

$$3x - y = 12 \qquad\qquad 3x - y = 12 \qquad\qquad 3x - y = 12$$
$$3(0) - (-12) \stackrel{?}{=} 12 \qquad 3(1) - 9 \stackrel{?}{=} 12 \qquad 3(2) - (-6) \stackrel{?}{=} 12$$
$$0 + 12 \stackrel{?}{=} 12 \qquad\qquad 3 - 9 \stackrel{?}{=} 12 \qquad\qquad 6 + 6 \stackrel{?}{=} 12$$
$$12 = 12 \quad \text{True} \qquad -6 = 12 \quad \text{False} \qquad 12 = 12 \quad \text{True}$$

Thus, $(1, 9)$ is not a solution of $3x - y = 12$, but both $(0, -12)$ and $(2, -6)$ are solutions. ☐

PRACTICE
2 Determine whether $(1, 4), (0, 6)$, and $(3, -4)$ are solutions of the equation $4x + y = 8$.

OBJECTIVE 3 ▶ Graphing linear equations. The equation $3x - y = 12$, from Example 2, actually has an infinite number of ordered pair solutions. Since it is impossible to list all solutions, we visualize them by graphing.

A few more ordered pairs that satisfy $3x - y = 12$ are $(4, 0), (3, -3), (5, 3)$, and $(1, -9)$. These ordered pair solutions along with the ordered pair solutions from Example 2 are plotted on the following graph. The graph of $3x - y = 12$ is the single line containing these points. Every ordered pair solution of the equation corresponds to a point on this line, and every point on this line corresponds to an ordered pair solution.

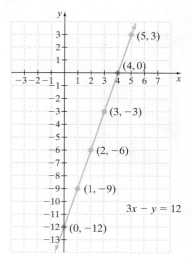

x	y	$3x - y = 12$
5	3	$3 \cdot 5 - 3 = 12$
4	0	$3 \cdot 4 - 0 = 12$
3	−3	$3 \cdot 3 - (-3) = 12$
2	−6	$3 \cdot 2 - (-6) = 12$
1	−9	$3 \cdot 1 - (-9) = 12$
0	−12	$3 \cdot 0 - (-12) = 12$

The equation $3x - y = 12$ is called a linear equation in two variables, and **the graph of every linear equation in two variables is a line.**

Linear Equation in Two Variables

A linear equation in two variables is an equation that can be written in the form

$$Ax + By = C$$

where A and B are not both 0. This form is called **standard form.**

Some examples of equations in standard form:

$$3x - y = 12$$
$$-2.1x + 5.6y = 0$$

▶ **Helpful Hint**

Remember: A linear equation is written in standard form when all of the variable terms are on one side of the equation and the constant is on the other side.

Many real-life applications are modeled by linear equations. Suppose you have a part-time job at a store that sells office products.

Your pay is $3000 plus 20% or $\frac{1}{5}$ of the price of the products you sell. If we let x represent products sold and y represent monthly salary, the linear equation that models your salary is

$$y = 3000 + \frac{1}{5}x$$

(Although this equation is not written in standard form, it is a linear equation. To see this, subtract $\frac{1}{5}x$ from both sides.)

Some ordered pair solutions of this equation are below.

Products Sold	x	0	1000	2000	3000	4000	10,000
Monthly Salary	y	3000	3200	3400	3600	3800	5000

For example, we say that the ordered pair (1000, 3200) is a solution of the equation $y = 3000 + \frac{1}{5}x$ because when x is replaced with 1000 and y is replaced with 3200, a true statement results.

$$y = 3000 + \frac{1}{5}x$$

$$3200 \stackrel{?}{=} 3000 + \frac{1}{5}(1000) \quad \text{Let } x = 1000 \text{ and } y = 3200.$$

$$3200 \stackrel{?}{=} 3000 + 200$$

$$3200 = 3200 \qquad\qquad \text{True}$$

A portion of the graph of $y = 3000 + \frac{1}{5}x$ is shown in the next example.

Since we assume that the smallest amount of product sold is none, or 0, then x must be greater than or equal to 0. Therefore, only the part of the graph that lies in Quadrant I is shown. Notice that the graph gives a visual picture of the correspondence between products sold and salary.

> ▶ **Helpful Hint**
>
> A line contains an infinite number of points and each point corresponds to an ordered pair that is a solution of its corresponding equation.

EXAMPLE 3 Use the graph of $y = 3000 + \frac{1}{5}x$ to answer the following questions.

a. If the salesperson has $8000 of products sold for a particular month, what is the salary for that month?

b. If the salesperson wants to make more than $5000 per month, what must be the total amount of products sold?

Solution

a. Since x is products sold, find 8000 along the x-axis and move vertically up until you reach a point on the line. From this point on the line, move horizontally to the left until you reach the y-axis. Its value on the y-axis is 4600, which means if $8000 worth of products is sold, the salary for the month is $4600.

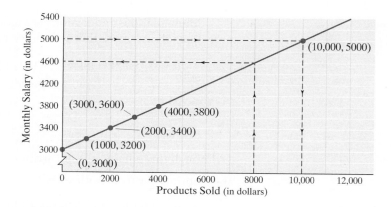

b. Since y is monthly salary, find 5000 along the y-axis and move horizontally to the right until you reach a point on the line. Either read the corresponding x-value from the labeled ordered pair, or move vertically downward until you reach the x-axis. The corresponding x-value is 10,000. This means that $10,000 worth of products sold gives a salary of $5000 for the month. For the salary to be greater than $5000, products sold must be greater that $10,000. ☐

PRACTICE
3   Use the graph in Example 3 to answer the following questions.

a. If the salesperson has $6000 of products sold for a particular month, what is the salary for that month?

b. If the salesperson wants to make more than $4800 per month, what must be the total amount of products sold?

Recall from geometry that a line is determined by two points. This means that to graph a linear equation in two variables, just two solutions are needed. We will find a third solution, just to check our work. To find ordered pair solutions of linear equations in two variables, we can choose an x-value and find its corresponding y-value, or we can choose a y-value and find its corresponding x-value. The number 0 is often a convenient value to choose for x and also for y.

EXAMPLE 4   Graph the equation $y = -2x + 3$.

Solution   This is a linear equation. (In standard form it is $2x + y = 3$.) Find three ordered pair solutions, and plot the ordered pairs. The line through the plotted points is the graph. Since the equation is solved for y, let's choose three x-values. We'll choose 0, 2, and then -1 for x to find our three ordered pair solutions.

Let $x = 0$	Let $x = 2$	Let $x = -1$
$y = -2x + 3$	$y = -2x + 3$	$y = -2x + 3$
$y = -2 \cdot 0 + 3$	$y = -2 \cdot 2 + 3$	$y = -2(-1) + 3$
$y = 3$ Simplify.	$y = -1$ Simplify.	$y = 5$ Simplify.

The three ordered pairs $(0, 3)$, $(2, -1)$ and $(-1, 5)$ are listed in the table and the graph is shown.

x	y
0	3
2	-1
-1	5

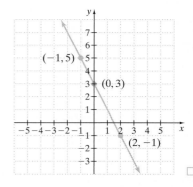

PRACTICE
4   Graph the equation $y = -3x - 2$.

Notice that the graph crosses the y-axis at the point $(0, 3)$. This point is called the **y-intercept.** (You may sometimes see just the number 3 called the y-intercept.) This graph also crosses the x-axis at the point $\left(\frac{3}{2}, 0 \right)$. This point is called the **x-intercept.** (You may also see just the number $\frac{3}{2}$ called the x-intercept.)

Since every point on the y-axis has an x-value of 0, we can find the y-intercept of a graph by letting $x = 0$ and solving for y. Also, every point on the x-axis has a y-value of 0. To find the x-intercept, we let $y = 0$ and solve for x.

Finding x- and y-Intercepts

To find an x-intercept, let $y = 0$ and solve for x.
To find a y-intercept, let $x = 0$ and solve for y.

We will study intercepts further in Section 3.3.

EXAMPLE 5   Graph the linear equation $y = \frac{1}{3}x$.

Solution   To graph, we find ordered pair solutions, plot the ordered pairs, and draw a line through the plotted points. We will choose x-values and substitute in the equation. To avoid fractions, we choose x-values that are multiples of 3. To find the y-intercept, we let $x = 0$.

> ▶ **Helpful Hint**
> Notice that by using multiples of 3 for x, we avoid fractions.

> ▶ **Helpful Hint**
> Since the equation $y = \frac{1}{3}x$ is solved for y, we choose x-values for finding points. This way, we simply need to evaluate an expression to find the x-value, as shown.

$$y = \frac{1}{3}x$$

If $x = 0$, then $y = \frac{1}{3}(0)$, or 0.

If $x = 6$, then $y = \frac{1}{3}(6)$, or 2.

If $x = -3$, then $y = \frac{1}{3}(-3)$, or -1.

x	y
0	0
6	2
−3	−1

This graph crosses the x-axis at $(0, 0)$ and the y-axis at $(0, 0)$. This means that the x-intercept is $(0, 0)$ and that the y-intercept is $(0, 0)$.

PRACTICE
5   Graph the linear equation $y = -\frac{1}{2}x$.

OBJECTIVE 4 ▶ Graphing nonlinear equations. Not all equations in two variables are linear equations, and not all graphs of equations in two variables are lines.

EXAMPLE 6   Graph $y = x^2$.

Solution   This equation is not linear because the x^2 term does not allow us to write it in the form $Ax + By = C$. Its graph is not a line. We begin by finding ordered pair solutions. Because this graph is solved for y, we choose x-values and find corresponding y-values.

If $x = -3$, then $y = (-3)^2$, or 9.

If $x = -2$, then $y = (-2)^2$, or 4.

If $x = -1$, then $y = (-1)^2$, or 1.

If $x = 0$, then $y = 0^2$, or 0.

If $x = 1$, then $y = 1^2$, or 1.

If $x = 2$, then $y = 2^2$, or 4.

If $x = 3$, then $y = 3^2$, or 9.

x	y
−3	9
−2	4
−1	1
0	0
1	1
2	4
3	9

Study the table a moment and look for patterns. Notice that the ordered pair solution $(0, 0)$ contains the smallest y-value because any other x-value squared will give a positive result. This means that the point $(0, 0)$ will be the lowest point on the graph. Also notice that all other y-values correspond to two different x-values. For example, $3^2 = 9$ and also $(-3)^2 = 9$. This means that the graph will be a mirror image of itself across the y-axis. Connect the plotted points with a smooth curve to sketch the graph.

This curve is given a special name, a parabola. We will study more about parabolas in later chapters.

PRACTICE
6   Graph $y = 2x^2$.

EXAMPLE 7   Graph the equation $y = |x|$.

<u>Solution</u>   This is not a linear equation since it cannot be written in the form $Ax + By = C$. Its graph is not a line. Because we do not know the shape of this graph, we find many ordered pair solutions. We will choose x-values and substitute to find corresponding y-values.

If $x = -3$, then $y = |-3|$, or 3.

If $x = -2$, then $y = |-2|$, or 2.

If $x = -1$, then $y = |-1|$, or 1.

If $x = 0$, then $y = |0|$, or 0.

If $x = 1$, then $y = |1|$, or 1.

If $x = 2$, then $y = |2|$, or 2.

If $x = 3$, then $y = |3|$, or 3.

x	y
-3	3
-2	2
-1	1
0	0
1	1
2	2
3	3

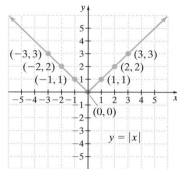

Again, study the table of values for a moment and notice any patterns.

From the plotted ordered pairs, we see that the graph of this absolute value equation is V-shaped.

PRACTICE
7   Graph $y = -|x|$.

Graphing Calculator Explorations

In this section, we begin a study of graphing calculators and graphing software packages for computers. These graphers use the same point plotting technique that we introduced in this section. The advantage of this graphing technology is, of course, that graphing calculators and computers can find and plot ordered pair solutions much faster than we can. Note, however, that the features described in these boxes may not be available on all graphing calculators.

The rectangular screen where a portion of the rectangular coordinate system is displayed is called a **window.** We call it a **standard window** for graphing when both the x- and y-axes display coordinates between -10 and 10. This information is often displayed in the window menu on a graphing calculator as

Xmin $= -10$

Xmax $= 10$

Xscl $= 1$ The scale on the x-axis is one unit per tick mark.

Ymin $= -10$

Ymax $= 10$

Yscl $= 1$ The scale on the y-axis is one unit per tick mark.

To use a graphing calculator to graph the equation $y = -5x + 4$, press the
$\boxed{\text{Y} =}$ key and enter the keystrokes

$\boxed{(-)}$ $\boxed{5}$ $\boxed{x}$ $\boxed{+}$ $\boxed{4}$.
$\uparrow$

(Check your owner's manual to make sure the "negative" key is pressed here and not the "subtraction" key.)

The top row should now read $Y_1 = -5x + 4$. Next press the GRAPH key, and the display should look like this:

Use a standard window and graph the following equations. (Unless otherwise stated, we will use a standard window when graphing.)

1. $y = -3.2x + 7.9$ **2.** $y = -x + 5.85$

3. $y = \dfrac{1}{4}x - \dfrac{2}{3}$ **4.** $y = \dfrac{2}{3}x - \dfrac{1}{5}$

5. $y = |x - 3| + 2$ **6.** $y = |x + 1| - 1$

7. $y = x^2 + 3$ **8.** $y = (x + 3)^2$

VOCABULARY & READINESS CHECK

Determine the coordinates of each point on the graph.

1. Point A **2.** Point B

3. Point C **4.** Point D

5. Point E **6.** Point F

7. Point G **8.** Point H

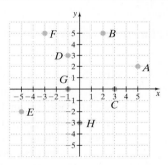

Without graphing, visualize the location of each point. Then give its location by quadrant or x- or y-axis.

9. $(2, 3)$ **10.** $(0, 5)$ **11.** $(-2, 7)$

12. $(-3, 0)$ **13.** $(-1, -4)$ **14.** $(4, -2)$

15. $(0, -100)$ **16.** $(10, 30)$ **17.** $(-10, -30)$

18. $(0, 0)$ **19.** $(-87, 0)$ **20.** $(-42, 17)$

3.1 EXERCISE SET

Plot each point and name the quadrant or axis in which the point lies. See Example 1.

1. $(3, 2)$ **2.** $(2, -1)$

3. $(-5, 3)$ **4.** $(-3, -1)$

5. $\left(5\dfrac{1}{2}, -4\right)$ **6.** $\left(-2, 6\dfrac{1}{3}\right)$

7. $(0, 3.5)$ **8.** $(-5.2, 0)$

9. $(-2, -4)$ **10.** $(-4.2, 0)$

Given that x is a positive number and that y is a positive number, determine the quadrant or axis in which each point lies. See Example 1.

11. $(x, -y)$ **12.** $(-x, y)$

13. $(x, 0)$ **14.** $(0, -y)$

15. $(-x, -y)$ **16.** $(0, 0)$

Determine whether each ordered pair is a solution of the given equation. See Example 2.

17. $y = 3x - 5$; $(0, 5), (-1, -8)$

18. $y = -2x + 7$; $(1, 5), (-2, 3)$

19. $-6x + 5y = -6$; $(1, 0), \left(2, \dfrac{6}{5}\right)$

20. $5x - 3y = 9$; $(0, 3), \left(\dfrac{12}{5}, -1\right)$

21. $y = 2x^2$; $(1, 2), (3, 18)$

22. $y = 2|x|$; $(-1, 2), (0, 2)$

23. $y = x^3$; $(2, 8), (3, 9)$

24. $y = x^4$; $(-1, 1), (2, 16)$

25. $y = \sqrt{x} + 2$; $(1, 3), (4, 4)$

26. $y = \sqrt[3]{x} - 4$; $(1, -3), (8, 6)$

MIXED PRACTICE

Determine whether each equation is linear or not. Then graph the equation by finding and plotting ordered-pair solutions. See Examples 3 through 7.

27. $x + y = 3$

28. $y - x = 8$

29. $y = 4x$

30. $y = 6x$

31. $y = 4x - 2$

32. $y = 6x - 5$

33. $y = |x| + 3$

34. $y = |x| + 2$

35. $2x - y = 5$

36. $4x - y = 7$

37. $y = 2x^2$

38. $y = 3x^2$

39. $y = x^2 - 3$

40. $y = x^2 + 3$

41. $y = -2x$

42. $y = -3x$

43. $y = -2x + 3$

44. $y = -3x + 2$

45. $y = |x + 2|$

46. $y = |x - 1|$

47. $y = x^3$
   (*Hint:* Let $x = -3, -2, -1, 0, 1, 2$.)

48. $y = x^3 - 2$
   (*Hint:* Let $x = -3, -2, -1, 0, 1, 2$.)

49. $y = -|x|$

50. $y = -x^2$

51. $y = \dfrac{1}{3}x - 1$

52. $y = \dfrac{1}{2}x - 3$

53. $y = -\dfrac{3}{2}x + 1$

54. $y = -\dfrac{2}{3}x + 1$

REVIEW AND PREVIEW

Solve the following equations. See Section 2.1.

55. $3(x - 2) + 5x = 6x - 16$

56. $5 + 7(x + 1) = 12 + 10x$

57. $3x + \dfrac{2}{5} = \dfrac{1}{10}$

58. $\dfrac{1}{6} + 2x = \dfrac{2}{3}$

Solve the following inequalities. See Section 2.4.

59. $3x \le -15$

60. $-3x > 18$

61. $2x - 5 > 4x + 3$

62. $9x + 8 \le 6x - 4$

CONCEPT EXTENSIONS

Solve. See the Concept Check in this section.

63. Which correctly describes the location of the point $(-1, 5.3)$ in a rectangular coordinate system?

   a. 1 unit to the right of the y-axis and 5.3 units above the x-axis

   b. 1 unit to the left of the y-axis and 5.3 units above the x-axis

   c. 1 unit to the left of the y-axis and 5.3 units below the x-axis

   d. 1 unit to the right of the y-axis and 5.3 units below the x-axis

64. Which correctly describes the location of the point $\left(0, -\dfrac{3}{4}\right)$ in a rectangular coordinate system?

   a. on the x-axis and $\dfrac{3}{4}$ unit to the left of the y-axis

   b. on the x-axis and $\dfrac{3}{4}$ unit to the right of the y-axis

   c. on the y-axis and $\dfrac{3}{4}$ unit above the x-axis

   d. on the y-axis and $\dfrac{3}{4}$ unit below the x-axis

For Exercises 65 through 68, match each description with the graph that best illustrates it.

65. Moe worked 40 hours per week until the fall semester started. He quit and didn't work again until he worked 60 hours a week during the holiday season starting mid-December.

66. Kawana worked 40 hours a week for her father during the summer. She slowly cut back her hours to not working at all during the fall semester. During the holiday season in December, she started working again and increased her hours to 60 hours per week.

67. Wendy worked from July through February, never quitting. She worked between 10 and 30 hours per week.

68. Bartholomew worked from July through February. The rest of the time, he worked between 10 and 40 hours per week. During the holiday season between mid-November and the beginning of January, he worked 40 hours per week.

a.

b.

c.

d.

The graph below shows first-class postal rates and the years it increased. Use this graph for Exercises 69 through 72.

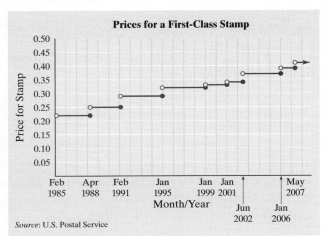

Prices for a First-Class Stamp

Source: U.S. Postal Service

For income tax purposes, Jason Verges, owner of Copy Services, uses a method called **straight-line depreciation** to show the loss in value of a copy machine he recently purchased. Jason assumes that he can use the machine for 7 years. The following graph shows the value of the machine over the years. Use this graph to answer Exercises 77 through 82.

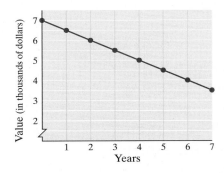

69. What was the first year that the price for a first-class stamp rose above $0.25?

70. What was the first year that the price for a first-class stamp rose above $0.30?

71. Why do you think that this graph is shaped the way it is?

72. The U.S. Postal Service issued first-class stamps as far back as 1885. The cost for a first-class stamp then was $0.02. By how much had it increased by 2007?

73. Graph $y = x^2 - 4x + 7$. Let $x = 0, 1, 2, 3, 4$ to generate ordered pair solutions.

74. Graph $y = x^2 + 2x + 3$. Let $x = -3, -2, -1, 0, 1$ to generate ordered pair solutions.

75. The perimeter y of a rectangle whose width is a constant 3 inches and whose length is x inches is given by the equation

$$y = 2x + 6$$

a. Draw a graph of this equation.

b. Read from the graph the perimeter y of a rectangle whose length x is 4 inches.

x inches

3 inches

76. The distance y traveled in a train moving at a constant speed of 50 miles per hour is given by the equation

$$y = 50x$$

where x is the time in hours traveled.

a. Draw a graph of this equation.

b. Read from the graph the distance y traveled after 6 hours.

77. What was the purchase price of the copy machine?

78. What is the depreciated value of the machine in 7 years?

79. What loss in value occurred during the first year?

80. What loss in value occurred during the second year?

81. Why do you think that this method of depreciating is called straight-line depreciation?

82. Why is the line tilted downward?

83. On the same set of axes, graph $y = 2x$, $y = 2x - 5$, and $y = 2x + 5$. What patterns do you see in these graphs?

84. On the same set of axes, graph $y = 2x$, $y = x$, and $y = -2x$. Describe the differences and similarities in these graphs.

85. Explain why we generally use three points to graph a line, when only two points are needed.

Write each statement as an equation in two variables. Then graph each equation.

86. The y-value is 5 more than three times the x-value.

87. The y-value is -3 decreased by twice the x-value.

88. The y-value is 2 more than the square of the x-value.

89. The y-value is 5 decreased by the square of the x-value.

Use a graphing calculator to verify the graphs of the following exercises.

90. Exercise 39

91. Exercise 40

92. Exercise 47

93. Exercise 48

How Well Do You Know Your Textbook?

The questions below will determine whether you are familiar with your textbook. For help, see Section 1.1 in this text.

1. What does the 🖩 icon mean?

2. What does the ⟍ icon mean?

3. What does the △ icon mean?

4. Which exercise set answers are given in the back of your text?

5. Where can you find a review for each chapter? What answers to this review can be found in the back of your text?

6. Each chapter contains an overview of the chapter along with examples. What is this feature called?

7. Each chapter contains a review of vocabulary. What is this feature called?

8. There is a CD in your text. What content is contained on this CD?

9. What is the location of the section that is entirely devoted to study skills?

10. There is a Practice exercise located after each worked example in the text. What are they and how can they be used?

11. There is a Practice Final Exam in your text. Where is it located?

3.2 INTRODUCTION TO FUNCTIONS

OBJECTIVES

1 Define relation, domain, and range.

2 Identify functions.

3 Use the vertical line test for functions.

4 Find the domain and range of a function.

5 Use function notation.

OBJECTIVE 1 ▶ Defining relation, domain, and range. Recall our example from the last section about products sold and monthly salary. We modeled the data given by the equation $y = 3000 + \frac{1}{5}x$. This equation describes a relationship between x-values and y-values. For example, if $x = 1000$, then this equation describes how to find the y-value related to $x = 1000$. In words, the equation $y = 3000 + \frac{1}{5}x$ says that 3000 plus $\frac{1}{5}$ of the x-value gives the corresponding y-value. The x-value of 1000 corresponds to the y-value of $3000 + \frac{1}{5} \cdot 1000 = 3200$ for this equation, and we have the ordered pair $(1000, 3200)$.

There are other ways of describing relations or correspondences between two numbers or, in general, a first set (sometimes called the set of *inputs*) and a second set (sometimes called the set of *outputs*). For example,

First Set: Input	— *Correspondence*	→ *Second Set: Output*
People in a certain city	— Each person's age	→ The set of nonnegative integers

A few examples of ordered pairs from this relation might be (Ana, 4); (Bob, 36); (Trey, 21); and so on.

Below are just a few other ways of describing relations between two sets and the ordered pairs that they generate.

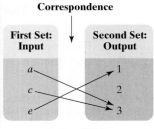

Correspondence

Ordered Pairs
$(a, 3), (c, 3), (e, 1)$

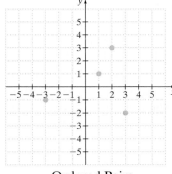

Ordered Pairs
$(-3, -1), (1, 1), (2, 3), (3, -2)$

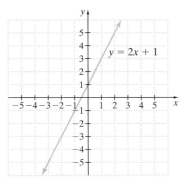

Some Ordered Pairs
$(1, 3), (0, 1),$ and so on

> **Relation, Domain, and Range**
>
> A **relation** is a set of ordered pairs.
> The **domain** of the relation is the set of all first components of the ordered pairs.
> The **range** of the relation is the set of all second components of the ordered pairs.

For example, the domain for our relation in the bottom left of the previous page is $\{a, c, e\}$ and the range is $\{1, 3\}$. Notice that the range does not include the element 2 of the second set. This is because no element of the first set is assigned to this element. If a relation is defined in terms of x- and y-values, we will agree that the domain corresponds to x-values and that the range corresponds to y-values that have x-values assigned to them.

> ▶ **Helpful Hint**
>
> Remember that the range only includes elements that are paired with domain values. For the correspondence below, the range is $\{a\}$.
>
>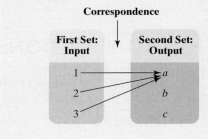

EXAMPLE 1   Determine the domain and range of each relation.

a. $\{(2, 3), (2, 4), (0, -1), (3, -1)\}$

b.

c.

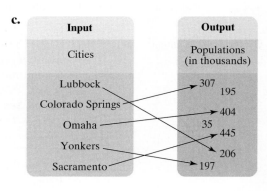

Solution

a. The domain is the set of all first coordinates of the ordered pairs, $\{2, 0, 3\}$. The range is the set of all second coordinates, $\{3, 4, -1\}$.

b. Ordered pairs are not listed here, but are given in graph form. The relation is $\{(-4, 1), (-3, 1), (-2, 1), (-1, 1), (0, 1), (1, 1), (2, 1), (3, 1)\}$. The domain is $\{-4, -3, -2, -1, 0, 1, 2, 3\}$. The range is $\{1\}$.

c. The domain is the set of inputs, {Lubbock, Colorado Springs, Omaha, Yonkers, Sacramento}. The range is the numbers in the set of outputs that correspond to elements in the set of inputs {307, 404, 445, 206, 197}.

> ▶ **Helpful Hint**
>
> Domain or range elements that occur more than once need only to be listed once.

PRACTICE
1   Determine the domain and range of each relation.

a. {(4, 1)(4, −3)(5, −2)(5, 6)}

b.

c.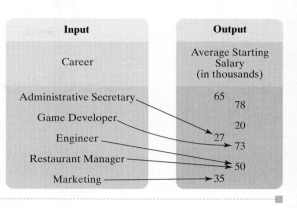

OBJECTIVE 2 ▶ Identifying functions. Now we consider a special kind of relation called a function.

> **Function**
>
> A **function** is a relation in which each first component in the ordered pairs corresponds to *exactly* one second component.

> ▶ **Helpful Hint**
>
> A function is a special type of relation, so all functions are relations, but not all relations are functions.

EXAMPLE 2   Which of the following relations are also functions?

a. {(−2, 5), (2, 7), (−3, 5), (9, 9)}

b.

c.

Input	Correspondence	Output
People in a certain city	Each person's age	The set of nonnegative integers

Solution

a. Although the ordered pairs (−2, 5) and (−3, 5) have the same *y*-value, each *x*-value is assigned to only one *y*-value, so this set of ordered pairs is a function.

b. The *x*-value 0 is assigned to two *y*-values, −2 and 3, in this graph so this relation does not define a function.

c. This relation is a function because although two different people may have the same age, each person has only one age. This means that each element in the first set is assigned to only one element in the second set.   □

PRACTICE
2 Which of the following relations are also functions?

a. $\{(3, 1), (-3, -4), (8, 5), (9, 1)\}$

b.

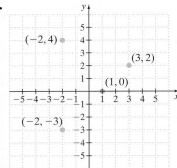

c.

Input	Correspondence	Output
People in a certain city	Birth date (day of month)	Set of nonnegative integers

Concept Check ☑

Explain why a function can contain both the ordered pairs $(1, 3)$ and $(2, 3)$ but not both $(3, 1)$ and $(3, 2)$.

We will call an equation such as $y = 2x + 1$ a **relation** since this equation defines a set of ordered pair solutions.

EXAMPLE 3 Is the relation $y = 2x + 1$ also a function?*

Solution The relation $y = 2x + 1$ is a function if each x-value corresponds to just one y-value. For each x-value substituted in the equation $y = 2x + 1$, the multiplication and addition performed on each gives a single result, so only one y-value will be associated with each x-value. Thus, $y = 2x + 1$ is a function.

*For further discussion including the graph, see Objective 3. ☐

PRACTICE
3 Is the relation $y = -3x + 5$ also a function?

EXAMPLE 4 Is the relation $x = y^2$ also a function?*

Solution In $x = y^2$, if $y = 3$, then $x = 9$. Also, if $y = -3$, then $x = 9$. In other words, we have the ordered pairs $(9, 3)$ and $(9, -3)$. Since the x-value 9 corresponds to two y-values, 3 and -3, $x = y^2$ is not a function.

*For further discussion including the graph, see Objective 3. ☐

PRACTICE
4 Is the relation $y = -x^2$ also a function?

Answer to Concept Check:
Two different ordered pairs can have the same y-value, but not the same x-value in a function.

OBJECTIVE 3 ▶ Using the vertical line test. As we have seen so far, not all relations are functions. Consider the graphs of $y = 2x + 1$ and $x = y^2$ shown next. For the graph of $y = 2x + 1$, notice that each x-value corresponds to only one y-value. Recall from Example 3 that $y = 2x + 1$ is a function.

Graph of Example 3:
$$y = 2x + 1$$

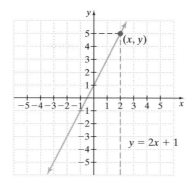

Graph of Example 4:
$$x = y^2$$

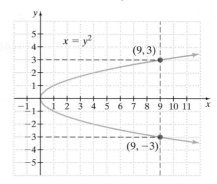

For the graph of $x = y^2$ the x-value 9, for example, corresponds to two y-values, 3 and -3, as shown by the vertical line. Recall from Example 4 that $x = y^2$ is not a function.

Graphs can be used to help determine whether a relation is also a function by the following vertical line test.

Vertical Line Test

If no vertical line can be drawn so that it intersects a graph more than once, the graph is the graph of a function.

EXAMPLE 5   Which of the following graphs are graphs of functions?

a.

b.

c.

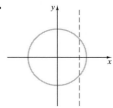

Solution

Yes, this is the graph of a function since no vertical line will intersect this graph more than once.

Yes, this is the graph of a function.

No, this is not the graph of a function. Note that vertical lines can be drawn that intersect the graph in two points.

d.

e.

Solution

Yes, this is the graph of a function.

No, this is not the graph of a function. A vertical line can be drawn that intersects this line at every point.   □

PRACTICE
5 Which of the following graphs are graphs of functions?

a.

b.

c.

d.

e.

Recall that the graph of a linear equation in two variables is a line, and a line that is not vertical will pass the vertical line test. Thus, **all linear equations are functions except those whose graph is a vertical line.**

Concept Check ☑

Determine which equations represent functions. Explain your answer.

a. $y = |x|$ **b.** $y = x^2$ **c.** $x + y = 6$

OBJECTIVE 4 ▶ Finding the domain and range of a function. Next, we practice finding the domain and range of a relation from its graph.

EXAMPLE 6 Find the domain and range of each relation. Determine whether the relation is also a function.

a.

b.

c.

d.

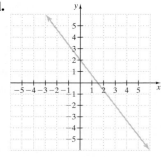

**Solution**   By the vertical line test, graphs **a**, **c**, and **d** are graphs of functions. The domain is the set of values of x and the range is the set of values of y. We read these values from each graph.

a.

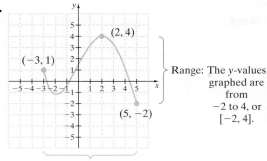

Range: The y-values graphed are from -2 to 4, or $[-2, 4]$.

Domain:
The x-values graphed are from -3 to 5, or $[-3, 5]$.

b.

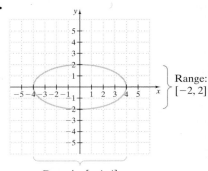

Range: $[-2, 2]$

Domain: $[-4, 4]$

c.

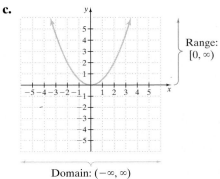

Range: $[0, \infty)$

Domain: $(-\infty, \infty)$

d.

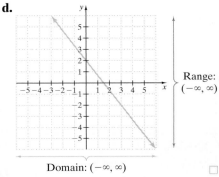

Range: $(-\infty, \infty)$

Domain: $(-\infty, \infty)$

PRACTICE

6   Find the domain and range of each relation. Determine whether each relation is also a function.

a.

b.

c.

d.

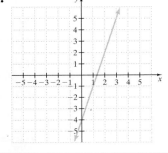

OBJECTIVE 5 ▶ Using function notation. Many times letters such as f, g, and h are used to name functions.

> **Function Notation**
>
> To denote that y is a function of x, we can write
>
> $$y = \underbrace{f(x)}_{\text{Function Notation}} \quad \text{(Read "f of x.")}$$
>
> This notation means that **y is a function of x** or that y *depends on x*. For this reason, y is called the **dependent variable** and x the **independent variable.**

For example, to use function notation with the function $y = 4x + 3$, we write $f(x) = 4x + 3$. The notation $f(1)$ means to replace x with 1 and find the resulting y or function value. Since

$$f(x) = 4x + 3$$

then

$$f(1) = 4(1) + 3 = 7$$

This means that when $x = 1$, y or $f(x) = 7$. The corresponding ordered pair is $(1, 7)$. Here, the input is 1 and the output is $f(1)$ or 7. Now let's find $f(2)$, $f(0)$, and $f(-1)$.

$f(x) = 4x + 3$	$f(x) = 4x + 3$	$f(x) = 4(x) + 3$
$f(2) = 4(2) + 3$	$f(0) = 4(0) + 3$	$f(-1) = 4(-1) + 3$
$= 8 + 3$	$= 0 + 3$	$= -4 + 3$
$= 11$	$= 3$	$= -1$

> ▶ **Helpful Hint**
> Make sure you remember that $f(2) = 11$ corresponds to the ordered pair $(2, 11)$.

Ordered Pairs:

$(2, 11)$	$(0, 3)$	$(-1, -1)$

> ▶ **Helpful Hint**
> Note that $f(x)$ is a special symbol in mathematics used to denote a function. The symbol $f(x)$ is read "f of x." It does *not* mean $f \cdot x$ (f times x).

EXAMPLE 7 If $f(x) = 7x^2 - 3x + 1$ and $g(x) = 3x - 2$, find the following.

a. $f(1)$ **b.** $g(1)$ **c.** $f(-2)$ **d.** $g(0)$

Solution

a. Substitute 1 for x in $f(x) = 7x^2 - 3x + 1$ and simplify.

$f(x) = 7x^2 - 3x + 1$

$f(1) = 7(1)^2 - 3(1) + 1 = 5$

b. $g(x) = 3x - 2$

$g(1) = 3(1) - 2 = 1$

c. $f(x) = 7x^2 - 3x + 1$

$f(-2) = 7(-2)^2 - 3(-2) + 1 = 35$

d. $g(x) = 3x - 2$

$g(0) = 3(0) - 2 = -2$

PRACTICE
7 If $f(x) = 3x - 2$ and $g(x) = 5x^2 + 2x - 1$, find the following.

a. $f(1)$ **b.** $g(1)$ **c.** $f(0)$ **d.** $g(-2)$

Concept Check ☑

Suppose $y = f(x)$ and we are told that $f(3) = 9$. Which is not true?

a. When $x = 3$, $y = 9$.

b. A possible function is $f(x) = x^2$.

c. A point on the graph of the function is $(3, 9)$.

d. A possible function is $f(x) = 2x + 4$.

If it helps, think of a function, f, as a machine that has been programmed with a certain correspondence or rule. An input value (a member of the domain) is then fed into the machine, the machine does the correspondence or rule and the result is the output (a member of the range).

EXAMPLE 8 Given the graphs of the functions f and g, find each function value by inspecting the graphs.

 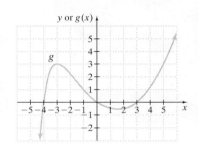

a. $f(4)$ **b.** $f(-2)$ **c.** $g(5)$ **d.** $g(0)$

e. Find all x-values such that $f(x) = 1$.

f. Find all x-values such that $g(x) = 0$.

Solution

a. To find $f(4)$, find the y-value when $x = 4$. We see from the graph that when $x = 4$, y or $f(x) = 2$. Thus, $f(4) = 2$.

b. $f(-2) = 1$ from the ordered pair $(-2, 1)$.

c. $g(5) = 3$ from the ordered pair $(5, 3)$.

d. $g(0) = 0$ from the ordered pair $(0, 0)$.

e. To find x-values such that $f(x) = 1$, we are looking for any ordered pairs on the graph of f whose $f(x)$ or y-value is 1. They are $(2, 1)$ and $(-2, 1)$. Thus $f(2) = 1$ and $f(-2) = 1$. The x-values are 2 and -2.

f. Find ordered pairs on the graph of g whose $g(x)$ or y-value is 0. They are $(3, 0)$ $(0, 0)$ and $(-4, 0)$. Thus $g(3) = 0$, $g(0) = 0$, and $g(-4) = 0$. The x-values are 3, 0, and -4. ☐

8 Given the graphs of the functions f and g, find each function value by inspecting the graphs.

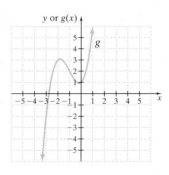

a. $f(1)$ **b.** $f(0)$ **c.** $g(-2)$ **d.** $g(0)$

e. Find all x-values such that $f(x) = 1$.

f. Find all x-values such that $g(x) = -2$.

Many types of real-world paired data form functions. The broken-line graph below shows the research and development spending by the Pharmaceutical Manufacturers Association.

EXAMPLE 9 The following graph shows the research and development expenditures by the Pharmaceutical Manufacturers Association as a function of time.

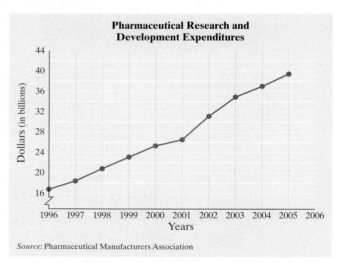

Pharmaceutical Research and Development Expenditures

Source: Pharmaceutical Manufacturers Association

a. Approximate the money spent on research and development in 2002.

b. In 1958, research and development expenditures were \$200 million. Find the increase in expenditures from 1958 to 2004.

Solution

a. Find the year 2002 and move upward until you reach the graph. From the point on the graph move horizontally, to the left, until the other axis is reached. In 2002, approximately \$31 billion was spent.

b. In 2004, approximately \$37 billion, or \$37,000 million was spent. The increase in spending from 1958 to 2004 is \$37,000 − \$200 = \$36,800 million or \$36.8 billion. □

9 Use the graph in Example 9 and approximate the money spent in 2003.

Notice that the graph in Example 9 is the graph of a function since for each year there is only one total amount of money spent by the Pharmaceutical Manufacturers Association on research and development. Also notice that the graph resembles the graph of a line. Often, businesses depend on equations that "closely fit" data-defined functions like this one in order to model the data and predict future trends. For example, by a method called **least squares,** the function $f(x) = 2.602x - 5178$ approximates the data shown. For this function, x is the year and $f(x)$ is total money spent. Its graph and the actual data function are shown next.

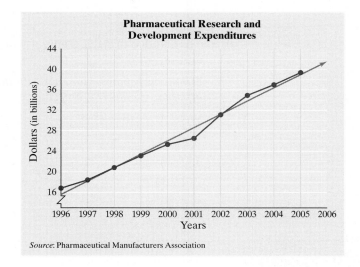

Pharmaceutical Research and Development Expenditures

Source: Pharmaceutical Manufacturers Association

EXAMPLE 10   Use the function $f(x) = 2.602x - 5178$ to predict the amount of money that will be spent by the Pharmaceutical Manufacturers Association on research and development in 2014.

Solution   To predict the amount of money that will be spent in the year 2014 we use $f(x) = 2.602x - 5178$ and find $f(2014)$.

$$f(x) = 2.602x - 5178$$
$$f(2014) = 2.602(2014) - 5178$$
$$= 62.428$$

We predict that in the year 2014, \$62.428 billion dollars will be spent on research and development by the Pharmaceutical Manufacturers Association.   □

PRACTICE
10   Use $f(x) = 2.602x - 5178$ to approximate the money spent in 2012.

Graphing Calculator Explorations

It is possible to use a graphing calculator to sketch the graph of more than one equation on the same set of axes. For example, graph the functions $f(x) = x^2$ and $g(x) = x^2 + 4$ on the same set of axes.

To graph on the same set of axes, press the $\boxed{Y =}$ key and enter the equations on the first two lines.

$$Y_1 = x^2$$
$$Y_2 = x^2 + 4$$

Then press the ⎡ GRAPH ⎤ key as usual. The screen should look like this.

Notice that the graph of y or $g(x) = x^2 + 4$ is the graph of $y = x^2$ moved 4 units upward.

Graph each pair of functions on the same set of axes. Describe the similarities and differences in their graphs.

1. $f(x) = |x|$
$\quad$ $g(x) = |x| + 1$

2. $f(x) = x^2$
$\quad$ $h(x) = x^2 - 5$

3. $f(x) = x$
$\quad$ $H(x) = x - 6$

4. $f(x) = |x|$
$\quad$ $G(x) = |x| + 3$

5. $f(x) = -x^2$
$\quad$ $F(x) = -x^2 + 7$

6. $f(x) = x$
$\quad$ $F(x) = x + 2$

VOCABULARY & READINESS CHECK

Use the choices below to fill in each blank. Some choices may not be used. These exercises have to do with functions and the rectangular coordinate system (Sections 3.1 and 3.2)

x	domain	vertical	relation	$(1.7, -2)$	line	parabola
y	range	horizontal	function	$(-2, 1.7)$	origin	V-shaped

1. The intersection of the x-axis and y-axis is a point, called the _____.

2. To find an x-intercept, let _____ = 0 and solve for _____.

3. To find a y-intercept, let _____ = 0 and solve for _____.

4. The graph of $Ax + By = C$, where A and B are not both 0 is a _____.

5. The graph of $y = |x|$ looks _____.

6. The graph of $y = x^2$ is a _____.

7. A _____ is a set of ordered pairs.

8. The _____ of a relation is the set of all second components of the ordered pairs.

9. The _____ of a relation is the set of all first components of the ordered pairs.

10. A _____ is a relation in which each first component in the ordered pairs corresponds to *exactly* one second component.

11. By the vertical line test, all linear equations are functions except those whose graphs are _____ lines.

12. If $f(-2) = 1.7$, the corresponding ordered pair is _____.

3.2 │ EXERCISE SET

Find the domain and the range of each relation. Also determine
whether the relation is a function. See Examples 1 and 2.

1. $\{(-1, 7), (0, 6), (-2, 2), (5, 6)\}$

2. $\{(4, 9), (-4, 9), (2, 3), (10, -5)\}$

3. $\{(-2, 4), (6, 4), (-2, -3), (-7, -8)\}$

4. $\{(6, 6), (5, 6), (5, -2), (7, 6)\}$

5. $\{(1, 1), (1, 2), (1, 3), (1, 4)\}$

6. $\{(1, 1), (2, 1), (3, 1), (4, 1)\}$

7. $\left\{\left(\dfrac{3}{2}, \dfrac{1}{2}\right), \left(1\dfrac{1}{2}, -7\right), \left(0, \dfrac{4}{5}\right)\right\}$

8. $\{(\pi, 0), (0, \pi), (-2, 4), (4, -2)\}$

9. $\{(-3, -3), (0, 0), (3, 3)\}$

10. $\left\{\left(\dfrac{1}{2}, \dfrac{1}{4}\right), \left(0, \dfrac{7}{8}\right), (0.5, \pi)\right\}$

11.

12.

13.

14.

15.

16.

17.

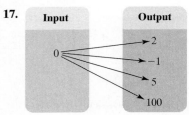

18.

Input	Output

In Exercises 19 through 22, determine whether the relation is a function. See Example 2.

First Set: Input	Correspondence	Second Set: Output
19. Class of algebra students	Final grade average	non negative numbers
20. People who live in Cincinnati, Ohio	Birth date	days of the year
21. blue, green, brown	Eye color	People who live in Cincinnati, Ohio
22. Whole numbers from 0 to 4	Number of children	50 Women in a water aerobics class

Use the vertical line test to determine whether each graph is the graph of a function. See Example 5.

23.

24.

25.

26.

27.

28.

Find the domain and the range of each relation. Use the vertical line test to determine whether each graph is the graph of a function. See Example 6.

29.

30.

31.

32.

33.

34.

35.

36.

37.

38.

39.

40.

41. In your own words define **(a)** function; **(b)** domain; **(c)** range.

42. Explain the vertical line test and how it is used.

MIXED PRACTICE

Decide whether each is a function. See Examples 3 through 6.

43. $y = x + 1$

44. $y = x - 1$

45. $x = 2y^2$

46. $y = x^2$

47. $y - x = 7$

48. $2x - 3y = 9$

49. $y = \dfrac{1}{x}$

50. $y = \dfrac{1}{x - 3}$

51. $y = 5x - 12$

52. $y = \dfrac{1}{2}x + 4$

53. $x = y^2$

54. $x = |y|$

If $f(x) = 3x + 3$, $g(x) = 4x^2 - 6x + 3$, and $h(x) = 5x^2 - 7$, find the following. See Example 7.

55. $f(4)$

56. $f(-1)$

57. $h(-3)$

58. $h(0)$

59. $g(2)$

60. $g(1)$

61. $g(0)$

62. $h(-2)$

Given the following functions, find the indicated values. See Example 7.

63. $f(x) = \dfrac{1}{2}x;$

    a. $f(0)$ **b.** $f(2)$ **c.** $f(-2)$

64. $g(x) = -\dfrac{1}{3}x;$

    a. $g(0)$ **b.** $g(-1)$ **c.** $g(3)$

65. $g(x) = 2x^2 + 4;$

    a. $g(-11)$ **b.** $g(-1)$ **c.** $g\left(\dfrac{1}{2}\right)$

66. $h(x) = -x^2;$

    a. $h(-5)$ **b.** $h\left(-\dfrac{1}{3}\right)$ **c.** $h\left(\dfrac{1}{3}\right)$

67. $f(x) = -5;$

    a. $f(2)$ **b.** $f(0)$ **c.** $f(606)$

68. $h(x) = 7;$

    a. $h(7)$ **b.** $h(542)$ **c.** $h\left(-\dfrac{3}{4}\right)$

69. $f(x) = 1.3x^2 - 2.6x + 5.1$

    a. $f(2)$ **b.** $f(-2)$ **c.** $f(3.1)$

70. $g(x) = 2.7x^2 + 6.8x - 10.2$

    a. $g(1)$ **b.** $g(-5)$ **c.** $g(7.2)$

Use the graph of the functions below to answer Exercises 71 through 82. See Example 8.

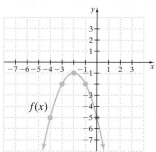

71. If $f(1) = -10$, write the corresponding ordered pair.

72. If $f(-5) = -10$, write the corresponding ordered pair.

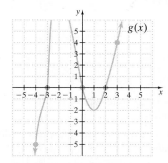

73. If $g(4) = 56$, write the corresponding ordered pair.

74. If $g(-2) = 8$, write the corresponding ordered pair.

75. Find $f(-1)$.

76. Find $f(-2)$.

77. Find $g(2)$.

78. Find $g(-4)$.

79. Find all values of x such that $f(x) = -5$.

80. Find all values of x such that $f(x) = -2$.

81. Find all positive values of x such that $g(x) = 4$.

82. Find all values of x such that $g(x) = 0$.

83. What is the greatest number of x-intercepts that a function may have? Explain your answer.

84. What is the greatest number of y-intercepts that a function may have? Explain your answer.

Use the graph in Example 9 to answer the following. Also see Example 10.

85. a. Use the graph to approximate the money spent on research and development in 1996.

    b. Recall that the function $f(x) = 2.602x - 5178$ approximates the graph in Example 9. Use this equation to approximate the money spent on research and development in 1996.

86. a. Use the graph to approximate the money spent on research and development in 1999.

    b. Use the function $f(x) = 2.602x - 5178$ to approximate the money spent on research and development in 1999.

The function $f(x) = 0.42x + 10.5$, can be used to predict diamond production. For this function, x is the number of years after 2000, and $f(x)$ is the value (in billions of dollars) of the years diamond production. (See the Chapter 3 opener.)

87. Use the function in the directions above to predict diamond production in 2012.

88. Use the function in the directions above to predict diamond production in 2015.

89. Since $y = x + 7$ describes a function, rewrite the equation using function notation.

90. In your own words, explain how to find the domain of a function given its graph.

The function $A(r) = \pi r^2$ may be used to find the area of a circle if we are given its radius.

91. Find the area of a circle whose radius is 5 centimeters. (Do not approximate π.)

92. Find the area of a circular garden whose radius is 8 feet. (Do not approximate π.)

The function $V(x) = x^3$ may be used to find the volume of a cube if we are given the length x of a side.

93. Find the volume of a cube whose side is 14 inches.

94. Find the volume of a die whose side is 1.7 centimeters.

Forensic scientists use the following functions to find the height of a woman if they are given the height of her femur bone f or her tibia bone t in centimeters.

$$H(f) = 2.59f + 47.24$$
$$H(t) = 2.72t + 61.28$$

95. Find the height of a woman whose femur measures 46 centimeters.

96. Find the height of a woman whose tibia measures 35 centimeters.

The dosage in milligrams D of Ivermectin, a heartworm preventive, for a dog who weighs x pounds is given by

$$D(x) = \frac{136}{25}x$$

97. Find the proper dosage for a dog that weighs 30 pounds.

98. Find the proper dosage for a dog that weighs 50 pounds.

99. The per capita consumption (in pounds) of all poultry in the United States is approximated by the function $C(x) = 2.28x + 94.86$, where x is the number of years since 2001. (*Source*: Based on actual and estimated data from the Economic Research Service, U.S. Department of Agriculture)

    a. Find and interpret $C(5)$.

    b. Estimate the per capita consumption of all poultry in the United States in 2007.

100. The average length of U.S. hospital stays has been decreasing, following the equation $y = -0.09x + 8.02$ where x is the number of years since 1970. (*Source:* National Center for Health Statistics)

    a. What was the length of the average hospital stay in 1995?

    b. If this trend continues, what will the average length be in 2011?

REVIEW AND PREVIEW

Complete the given table and use the table to graph the linear equation. See Section 3.1.

101. $x - y = -5$

x	0		1
y		0	

102. $2x + 3y = 10$

x	0		
y		0	2

103. $7x + 4y = 8$

x	0		
y		0	-1

104. $5y - x = -15$

x	0		-2
y		0	

105. $y = 6x$

x	0	-1	
y		0	

106. $y = -2x$

x	0	-2	
y		0	

△ **107.** Is it possible to find the perimeter of the following geometric figure? If so, find the perimeter.

45 meters

40 meters

CONCEPT EXTENSIONS

For Exercises 108 through 111, suppose that $y = f(x)$ and it is true that $f(7) = 50$. Determine whether each is true or false. See the second Concept Check in this section.

108. An ordered-pair solution of the function is $(7, 50)$.

109. When x is 50, y is 7.

110. A possible function is $f(x) = x^2 + 1$.

111. A possible function is $f(x) = 10x - 20$.

Given the following functions, find the indicated values.

112. $f(x) = 2x + 7$;
  a. $f(2)$ **b.** $f(a)$

113. $g(x) = -3x + 12$;
  a. $g(s)$ **b.** $g(r)$

114. $h(x) = x^2 + 7$;
  a. $h(3)$ **b.** $h(a)$

115. $f(x) = x^2 - 12$;
  a. $f(12)$ **b.** $f(a)$

116. Describe a function whose domain is the set of people in your hometown.

117. Describe a function whose domain is the set of people in your algebra class.

3.3 GRAPHING LINEAR FUNCTIONS

OBJECTIVES

1 Graph linear functions.

2 Graph linear functions by finding intercepts.

3 Graph vertical and horizontal lines.

OBJECTIVE 1 ▶ Graphing linear functions. In this section, we identify and graph linear functions. By the vertical line test, we know that all linear equations except those whose graphs are vertical lines are functions. For example, we know from Section 3.1 that $y = 2x$ is a linear equation in two variables. Its graph is shown.

x	$y = 2x$
1	2
0	0
-1	-2

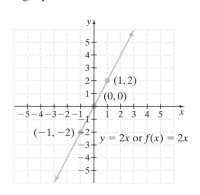

Because this graph passes the vertical line test, we know that $y = 2x$ is a function. If we want to emphasize that this equation describes a function, we may write $y = 2x$ as $f(x) = 2x$.

EXAMPLE 1 Graph $g(x) = 2x + 1$. Compare this graph with the graph of $f(x) = 2x$.

Solution To graph $g(x) = 2x + 1$, find three ordered pair solutions.

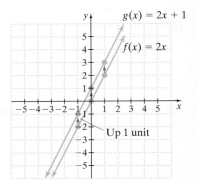

x	f(x) = 2x	**g (x) = 2x + 1**
0	0	1
−1	−2	−1
1	2	3

add 1

Notice that y-values for the graph of $g(x) = 2x + 1$ are obtained by adding 1 to each y-value of each corresponding point of the graph of $f(x) = 2x$. The graph of $g(x) = 2x + 1$ is the same as the graph of $f(x) = 2x$ shifted upward 1 unit. □

PRACTICE
1 Graph $g(x) = 4x - 3$ and $f(x) = 4x$ on the same axes.

In general, a **linear function** is a function that can be written in the form $f(x) = mx + b$. For example, $g(x) = 2x + 1$ is in this form, with $m = 2$ and $b = 1$.

EXAMPLE 2 Graph the linear functions $f(x) = -3x$ and $g(x) = -3x - 6$ on the same set of axes.

Solution To graph $f(x)$ and $g(x)$, find ordered pair solutions.

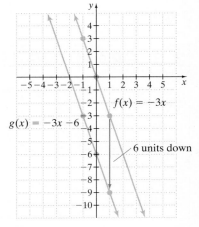

x	f(x) = −3x	**g (x) = −3x − 6**
0	0	−6
1	−3	−9
−1	3	−3
−2	6	0

subtract 6

subtract 6

Each y-value for the graph of $g(x) = -3x - 6$ is obtained by subtracting 6 from the y-value of the corresponding point of the graph of $f(x) = -3x$. The graph of $g(x) = -3x - 6$ is the same as the graph of $f(x) = -3x$ shifted down 6 units. □

PRACTICE
2 Graph the linear functions $f(x) = -2x$ and $g(x) = -2x + 5$ on the same set of axes.

OBJECTIVE 2 ▶ Graphing linear functions using intercepts. Notice that the y-intercept of the graph of $g(x) = -3x - 6$ in the preceding figure is $(0, -6)$. In general, if *a linear function is written in the form* $f(x) = mx + b$ *or* $y = mx + b$, *the y-intercept is* $(0, b)$. This is because if x is 0, then $f(x) = mx + b$ becomes $f(0) = m \cdot 0 + b = b$, and we have the ordered pair solution $(0, b)$. We will study this form more in the next section.

EXAMPLE 3 Find the y-intercept of the graph of each equation.

a. $f(x) = \dfrac{1}{2}x + \dfrac{3}{7}$ **b.** $y = -2.5x - 3.2$

Solution

a. The y-intercept of $f(x) = \dfrac{1}{2}x + \dfrac{3}{7}$ is $\left(0, \dfrac{3}{7}\right)$.

b. The y-intercept of $y = -2.5x - 3.2$ is $(0, -3.2)$.

PRACTICE
3 Find the y-intercept of the graph of each equation.

a. $f(x) = \dfrac{3}{4}x - \dfrac{2}{5}$ **b.** $y = 2.6x + 4.1$

In general, to find the y-intercept of the graph of an equation not in the form $y = mx + b$, let $x = 0$ since any point on the y-axis has an x-coordinate of 0. To find the x-intercept of a line, let $y = 0$ or $f(x) = 0$ since any point on the x-axis has a y-coordinate of 0.

> **Finding x- and y-Intercepts**
> To find an x-intercept, let $y = 0$ or $f(x) = 0$ and solve for x.
> To find a y-intercept, let $x = 0$ and solve for y.

Intercepts are usually easy to find and plot since one coordinate is 0.

EXAMPLE 4 Find the intercepts and graph: $3x + 4y = -12$.

Solution To find the y-intercept, we let $x = 0$ and solve for y. To find the x-intercept, we let $y = 0$ and solve for x. Let's let $x = 0$, $y = 0$, and then let $x = 2$ to find a third point as a check.

Let $x = 0$.	Let $y = 0$.	Let $x = 2$.
$3x + 4y = -12$	$3x + 4y = -12$	$3x + 4y = -12$
$3 \cdot 0 + 4y = -12$	$3x + 4 \cdot 0 = -12$	$3 \cdot 2 + 4y = -12$
$4y = -12$	$3x = -12$	$6 + 4y = -12$
$y = -3$	$x = -4$	$4y = -18$
		$y = -\dfrac{18}{4} = -4\dfrac{1}{2}$
$(0, -3)$	$(-4, 0)$	$\left(2, -4\dfrac{1}{2}\right)$

The ordered pairs are on the table below. The graph of $3x + 4y = -12$ is the line drawn through these points, as shown.

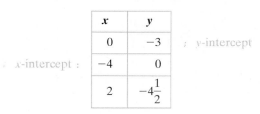

x	y	
0	-3	; y-intercept
-4	0	
2	$-4\dfrac{1}{2}$	

x-intercept :

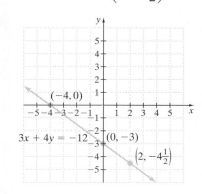

PRACTICE
4 Find the intercepts and graph: $4x - 5y = -20$.

Notice that the equation $3x + 4y = -12$ describes a linear function—"linear" because its graph is a line and "function" because the graph passes the vertical line test.

If we want to emphasize that the equation $3x + 4y = -12$ from Example 4 describes a function, first solve the equation for y.

$$3x + 4y = -12$$
$$4y = -3x - 12 \quad \text{Subtract } x \text{ from both sides.}$$
$$\frac{4y}{4} = \frac{-3x}{4} - \frac{12}{4} \quad \text{Divide both sides by } -3.$$
$$y = -\frac{3}{4}x - 3 \quad \text{Simplify.}$$

Next, let

$$y = f(x).$$
$$f(x) = -\frac{3}{4}x - 3$$

> ▶ **Helpful Hint**
>
> Any linear equation that describes a function can be written using function notation. To do so,
>
> **1.** solve the equation for y and then
> **2.** replace y with $f(x)$, as we did above.

EXAMPLE 5 Graph $x = -2y$ by plotting intercepts.

Solution Let $y = 0$ to find the x-intercept and $x = 0$ to find the y-intercept.

$$\text{If } y = 0 \quad \text{then} \qquad \text{If } x = 0 \quad \text{then}$$
$$x = -2(0) \quad \text{or} \qquad 0 = -2y \quad \text{or}$$
$$x = 0 \qquad\qquad\qquad 0 = y$$
$$(0, 0) \qquad\qquad\qquad (0, 0)$$

Ordered pairs Both the x-intercept and y-intercept are $(0, 0)$. This happens when the graph passes through the origin. Since two points are needed to determine a line, we must find at least one more ordered pair that satisfies $x = -2y$. Let $y = -1$ to find a second ordered pair solution and let $y = 1$ as a check point.

$$\text{If } y = -1 \quad \text{then} \quad \text{If } y = 1 \quad \text{then}$$
$$x = -2(-1) \quad \text{or} \quad x = -2(1) \quad \text{or}$$
$$x = 2 \qquad\qquad\quad x = -2$$

The ordered pairs are $(0, 0)$, $(2, -1)$, and $(-2, 1)$. Plot these points to graph $x = -2y$.

x	y
0	0
2	-1
-2	1

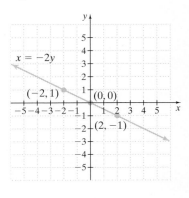

PRACTICE
5 Graph $y = -3x$ by plotting intercepts.

OBJECTIVE 3 ▶ Graphing vertical and horizontal lines. The equations $x = c$ and $y = c$, where c is a real number constant, are both linear equations in two variables. Why? Because $x = c$ can be written as $x + 0y = c$ and $y = c$ can be written as $0x + y = c$. We graph these two special linear equations below.

EXAMPLE 6 Graph $x = 2$.

Solution The equation $x = 2$ can be written as $x + 0y = 2$. For any y-value chosen, notice that x is 2. No other value for x satisfies $x + 0y = 2$. Any ordered pair whose x-coordinate is 2 is a solution to $x + 0y = 2$ because 2 added to 0 times any value of y is $2 + 0$, or 2. We will use the ordered pairs $(2, 3), (2, 0)$ and $(2, -3)$ to graph $x = 2$.

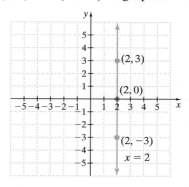

x	y
2	3
2	0
2	-3

x-intercept :

The graph is a vertical line with x-intercept $(2, 0)$. Notice that this graph is not the graph of a function, and it has no y-intercept because x is never 0. ☐

PRACTICE
6 Graph $x = -4$.

EXAMPLE 7 Graph $y = -3$.

Solution The equation $y = -3$ can be written as $0x + y = -3$. For any x-value chosen, y is -3. If we choose 4, 0, and -2 as x-values, the ordered pair solutions are $(4, -3), (0, -3)$, and $(-2, -3)$. We will use these ordered pairs to graph $y = -3$.

x	y
4	-3
0	-3
-2	-3

; y-intercept

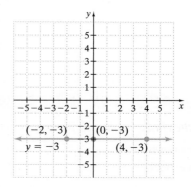

The graph is a horizontal line with y-intercept $(0, -3)$ and no x-intercept. Notice that this graph is the graph of a function. ☐

PRACTICE
7 Graph $y = 4$.

From Examples 6 and 7, we have the following generalization.

Graphing Vertical and Horizontal Lines

The graph of $x = c$, where c is a real number, is a vertical line with x-intercept $(c, 0)$.

The graph of $y = c$, where c is a real number, is a horizontal line with y-intercept $(0, c)$.

not a function

a function

Graphing Calculator Explorations

You may have noticed by now that to use the $\boxed{Y =}$ key on a graphing calculator to graph an equation, the equation must be solved for y.

Graph each function by first solving the function for y.

1. $x = 3.5y$

2. $-2.7y = x$

3. $5.78x + 2.31y = 10.98$

4. $-7.22x + 3.89y = 12.57$

5. $y - |x| = 3.78$

6. $3y - 5x^2 = 6x - 4$

7. $y - 5.6x^2 = 7.7x + 1.5$

8. $y + 2.6|x| = -3.2$

VOCABULARY & READINESS CHECK

Use the choices below to fill in each blank. Some choices may be used more than once and some not at all.

horizontal	y	$(c, 0)$	$(b, 0)$	$(m, 0)$	linear
vertical	x	$(0, c)$	$(0, b)$	$(0, m)$	$f(x)$

1. A _____ function can be written in the form $f(x) = mx + b$.

2. In the form $f(x) = mx + b$, the y-intercept is _____.

3. The graph of $x = c$ is a _____ line with x-intercept _____.

4. The graph of $y = c$ is a _____ line with y-intercept _____.

5. To find an x-intercept, let ____ $= 0$ or _____ $= 0$ and solve for ____.

6. To find a y-intercept, let _____ $= 0$ and solve for _____.

3.3 | EXERCISE SET

 MyMathLab   PRACTICE   WATCH   DOWNLOAD   READ   REVIEW

Graph each linear function. See Examples 1 and 2.

1. $f(x) = -2x$

2. $f(x) = 2x$

 3. $f(x) = -2x + 3$

4. $f(x) = 2x + 6$

5. $f(x) = \frac{1}{2}x$

6. $f(x) = \frac{1}{3}x$

7. $f(x) = \frac{1}{2}x - 4$

8. $f(x) = \frac{1}{3}x - 2$

The graph of $f(x) = 5x$ follows. Use this graph to match each linear function with its graph. See Examples 1 through 3.

y = 5x

A   B

C   D

9. $f(x) = 5x - 3$

10. $f(x) = 5x - 2$

11. $f(x) = 5x + 1$

12. $f(x) = 5x + 3$

Graph each linear function by finding x- and y-intercepts. Then write each equation using function notation. See Examples 4 and 5.

13. $x - y = 3$

14. $x - y = -4$

15. $x = 5y$

16. $2x = y$

17. $-x + 2y = 6$

18. $x - 2y = -8$

19. $2x - 4y = 8$

20. $2x + 3y = 6$

21. In your own words, explain how to find x- and y-intercepts.

22. Explain why it is a good idea to use three points to graph a linear equation.

Graph each linear equation. See Examples 6 and 7.

23. $x = -1$

24. $y = 5$

25. $y = 0$

26. $x = 0$

27. $y + 7 = 0$

28. $x - 3 = 0$

Match each equation below with its graph.

A B

C D

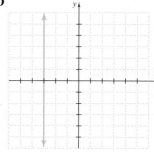

29. $y = 2$

30. $x = -3$

31. $x - 2 = 0$

32. $y + 1 = 0$

33. Discuss whether a vertical line ever has a y-intercept.

34. Discuss whether a horizontal line ever has an x-intercept.

MIXED PRACTICE

Graph each linear equation. See Examples 1 through 7.

35. $x + 2y = 8$

36. $x - 3y = 3$

37. $3x + 5y = 7$

38. $3x - 2y = 5$

39. $x + 8y = 8$

40. $x - 3y = 9$

41. $5 = 6x - y$

42. $4 = x - 3y$

43. $-x + 10y = 11$

44. $-x + 9 = -y$

45. $y = \dfrac{3}{2}$

46. $x = \dfrac{3}{2}$

47. $2x + 3y = 6$

48. $4x + y = 5$

49. $x + 3 = 0$

50. $y - 6 = 0$

51. $f(x) = \dfrac{3}{4}x + 2$

52. $f(x) = \dfrac{4}{3}x + 2$

53. $f(x) = x$

54. $f(x) = -x$

55. $f(x) = \dfrac{1}{2}x$

56. $f(x) = -2x$

57. $f(x) = 4x - \dfrac{1}{3}$

58. $f(x) = -3x + \dfrac{3}{4}$

59. $x = -3$

60. $f(x) = 3$

REVIEW AND PREVIEW

Solve the following. See Sections 2.6 and 2.7.

61. $|x - 3| = 6$

62. $|x + 2| < 4$

63. $|2x + 5| > 3$

64. $|5x| = 10$

65. $|3x - 4| \le 2$

66. $|7x - 2| \ge 5$

Simplify. See Section 1.3.

67. $\dfrac{-6 - 3}{2 - 8}$

68. $\dfrac{4 - 5}{-1 - 0}$

69. $\dfrac{-8 - (-2)}{-3 - (-2)}$

70. $\dfrac{12 - 3}{10 - 9}$

71. $\dfrac{0 - 6}{5 - 0}$

72. $\dfrac{2 - 2}{3 - 5}$

CONCEPT EXTENSIONS

Solve.

73. Broyhill Furniture found that it takes 2 hours to manufacture each table for one of its special dining room sets. Each chair takes 3 hours to manufacture. A total of 1500 hours is available to produce tables and chairs of this style. The linear equation that models this situation is $2x + 3y = 1500$, where x represents the number of tables produced and y the number of chairs produced.

   a. Complete the ordered pair solution (0,) of this equation. Describe the manufacturing situation this solution corresponds to.

   b. Complete the ordered pair solution (, 0) for this equation. Describe the manufacturing situation this solution corresponds to.

   c. If 50 tables are produced, find the greatest number of chairs the company can make.

74. While manufacturing two different camera models, Kodak found that the basic model costs \$55 to produce, whereas the deluxe model costs \$75. The weekly budget for these two models is limited to \$33,000 in production costs. The linear equation that models this situation is $55x + 75y = 33,000$, where x represents the number of basic models and y the number of deluxe models.

   a. Complete the ordered pair solution (0,) of this equation. Describe the manufacturing situation this solution corresponds to.

   b. Complete the ordered pair solution (, 0) of this equation. Describe the manufacturing situation this solution corresponds to.

   c. If 350 deluxe models are produced, find the greatest number of basic models that can be made in one week.

75. The cost of renting a car for a day is given by the linear function $C(x) = 0.2x + 24$, where $C(x)$ is in dollars and x is the number of miles driven.

   a. Find the cost of driving the car 200 miles.

   b. Graph $C(x) = 0.2x + 24$.

   c. How can you tell from the graph of $C(x)$ that as the number of miles driven increases, the total cost increases also?

76. The cost of renting a piece of machinery is given by the linear function $C(x) = 4x + 10$, where $C(x)$ is in dollars and x is given in hours.

   a. Find the cost of renting the piece of machinery for 8 hours.

   b. Graph $C(x) = 4x + 10$.

   c. How can you tell from the graph of $C(x)$ that as the number of hours increases, the total cost increases also?

77. The yearly cost of tuition (in-state) and required fees for attending a public two-year college full time can be estimated by the linear function $f(x) = 107.3x + 1245.62$, where x is the number of years after 2000 and $f(x)$ is the total cost. (*Source:* U.S. National Center for Education Statistics)

   a. Use this function to approximate the yearly cost of attending a two-year college in the year 2015. [*Hint:* Find $f(15)$.]

   b. Use the given function to predict in what year the yearly cost of tuition and required fees will exceed \$2500. [*Hint:* Let $f(x) = 2500$, solve for x, then round your solution up to the next whole year.

   c. Use this function to approximate the yearly cost of attending a two-year college in the present year. If you attend a two-year college, is this amount greater than or less than the amount that is currently charged by the college you attend?

78. The yearly cost of tuition (in-state) and required fees for attending a public four-year college full time can be estimated by the linear function $f(x) = 291.5x + 2944.05$, where x is the number of years after 2000 and $f(x)$ is the total cost in dollars. (*Source:* U.S. National Center for Education Statistics)

  a. Use this function to approximate the yearly cost of attending a four-year college in the year 2015. [*Hint:* Find $f(15)$.]

  b. Use the given function to predict in what year the yearly cost of tuition and required fees will exceed \$6000. [*Hint:* Let $f(x) = 6000$, solve for x, then round your solution up to the next whole year.]

  c. Use this function to approximate the yearly cost of attending a four-year college in the present year. If you attend a four-year college, is this amount greater than or less than the amount that is currently charged by the college you attend?

Use a graphing calculator to verify the results of each exercise.

79. Exercise 9   **80.** Exercise 10

81. Exercise 17   **82.** Exercise 18

83. The graph of $f(x)$ or $y = -4x$ is given below. Without actually graphing, describe the shape and location of

  a. $y = -4x + 2$ **b.** $y = -4x - 5$

It is true that for any function $f(x)$, the graph of $f(x) + K$ is the same as the graph of $f(x)$ shifted K units up if K is positive and $|K|$ units down if K is negative. (We study this further in Section 3.7.)

The graph of $y = |x|$ is

Without actually graphing, match each equation with its graph.

  a. $y = |x| - 1$

  b. $y = |x| + 1$

  c. $y = |x| - 3$

  d. $y = |x| + 3$

84.

85.

86.

87.

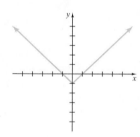

📖 **STUDY SKILLS BUILDER**

Are You Organized?

When it's time to study for a test, are your notes neat and organized? Have you ever had trouble reading your own mathematics handwriting? (Be honest—I have.)

When any of these things happen, it's time to get organized. Here are a few suggestions:

Write your notes and complete your homework assignment in a notebook with pockets (spiral or ring binder.) When you receive graded papers or handouts, place them in the notebook pocket so that you will not lose them.

Remember to mark (possibly with an exclamation point) any note(s) that seem extra important to you. Also mark (possibly with a question mark) any notes or homework that you are having trouble with.

Also, if you are having trouble reading your own handwriting, *slow down* and write your mathematics work clearly!

Exercises

1. Have you been completing your assignments on time?
2. Have you been correcting any exercises you may be having difficulty with?
3. If you are having trouble with a mathematical concept or correcting any homework exercises, have you visited your instructor, a tutor, or your campus math lab?
4. Are you taking lecture notes in your mathematics course? (By the way, these notes should include all worked-out examples solved by your instructor.)
5. Is your mathematics course material (handouts, graded papers, lecture notes) organized?
6. If your answer to Exercise 5 is no, take a moment and review your course material. List at least two ways that you might better organize it. Then read the Study Skills Builder on organizing a notebook in Chapter 2.

3.4 THE SLOPE OF A LINE

OBJECTIVES

1 Find the slope of a line given two points on the line.

2 Find the slope of a line given the equation of a line.

3 Interpret the slope–intercept form in an application.

4 Find the slopes of horizontal and vertical lines.

5 Compare the slopes of parallel and perpendicular lines.

OBJECTIVE 1 ▶ Finding slope given two points. You may have noticed by now that different lines often tilt differently. It is very important in many fields to be able to measure and compare the tilt, or **slope,** of lines. For example, a wheelchair ramp with a slope of $\frac{1}{12}$ means that the ramp rises 1 foot for every 12 horizontal feet. A road with a slope or grade of 11% $\left(\text{or } \frac{11}{100}\right)$ means that the road rises 11 feet for every 100 horizontal feet.

We measure the slope of a line as a ratio of **vertical change** to **horizontal change.** Slope is usually designated by the letter m.

Suppose that we want to measure the slope of the following line.

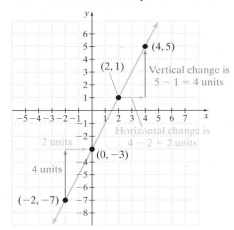

The vertical change between *both* pairs of points on the line is 4 units per horizontal change of 2 units. Then

$$\text{slope } m = \frac{\text{change in } y \text{ (vertical change)}}{\text{change in } x \text{ (horizontal change)}} = \frac{4}{2} = 2$$

We can also think of slope as a **rate of change** between points. A slope of 2 or $\frac{2}{1}$ means that between pairs of points on the line, the rate of change is a vertical change of 2 units per horizontal change of 1 unit.

Consider the line in the box below, which passes through the points (x_1, y_1) and (x_2, y_2). (The notation x_1 is read "x-sub-one.") The vertical change, or *rise*, between these points is the difference of the y-coordinates: $y_2 - y_1$. The horizontal change, or *run*, between the points is the difference of the x-coordinates: $x_2 - x_1$.

Slope of a Line

Given a line passing through points (x_1, y_1) and (x_2, y_2) the **slope** m of the line is

$m = \dfrac{\text{rise}}{\text{run}} = \dfrac{y_2 - y_1}{x_2 - x_1}$, as long as $x_2 \neq x_1$.

Concept Check ☑

In the definition of slope, we state that $x_2 \neq x_1$. Explain why.

EXAMPLE 1   Find the slope of the line containing the points $(0, 3)$ and $(2, 5)$. Graph the line.

Solution   We use the slope formula. It does not matter which point we call (x_1, y_1) and which point we call (x_2, y_2). We'll let $(x_1, y_1) = (0, 3)$ and $(x_2, y_2) = (2, 5)$.

$$m = \frac{y_2 - y_1}{x_2 - x_1}$$

$$= \frac{5 - 3}{2 - 0} = \frac{2}{2} = 1$$

Notice in this example that the slope is *positive* and that the graph of the line containing $(0, 3)$ and $(2, 5)$ moves *upward,* or increases, as we go from left to right.   □

PRACTICE

1   Find the slope of the line containing the points $(4, 0)$ and $(-2, 3)$. Graph the line.

Answer to Concept Check:
So that the denominator is not 0

> **Helpful Hint**
>
> The slope of a line is the same no matter which 2 points of a line you choose to calculate slope. The line in Example 1 also contains the point $(-3, 0)$. Below, we calculate the slope of the line using $(0, 3)$ as (x_1, y_1) and $(-3, 0)$ as (x_2, y_2).
>
> $$m = \frac{y_2 - y_1}{x_2 - x_1} = \frac{0 - 3}{-3 - 0} = \frac{-3}{-3} = 1 \quad \text{Same slope as found in Example 1.}$$

EXAMPLE 2 Find the slope of the line containing the points $(5, -4)$ and $(-3, 3)$. Graph the line.

Solution We use the slope formula, and let $(x_1, y_1) = (5, -4)$ and $(x_2, y_2) = (-3, 3)$.

$$m = \frac{y_2 - y_1}{x_2 - x_1}$$

$$= \frac{3 - (-4)}{-3 - 5} = \frac{7}{-8} = -\frac{7}{8}$$

> **Helpful Hint**
>
> When we are trying to find the slope of a line through two given points, it makes no difference which given point is called (x_1, y_1) and which is called (x_2, y_2). Once an x-coordinate is called x_1, however, make sure its corresponding y-coordinate is called y_1.

Notice in this example that the slope is negative and that the graph of the line through $(5, -4)$ and $(-3, 3)$ moves downward, or decreases, as we go from left to right. □

PRACTICE

2 Find the slope of the line containing the points $(-5, -4)$ and $(5, 2)$. Graph the line.

Concept Check ☑

Find and correct the error in the following calculation of slope of the line containing the points $(12, 2)$ and $(4, 7)$.

$$m = \frac{12 - 4}{2 - 7} = \frac{8}{-5} = -\frac{8}{5}$$

OBJECTIVE 2 ▶ Finding slope given an equation. As we have seen, the slope of a line is defined by two points on the line. Thus, if we know the equation of a line, we can find its slope.

EXAMPLE 3 Find the slope of the line whose equation is $f(x) = \frac{2}{3}x + 4$.

Solution Two points are needed on the line defined by $f(x) = \frac{2}{3}x + 4$ or $y = \frac{2}{3}x + 4$ to find its slope. We will use intercepts as our two points.

If $x = 0$, then	If $y = 0$, then
$y = \frac{2}{3} \cdot 0 + 4$	$0 = \frac{2}{3}x + 4$
$y = 4$	$-4 = \frac{2}{3}x \qquad$ Subtract 4.
	$\frac{3}{2}(-4) = \frac{3}{2} \cdot \frac{2}{3}x \qquad$ Multiply by $\frac{3}{2}$.
	$-6 = x$

Answer to Concept Check:

$$m = \frac{2 - 7}{12 - 4} = \frac{-5}{8} = -\frac{5}{8}$$

Use the points $(0, 4)$ and $(-6, 0)$ to find the slope. Let (x_1, y_1) be $(0, 4)$ and (x_2, y_2) be $(-6, 0)$. Then

$$m = \frac{y_2 - y_1}{x_2 - x_1} = \frac{0 - 4}{-6 - 0} = \frac{-4}{-6} = \frac{2}{3}$$ □

PRACTICE

3   Find the slope of the line whose equation is $f(x) = -4x + 6$.

Analyzing the results of Example 3, you may notice a striking pattern:

The slope of $y = \frac{2}{3}x + 4$ is $\frac{2}{3}$, the same as the coefficient of x.

Also, the y-intercept is $(0, 4)$, as expected.

When a linear equation is written in the form $f(x) = mx + b$ or $y = mx + b$, m is the slope of the line and $(0, b)$ is its y-intercept. The form $y = mx + b$ is appropriately called the **slope–intercept form.**

> **Slope–Intercept Form**
>
> When a linear equation in two variables is written in slope–intercept form,
>
> $$\underset{\uparrow}{\text{slope}} \quad \underset{\uparrow}{\text{y-intercept is }(0, b)}$$
> $$y = mx + b$$
>
> then m is the slope of the line and $(0, b)$ is the y-intercept of the line.

EXAMPLE 4   Find the slope and the y-intercept of the line $3x - 4y = 4$.

Solution   We write the equation in slope–intercept form by solving for y.

$$3x - 4y = 4$$
$$-4y = -3x + 4 \qquad \text{Subtract } 3x \text{ from both sides.}$$
$$\frac{-4y}{-4} = \frac{-3x}{-4} + \frac{4}{-4} \qquad \text{Divide both sides by } -4.$$
$$y = \frac{3}{4}x - 1 \qquad \text{Simplify.}$$

The coefficient of x, $\frac{3}{4}$, is the slope, and the y-intercept is $(0, -1)$.   □

PRACTICE

4   Find the slope and the y-intercept of the line $2x - 3y = 9$.

OBJECTIVE 3 ▶ Interpreting slope-intercept form. On the following page is the graph of one-day ticket prices at Disney World for the years shown.

Notice that the graph resembles the graph of a line. Recall that businesses often depend on equations that "closely fit" graphs like this one to model the data and to predict future trends. By the **least squares** method, the linear function $f(x) = 2.7x + 38.64$ approximates the data shown, where x is the number of years since 1996 and y is the ticket price for that year.

> ▶ **Helpful Hint**
>
> The notation 0 4 1996 below the graph on the next page means that the number 0 corresponds to the year 1996, 1 corresponds to the year 1997, and so on.

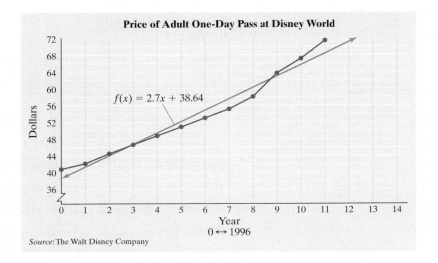

Price of Adult One-Day Pass at Disney World

$f(x) = 2.7x + 38.64$

Dollars

Year
0 ↔ 1996

Source: The Walt Disney Company

EXAMPLE 5   Predicting Future Prices

The adult one-day pass price $f(x)$ for Disney World is given by

$$f(x) = 2.7x + 38.64$$

where x is the number of years since 1996

a. Use this equation to predict the ticket price for the year 2010.

b. What does the slope of this equation mean?

c. What does the y-intercept of this equation mean?

Solution

a. To predict the price of a pass in 2010, we need to find $f(14)$. (Since year 1996 corresponds to $x = 0$, year 2010 corresponds to $x = 14$.)

$$f(x) = 2.7x + 38.64$$
$$f(14) = 2.7(14) + 38.64 \quad \text{Let } x = 14.$$
$$= 76.44$$

We predict that in the year 2010 the price of an adult one-day pass to Disney World will be about \$76.44.

b. The slope of $f(x) = 2.7x + 38.64$ is 2.7. We can think of this number as $\dfrac{\text{rise}}{\text{run}}$ or $\dfrac{2.7}{1}$. This means that the ticket price increases on the average by \$2.70 every 1 year.

c. The y-intercept of $f(x) = 2.7x + 38.64$ is $(0, \ 38.64)$.
     ↑   ↑
   year   price

This means that at year 0, or 1996, the ticket price was about \$38.64.   □

PRACTICE
5   Use the equation from Example 5 to predict the ticket price for the year 2012.

OBJECTIVE 4 ▶ Finding slopes of horizontal and vertical lines. Next we find the slopes of two special types of lines: vertical lines and horizontal lines.

EXAMPLE 6   Find the slope of the line $x = -5$.

Solution Recall that the graph of $x = -5$ is a vertical line with x-intercept $(-5, 0)$. To find the slope, we find two ordered pair solutions of $x = -5$. Of course, solutions of $x = -5$ must have an x-value of -5. We will let $(x_1, y_1) = (-5, 0)$ and $(x_2, y_2) = (-5, 4)$.

Then

$$m = \frac{y_2 - y_1}{x_2 - x_1}$$

$$= \frac{4 - 0}{-5 - (-5)}$$

$$= \frac{4}{0}$$

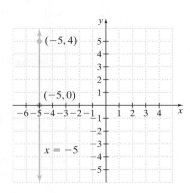

Since $\frac{4}{0}$ is undefined, we say that the slope of the vertical line $x = -5$ is undefined.   □

PRACTICE
6   Find the slope of the line $x = 4$.

EXAMPLE 7   Find the slope of the line $y = 2$.

Solution   Recall that the graph of $y = 2$ is a horizontal line with y-intercept $(0, 2)$. To find the slope, we find two points on the line, such as $(0, 2)$ and $(1, 2)$, and use these points to find the slope.

$$m = \frac{2 - 2}{1 - 0}$$

$$= \frac{0}{1}$$

$$= 0$$

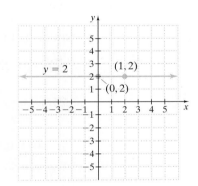

The slope of the horizontal line $y = 2$ is 0.   □

PRACTICE
7   Find the slope of the line $y = -3$.

From the previous two examples, we have the following generalization.

The slope of any vertical line is undefined.
The slope of any horizontal line is 0.

▶ Helpful Hint

Slope of 0 and undefined slope are not the same. Vertical lines have undefined slope, whereas horizontal lines have slope of 0.

The following four graphs summarize the overall appearance of lines with positive, negative, zero, or undefined slopes.

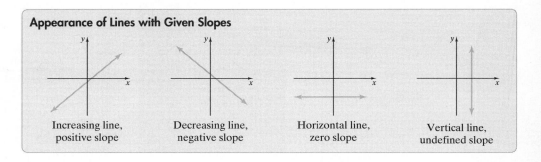

Appearance of Lines with Given Slopes

Increasing line, positive slope | Decreasing line, negative slope | Horizontal line, zero slope | Vertical line, undefined slope

The appearance of a line can give us further information about its slope.

The graphs of $y = \frac{1}{2}x + 1$ and $y = 5x + 1$ are shown to the right. Recall that the graph of $y = \frac{1}{2}x + 1$ has a slope of $\frac{1}{2}$ and that the graph of $y = 5x + 1$ has a slope of 5.

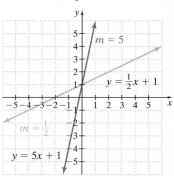

Notice that the line with the slope of 5 is steeper than the line with the slope of $\frac{1}{2}$. This is true in general for positive slopes.

For a line with positive slope m, as m increases, the line becomes steeper.

To see why this is so, compare the slopes from above.

$\frac{1}{2}$ means a vertical change of 1 unit per horizontal change of 2 units

5 or $\frac{10}{2}$ means a vertical change of 10 units per horizontal change of 2 units

For larger positive slopes, the vertical change is greater for the same horizontal change. Thus, larger positive slopes mean steeper lines.

OBJECTIVE 5 ▶ Comparing slopes of parallel and perpendicular lines. Slopes of lines can help us determine whether lines are parallel. Parallel lines are distinct lines with the same steepness, so it follows that they have the same slope.

Parallel Lines

Two nonvertical lines are parallel if they have the same slope and different y-intercepts.

Different y-intercepts

Same slope

How do the slopes of perpendicular lines compare? (Two lines intersecting at right angles are called **perpendicular lines.**) Suppose that a line has a slope of $\frac{a}{b}$. If the line is rotated 90°, the rise and run are now switched, except that the run is now negative. This means that the new slope is $-\dfrac{b}{a}$. Notice that

$$\left(\frac{a}{b}\right)\cdot\left(-\frac{b}{a}\right) = -1$$

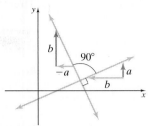

This is how we tell whether two lines are perpendicular.

Perpendicular Lines
Two nonvertical lines are perpendicular if the product of their slopes is −1.

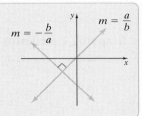

In other words, two nonvertical lines are perpendicular if the slope of one is the negative reciprocal of the slope of the other.

EXAMPLE 8   Are the following pairs of lines parallel, perpendicular, or neither?

a. $3x + 7y = 4$
  $6x + 14y = 7$

b. $-x + 3y = 2$
  $2x + 6y = 5$

Solution   Find the slope of each line by solving each equation for y.

a.

$3x + 7y = 4$	$6x + 14y = 7$
$7y = -3x + 4$	$14y = -6x + 7$
$\dfrac{7y}{7} = \dfrac{-3x}{7} + \dfrac{4}{7}$	$\dfrac{14y}{14} = \dfrac{-6x}{14} + \dfrac{7}{14}$
$y = -\dfrac{3}{7}x + \dfrac{4}{7}$	$y = -\dfrac{3}{7}x + \dfrac{1}{2}$

slope y-intercept   slope y-intercept
$\left(0, \dfrac{4}{7}\right)$ $\left(0, \dfrac{1}{2}\right)$

The slopes of both lines are $-\dfrac{3}{7}$.

The y-intercepts are different, so the lines are not the same.

Therefore, the lines are parallel.

b.

$-x + 3y = 2$	$2x + 6y = 5$
$3y = x + 2$	$6y = -2x + 5$
$\dfrac{3y}{3} = \dfrac{x}{3} + \dfrac{2}{3}$	$\dfrac{6y}{6} = \dfrac{-2x}{6} + \dfrac{5}{6}$
$y = \dfrac{1}{3}x + \dfrac{2}{3}$	$y = -\dfrac{1}{3}x + \dfrac{5}{6}$

slope y-intercept   slope y-intercept
$\left(0, \dfrac{2}{3}\right)$ $\left(0, \dfrac{5}{6}\right)$

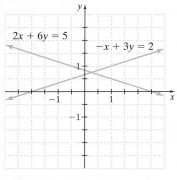

$2x + 6y = 5$

$-x + 3y = 2$

The slopes are not the same and their product is not -1. $\left[\left(\dfrac{1}{3}\right) \cdot \left(-\dfrac{1}{3}\right) = -\dfrac{1}{9}\right]$

Therefore, the lines are neither parallel nor perpendicular.

PRACTICE

8   Are the following pairs of lines parallel, perpendicular, or neither?

a. $x - 2y = 3$ **b.** $4x - 3y = 2$

    $2x + y = 3$ $-8x + 6y = -6$

Concept Check ✓

What is *different* about the equations of two parallel lines?

Answer to Concept Check:
y-intercepts are different

Graphing Calculator Explorations

Many graphing calculators have a TRACE feature. This feature allows you to trace along a graph and see the corresponding *x*- and *y*-coordinates appear on the screen. Use this feature for the following exercises.

Graph each function and then use the TRACE feature to complete each ordered pair solution. (Many times the tracer will not show an exact *x*- or *y*-value asked for. In each case, trace as closely as you can to the given *x*- or *y*-coordinate and approximate the other, unknown coordinate to one decimal place.)

1. $y = 2.3x + 6.7$
    $x = 5.1,\ y = ?$

2. $y = -4.8x + 2.9$
    $x = -1.8,\ y = ?$

3. $y = -5.9x - 1.6$
    $x = ?,\ y = 7.2$

4. $y = 0.4x - 8.6$
    $x = ?,\ y = -4.4$

5. $y = x^2 + 5.2x - 3.3$
    $x = 2.3,\ y = ?$
    $x = ?,\ y = 36$
    (There will be two answers here.)

6. $y = 5x^2 - 6.2x - 8.3$
    $x = 3.2,\ y = ?$
    $x = ?,\ y = 12$
    (There will be two answers here.)

VOCABULARY & READINESS CHECK

Use the choices below to fill in each blank. Some choices may be used more than once and some not at all.

horizontal	the same	-1	*y*-intercepts	$(0, b)$	slope
vertical	different	*m*	*x*-intercepts	$(b, 0)$	slope-intercept

1. The measure of the steepness or tilt of a line is called _____.

2. The slope of a line through two points is measured by the ratio of _____ change to _____ change.

3. If a linear equation is in the form $y = mx + b$, or $f(x) = mx + b$, the slope of the line is _____ and the *y*-intercept is _____.

4. The form $y = mx + b$ or $f(x) = mx + b$ is the _____ form.

5. The slope of a _____ line is 0.

6. The slope of a _____ line is undefined.

7. Two non-vertical perpendicular lines have slopes whose product is _____.

8. Two non-vertical lines are parallel if they have _____ slope and different _____.

Decide whether a line with the given slope slants upward or downward from left to right, or is horizontal or vertical.

9. $m = \dfrac{7}{6}$ **10.** $m = -3$ **11.** $m = 0$ **12.** *m* is undefined

3.4 EXERCISE SET

MyMathLab   PRACTICE   WATCH   DOWNLOAD   READ   REVIEW

Find the slope of the line that goes through the given points. See Examples 1 and 2.

1. $(3, 2), (8, 11)$

2. $(1, 6), (7, 11)$

3. $(3, 1), (1, 8)$

4. $(2, 9), (6, 4)$

5. $(-2, 8), (4, 3)$

6. $(3, 7), (-2, 11)$

7. $(-2, -6), (4, -4)$

8. $(-3, -4), (-1, 6)$

9. $(-3, -1), (-12, 11)$

10. $(3, -1), (-6, 5)$

11. $(-2, 5), (3, 5)$

12. $(4, 2), (4, 0)$

13. $(-1, 1), (-1, -5)$

14. $(-2, -5), (3, -5)$

15. $(0, 6), (-3, 0)$

16. $(5, 2), (0, 5)$

17. $(-1, 2), (-3, 4)$

18. $(3, -2), (-1, -6)$

Two lines are graphed on each set of axes. Decide whether l_1 or l_2 has the greater slope. See the boxed material on page 160.

19.

20.

21.

22.

23.

24.
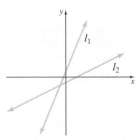

Find the slope and the y-intercept of each line. See Examples 3 and 4.

25. $f(x) = 5x - 2$

26. $f(x) = -2x + 6$

27. $2x + y = 7$

28. $-5x + y = 10$

29. $2x - 3y = 10$

30. $-3x - 4y = 6$

31. $f(x) = \dfrac{1}{2}x$

32. $f(x) = -\dfrac{1}{4}x$

Match each graph with its equation. See Examples 1 and 2.

A

B

C

D
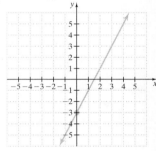

33. $f(x) = 2x + 3$

34. $f(x) = 2x - 3$

35. $f(x) = -2x + 3$

36. $f(x) = -2x - 3$

Find the slope of each line. See Examples 6 and 7.

37. $x = 1$

38. $y = -2$

39. $y = -3$

40. $x = 4$

41. $x + 2 = 0$

42. $y - 7 = 0$

43. Explain how merely looking at a line can tell us whether its slope is negative, positive, undefined, or zero.

44. Explain why the graph of $y = b$ is a horizontal line.

MIXED PRACTICE

Find the slope and the y-intercept of each line. See Examples 3 through 7.

45. $f(x) = -x + 5$

46. $f(x) = x + 2$

47. $-6x + 5y = 30$

48. $4x - 7y = 28$

49. $3x + 9 = y$

50. $2y - 7 = x$

51. $y = 4$

52. $x = 7$

53. $f(x) = 7x$

54. $f(x) = \dfrac{1}{7}x$

55. $6 + y = 0$

56. $x - 7 = 0$

57. $2 - x = 3$

58. $2y + 4 = -7$

Determine whether the lines are parallel, perpendicular, or neither. See Example 8.

△ **59.** $f(x) = -3x + 6$
$g(x) = 3x + 5$

△ **60.** $f(x) = 5x - 6$
$g(x) = 5x + 2$

△ **61.** $-4x + 2y = 5$
$2x - y = 7$

△ **62.** $2x - y = -10$
$2x + 4y = 2$

△ **63.** $-2x + 3y = 1$
$3x + 2y = 12$

△ **64.** $x + 4y = 7$
$2x - 5y = 0$

65. Explain whether two lines, both with positive slopes, can be perpendicular.

66. Explain why it is reasonable that nonvertical parallel lines have the same slope.

Use the points shown on the graphs to determine the slope of each line. See Examples 1 and 2.

67.

68.

69.

70.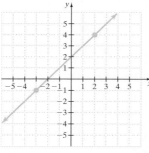

Find each slope. See Examples 1 and 2.

71. Find the pitch, or slope, of the roof shown.

8 ft
12 ft

72. Upon takeoff, a Delta Airlines jet climbs to 3 miles as it passes over 25 miles of land below it. Find the slope of its climb.

3 mi
25 mi

73. Driving down Bald Mountain in Wyoming, Bob Dean finds that he descends 1600 feet in elevation by the time he is 2.5 miles (horizontally) away from the high point on the mountain road. Find the slope of his descent rounded to two decimal places (1 mile = 5280 feet).

74. Find the grade, or slope, of the road shown.

15 ft
100 ft

Solve. See Example 5.

75. The annual average income y of an American man over 25 with an associate's degree is approximated by the linear equation $y = 694.9x + 43,884.9$, where x is the number of years after 2000. (*Source:* Based on data from the U.S. Bureau of the Census).

a. Predict the average income of an American man with an associate's degree in 2009.

b. Find and interpret the slope of the equation.

c. Find and interpret the y-intercept of the equation.

76. The annual average income of an American woman over 25 with a bachelor's degree is given by the linear equation $y = 1059.6x + 36,827.4$, where x is the number of years after 2000. (*Source:* Based on data from the U.S. Bureau of the Census).

a. Find the average income of an American woman with a bachelor's degree in 2009.

b. Find and interpret the slope of the equation.

c. Find and interpret the y-intercept of the equation.

77. With wireless Internet (WiFi) gaining popularity, the number of public wireless Internet access points (in thousands) is projected to grow from 2003 to 2008 according to the equation

$$-66x + 2y = 84$$

where x is the number of years after 2003.

a. Find the slope and *y*-intercept of the linear equation.

b. What does the slope mean in this context?

c. What does the *y*-intercept mean in this context?

78. One of the faster growing occupations over the next few years is expected to be nursing. The number of people *y* in thousands employed in nursing in the United States can be estimated by the linear equation $-266x + 10y = 27{,}409$, where *x* is the number of years after 2000. (*Source:* Based on data from American Nurses Association)

a. Find the slope and *y*-intercept of the linear equation.

b. What does the slope mean in this context?

c. What does the *y*-intercept mean in this context?

79. In an earlier section, it was given that the yearly cost of tuition and required fees for attending a public four-year college full-time can be estimated by the linear function

$$f(x) = 291.5x + 2944.05$$

where *x* is the number of years after 2000 and $f(x)$ is the total cost. (*Source:* U.S. National Center for Education Statistics)

a. Find and interpret the slope of this equation.

b. Find and interpret the *y*-intercept of this equation.

80. In an earlier section, it was given that the yearly cost of tuition and required fees for attending a public two-year college full-time can be estimated by the linear function

$$f(x) = 107.3x + 1245.62$$

where *x* is the number of years after 2000 and $f(x)$ is the total cost. (*Source:* U.S. National Center for Education Statistics)

a. Find and interpret the slope of this equation.

b. Find and interpret the *y*-intercept of this equation.

REVIEW AND PREVIEW

Simplify and solve for y. See Section 2.3.

81. $y - 2 = 5(x + 6)$

82. $y - 0 = -3[x - (-10)]$

83. $y - (-1) = 2(x - 0)$

84. $y - 9 = -8[x - (-4)]$

CONCEPT EXTENSIONS

Each slope calculation is incorrect. Find the error and correct the calculation. See the Concept Check in this section.

85. $(-2, 6)$ and $(7, -14)$

$$m = \frac{-14 \cancel{- 6}}{7 \cancel{- 2}} = \frac{-20}{5} = -4$$

86. $(-1, 4)$ and $(-3, 9)$

$$m = \frac{9 \cancel{- 4}}{-3 \cancel{- 1}} = \frac{5}{-4} \text{ or } -\frac{5}{4}$$

87. $(-8, -10)$ and $(-11, -5)$

$$m = \frac{-10 \cancel{- 5}}{-8 \cancel{- 11}} = \frac{-15}{-19} = \frac{15}{19}$$

88. $(0, -4)$ and $(-6, -6)$

$$m = \frac{0 \cancel{- (-6)}}{-4 \cancel{- (-6)}} = \frac{6}{2} = 3$$

89. Find the slope of a line parallel to the line $f(x) = -\frac{7}{2}x - 6$.

△ **90.** Find the slope of a line parallel to the line $f(x) = x$.

△ **91.** Find the slope of a line perpendicular to the line

$$f(x) = -\frac{7}{2}x - 6.$$

△ **92.** Find the slope of a line perpendicular to the line $f(x) = x$.

△ **93.** Find the slope of a line parallel to the line $5x - 2y = 6$.

△ **94.** Find the slope of a line parallel to the line $-3x + 4y = 10$.

△ **95.** Find the slope of a line perpendicular to the line $5x - 2y = 6$.

96. Each line below has negative slope.

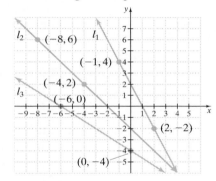

a. Find the slope of each line.

b. Use the result of Part **a** to fill in the blank. For lines with negative slopes, the steeper line has the _____ (greater/lesser) slope.

97. The following graph shows the altitude of a seagull in flight over a time period of 30 seconds.

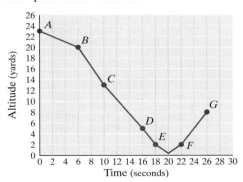

a. Find the coordinates of point *B*.

b. Find the coordinates of point *C*.

c. Find the rate of change of altitude between points *B* and *C*. (Recall that the rate of change between points is the slope between points. This rate of change will be in yards per second.)

    d. Find the rate of change of altitude (in yards per second) between points F and G.

98. Professional plumbers suggest that a sewer pipe should be sloped 0.25 inch for every foot. Find the recommended slope for a sewer pipe. (*Source: Rules of Thumb* by Tom Parker, 1983, Houghton Mifflin Company)

99. Support the result of Exercise 61 by graphing the pair of equations on a graphing calculator.

100. Support the result of Exercise 62 by graphing the pair of equations on a graphing calculator. (*Hint:* Use the window showing $[-15, 15]$ on the x-axis and $[-10, 10]$ on the y-axis.)

101. a. On a single screen, graph $y = \frac{1}{2}x + 1$, $y = x + 1$ and $y = 2x + 1$. Notice the change in slope for each graph.

    b. On a single screen, graph $y = -\frac{1}{2}x + 1$, $y = -x + 1$ and $y = -2x + 1$. Notice the change in slope for each graph.

    c. Determine whether the following statement is true or false for slope m of a given line. As $|m|$ becomes greater, the line becomes steeper.

3.5 EQUATIONS OF LINES

OBJECTIVES

1. Use the slope–intercept form to write the equation of a line.

2. Graph a line using its slope and y-intercept.

3. Use the point–slope form to write the equation of a line.

4. Write equations of vertical and horizontal lines.

5. Find equations of parallel and perpendicular lines.

OBJECTIVE 1 ▶ Using slope-intercept form to write equations of lines. In the last section, we learned that the slope–intercept form of a linear equation is $y = mx + b$. When a linear equation is written in this form, the slope of the line is the same as the coefficient m of x. Also, the y-intercept of the line is $(0, b)$. For example, the slope of the line defined by $y = 2x + 3$ is, 2, and its y-intercept is $(0, 3)$.

    We may also use the slope–intercept form to write the equation of a line given its slope and y-intercept. The equation of a line is a linear equation in 2 variables that, if graphed, would produce the line described.

EXAMPLE 1 Write an equation of the line with y-intercept $(0, -3)$ and slope of $\frac{1}{4}$.

Solution We want to write a linear equation in 2 variables that describes the line with y-intercept $(0, -3)$ and has a slope of $\frac{1}{4}$. We are given the slope and the y-intercept. Let $m = \frac{1}{4}$ and $b = -3$, and write the equation in slope–intercept form, $y = mx + b$.

$$y = mx + b$$
$$y = \frac{1}{4}x + (-3) \quad \text{Let } m = \frac{1}{4} \text{ and } b = -3.$$
$$y = \frac{1}{4}x - 3 \quad \text{Simplify.} \qquad \square$$

PRACTICE

1 Write an equation of the line with y-intercept $(0, 4)$ and slope of $-\frac{3}{4}$.

Concept Check ☑

What is wrong with the following equation of a line with y-intercept $(0, 4)$ and slope 2?

$$y = 4x + 2$$

Answer to Concept Check:
y-intercept and slope were switched, should be $y = 2x + 4$

OBJECTIVE 2 ▶ Graph a line using slope and y-intercept. Given the slope and y-intercept of a line, we may graph the line as well as write its equation. Let's graph the line from Example 1.

EXAMPLE 2   Graph $y = \frac{1}{4}x - 3$.

Solution   Recall that the slope of the graph of $y = \frac{1}{4}x - 3$ is $\frac{1}{4}$ and the y-intercept is $(0, -3)$. To graph the line, we first plot the y-intercept $(0, -3)$. To find another point on the line, we recall that slope is $\frac{\text{rise}}{\text{run}} = \frac{1}{4}$. Another point may then be plotted by starting at $(0, -3)$, rising 1 unit up, and then running 4 units to the right. We are now at the point $(4, -2)$. The graph is the line through these two points.

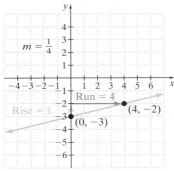

Notice that the line does have a y-intercept of $(0, -3)$ and a slope of $\frac{1}{4}$.   □

PRACTICE
2   Graph $y = \frac{3}{4}x + 2$.

EXAMPLE 3   Graph $2x + 3y = 12$.

Solution   First, we solve the equation for y to write it in slope–intercept form. In slope–intercept form, the equation is $y = -\frac{2}{3}x + 4$. Next we plot the y-intercept $(0, 4)$. To find another point on the line, we use the slope $-\frac{2}{3}$, which can be written as $\frac{\text{rise}}{\text{run}} = \frac{-2}{3}$. We start at $(0, 4)$ and move down 2 units since the numerator of the slope is -2; then we move 3 units to the right since the denominator of the slope is 3. We arrive at the point $(3, 2)$. The line through these points is the graph, shown below to the left.

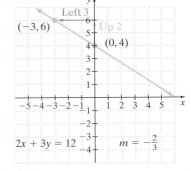

The slope $\frac{-2}{3}$ can also be written as $\frac{2}{-3}$, so to find another point in Example 3 we could start at $(0, 4)$ and move up 2 units and then 3 units to the left. We would arrive at the point $(-3, 6)$. The line through $(-3, 6)$ and $(0, 4)$ is the same line as shown previously through $(3, 2)$ and $(0, 4)$. See the graph above to the right.   □

PRACTICE
3   Graph $x + 2y = 6$.

OBJECTIVE 3 ▶ Using point-slope form to write equations of lines. When the slope of a line and a point on the line are known, the equation of the line can also be found. To do this, use the slope formula to write the slope of a line that passes through points (x_1, y_1) and (x, y). We have

$$m = \frac{y - y_1}{x - x_1}$$

Multiply both sides of this equation by $x - x_1$ to obtain

$$y - y_1 = m(x - x_1)$$

This form is called the **point–slope form** of the equation of a line.

Point-Slope Form of the Equation of a Line
The **point-slope form** of the equation of a line is

slope
↓
$$y - y_1 = m(x - x_1)$$
└─point─┘

where m is the slope of the line and (x_1, y_1) is a point on the line.

EXAMPLE 4 Find an equation of the line with slope -3 containing the point $(1, -5)$. Write the equation in slope–intercept form $y = mx + b$.

Solution Because we know the slope and a point of the line, we use the point–slope form with $m = -3$ and $(x_1, y_1) = (1, -5)$.

$$\begin{aligned}
y - y_1 &= m(x - x_1) &&\text{Point-slope form} \\
y - (-5) &= -3(x - 1) &&\text{Let } m = -3 \text{ and } (x_1, y_1) = (1, -5). \\
y + 5 &= -3x + 3 &&\text{Apply the distributive property.} \\
y &= -3x - 2 &&\text{Write in slope-intercept form.}
\end{aligned}$$

In slope–intercept form, the equation is $y = -3x - 2$. □

PRACTICE
4 Find an equation of the line with slope -4 containing the point $(-2, 5)$. Write the equation in slope-intercept form $y = mx + b$.

▶ **Helpful Hint**
Remember, "slope-intercept form" means the equation is "solved for y."

EXAMPLE 5 Find an equation of the line through points $(4, 0)$ and $(-4, -5)$. Write the equation using function notation.

Solution First, find the slope of the line.

$$m = \frac{-5 - 0}{-4 - 4} = \frac{-5}{-8} = \frac{5}{8}$$

Next, make use of the point–slope form. Replace (x_1, y_1) by either $(4, 0)$ or $(-4, -5)$ in the point–slope equation. We will choose the point $(4, 0)$. The line through $(4, 0)$ with

slope $\dfrac{5}{8}$ is

$$y - y_1 = m(x - x_1) \quad \text{Point–slope form.}$$

$$y - 0 = \frac{5}{8}(x - 4) \quad \text{Let } m = \frac{5}{8} \text{ and } (x_1, y_1) = (4, 0).$$

$$8y = 5(x - 4) \quad \text{Multiply both sides by 8.}$$

$$8y = 5x - 20 \quad \text{Apply the distributive property.}$$

To write the equation using function notation, we solve for y, then replace y with $f(x)$.

$$8y = 5x - 20$$

$$y = \frac{5}{8}x - \frac{20}{8} \quad \text{Divide both sides by 8.}$$

$$f(x) = \frac{5}{8}x - \frac{5}{2} \quad \text{Write using function notation.} \qquad \square$$

PRACTICE
5   Find an equation of the line through points $(-1, 2)$ and $(2, 0)$. Write the equation using function notation.

> ▶ **Helpful Hint**
> If two points of a line are given, either one may be used with the point-slope form to write an equation of the line.

EXAMPLE 6   Find an equation of the line graphed. Write the equation in standard form.

Solution   First, find the slope of the line by identifying the coordinates of the noted points on the graph.
The points have coordinates $(-1, 2)$ and $(3, 5)$.

$$m = \frac{5 - 2}{3 - (-1)} = \frac{3}{4}$$

Next, use the point-slope form. We will choose $(3, 5)$ for (x_1, y_1), although it makes no difference which point we choose. The line through $(3, 5)$ with slope $\dfrac{3}{4}$ is

$$y - y_1 = m(x - x_1) \quad \text{Point-slope form}$$

$$y - 5 = \frac{3}{4}(x - 3) \quad \text{Let } m = \frac{3}{4} \text{ and } (x_1, y_1) = (3, 5).$$

$$4(y - 5) = 3(x - 3) \quad \text{Multiply both sides by 4.}$$

$$4y - 20 = 3x - 9 \quad \text{Apply the distributive property.}$$

To write the equation in standard form, move x- and y-terms to one side of the equation and any numbers (constants) to the other side.

$$4y - 20 = 3x - 9$$

$$-3x + 4y = 11 \quad \text{Subtract } 3x \text{ from both sides and add 20 to both sides.}$$

The equation of the graphed line is $-3x + 4y = 11$. $\qquad \square$

PRACTICE
6   Find an equation of the line graphed. Write the equation in standard form.

The point–slope form of an equation is very useful for solving real-world problems.

EXAMPLE 7 Predicting Sales

Southern Star Realty is an established real estate company that has enjoyed constant growth in sales since 2000. In 2002 the company sold 200 houses, and in 2007 the company sold 275 houses. Use these figures to predict the number of houses this company will sell in the year 2016.

Solution

1. UNDERSTAND. Read and reread the problem. Then let

   x = the number of years after 2000 and

   y = the number of houses sold in the year corresponding to x.

   The information provided then gives the ordered pairs $(2, 200)$ and $(7, 275)$. To better visualize the sales of Southern Star Realty, we graph the linear equation that passes through the points $(2, 200)$ and $(7, 275)$.

 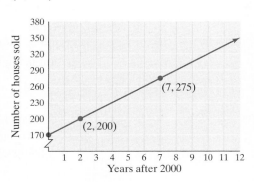

2. TRANSLATE. We write a linear equation that passes through the points $(2, 200)$ and $(7, 275)$. To do so, we first find the slope of the line.

$$m = \frac{275 - 200}{7 - 2} = \frac{75}{5} = 15$$

Then, using the point–slope form and the point $(2, 200)$ to write the equation, we have

$$y - y_1 = m(x - x_1)$$

$$y - 200 = 15(x - 2) \quad \text{Let } m = 15 \text{ and } (x_1, y_1) = (2, 200).$$

$$y - 200 = 15x - 30 \quad \text{Multiply.}$$

$$y = 15x + 170 \quad \text{Add 200 to both sides.}$$

3. SOLVE. To predict the number of houses sold in the year 2016, we use $y = 15x + 170$ and complete the ordered pair $(16, \ )$, since $2016 - 2000 = 16$.

$$y = 15(16) + 170 \quad \text{Let } x = 16.$$

$$y = 410$$

4. INTERPRET.

Check: Verify that the point $(16, 410)$ is a point on the line graphed in step 1.

State: Southern Star Realty should expect to sell 410 houses in the year 2016. □

PRACTICE

7 Southwest Florida, including Fort Myers and Cape Coral, has been a growing real estate market in past years. In 2002, there were 7513 house sales in the area, and in 2006, there were 9198 house sales. Use these figures to predict the number of house sales there will be in 2014.

OBJECTIVE 4 ▶ Writing equations of vertical and horizontal lines. A few special types of linear equations are linear equations whose graphs are vertical and horizontal lines.

> **EXAMPLE 8** Find an equation of the horizontal line containing the point $(2, 3)$.
>
> *Solution* Recall that a horizontal line has an equation of the form $y = b$. Since the line contains the point $(2, 3)$, the equation is $y = 3$, as shown to the right.

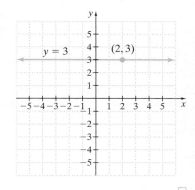

> **PRACTICE**
> **8** Find the equation of the horizontal line containing the point $(6, -2)$.

> **EXAMPLE 9** Find an equation of the line containing the point $(2, 3)$ with undefined slope.
>
> *Solution* Since the line has undefined slope, the line must be vertical. A vertical line has an equation of the form $x = c$. Since the line contains the point $(2, 3)$, the equation is $x = 2$, as shown to the right.

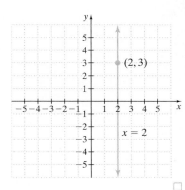

> **PRACTICE**
> **9** Find an equation of the line containing the point $(6, -2)$ with undefined slope.

OBJECTIVE 5 ▶ Finding equations of parallel and perpendicular lines. Next, we find equations of parallel and perpendicular lines.

> △ **EXAMPLE 10** Find an equation of the line containing the point $(4, 4)$ and parallel to the line $2x + 3y = -6$. Write the equation in standard form.
>
> *Solution* Because the line we want to find is *parallel* to the line $2x + 3y = -6$, the two lines must have equal slopes. Find the slope of $2x + 3y = -6$ by writing it in the form $y = mx + b$. In other words, solve the equation for y.
>
> $$2x + 3y = -6$$
>
> $$3y = -2x - 6 \qquad \text{Subtract } 2x \text{ from both sides.}$$
>
> $$y = \frac{-2x}{3} - \frac{6}{3} \qquad \text{Divide by 3.}$$
>
> $$y = -\frac{2}{3}x - 2 \qquad \text{Write in slope-intercept form.}$$

The slope of this line is $-\dfrac{2}{3}$. Thus, a line parallel to this line will also have a slope of $-\dfrac{2}{3}$. The equation we are asked to find describes a line containing the point $(4, 4)$ with a slope of $-\dfrac{2}{3}$. We use the point-slope form.

$$y - y_1 = m(x - x_1)$$

$$y - 4 = -\frac{2}{3}(x - 4) \quad \text{Let } m = -\frac{2}{3}, x_1 = 4, \text{ and } y_1 = 4.$$

$$3(y - 4) = -2(x - 4) \quad \text{Multiply both sides by 3.}$$

$$3y - 12 = -2x + 8 \quad \text{Apply the distributive property.}$$

$$2x + 3y = 20 \quad \text{Write in standard form.} \qquad \square$$

> ▶ **Helpful Hint**
> Multiply both sides of the equation $2x + 3y = 20$ by -1 and it becomes $-2x - 3y = -20$. Both equations are in standard form, and their graphs are the same line.

PRACTICE

10 Find an equation of the line containing the point $(8, -3)$ and parallel to the line $3x + 4y = 1$. Write the equation in standard form.

EXAMPLE 11 Write a function that describes the line containing the point $(4, 4)$ and is perpendicular to the line $2x + 3y = -6$.

Solution In the previous example, we found that the slope of the line $2x + 3y = -6$ is $-\dfrac{2}{3}$. A line perpendicular to this line will have a slope that is the negative reciprocal of $-\dfrac{2}{3}$, or $\dfrac{3}{2}$. From the point-slope equation, we have

$$y - y_1 = m(x - x_1)$$

$$y - 4 = \frac{3}{2}(x - 4) \quad \text{Let } x_1 = 4, y_1 = 4 \text{ and } m = \frac{3}{2}.$$

$$2(y - 4) = 3(x - 4) \quad \text{Multiply both sides by 2.}$$

$$2y - 8 = 3x - 12 \quad \text{Apply the distributive property.}$$

$$2y = 3x - 4 \quad \text{Add 8 to both sides.}$$

$$y = \frac{3}{2}x - 2 \quad \text{Divide both sides by 2.}$$

$$f(x) = \frac{3}{2}x - 2 \quad \text{Write using function notation.} \qquad \square$$

PRACTICE

11 Write a function that describes the line containing the point $(8, -3)$ and is perpendicular to the line $3x + 4y = 1$.

Forms of Linear Equations

$Ax + By = C$	**Standard form** of a linear equation A and B are not both 0.
$y = mx + b$	**Slope–intercept form** of a linear equation The slope is m, and the y-intercept is $(0, b)$.
$y - y_1 = m(x - x_1)$	**Point–slope form** of a linear equation The slope is m, and (x_1, y_1) is a point on the line.
$y = c$	**Horizontal line** The slope is 0, and the y-intercept is $(0, c)$.
$x = c$	**Vertical line** The slope is undefined and the x-intercept is $(c, 0)$.

Parallel and Perpendicular Lines

Nonvertical parallel lines have the same slope. The product of the slopes of two nonvertical perpendicular lines is -1.

VOCABULARY & READINESS CHECK

State the slope and the y-intercept of each line with the given equation.

1. $y = -4x + 12$

2. $y = \frac{2}{3}x - \frac{7}{2}$

3. $y = 5x$

4. $y = -x$

5. $y = \frac{1}{2}x + 6$

6. $y = -\frac{2}{3}x + 5$

Decide whether the lines are parallel, perpendicular, or neither.

7. $y = 12x + 6$
     $y = 12x - 2$

8. $y = -5x + 8$
     $y = -5x - 8$

9. $y = -9x + 3$
     $y = \frac{3}{2}x - 7$

10. $y = 2x - 12$
      $y = \frac{1}{2}x - 6$

3.5 | EXERCISE SET

MyMathLab *Powered by CourseCompass™ and MathXL®*   MathⓍP PRACTICE   WATCH   DOWNLOAD   READ   REVIEW

Use the slope-intercept form of the linear equation to write the equation of each line with the given slope and y-intercept. See Example 1.

1. Slope -1; y-intercept $(0, 1)$

2. Slope $\frac{1}{2}$; y-intercept $(0, -6)$

3. Slope 2; y-intercept $\left(0, \frac{3}{4}\right)$

4. Slope -3;   y-intercept $\left(0, -\frac{1}{5}\right)$

5. Slope $\frac{2}{7}$; y-intercept $(0, 0)$

6. Slope $-\frac{4}{5}$; y-intercept $(0, 0)$

Graph each linear equation. See Examples 2 and 3.

7. $y = 5x - 2$

8. $y = 2x + 1$

9. $4x + y = 7$

10. $3x + y = 9$

11. $-3x + 2y = 3$

12. $-2x + 5y = -16$

Find an equation of the line with the given slope and containing the given point. Write the equation in slope-intercept form. See Example 4.

13. Slope 3; through $(1, 2)$

14. Slope 4; through $(5, 1)$

15. Slope -2; through $(1, -3)$

16. Slope -4; through $(2, -4)$

17. Slope $\frac{1}{2}$; through $(-6, 2)$

18. Slope $\frac{2}{3}$; through $(-9, 4)$

19. Slope $-\frac{9}{10}$; through $(-3, 0)$

20. Slope $-\frac{1}{5}$; through $(4, -6)$

Find an equation of the line passing through the given points. Use function notation to write the equation. See Example 5.

21. $(2, 0), (4, 6)$

22. $(3, 0), (7, 8)$

23. $(-2, 5), (-6, 13)$

24. $(7, -4), (2, 6)$

25. $(-2, -4), (-4, -3)$

26. $(-9, -2), (-3, 10)$

27. $(-3, -8), (-6, -9)$

28. $(8, -3), (4, -8)$

29. $\left(\frac{3}{5}, \frac{4}{10}\right)$ and $\left(-\frac{1}{5}, \frac{7}{10}\right)$

30. $\left(\frac{1}{2}, -\frac{1}{4}\right)$ and $\left(\frac{3}{2}, \frac{3}{4}\right)$

Find an equation of each line graphed. Write the equation in standard form. See Example 6.

31.

32.

33.

34.

Use the graph of the following function f(x) to find each value.

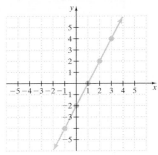

35. $f(0)$

36. $f(-1)$

37. $f(2)$

38. $f(1)$

39. Find x such that $f(x) = -6$.

40. Find x such that $f(x) = 4$.

Write an equation of each line. See Examples 8 and 9.

41. Slope 0; through $(-2, -4)$

42. Horizontal; through $(-3, 1)$

43. Vertical; through $(4, 7)$

44. Vertical; through $(2, 6)$

45. Horizontal; through $(0, 5)$

46. Undefined slope; through $(0, 5)$

Find an equation of each line. Write the equation using function notation. See Examples 10 and 11.

47. Through $(3, 8)$; parallel to $f(x) = 4x - 2$

48. Through $(1, 5)$; parallel to $f(x) = 3x - 4$

49. Through $(2, -5)$; perpendicular to $3y = x - 6$

50. Through $(-4, 8)$; perpendicular to $2x - 3y = 1$

51. Through $(-2, -3)$; parallel to $3x + 2y = 5$

52. Through $(-2, -3)$; perpendicular to $3x + 2y = 5$

MIXED PRACTICE

Find the equation of each line. Write the equation in standard form unless indicated otherwise. See Examples 1, 4, 5 and 8 through 11.

53. Slope 2; through $(-2, 3)$

54. Slope 3; through $(-4, 2)$

55. Through $(1, 6)$ and $(5, 2)$; use function notation.

56. Through $(2, 9)$ and $(8, 6)$

57. With slope $-\frac{1}{2}$; y-intercept 11

58. With slope -4; y-intercept $\frac{2}{9}$; use function notation.

59. Through $(-7, -4)$ and $(0, -6)$

60. Through $(2, -8)$ and $(-4, -3)$

61. Slope $-\frac{4}{3}$; through $(-5, 0)$

62. Slope $-\frac{3}{5}$; through $(4, -1)$

63. Vertical line; through $(-2, -10)$

64. Horizontal line; through $(1, 0)$

65. Through $(6, -2)$; parallel to the line $2x + 4y = 9$

66. Through $(8, -3)$; parallel to the line $6x + 2y = 5$

67. Slope 0; through $(-9, 12)$

68. Undefined slope; through $(10, -8)$

69. Through $(6, 1)$; parallel to the line $8x - y = 9$

70. Through $(3, 5)$; perpendicular to the line $2x - y = 8$

71. Through $(5, -6)$; perpendicular to $y = 9$

72. Through $(-3, -5)$; parallel to $y = 9$

73. Through $(2, -8)$ and $(-6, -5)$; use function notation.

74. Through $(-4, -2)$ and $(-6, 5)$; use function notation.

Solve. See Example 7.

75. Del Monte Fruit Company recently released a new applesauce. By the end of its first year, profits on this product amounted to \$30,000. The anticipated profit for the end of the fourth year is \$66,000. The ratio of change in time to change in profit is constant. Let x be years and P be profit.

   a. Write a linear function $P(x)$ that expresses profit as a function of time.

   b. Use this function to predict the company's profit at the end of the seventh year.

   c. Predict when the profit should reach \$126,000.

76. The value of a computer bought in 2003 depreciates, or decreases, as time passes. Two years after the computer was bought, it was worth \$2000; 4 years after it was bought, it was worth \$800.

   a. If this relationship between number of years past 2003 and value of computer is linear, write an equation describing this relationship. [Use ordered pairs of the form (years past 2003, value of computer).]

   b. Use this equation to estimate the value of the computer in the year 2008.

77. The Pool Fun Company has learned that, by pricing a newly released Fun Noodle at \$3, sales will reach 10,000 Fun Noodles per day during the summer. Raising the price to \$5 will cause the sales to fall to 8000 Fun Noodles per day.

   a. Assume that the relationship between sales price and number of Fun Noodles sold is linear and write an equation describing this relationship.

   b. Predict the daily sales of Fun Noodles if the price is \$3.50.

78. The value of a building bought in 1990 appreciates, or increases, as time passes. Seven years after the building was bought, it was worth \$165,000; 12 years after it was bought, it was worth \$180,000.

   a. If this relationship between number of years past 1990 and value of building is linear, write an equation describing this relationship. [Use ordered pairs of the form (years past 1990, value of building).]

   b. Use this equation to estimate the value of the building in the year 2010.

79. In 2006, the median price of an existing home in the United States was approximately \$222,000. In 2001, the median price of an existing home was \$150,900. Let y be the median price of an existing home in the year x, where $x = 0$ represents 2001. (*Source:* National Association of REALTORS®)

   a. Write a linear equation that models the median existing home price in terms of the year x. [*Hint:* The line must pass through the points $(0, 150,900)$ and $(5, 222,000)$.]

b. Use this equation to predict the median existing home price for the year 2010.

c. Interpret the slope of the equation found in part **a.**

80. The number of births (in thousands) in the United States in 2000 was 4060. The number of births (in thousands) in the United States in 2004 was 4116. Let y be the number of births (in thousands) in the year x, where $x = 0$ represents 2000. (*Source:* National Center for Health Statistics)

a. Write a linear equation that models the number of births (in thousands) in terms of the year x. (See hint for Exercise 79a.)

b. Use this equation to predict the number of births in the United States for the year 2013.

c. Interpret the slope of the equation in part a.

81. The number of people employed in the United States as medical assistants was 387 thousand in 2004. By the year 2014, this number is expected to rise to 589 thousand. Let y be the number of medical assistants (in thousands) employed in the United States in the year x, where $x = 0$ represents 2004. (*Source:* Bureau of Labor Statistics)

a. Write a linear equation that models the number of people (in thousands) employed as medical assistants in the year x. (See hint for Exercise 79a.)

b. Use this equation to estimate the number of people who will be employed as medical assistants in the year 2013.

82. The number of people employed in the United States as systems analysts was 487 thousand in 2004. By the year 2014, this number is expected to rise to 640 thousand. Let y be the number of systems analysts (in thousands) employed in the United States in the year x, where $x = 0$ represents 2004. (*Source:* Bureau of Labor Statistics)

a. Write a linear equation that models the number of people (in thousands) employed as systems analysts in the year x. (See hint for Exercise 79a.)

b. Use this equation to estimate the number of people who will be employed as systems analysts in the year 2012.

REVIEW AND PREVIEW

Solve. Write the solution in interval notation. See Section 2.4.

83. $2x - 7 \leq 21$

84. $-3x + 1 > 0$

85. $5(x - 2) \geq 3(x - 1)$

86. $-2(x + 1) \leq -x + 10$

87. $\dfrac{x}{2} + \dfrac{1}{4} < \dfrac{1}{8}$

88. $\dfrac{x}{5} - \dfrac{3}{10} \geq \dfrac{x}{2} - 1$

CONCEPT EXTENSIONS

Answer true or false.

89. A vertical line is always perpendicular to a horizontal line.

90. A vertical line is always parallel to a vertical line.

Example:

Find an equation of the perpendicular bisector of the line segment whose endpoints are (2, 6) and (0, −2).

Solution:

A perpendicular bisector is a line that contains the midpoint of the given segment and is perpendicular to the segment.

Step 1: The midpoint of the segment with endpoints $(2, 6)$ and $(0, -2)$ is $(1, 2)$.

Step 2: The slope of the segment containing points $(2, 6)$ and $(0, -2)$ is 4.

Step 3: A line perpendicular to this line segment will have slope of $-\dfrac{1}{4}$.

Step 4: The equation of the line through the midpoint $(1, 2)$ with a slope of $-\dfrac{1}{4}$ will be the equation of the perpendicular bisector. This equation in standard form is $x + 4y = 9$.

Find an equation of the perpendicular bisector of the line segment whose endpoints are given. See the previous example.

△ **91.** $(3, -1); (-5, 1)$

△ **92.** $(-6, -3); (-8, -1)$

△ **93.** $(-2, 6); (-22, -4)$

△ **94.** $(5, 8); (7, 2)$

△ **95.** $(2, 3); (-4, 7)$

△ **96.** $(-6, 8); (-4, -2)$

✎ **97.** Describe how to check to see if the graph of $2x - 4y = 7$ passes through the points $(1.4, -1.05)$ and $(0, -1.75)$. Then follow your directions and check these points.

▦ *Use a graphing calculator with a TRACE feature to see the results of each exercise.*

98. Exercise 56; graph the equation and verify that it passes through $(2, 9)$ and $(8, 6)$.

99. Exercise 55; graph the function and verify that it passes through $(1, 6)$ and $(5, 2)$.

100. Exercise 62; graph the equation. See that it has a negative slope and passes through $(4, -1)$.

101. Exercise 61; graph the equation. See that it has a negative slope and passes through $(-5, 0)$.

102. Exercise 48: Graph the equation and verify that it passes through $(1, 5)$ and is parallel to $y = 3x - 4$.

103. Exercise 47: Graph the equation and verify that it passes through $(3, 8)$ and is parallel to $y = 4x - 2$.

INTEGRATED REVIEW   LINEAR EQUATIONS IN TWO VARIABLES

Sections 3.1–3.5

Below is a review of equations of lines.

Forms of Linear Equations

$Ax + By = C$	**Standard form** of a linear equation A and B are not both 0.
$y = mx + b$	**Slope-intercept form** of a linear equation. The slope is m, and the y-intercept is $(0, b)$.
$y - y_1 = m(x - x_1)$	**Point-slope form** of a linear equation. The slope is m, and (x_1, y_1) is a point on the line.
$y = c$	**Horizontal line** The slope is 0, and the y-intercept is $(0, c)$.
$x = c$	**Vertical line** The slope is undefined and the x-intercept is $(c, 0)$.

Parallel and Perpendicular Lines

Nonvertical parallel lines have the same slope. The product of the slopes of two nonvertical perpendicular lines is -1.

Graph each linear equation.

1. $y = -2x$ **2.** $3x - 2y = 6$ **3.** $x = -3$ **4.** $y = 1.5$

Find the slope of the line containing each pair of points.

5. $(-2, -5), (3, -5)$ **6.** $(5, 2), (0, 5)$

Find the slope and y-intercept of each line.

7. $y = 3x - 5$ **8.** $5x - 2y = 7$

Determine whether each pair of lines is parallel, perpendicular, or neither.

9. $y = 8x - 6$
$y = 8x + 6$

10. $y = \dfrac{2}{3}x + 1$
$2y + 3x = 1$

Find the equation of each line. Write the equation in the form $x = a$, $y = b$, or $y = mx + b$. For Exercises 14 through 17, write the equation in the form $f(x) = mx + b$.

11. Through $(1, 6)$ and $(5, 2)$

12. Vertical line; through $(-2, -10)$

13. Horizontal line; through $(1, 0)$

14. Through $(2, -9)$ and $(-6, -5)$

15. Through $(-2, 4)$ with slope -5

16. Slope -4; y-intercept $\left(0, \dfrac{1}{3}\right)$

17. Slope $\dfrac{1}{2}$; y-intercept $(0, -1)$

18. Through $\left(\dfrac{1}{2}, 0\right)$ with slope 3

19. Through $(-1, -5)$; parallel to $3x - y = 5$

20. Through $(0, 4)$; perpendicular to $4x - 5y = 10$

21. Through $(2, -3)$; perpendicular to $4x + y = \dfrac{2}{3}$

22. Through $(-1, 0)$; parallel to $5x + 2y = 2$

23. Undefined slope; through $(-1, 3)$

24. $m = 0$; through $(-1, 3)$

CHAPTER 3 GROUP ACTIVITY

Modeling Real Data

The number of children who live with only one parent has been steadily increasing in the United States since the 1960s. According to the U.S. Bureau of the Census, the percent of children living with both parents is declining. The following table shows the percent of children (under age 18) living with *both* parents during selected years from 1980 to 2005. In this project, you will have the opportunity to use the data in the table to find a linear function $f(x)$ that represents the data, reflecting the change in living arrangements for children. This project may be completed by working in groups or individually.

Percent of U.S. Children Who Live with Both Parents

Year	*1980*	*1985*	*1990*	*1995*	*2000*	*2005*
x	0	5	10	15	20	25
Percent, y	77	74	73	69	67	68

Source: U.S. Bureau of the Census

1. Plot the data given in the table as ordered pairs.
2. Use a straight edge to draw on your graph what appears to be the line that "best fits" the data you plotted.
3. Estimate the coordinates of two points that fall on your best-fitting line. Use these points to find a linear function $f(x)$ for the line.
4. What is the slope of your line? Interpret its meaning. Does it make sense in the context of this situation?
5. Find the value of $f(50)$. Write a sentence interpreting its meaning in context.

6. Compare your linear function with that of another student or group. Are they different? If so, explain why.

(Optional) Enter the data from the table into a graphing calculator. Use the linear regression feature of the calculator to find a linear function for the data. Compare this function to the one you found in Question 3. How are they alike or different? Find the value of $f(50)$ using the model you found with the graphing calculator. Compare it to the value of $f(50)$ you found in Question 5.

CHAPTER 3 VOCABULARY CHECK

Fill in each blank with one of the words or phrases listed below.

relation	standard	slope–intercept	range	point–slope
line	slope	x	parallel	perpendicular
function	domain	y	linear function	linear inequality

1. A _____ is a set of ordered pairs.
2. The graph of every linear equation in two variables is a _____.
3. The statement $-x + 2y > 0$ is called a _____ in two variables.
4. _____ form of linear equation in two variables is $Ax + By = C$.
5. The _____ of a relation is the set of all second components of the ordered pairs of the relation.
6. _____ lines have the same slope and different y-intercepts.
7. _____ form of a linear equation in two variables is $y = mx + b$.
8. A _____ is a relation in which each first component in the ordered pairs corresponds to exactly one second component.
9. In the equation $y = 4x - 2$, the coefficient of x is the _____ of its corresponding graph.
10. Two lines are _____ if the product of their slopes is -1.
11. To find the x-intercept of a linear equation, let _____ = 0 and solve for the other variable.
12. The _____ of a relation is the set of all first components of the ordered pairs of the relation.
13. A _____ is a function that can be written in the form $f(x) = mx + b$.
14. To find the y-intercept of a linear equation, let _____ = 0 and solve for the other variable.
15. The equation $y - 8 = -5(x + 1)$ is written in _____ form.

> ▶ **Helpful Hint**
>
> Are you preparing for your test? Don't forget to take the Chapter 3 Test on page 200. Then check your answers at the back of the text and use the Chapter Test Prep Video CD to see the fully worked-out solutions to any of the exercises you want to review.

CHAPTER 3 HIGHLIGHTS

| **DEFINITIONS AND CONCEPTS** | **EXAMPLES** |

SECTION 3.1   GRAPHING EQUATIONS

The **rectangular coordinate system,** or **Cartesian coordinate system,** consists of a vertical and a horizontal number line intersecting at their 0 coordinate. The vertical number line is called the **y-axis,** and the horizontal number line is called the **x-axis.** The point of intersection of the axes is called the **origin.** The axes divide the plane into four regions called **quadrants.**

(continued)

DEFINITIONS AND CONCEPTS	EXAMPLES

To **plot** or **graph** an ordered pair means to find its corresponding point on a rectangular coordinate system.

To plot or graph the ordered pair $(-2, 5)$, start at the origin. Move 2 units to the left along the x-axis, then 5 units upward parallel to the y-axis.

An ordered pair is a **solution** of an equation in two variables if replacing the variables by the corresponding coordinates results in a true statement.

Determine whether $(-2, 3)$ is a solution of

$$3x + 2y = 0$$
$$3(-2) + 2(3) = 0$$
$$-6 + 6 = 0$$
$$0 = 0 \quad \text{True}$$

$(-2, 3)$ is a solution.

A **linear equation in two variables** is an equation that can be written in the form $Ax + By = C$, where A, B, and C are real numbers and A and B are not both 0. The form $Ax + By = C$ is called **standard form.**

Linear Equations in Two Variables

$$y = -2x + 5, \quad x = 7$$
$$y - 3 = 0, \quad 6x - 4y = 10$$

$6x - 4y = 10$ is in standard form.

The graph of a linear equation in two variables is a line. To graph a linear equation in two variables, find three ordered pair solutions. (Use the third ordered-pair to check.) Plot the solution points, and draw the line connecting the points.

Graph $3x + y = -6$.

x	y
0	-6
-2	0
-3	3

To graph an equation that is not linear, find a sufficient number of ordered pair solutions so that a pattern may be discovered.

Graph $y = x^3 + 2$.

x	y
-2	-6
-1	1
0	2
1	3
2	10

DEFINITIONS AND CONCEPTS	EXAMPLES

SECTION 3.2 INTRODUCTION TO FUNCTIONS

A **relation** is a set of ordered pairs. The **domain** of the relation is the set of all first components of the ordered pairs. The **range** of the relation is the set of all second components of the ordered pairs.

Relation

Domain: {cat, dog, too, give}
Range: {1, 2}

A **function** is a relation in which each element of the first set corresponds to exactly one element of the second set.

The previous relation is a function. Each word contains exactly one number of vowels.

Vertical Line Test

If no vertical line can be drawn so that it intersects a graph more than once, the graph is the graph of a function.

Find the domain and the range of the relation. Also determine whether the relation is a function.

By the vertical line test, this graph is the graph of a function.

The symbol $f(x)$ means **function of x** and is called **function notation**.

If $f(x) = 2x^2 - 5$, find $f(-3)$.
$$f(-3) = 2(-3)^2 - 5 = 2(9) - 5 = 13$$

SECTION 3.3 GRAPHING LINEAR FUNCTIONS

A **linear function** is a function that can be written in the form $f(x) = mx + b$.

To graph a linear function, find three ordered pair solutions. (Use the third ordered-pair to check.) Graph the solutions and draw a line through the plotted points.

Linear Functions
$$f(x) = -3, g(x) = 5x, h(x) = -\frac{1}{3}x - 7$$
Graph $f(x) = -2x$.

x	$y \, or \, f(x)$
-1	2
0	0
2	-4

(continued)

DEFINITIONS AND CONCEPTS	**EXAMPLES**

The graph of $y = mx + b$ is the same as the graph of $y = mx$, but shifted b units up if b is positive and b units down if b is negative.

Graph $g(x) = -2x + 3$.

This is the same as the graph of $f(x) = -2x$ shifted 3 units up.

The x-coordinate of a point where a graph crosses the x-axis is called an **x-intercept.** The y-coordinate of a point where a graph crosses the y-axis is called a **y-intercept.**

To find an x-intercept, let $y = 0$ or $f(x) = 0$ and solve for x.

To find a y-intercept, let $x = 0$ and solve for y.

Graph $5x - y = -5$ by finding intercepts.

If $x = 0$, then	If $y = 0$, then
$5x - y = -5$	$5x - y = -5$
$5 \cdot 0 - y = -5$	$5x - 0 = -5$
$-y = -5$	$5x = -5$
$y = 5$	$x = -1$
$(0, 5)$	$(-1, 0)$

Ordered pairs are $(0, 5)$ and $(-1, 0)$.

The graph of $x = c$ is a vertical line with x-intercept $(c, 0)$.

The graph of $y = c$ is a horizontal line with y-intercept $(0, c)$.

DEFINITIONS AND CONCEPTS	EXAMPLES

The **slope** m of the line through (x_1, y_1) and (x_2, y_2) is given by

$$m = \frac{y_2 - y_1}{x_2 - x_1} \text{ as long } x_2 \neq x_1$$

Find the slope of the line through $(-1, 7)$ and $(-2, -3)$.

$$m = \frac{y_2 - y_1}{x_2 - x_1} = \frac{-3 - 7}{-2 - (-1)} = \frac{-10}{-1} = 10$$

The **slope-intercept form** of a linear equation is $y = mx + b$, where m is the slope of the line and b is the y-intercept.

Find the slope and y-intercept of $-3x + 2y = -8$.

$$2y = 3x - 8$$
$$\frac{2y}{2} = \frac{3x}{2} - \frac{8}{2}$$
$$y = \frac{3}{2}x - 4$$

The slope the line is $\frac{3}{2}$, and the y-intercept is $(0, -4)$.

Nonvertical parallel lines have the same slope.

If the product of the slopes of two lines is -1, then the lines are perpendicular.

The slope of a horizontal line is 0.

The slope of a vertical line is undefined.

The slope of $y = -2$ is 0.

The slope of $x = 5$ is undefined.

We can use the slope–intercept form to write an equation of a line given its slope and y-intercept.

Write an equation of the line with y-intercept $(0, -1)$ and slope $\frac{2}{3}$.

$$y = mx + b$$
$$y = \frac{2}{3}x - 1$$

The point–slope form of the equation of a line is $y - y_1 = m(x - x_1)$, where m is the slope of the line and (x_1, y_1) is a point on the line.

Find an equation of the line with slope 2 containing the point $(1, -4)$. Write the equation in standard form: $Ax + By = C$.

$$y - y_1 = m(x - x_1)$$
$$y - (-4) = 2(x - 1)$$
$$y + 4 = 2x - 2$$
$$-2x + y = -6 \qquad \text{Standard form}$$

📖 **STUDY SKILLS BUILDER**

Are You Prepared for a Test on Chapter 3?

Below I have listed some common trouble areas for students in Chapter 3. After studying for your test—but before taking your test—read these.

- Don't forget that the graph of an ordered pair is a *single* point in the rectangular coordinate plane.
- Remember that the slope of a horizontal line is 0 while a vertical line has undefined slope or no slope.
- For a linear equation such as $2y = 3x - 6$, the slope is not the coefficient of x unless the equation is solved for y. Solving this equation for y, we have $y = \frac{3}{2}x - 3$.

  The slope is $\frac{3}{2}$ and the y-intercept is $(0, -3)$.

Slope	Parallel line	Perpendicular line
$m = 6$	$m = 6$	$m = -\frac{1}{6}$
$m = -\frac{2}{3}$	$m = -\frac{2}{3}$	$m = \frac{3}{2}$

- Parallel lines have the same slope while perpendicular lines have negative reciprocal slopes.
- Don't forget that the statement $f(2) = 3$ corresponds to the ordered pair $(2, 3)$.

Remember: this is simply a checklist of common trouble areas. For a review of Chapter 3, see the Highlights and Chapter Review at the end of this chapter.

CHAPTER 3 REVIEW

(3.1) *Plot the points and name the quadrant or axis in which each point lies.*

1. $A(2, -1)$, $B(-2, 1)$, $C(0, 3)$, $D(-3, -5)$
2. $A(-3, 4)$, $B(4, -3)$, $C(-2, 0)$, $D(-4, 1)$

Determine whether each ordered pair is a solution to the given equation.

3. $7x - 8y = 56$; $(0, 56)$, $(8, 0)$
4. $-2x + 5y = 10$; $(-5, 0)$, $(1, 1)$
5. $x = 13$; $(13, 5)$, $(13, 13)$
6. $y = 2$; $(7, 2)$, $(2, 7)$

Determine whether each equation is linear or not. Then graph the equation.

7. $y = 3x$
8. $y = 5x$
9. $3x - y = 4$
10. $x - 3y = 2$
11. $y = |x| + 4$
12. $y = x^2 + 4$
13. $y = -\frac{1}{2}x + 2$
14. $y = -x + 5$
15. $y = 2x - 1$
16. $y = \frac{1}{3}x + 1$
17. $y = -1.36x$
18. $y = 2.1x + 5.9$

(3.2) *Find the domain and range of each relation. Also determine whether the relation is a function.*

19. $\left\{ \left(-\frac{1}{2}, \frac{3}{4} \right), (6, 0.75), (0, -12), (25, 25) \right\}$

20. $\left\{ \left(\frac{3}{4}, -\frac{1}{2} \right), (0.75, 6), (-12, 0), (25, 25) \right\}$

21.

22.

23.

24.

25.

26.

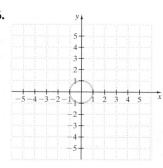

If $f(x) = x - 5$, $g(x) = -3x$, and $h(x) = 2x^2 - 6x + 1$, find the following.

27. $f(2)$

28. $g(0)$

29. $g(-6)$

30. $h(-1)$

31. $h(1)$

32. $f(5)$

The function $J(x) = 2.54x$ may be used to calculate the weight of an object on Jupiter J given its weight on Earth x.

33. If a person weighs 150 pounds on Earth, find the equivalent weight on Jupiter.

34. A 2000-pound probe on Earth weighs how many pounds on Jupiter?

Use the graph of the function below to answer Exercises 35 through 38.

35. Find $f(-1)$.

36. Find $f(1)$.

37. Find all values of x such that $f(x) = 1$.

38. Find all values of x such that $f(x) = -1$.

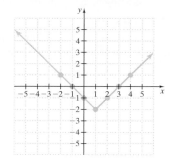

(3.3) Graph each linear function.

39. $f(x) = x$

40. $f(x) = -\dfrac{1}{3}x$

41. $g(x) = 4x - 1$

The graph of $f(x) = 3x$ is sketched below. Use this graph to match each linear function with its graph.

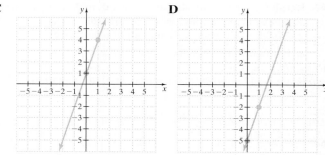

42. $f(x) = 3x + 1$

43. $f(x) = 3x - 2$

44. $f(x) = 3x + 2$

45. $f(x) = 3x - 5$

Graph each linear equation by finding intercepts if possible.

46. $4x + 5y = 20$

47. $3x - 2y = -9$

48. $4x - y = 3$

49. $2x + 6y = 9$

50. $y = 5$

51. $x = -2$

Graph each linear equation.

52. $x - 2 = 0$

53. $y + 3 = 0$

54. The cost C, in dollars, of renting a minivan for a day is given by the linear function $C(x) = 0.3x + 42$, where x is number of miles driven.

   a. Find the cost of renting the minivan for a day and driving it 150 miles.

   b. Graph $C(x) = 0.3x + 42$.

(3.4) Find the slope of the line through each pair of points.

55. $(2, 8)$ and $(6, -4)$

56. $(-3, 9)$ and $(5, 13)$

57. $(-7, -4)$ and $(-3, 6)$

58. $(7, -2)$ and $(-5, 7)$

Find the slope and y-intercept of each line.

59. $6x - 15y = 20$

60. $4x + 14y = 21$

Find the slope of each line.

61. $y - 3 = 0$ **62.** $x = -5$

Two lines are graphed on each set of axes. Decide whether l_1 or l_2 has the greater slope.

63.

64.

65.

66.

67. Recall from Exercise 54, that the cost C, in dollars, of renting a minivan for a day is given by the linear equation $y = 0.3x + 42$, where x is number of miles driven.

   a. Find and interpret the slope of this equation.

   b. Find and interpret the y-intercept of this equation.

Decide whether the lines are parallel, perpendicular, or neither.

△ **68.** $f(x) = -2x + 6$ △ **69.** $-x + 3y = 2$
         $g(x) = 2x - 1$ $6x - 18y = 3$

(3.5) Graph each linear equation using the slope and y-intercept.

70. $y = -x + 1$ **71.** $y = 4x - 3$
72. $3x - y = 6$ **73.** $y = -5x$

Find an equation of the line satisfying the given conditions.

74. Horizontal; through $(3, -1)$

75. Vertical; through $(-2, -4)$

△ **76.** Parallel to the line $x = 6$; through $(-4, -3)$

77. Slope 0; through $(2, 5)$

Find the standard form equation of each line satisfying the given conditions.

78. Through $(-3, 5)$; slope 3

79. Slope 2; through $(5, -2)$

80. Through $(-6, -1)$ and $(-4, -2)$

81. Through $(-5, 3)$ and $(-4, -8)$

△ **82.** Through $(-2, 3)$; perpendicular to $x = 4$

△ **83.** Through $(-2, -5)$; parallel to $y = 8$

Find the equation of each line satisfying the given conditions. Write each equation using function notation.

84. Slope $-\dfrac{2}{3}$; y-intercept $(0, 4)$

85. Slope -1; y-intercept $(0, -2)$

△ **86.** Through $(2, -6)$; parallel to $6x + 3y = 5$

△ **87.** Through $(-4, -2)$; parallel to $3x + 2y = 8$

△ **88.** Through $(-6, -1)$; perpendicular to $4x + 3y = 5$

△ **89.** Through $(-4, 5)$; perpendicular to $2x - 3y = 6$

90. In 2005, the percent of U.S. drivers wearing seat belts was 82%. The number of drivers wearing seat belts in 2000 was 71%. Let y be the number of drivers wearing seat belts in the year x, where $x = 0$ represents 2000. (*Source:* Strategis Group for Personal Communications Asso.)

   a. Write a linear equation that models the percent of U.S. drivers wearing seat belts in terms of the year x. [*Hint:* Write 2 ordered pairs of the form (years past 2000, percent of drivers).]

   b. Use this equation to predict the number of U.S. drivers wearing seat belts in the year 2009. (Round to the nearest percent.)

91. In 1998, the number of people (in millions) reporting arthritis was 43. The number of people (in millions) predicted to be reporting arthritis in 2020 is 60. Let y be the number of people (in millions) reporting arthritis in the year x, where $x = 0$ represents 1998. (*Source:* Arthritis Foundation)

   a. Write a linear equation that models the number of people (in millions) reporting arthritis in terms of the year x (See the hint for Exercise 90.)

   b. Use this equation to predict the number of people reporting arthritis in 2010. (Round to the nearest million.)

CHAPTER 3 TEST TEST PREP VIDEO

Remember to use the Chapter Test Prep Video CD to see the fully worked-out solutions to any of the exercises you want to review.

1. Plot the points, and name the quadrant or axis in which each is located: $A(6, -2)$, $B(4, 0)$, $C(-1, 6)$.

Graph each line.

2. $2x - 3y = -6$

3. $4x + 6y = 7$

4. $f(x) = \frac{2}{3}x$

5. $y = -3$

6. Find the slope of the line that passes through $(5, -8)$ and $(-7, 10)$.

7. Find the slope and the y-intercept of the line $3x + 12y = 8$.

Graph each nonlinear function. Suggested x-values have been given for ordered pair solutions.

8. $f(x) = (x - 1)^2$ Let $x = -2, -1, 0, 1, 2, 3, 4$

9. $g(x) = |x| + 2$ Let $x = -3, -2, -1, 0, 1, 2, 3$

Find an equation of each line satisfying the given conditions. Write Exercises 10–14 in standard form. Write Exercises 15–17 using function notation.

10. Horizontal; through $(2, -8)$

11. Vertical; through $(-4, -3)$

12. Perpendicular to $x = 5$; through $(3, -2)$

13. Through $(4, -1)$; slope -3

14. Through $(0, -2)$; slope 5

15. Through $(4, -2)$ and $(6, -3)$

16. Through $(-1, 2)$; perpendicular to $3x - y = 4$

17. Parallel to $2y + x = 3$; through $(3, -2)$

18. Line L_1 has the equation $2x - 5y = 8$. Line L_2 passes through the points $(1, 4)$ and $(-1, -1)$. Determine whether these lines are parallel lines, perpendicular lines, or neither.

Graph each inequality.

19. $x \leq -4$

20. $2x - y > 5$

21. The intersection of $2x + 4y < 6$ and $y \leq -4$

Find the domain and range of each relation. Also determine whether the relation is a function.

22.

23.

24.

25.

26. The average yearly earnings for high school graduates age 18 and older is given by the linear function

$$f(x) = 1031x + 25{,}193$$

where x is the number of years since 2000 that a person graduated. (*Source:* U.S. Census Bureau)

a. Find the average earnings in 2000 for high school graduates.

b. Find the average earnings for high school graduates in the year 2007.

c. Predict the first whole year that the average earnings for high school graduates will be greater than $40,000.

d. Find and interpret the slope of this equation.

e. Find and interpret the y-intercept of this equation.

CHAPTER 3 CUMULATIVE REVIEW

1. Evaluate: $3x - y$ when $x = 15$ and $y = 4$.

2. Add.

   a. $-4 + (-3)$

   b. $\dfrac{1}{2} - \left(-\dfrac{1}{3}\right)$

   c. $7 - 20$

3. Determine whether the following statements are true or false.

   a. 3 is a real number.

   b. $\frac{1}{5}$ is an irrational number.

   c. Every rational number is an integer.

   d. $\{1, 5\} \subseteq \{2, 3, 4, 5\}$

4. Write the opposite of each.

   a. -7

   b. 0

   c. $\dfrac{1}{4}$

5. Subtract.

   a. $2 - 8$

   b. $-8 - (-1)$

   c. $-11 - 5$

   d. $10.7 - (-9.8)$

   e. $\dfrac{2}{3} - \dfrac{1}{2}$

   △ **f.** $1 - 0.06$

   g. Subtract 7 from 4.

6. Multiply or divide.

   a. $\dfrac{-42}{-6}$

   b. $\dfrac{0}{14}$

   c. $-1(-5)(-2)$

7. Simplify each expression.

   a. 3^2

   b. $\left(\dfrac{1}{2}\right)^4$

   c. -5^2

   d. $(-5)^2$

   e. -5^3

   f. $(-5)^3$

8. Which property is illustrated?

   a. $5(x + 7) = 5 \cdot x + 5 \cdot 7$

   b. $5(x + 7) = 5(7 + x)$

9. Insert $<, >,$ or $=$ between each pair of numbers to form a true statement.

   a. $-1 \quad -2$

   b. $\dfrac{12}{4} \quad 3$

   c. $-5 \quad 0$

   d. $-3.5 \quad -3.05$

10. Evaluate $2x^2$ for

   a. $x = 7$

   b. $x = -7$

11. Write the multiplicative inverse, or reciprocal, of each.

   a. 11

   b. -9

   c. $\dfrac{7}{4}$

12. Simplify $-2 + 3[5 - (7 - 10)]$.

13. Solve: $0.6 = 2 - 3.5c$

14. Solve: $2(x - 3) = -40$.

15. Solve for x: $3x + 5 = 3(x + 2)$

16. Solve: $5(x - 7) = 4x - 35 + x$.

17. Write the following as algebraic expressions. Then simplify.

   a. The sum of three consecutive integers, if x is the first consecutive integer.

   b. The perimeter of a triangle with sides of length x, $5x$, and $6x - 3$.

18. Find 25% of 16.

19. Kelsey Ohleger was helping her friend Benji Burnstine study for an algebra exam. Kelsey told Benji that her three latest art history quiz scores are three consecutive even integers whose sum is 264. Help Benji find the scores.

20. Find 3 consecutive odd integers whose sum is 213.

21. Solve $V = lwh$ for h.

22. Solve $7x + 3y = 21$ for y

23. Solve: $x - 2 < 5$.

24. Solve: $-x - 17 \geq 9$.

25. Solve: $\dfrac{2}{5}(x - 6) \geq x - 1$

26. $3x + 10 > \dfrac{5}{2}(x - 1)$.

27. Solve: $2x \geq 0$ and $4x - 1 \leq -9$

28. Solve: $x - 2 < 6$ and $3x + 1 > 1$.

29. Solve: $5x - 3 \leq 10$ or $x + 1 \geq 5$

30. Solve: $x - 2 < 6$ or $3x + 1 > 1$.

31. Solve: $|5w + 3| = 7$

32. Solve: $|5x - 2| = 3$.

33. Solve: $|3x + 2| = |5x - 8|$

34. Solve: $|7x - 2| = |7x + 4|$

35. Solve: $|5x + 1| + 1 \leq 10$

36. Solve: $|-x + 8| - 2 \leq 8$

37. Solve for y: $|y - 3| > 7$

38. Solve for x: $|x + 3| > 1$.

39. Determine whether $(0, -12), (1, 9),$ and $(2, -6)$ are solutions of the equation $3x - y = 12$.

40. Find the slope and y-intercept of $7x + 2y = 10$.

41. Is the relation $y = 2x + 1$ also a function?

42. Determine whether the graph below is the graph of a function.

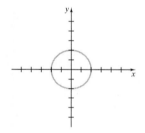

43. Find the y-intercept of the graph of each equation.

   a. $f(x) = \dfrac{1}{2}x + \dfrac{3}{7}$

   b. $y = -2.5x - 3.2$

44. Find the slope of the line through $(-1, 6)$ and $(0, 9)$.

45. Find the slope of the line whose equation is $f(x) = \dfrac{2}{3}x + 4$.

46. Find an equation of the vertical line through $\left(-2, -\dfrac{3}{4}\right)$.

47. Write an equation of the line with y-intercept $(0, -3)$ and slope of $\dfrac{1}{4}$.

48. Find an equation of the horizontal line through $\left(-2, -\dfrac{3}{4}\right)$.

4 Systems of Equations

In this chapter, two or more equations in two or more variables are solved simultaneously. Such a collection of equations is called a **system of equations.** Systems of equations are good mathematical models for many real-world problems because these problems may involve several related patterns.

My Space and Facebook are both popular social networking Web sites offering interactive, user-submitted network of friends, personal profiles, blogs, groups, music, videos, and photos.

My Space is currently the world's sixth most popular Web site in any language and the third most popular Web site in the United States. Facebook was launched in early 2004 and is currently the 7th most visited Web site.

In Section 4.3, Exercise 53, page 222, we will form and use the functions graphed below to solve the system of equations.

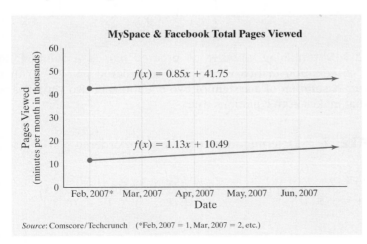

MySpace & Facebook Total Pages Viewed

$f(x) = 0.85x + 41.75$

$f(x) = 1.13x + 10.49$

Pages Viewed (minutes per month in thousands)

Date

Feb, 2007* Mar, 2007 Apr, 2007 May, 2007 Jun, 2007

Source: Comscore/Techcrunch (*Feb, 2007 = 1, Mar, 2007 = 2, etc.)

4.1 SOLVING SYSTEMS OF LINEAR EQUATIONS IN TWO VARIABLES

OBJECTIVES

1 Determine whether an ordered pair is a solution of a system of two linear equations.

2 Solve a system by graphing.

3 Solve a system by substitution.

4 Solve a system by elimination.

An important problem that often occurs in the fields of business and economics concerns the concepts of revenue and cost. For example, suppose that a small manufacturing company begins to manufacture and sell compact disc storage units. The revenue of a company is the company's income from selling these units, and the cost is the amount of money that a company spends to manufacture these units. The following coordinate system shows the graphs of revenue and cost for the storage units.

These lines intersect at the point (500, 25,000). This means that when 500 storage units are manufactured and sold, both cost and revenue are $25,000. In business, this point of intersection is called the **break-even point.** Notice that for *x*-values (units sold) less than 500, the cost graph is above the revenue graph, meaning that cost of manufacturing is greater than revenue, and so the company is losing money. For *x*-values (units sold) greater than 500, the revenue graph is above the cost graph, meaning that revenue is greater than cost, and so the company is making money.

Recall from Chapter 3 that each line is a graph of some linear equation in two variables. Both equations together form a **system of equations.** The common point of intersection is called the **solution of the system.** Some examples of systems of linear equations in two variables are

Systems of Linear Equations in Two Variables

$$\begin{cases} x - 2y = -7 \\ 3x + y = 0 \end{cases} \qquad \begin{cases} x = 5 \\ x + \dfrac{y}{2} = 9 \end{cases} \qquad \begin{cases} x - 3 = 2y + 6 \\ y = 1 \end{cases}$$

OBJECTIVE 1 ▶ Determining whether an ordered pair is a solution. Recall that a solution of an equation in two variables is an ordered pair (x, y) that makes the equation true. A **solution of a system** of two equations in two variables is an ordered pair (x, y) that makes both equations true.

EXAMPLE 1 Determine whether the given ordered pair is a solution of the system.

a. $\begin{cases} -x + y = 2 \\ 2x - y = -3 \end{cases}$ $(-1, 1)$ **b.** $\begin{cases} 5x + 3y = -1 \\ x - y = 1 \end{cases}$ $(-2, 3)$

Solution

a. We replace *x* with −1 and *y* with 1 in each equation.

$$-x + y = 2 \quad \text{First equation} \qquad\qquad 2x - y = -3 \quad \text{Second equation}$$
$$-(-1) + (1) \stackrel{?}{=} 2 \quad \text{Let } x = -1 \text{ and } y = 1. \quad 2(-1) - (1) \stackrel{?}{=} -3 \quad \text{Let } x = -1 \text{ and } y = 1.$$
$$1 + 1 \stackrel{?}{=} 2 \qquad\qquad\qquad\qquad -2 - 1 \stackrel{?}{=} -3$$
$$2 = 2 \quad \text{True} \qquad\qquad\qquad\qquad -3 = -3 \quad \text{True}$$

Since $(-1, 1)$ makes *both* equations true, it is a solution. Using set notation, the solution set is $\{(-1, 1)\}$.

b. We replace x with -2 and y with 3 in each equation.

$$5x + 3y = -1 \quad \text{First equation} \qquad\qquad x - y = 1 \quad \text{Second equation}$$
$$5(-2) + 3(3) \stackrel{?}{=} -1 \quad \text{Let } x = -2 \text{ and } y = 3. \quad (-2) - (3) \stackrel{?}{=} 1 \quad \text{Let } x = -2 \text{ and } y = 3.$$
$$-10 + 9 \stackrel{?}{=} -1 \qquad\qquad\qquad\qquad -5 = 1 \quad \text{False}$$
$$-1 = -1 \quad \text{True}$$

Since the ordered pair $(-2, 3)$ does not make *both* equations true, it is not a solution of the system. $\square$

PRACTICE

1 Determine whether the given ordered pair is a solution of the system.

a. $\begin{cases} -x - 4y = 1 \\ 2x + y = 5 \end{cases}$ $(3, -1)$ **b.** $\begin{cases} 4x + y = -4 \\ -x + 3y = 8 \end{cases}$ $(-2, 4)$

> ▶ **Helpful Hint**
>
> Reading values from graphs may not be accurate. Until a proposed solution is checked in both equations of the system, we can only assume that we have *estimated* a solution.

OBJECTIVE 2 ▶ **Solving a system by graphing.** We can *estimate* the solutions of a system by graphing each equation on the same coordinate system and estimating the coordinates of any point of intersection.

EXAMPLE 2 Solve each system by graphing. If the system has just one solution, estimate the solution.

a. $\begin{cases} x + y = 2 \\ 3x - y = -2 \end{cases}$ **b.** $\begin{cases} x - 2y = 4 \\ x = 2y \end{cases}$ **c.** $\begin{cases} 2x + 4y = 10 \\ x + 2y = 5 \end{cases}$

Solution Since the graph of a linear equation in two variables is a line, graphing two such equations yields two lines in a plane.

a. $\begin{cases} x + y = 2 \\ 3x - y = -2 \end{cases}$

These lines intersect at one point as shown in the figure to the right. The coordinates of the point of intersection appear to be $(0, 2)$. Check this estimated solution by replacing x with 0 and y with 2 in **both** equations.

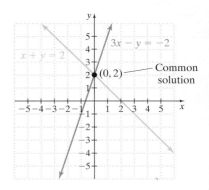

$$x + y = 2 \quad \text{First equation} \qquad\qquad 3x - y = -2 \quad \text{Second equation}$$
$$0 + 2 \stackrel{?}{=} 2 \quad \text{Let } x = 0 \text{ and } y = 2. \qquad 3 \cdot 0 - 2 \stackrel{?}{=} -2 \quad \text{Let } x = 0 \text{ and } y = 2.$$
$$2 = 2 \quad \text{True} \qquad\qquad\qquad\qquad -2 = -2 \quad \text{True}$$

The ordered pair $(0, 2)$ does satisfy both equations. We conclude therefore that $(0, 2)$ is the solution of the system. A system that has at least one solution, such as this one, is said to be **consistent.**

b. $\begin{cases} x - 2y = 4 \\ x \quad\;\; = 2y \end{cases}$

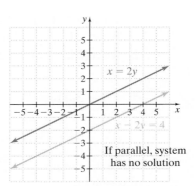

If parallel, system
has no solution

The lines appear to be parallel. To be sure, write each equation in point–slope form, $y = mx + b$.

| $x - 2y = 4$ | First equation | $x = 2y$ | Second equation |

$-2y = -x + 4$ Subtract x from both sides. $\dfrac{1}{2}x = y$ Divide both sides by 2.

$y = \dfrac{1}{2}x - 2$ Divide both sides by -2. $y = \dfrac{1}{2}x$

> **Helpful Hint**
> - If a system of equations has *at least one solution,* the system is *consistent.*
> - If a system of equations has *no solution,* the system is *inconsistent.*

The graphs of these equations have the same slope, $\dfrac{1}{2}$, but different y-intercepts, so we have confirmed that these lines are parallel. Therefore, the system has no solution since the equations have no common solution (there are no intersection points). A system that has no solution is said to be **inconsistent.**

c. $\begin{cases} 2x + 4y = 10 \\ x + 2y = 5 \end{cases}$

The graph of each equation appears to be in the same line. To confirm this, notice that if both sides of the second equation are multiplied by 2, the result is the first equation. This means that the equations have identical solutions. Any ordered pair solution of one equation satisfies the other equation also. Thus, these equations are said to be **dependent equations.** The solution set of the system is $\{(x, y)\,|\,x + 2y = 5\}$ or, equivalently, $\{(x, y)\,|\,2x + 4y = 10\}$ since the lines describe

If same line, system
has an infinite number
of solutions.

> **Helpful Hint**
> - If the graphs of two equations *differ,* they are *independent* equations.
> - If the graphs of two equations are the *same,* they are *dependent* equations.

identical ordered pairs. Written this way, the solution set is read "the set of all ordered pairs (x, y), such that $2x + 4y = 10$." There are therefore an infinite number of solutions to this system. ☐

PRACTICE

2 Solve each system by graphing. If the system has just one solution, estimate the solution.

a. $\begin{cases} 3x - 2y = 4 \\ -9x + 6y = -12 \end{cases}$ **b.** $\begin{cases} y = 5x \\ 2x + y = 7 \end{cases}$ **c.** $\begin{cases} y = \dfrac{3}{4}x + 1 \\ 3x - 4y = 12 \end{cases}$

Concept Check ☑️

The equations in the system are dependent and the system has an infinite number of solutions. Which ordered pairs below are solutions?

$$\begin{cases} -x + 3y = 4 \\ 2x + 8 = 6y \end{cases}$$

Answer to Concept Check: b, c   **a.** $(4, 0)$ **b.** $(-4, 0)$ **c.** $(-1, 1)$

We can summarize the information discovered in Example 2 as follows.

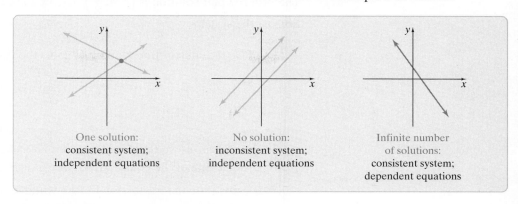

| One solution: consistent system; independent equations | No solution: inconsistent system; independent equations | Infinite number of solutions: consistent system; dependent equations |

Concept Check ☑

How can you tell just by looking at the following system that it has no solution?

$$\begin{cases} y = 3x + 5 \\ y = 3x - 7 \end{cases}$$

How can you tell just by looking at the following system that it has infinitely many solutions?

$$\begin{cases} x + y = 5 \\ 2x + 2y = 10 \end{cases}$$

OBJECTIVE 3 ▶ Solving a system by substitution. Graphing the equations of a system by hand is often a good method of finding approximate solutions of a system, but it is not a reliable method of finding exact solutions of a system. We turn instead to two algebraic methods of solving systems. We use the first method, the **substitution method,** to solve the system

$$\begin{cases} 2x + 4y = -6 & \text{First equation} \\ x = 2y - 5 & \text{Second equation} \end{cases}$$

EXAMPLE 3   Use the substitution method to solve the system.

$$\begin{cases} 2x + 4y = -6 & \text{First equation} \\ x = 2y - 5 & \text{Second equation} \end{cases}$$

Solution   In the second equation, we are told that x is equal to $2y - 5$. Since they are equal, we can *substitute* $2y - 5$ for x in the first equation. This will give us an equation in one variable, which we can solve for y.

$$2x + 4y = -6 \qquad \text{First equation}$$

$$2\overbrace{(2y - 5)} + 4y = -6 \qquad \text{Substitute } 2y - 5 \text{ for } x.$$

$$4y - 10 + 4y = -6$$

$$8y = 4$$

$$y = \frac{4}{8} = \frac{1}{2} \qquad \text{Solve for } y.$$

The y-coordinate of the solution is $\frac{1}{2}$. To find the x-coordinate, we replace y with $\frac{1}{2}$ in the second equation,

$$x = 2y - 5.$$

$$x = 2y - 5$$

$$x = 2\left(\frac{1}{2}\right) - 5 = 1 - 5 = -4$$

The ordered pair solution is $\left(-4, \frac{1}{2}\right)$. Check to see that $\left(-4, \frac{1}{2}\right)$ satisfies both equations of the system. □

PRACTICE

3 Use the substitution method to solve the system.

$$\begin{cases} y = 4x + 7 \\ 2x + y = 4 \end{cases}$$

> **Solving a System of Two Equations Using the Substitution Method**
>
> **STEP 1.** Solve one of the equations for one of its variables.
>
> **STEP 2.** Substitute the expression for the variable found in Step 1 into the other equation.
>
> **STEP 3.** Find the value of one variable by solving the equation from Step 2.
>
> **STEP 4.** Find the value of the other variable by substituting the value found in Step 3 into the equation from Step 1.
>
> **STEP 5.** Check the ordered pair solution in *both* original equations.

EXAMPLE 4 Use the substitution method to solve the system.

$$\begin{cases} -\dfrac{x}{6} + \dfrac{y}{2} = \dfrac{1}{2} \\ \dfrac{x}{3} - \dfrac{y}{6} = -\dfrac{3}{4} \end{cases}$$

Solution First we multiply each equation by its least common denominator to clear the system of fractions. We multiply the first equation by 6 and the second equation by 12.

$$\begin{cases} 6\left(-\dfrac{x}{6} + \dfrac{y}{2}\right) = 6\left(\dfrac{1}{2}\right) \\ 12\left(\dfrac{x}{3} - \dfrac{y}{6}\right) = 12\left(-\dfrac{3}{4}\right) \end{cases} \text{ simplifies to } \begin{cases} -x + 3y = 3 & \text{First equation} \\ 4x - 2y = -9 & \text{Second equation} \end{cases}$$

> **▶ Helpful Hint**
> To avoid tedious fractions, solve for a variable whose coefficient is 1 or −1, if possible.

To use the substitution method, we now solve the first equation for x.

$$-x + 3y = 3 \quad \text{First equation}$$
$$3y - 3 = x \quad \text{Solve for } x.$$

Next we replace x with $3y - 3$ in the second equation.

$$4x - 2y = -9 \quad \text{Second equation}$$

$$4(3y - 3) - 2y = -9$$
$$12y - 12 - 2y = -9$$
$$10y = 3$$
$$y = \frac{3}{10} \quad \text{Solve for } y.$$

To find the corresponding x-coordinate, we replace y with $\dfrac{3}{10}$ in the equation $x = 3y - 3$. Then

$$x = 3\left(\frac{3}{10}\right) - 3 = \frac{9}{10} - 3 = \frac{9}{10} - \frac{30}{10} = -\frac{21}{10}$$

The ordered pair solution is $\left(-\dfrac{21}{10}, \dfrac{3}{10}\right)$. Check to see that this solution satisfies both original equations.   □

PRACTICE
4   Use the substitution method to solve the system.

$$\begin{cases} -\dfrac{x}{3} + \dfrac{y}{4} = \dfrac{1}{2} \\ \dfrac{x}{4} - \dfrac{y}{2} = -\dfrac{1}{4} \end{cases}$$

> ▶ **Helpful Hint**
> If a system of equations contains equations with fractions, first clear the equations of fractions.

OBJECTIVE 4 ▶ Solving a system by elimination. The **elimination method,** or **addition method,** is a second algebraic technique for solving systems of equations. For this method, we rely on a version of the addition property of equality, which states that "equals added to equals are equal."

> If $A = B$ and $C = D$ then $A + C = B + D$.

EXAMPLE 5   Use the elimination method to solve the system.

$$\begin{cases} x - 5y = -12 & \text{First equation} \\ -x + y = 4 & \text{Second equation} \end{cases}$$

Solution   Since the left side of each equation is equal to the right side, we add equal quantities by adding the left sides of the equations and the right sides of the equations. This sum gives us an equation in one variable, y, which we can solve for y.

$$\begin{array}{ll} x - 5y = -12 & \text{First equation} \\ \underline{-x + y = 4} & \text{Second equation} \\ -4y = -8 & \text{Add.} \\ y = 2 & \text{Solve for } y. \end{array}$$

The y-coordinate of the solution is 2. To find the corresponding x-coordinate, we replace y with 2 in either original equation of the system. Let's use the second equation.

$$\begin{array}{ll} -x + y = 4 & \text{Second equation} \\ -x + 2 = 4 & \text{Let } y = 2. \\ -x = 2 & \\ x = -2 & \end{array}$$

The ordered pair solution is $(-2, 2)$. Check to see that $(-2, 2)$ satisfies both equations of the system.   □

PRACTICE
5   Use the elimination method to solve the system.

$$\begin{cases} 3x - y = 5 \\ 5x + y = 11 \end{cases}$$

The steps below summarize the elimination method.

Solving a System of Two Linear Equations Using the Elimination Method

STEP 1. Rewrite each equation in standard form, $Ax + By = C$.

STEP 2. If necessary, multiply one or both equations by some nonzero number so that the coefficients of a variable are opposites of each other.

STEP 3. Add the equations.

STEP 4. Find the value of one variable by solving the equation from Step 3.

STEP 5. Find the value of the second variable by substituting the value found in Step 4 into either original equation.

STEP 6. Check the proposed ordered pair solution in *both* original equations.

EXAMPLE 6 Use the elimination method to solve the system.

$$\begin{cases} 3x - 2y = 10 \\ 4x - 3y = 15 \end{cases}$$

Solution If we add the two equations, the sum will still be an equation in two variables. Notice, however, that we can eliminate y when the equations are added if we multiply both sides of the first equation by 3 and both sides of the second equation by -2. Then

$$\begin{cases} 3(3x - 2y) = 3(10) \\ -2(4x - 3y) = -2(15) \end{cases} \quad \text{simplifies to} \quad \begin{cases} 9x - 6y = 30 \\ -8x + 6y = -30 \end{cases}$$

Next we add the left sides and add the right sides.

$$\begin{array}{r} 9x - 6y = 30 \\ -8x + 6y = -30 \\ \hline x \qquad\quad = 0 \end{array}$$

To find y, we let $x = 0$ in either equation of the system.

$$\begin{aligned} 3x - 2y &= 10 && \text{First equation} \\ 3(0) - 2y &= 10 && \text{Let } x = 0. \\ -2y &= 10 \\ y &= -5 \end{aligned}$$

The ordered pair solution is $(0, -5)$. Check to see that $(0, -5)$ satisfies both equations of the system. ☐

PRACTICE
6 Use the elimination method to solve the system.

$$\begin{cases} 3x - 2y = -6 \\ 4x + 5y = -8 \end{cases}$$

EXAMPLE 7   Use the elimination method to solve the system.

$$\begin{cases} 3x + \dfrac{y}{2} = 2 \\ 6x + y = 5 \end{cases}$$

Solution   If we multiply both sides of the first equation by -2, the coefficients of x in the two equations will be opposites. Then

$$\begin{cases} -2\left(3x + \dfrac{y}{2}\right) = -2(2) \\ 6x + y = 5 \end{cases}$$ simplifies to $$\begin{cases} -6x - y = -4 \\ 6x + y = 5 \end{cases}$$

Now we can add the left sides and add the right sides.

$$\begin{array}{r} -6x - y = -4 \\ 6x + y = 5 \\ \hline 0 = 1 \quad \text{False} \end{array}$$

The resulting equation, $0 = 1$, is false for all values of y or x. Thus, the system has no solution. The solution set is $\{\ \}$ or $\varnothing$. This system is inconsistent, and the graphs of the equations are parallel lines. ☐

PRACTICE
7   Use the elimination method to solve the system.

$$\begin{cases} 8x + y = 6 \\ 2x + \dfrac{y}{4} = -2 \end{cases}$$

EXAMPLE 8   Use the elimination method to solve the system.

$$\begin{cases} -5x - 3y = 9 \\ 10x + 6y = -18 \end{cases}$$

Solution   To eliminate x when the equations are added, we multiply both sides of the first equation by 2. Then

$$\begin{cases} 2(-5x - 3y) = 2(9) \\ 10x + 6y = -18 \end{cases}$$ simplifies to $$\begin{cases} -10x - 6y = 18 \\ 10x + 6y = -18 \end{cases}$$

Next we add the equations.

$$\begin{array}{r} -10x - 6y = 18 \\ 10x + 6y = -18 \\ \hline 0 = 0 \end{array}$$

The resulting equation, $0 = 0$, is true for all possible values of y or x. Notice in the original system that if both sides of the first equation are multiplied by -2, the result is the second equation. This means that the two equations are equivalent. They have the same solution set and there are an infinite number of solutions. Thus, the equations of this system are dependent, and the solution set of the system is

$$\{(x, y)\,|\,-5x - 3y = 9\} \qquad \text{or, equivalently,} \qquad \{(x, y)\,|\,10x + 6y = -18\}. \quad ☐$$

PRACTICE
8   Use the elimination method to solve the system.

$$\begin{cases} -3x + 2y = -1 \\ 9x - 6y = 3 \end{cases}$$

▶ **Helpful Hint**

Remember that not all ordered pairs are solutions of the system in Example 8. Only the infinite number of ordered pairs that satisfy $-5x - 3y = 9$ or equivalently $10x + 6y = -18$.

Graphing Calculator Explorations

A graphing calculator may be used to approximate solutions of systems of equations by graphing each equation on the same set of axes and approximating any points of intersection. For example, approximate the solution of the system

$$\begin{cases} y = -2.6x + 5.6 \\ y = 4.3x - 4.9 \end{cases}$$

First use a standard window and graph both equations on a single screen.

The two lines intersect. To approximate the point of intersection, trace to the point of intersection and use an Intersect feature of the graphing calculator or a Zoom In feature.

Using either method, we find that the approximate point of intersection is (1.52, 1.64).

Solve each system of equations. Approximate the solutions to two decimal places.

1. $y = -1.65x + 3.65$
  $y = 4.56x - 9.44$

2. $y = 7.61x + 3.48$
  $y = -1.26x - 6.43$

3. $2.33x - 4.72y = 10.61$
  $5.86x + 6.22y = -8.89$

4. $-7.89x - 5.68y = 3.26$
  $-3.65x + 4.98y = 11.77$

VOCABULARY & READINESS CHECK

Match each graph with the solution of the corresponding system.

A   **B**   **C**   **D**

1. no solution   **2.** Infinite number of solutions   **3.** $(1, -2)$ **4.** $(-3, 0)$

4.1 | EXERCISE SET

MyMathLab

PRACTICE   WATCH   DOWNLOAD   READ   REVIEW

Determine whether each given ordered pair is a solution of each system. See Example 1.

1. $\begin{cases} x - y = 3 \\ 2x - 4y = 8 \end{cases}$ $(2, -1)$

2. $\begin{cases} x - y = -4 \\ 2x + 10y = 4 \end{cases}$ $(-3, 1)$

3. $\begin{cases} 2x - 3y = -9 \\ 4x + 2y = -2 \end{cases}$ $(3, 5)$

4. $\begin{cases} 2x - 5y = -2 \\ 3x + 4y = 4 \end{cases}$ $(4, 2)$

5. $\begin{cases} 3x + 7y = -19 \\ -6x = 5y + 8 \end{cases}$ $\left(\frac{2}{3}, -3\right)$

6. $\begin{cases} 4x + 5y = -7 \\ -8x = 3y - 1 \end{cases}$ $\left(\frac{3}{4}, -2\right)$

Solve each system by graphing. See Example 2.

7. $\begin{cases} x + y = 1 \\ x - 2y = 4 \end{cases}$

8. $\begin{cases} 2x - y = 8 \\ x + 3y = 11 \end{cases}$

9. $\begin{cases} 2y - 4x = 0 \\ x + 2y = 5 \end{cases}$

10. $\begin{cases} 4x - y = 6 \\ x - y = 0 \end{cases}$

11. $\begin{cases} 3x - y = 4 \\ 6x - 2y = 4 \end{cases}$

12. $\begin{cases} -x + 3y = 6 \\ 3x - 9y = 9 \end{cases}$

13. Can a system consisting of two linear equations have exactly two solutions? Explain why or why not.

14. Suppose the graph of the equations in a system of two equations in two variables consists of a circle and a line. Discuss the possible number of solutions for this system.

Solve each system of equations by the substitution method. See Examples 3 and 4.

15. $\begin{cases} x + y = 10 \\ y = 4x \end{cases}$

16. $\begin{cases} 5x + 2y = -17 \\ x = 3y \end{cases}$

17. $\begin{cases} 4x - y = 9 \\ 2x + 3y = -27 \end{cases}$

18. $\begin{cases} 3x - y = 6 \\ -4x + 2y = -8 \end{cases}$

19. $\begin{cases} \dfrac{1}{2}x + \dfrac{3}{4}y = -\dfrac{1}{4} \\ \dfrac{3}{4}x - \dfrac{1}{4}y = 1 \end{cases}$

20. $\begin{cases} \dfrac{2}{5}x + \dfrac{1}{5}y = -1 \\ x + \dfrac{2}{5}y = -\dfrac{8}{5} \end{cases}$

21. $\begin{cases} \dfrac{x}{3} + y = \dfrac{4}{3} \\ -x + 2y = 11 \end{cases}$

22. $\begin{cases} \dfrac{x}{8} - \dfrac{y}{2} = 1 \\ \dfrac{x}{3} - y = 2 \end{cases}$

Solve each system of equations by the elimination method. See Examples 5 through 8.

23. $\begin{cases} -x + 2y = 0 \\ x + 2y = 5 \end{cases}$

24. $\begin{cases} -2x + 3y = 0 \\ 2x + 6y = 3 \end{cases}$

25. $\begin{cases} 5x + 2y = 1 \\ x - 3y = 7 \end{cases}$

26. $\begin{cases} 6x - y = -5 \\ 4x - 2y = 6 \end{cases}$

27. $\begin{cases} \dfrac{3}{4}x + \dfrac{5}{2}y = 11 \\ \dfrac{1}{16}x - \dfrac{3}{4}y = -1 \end{cases}$

28. $\begin{cases} \dfrac{2}{3}x + \dfrac{1}{4}y = -\dfrac{3}{2} \\ \dfrac{1}{2}x - \dfrac{1}{4}y = -2 \end{cases}$

29. $\begin{cases} 3x - 5y = 11 \\ 2x - 6y = 2 \end{cases}$

30. $\begin{cases} 6x - 3y = -3 \\ 4x + 5y = -9 \end{cases}$

31. $\begin{cases} x - 2y = 4 \\ 2x - 4y = 4 \end{cases}$

32. $\begin{cases} -x + 3y = 6 \\ 3x - 9y = 9 \end{cases}$

33. $\begin{cases} 3x + y = 1 \\ 2y = 2 - 6x \end{cases}$

34. $\begin{cases} y = 2x - 5 \\ 8x - 4y = 20 \end{cases}$

MIXED PRACTICE

Solve each system of equations.

35. $\begin{cases} 2x + 5y = 8 \\ 6x + y = 10 \end{cases}$

36. $\begin{cases} x - 4y = -5 \\ -3x - 8y = 0 \end{cases}$

37. $\begin{cases} x + y = 1 \\ x - 2y = 4 \end{cases}$

38. $\begin{cases} 2x - y = 8 \\ x + 3y = 11 \end{cases}$

39. $\begin{cases} \dfrac{1}{3}x + y = \dfrac{4}{3} \\ -\dfrac{1}{4}x - \dfrac{1}{2}y = -\dfrac{1}{4} \end{cases}$

40. $\begin{cases} \dfrac{3}{4}x - \dfrac{1}{2}y = -\dfrac{1}{2} \\ x + y = -\dfrac{3}{2} \end{cases}$

41. $\begin{cases} 2x + 6y = 8 \\ 3x + 9y = 12 \end{cases}$

42. $\begin{cases} x = 3y - 1 \\ 2x - 6y = -2 \end{cases}$

43. $\begin{cases} 4x + 2y = 5 \\ 2x + y = -1 \end{cases}$

44. $\begin{cases} 3x + 6y = 15 \\ 2x + 4y = 3 \end{cases}$

45. $\begin{cases} 10y - 2x = 1 \\ 5y = 4 - 6x \end{cases}$

46. $\begin{cases} 3x + 4y = 0 \\ 7x = 3y \end{cases}$

47. $\begin{cases} 5x - 2y = 27 \\ -3x + 5y = 18 \end{cases}$

48. $\begin{cases} 3x + 4y = 2 \\ 2x + 5y = -1 \end{cases}$

49. $\begin{cases} x = 3y + 2 \\ 5x - 15y = 10 \end{cases}$

50. $\begin{cases} y = \dfrac{1}{7}x + 3 \\ x - 7y = -21 \end{cases}$

51. $\begin{cases} 2x - y = -1 \\ y = -2x \end{cases}$

52. $\begin{cases} x = \dfrac{1}{5}y \\ x - y = -4 \end{cases}$

53. $\begin{cases} 2x = 6 \\ y = 5 - x \end{cases}$

54. $\begin{cases} x = 3y + 4 \\ -y = 5 \end{cases}$

55. $\begin{cases} \dfrac{x + 5}{2} = \dfrac{6 - 4y}{3} \\ \dfrac{3x}{5} = \dfrac{21 - 7y}{10} \end{cases}$

56. $\begin{cases} \dfrac{y}{5} = \dfrac{8 - x}{2} \\ x = \dfrac{2y - 8}{3} \end{cases}$

57. $\begin{cases} 4x - 7y = 7 \\ 12x - 21y = 24 \end{cases}$

58. $\begin{cases} 2x - 5y = 12 \\ -4x + 10y = 20 \end{cases}$

59. $\begin{cases} \dfrac{2}{3}x - \dfrac{3}{4}y = -1 \\ -\dfrac{1}{6}x + \dfrac{3}{8}y = 1 \end{cases}$

60. $\begin{cases} \dfrac{1}{2}x - \dfrac{1}{3}y = -3 \\ \dfrac{1}{8}x + \dfrac{1}{6}y = 0 \end{cases}$

61. $\begin{cases} 0.7x - 0.2y = -1.6 \\ 0.2x - y = -1.4 \end{cases}$

62. $\begin{cases} -0.7x + 0.6y = 1.3 \\ 0.5x - 0.3y = -0.8 \end{cases}$

63. $\begin{cases} 4x - 1.5y = 10.2 \\ 2x + 7.8y = -25.68 \end{cases}$

64. $\begin{cases} x - 3y = -5.3 \\ 6.3x + 6y = 3.96 \end{cases}$

REVIEW AND PREVIEW

Determine whether the given replacement values make each equation true or false. See Section 1.3.

65. $3x - 4y + 2z = 5$; $x = 1$, $y = 2$, and $z = 5$

66. $x + 2y - z = 7$; $x = 2$, $y = -3$, and $z = 3$

67. $-x - 5y + 3z = 15$; $x = 0$, $y = -1$, and $z = 5$

68. $-4x + y - 8z = 4$; $x = 1$, $y = 0$, and $z = -1$

Add the equations. See Section 4.1.

69. $3x + 2y - 5z = 10$
$-3x + 4y + z = 15$

70. $x + 4y - 5z = 20$
$2x - 4y - 2z = -17$

71. $10x + 5y + 6z = 14$
$-9x + 5y - 6z = -12$

72. $-9x - 8y - z = 31$
$9x + 4y - z = 12$

CONCEPT EXTENSIONS

The concept of supply and demand is used often in business. In general, as the unit price of a commodity increases, the demand for that commodity decreases. Also, as a commodity's unit price increases, the manufacturer normally increases the supply. The point where supply is equal to demand is called the equilibrium point. The following shows the graph of a demand equation and the graph of a supply equation for previously rented DVDs. The x-axis represents the number of DVDs in thousands, and the y-axis represents the cost of a DVD. Use this graph to answer Exercises 73 through 76.

73. Find the number of DVDs and the price per DVD when supply equals demand.

74. When *x* is between 3 and 4, is supply greater than demand or is demand greater than supply?

75. When *x* is greater than 7, is supply greater than demand or is demand greater than supply?

76. For what *x*-values are the *y*-values corresponding to the supply equation greater than the *y*-values corresponding to the demand equation?

The revenue equation for a certain brand of toothpaste is $y = 2.5x$, where x is the number of tubes of toothpaste sold and y is the total income for selling x tubes. The cost equation is $y = 0.9x + 3000$, where x is the number of tubes of toothpaste manufactured and y is the cost of producing x tubes. The following set of axes shows the graph of the cost and revenue equations. Use this graph for Exercises 77 through 82.

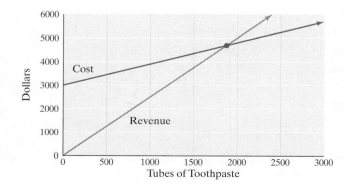

77. Find the coordinates of the point of intersection, or break-even point, by solving the system

$$\begin{cases} y = 2.5x \\ y = 0.9x + 3000 \end{cases}$$

78. Explain the meaning of the ordered pair point of intersection.

79. If the company sells 2000 tubes of toothpaste, does the company make money or lose money?

80. If the company sells 1000 tubes of toothpaste, does the company make money or lose money?

81. For what *x*-values will the company make a profit? (*Hint:* For what *x*-values is the revenue graph "higher" than the cost graph?)

82. For what *x*-values will the company lose money? (*Hint:* For what *x*-values is the revenue graph "lower" than the cost graph?)

83. Write a system of two linear equations in *x* and *y* that has the ordered pair solution (2, 5).

84. Which method would you use to solve the system?

$$\begin{cases} 5x - 2y = 6 \\ 2x + 3y = 5 \end{cases}$$

Explain your choice.

85. The amount *y* of red meat consumed per person in the United States (in pounds) in the year *x* can be modeled by the linear equation $y = -0.3x + 113$. The amount *y* of all poultry consumed per person in the United States (in pounds) in the year *x* can be modeled by the linear equation $y = x + 68$. In both models, $x = 0$ represents the year 2000. (*Source:* Based on data and forecasts from the Economic Research Service, U.S. Department of Agriculture)

a. What does the slope of each equation tell you about the patterns of red meat and poultry consumption in the United States?

b. Solve this system of equations. (Round your final results to the nearest whole numbers.)

c. Explain the meaning of your answer to part (b).

86. The number of books (in thousands) in the University of Texas libraries *y* for the years 2002 through 2005 can be modeled by the linear equation $y = 230x + 8146$. For the same time period, the number of books (in thousands) in the Columbia University libraries can be modeled by $y = 611x + 7378$, where *x* is the number of years since 2002. (*Source:* Association of Research Libraries)

a. What does the slope of each equation tell you about the pattern of books in these two university libraries?

b. Solve this system of equations. (Round your results to the nearest whole number.)

c. Explain the meaning of your answer to part (b).

Solve each system. To do so you may want to let $a = \dfrac{1}{x}$ (if x is in the denominator) and let $b = \dfrac{1}{y}$ (if y is in the denominator.)

87. $\begin{cases} \dfrac{1}{x} + y = 12 \\ \dfrac{3}{x} - y = 4 \end{cases}$

88. $\begin{cases} x + \dfrac{2}{y} = 7 \\ 3x + \dfrac{3}{y} = 6 \end{cases}$

89. $\begin{cases} \dfrac{1}{x} + \dfrac{1}{y} = 5 \\ \dfrac{1}{x} - \dfrac{1}{y} = 1 \end{cases}$

90. $\begin{cases} \dfrac{2}{x} + \dfrac{3}{y} = 5 \\ \dfrac{5}{x} - \dfrac{3}{y} = 2 \end{cases}$

93. $\begin{cases} \dfrac{2}{x} - \dfrac{4}{y} = 5 \\ \dfrac{1}{x} - \dfrac{2}{y} = \dfrac{3}{2} \end{cases}$

91. $\begin{cases} \dfrac{2}{x} + \dfrac{3}{y} = -1 \\ \dfrac{3}{x} - \dfrac{2}{y} = 18 \end{cases}$

92. $\begin{cases} \dfrac{3}{x} - \dfrac{2}{y} = -18 \\ \dfrac{2}{x} + \dfrac{3}{y} = 1 \end{cases}$

94. $\begin{cases} \dfrac{5}{x} + \dfrac{7}{y} = 1 \\ -\dfrac{10}{x} - \dfrac{14}{y} = 0 \end{cases}$

📖 STUDY SKILLS BUILDER

Are You Familiar with Your Textbook Supplements?

There are many student supplements available for additional study. Below, I have listed some of these. See the preface of this text or your instructor for further information.

- *Chapter Test Prep Video CD.* This material is found in your textbook and is fully explained. The CD contains video clip solutions to the Chapter Test exercises in this text and are excellent help when studying for chapter tests.

- *Lecture Video CDs.* These video segments are keyed to each section of the text. The material is presented by me, Elayn Martin-Gay, and I have placed a video icon by each exercise in the text that I have worked on the video.

- *The Student Solutions Manual.* This contains worked out solutions to odd-numbered exercises as well as every exercise in the Integrated Reviews, Chapter Reviews, Chapter Tests, and Cumulative Reviews.

- *Prentice Hall Tutor Center.* Mathematics questions may be phoned, faxed, or emailed to this center.

- *MyMathLab, MathXL, and Interact Math.* These are computer and Internet tutorials. This supplement may already be available to you somewhere on campus, for example at your local learning resource lab. Take a moment and find the name and location of any such lab on campus.

As usual, your instructor is your best source of information.

Let's see how you are doing with textbook supplements:

1. Name one way the Chapter Test Prep Video can help you prepare for a chapter test.

2. List any textbook supplements that you have found useful.

3. Have you located and visited a learning resource lab located on your campus?

4. List the textbook supplements that are currently housed in your campus' learning resource lab.

4.2 SOLVING SYSTEMS OF LINEAR EQUATIONS IN THREE VARIABLES

OBJECTIVE

1 Solve a system of three linear equations in three variables.

In this section, the algebraic methods of solving systems of two linear equations in two variables are extended to systems of three linear equations in three variables. We call the equation $3x - y + z = -15$, for example, a **linear equation in three variables** since there are three variables and each variable is raised only to the power 1. A solution of this equation is an **ordered triple (x, y, z)** that makes the equation a true statement. For example, the ordered triple $(2, 0, -21)$ is a solution of $3x - y + z = -15$ since replacing x with 2, y with 0, and z with -21 yields the true statement $3(2) - 0 + (-21) = -15$. The graph of this equation is a plane in three-dimensional space, just as the graph of a linear equation in two variables is a line in two-dimensional space.

Although we will not discuss the techniques for graphing equations in three variables, visualizing the possible patterns of intersecting planes gives us insight into the possible patterns of solutions of a system of three three-variable linear equations. There are four possible patterns.

1. Three planes have a single point in common. This point represents the single solution of the system. This system is **consistent.**

2. Three planes intersect at no point common to all three. This system has no solution. A few ways that this can occur are shown. This system is **inconsistent.**

3. Three planes intersect at all the points of a single line. The system has infinitely many solutions. This system is **consistent.**

4. Three planes coincide at all points on the plane. The system is consistent, and the equations are **dependent.**

OBJECTIVE 1 ▶ Solving a system of three linear equations in three variables. Just as with systems of two equations in two variables, we can use the elimination or substitution method to solve a system of three equations in three variables. To use the elimination method, we eliminate a variable and obtain a system of two equations in two variables. Then we use the methods we learned in the previous section to solve the system of two equations.

EXAMPLE 1   Solve the system.

$$\begin{cases} 3x - y + z = -15 & \text{Equation (1)} \\ x + 2y - z = 1 & \text{Equation (2)} \\ 2x + 3y - 2z = 0 & \text{Equation (3)} \end{cases}$$

Solution   Add equations (1) and (2) to eliminate z.

$$\begin{array}{r} 3x - y + z = -15 \\ \underline{x + 2y - z = 1} \\ 4x + y = -14 \quad \text{Equation (4)} \end{array}$$

Next, add two *other* equations and *eliminate z again.* To do so, multiply both sides of equation (1) by 2 and add this resulting equation to equation (3). Then

$$\begin{cases} 2(3x - y + z) = 2(-15) \\ 2x + 3y - 2z = 0 \end{cases} \quad \text{simplifies to} \quad \begin{cases} 6x - 2y + 2z = -30 \\ \underline{2x + 3y - 2z = 0} \\ 8x + y = -30 \quad \text{Equation (5)} \end{cases}$$

Now solve equations (4) and (5) for x and y. To solve by elimination, multiply both sides of equation (4) by -1 and add this resulting equation to equation (5). Then

$$\begin{cases} -1(4x + y) = -1(-14) \\ 8x + y = -30 \end{cases} \quad \text{simplifies to} \quad \begin{cases} -4x - y = 14 \\ \underline{8x + y = -30} \\ 4x = -16 \quad \text{Add the equations.} \\ x = -4 \quad \text{Solve for } x. \end{cases}$$

Replace x with -4 in equation (4) or (5).

$$4x + y = -14 \quad \text{Equation (4)}$$
$$4(-4) + y = -14 \quad \text{Let } x = -4.$$
$$y = 2 \quad \text{Solve for } y.$$

Finally, replace x with -4 and y with 2 in equation (1), (2), or (3).

$$x + 2y - z = 1 \quad \text{Equation (2)}$$
$$-4 + 2(2) - z = 1 \quad \text{Let } x = -4 \text{ and } y = 2.$$
$$-4 + 4 - z = 1$$
$$-z = 1$$
$$z = -1$$

The solution is $(-4, 2, -1)$. To check, let $x = -4$, $y = 2$, and $z = -1$ in all three original equations of the system.

Equation (1)	**Equation (2)**	**Equation (3)**
$3x - y + z = -15$	$x + 2y - z = 1$	$2x + 3y - 2z = 0$
$3(-4) - 2 + (-1) \overset{?}{=} -15$	$-4 + 2(2) - (-1) \overset{?}{=} 1$	$2(-4) + 3(2) - 2(-1) \overset{?}{=} 0$
$-12 - 2 - 1 \overset{?}{=} -15$	$-4 + 4 + 1 \overset{?}{=} 1$	$-8 + 6 + 2 \overset{?}{=} 0$
$-15 = -15$	$1 = 1$	$0 = 0$
True	True	True

All three statements are true, so the solution is $(-4, 2, -1)$.   □

PRACTICE
1   Solve the system. $\begin{cases} 3x + 2y - z = 0 \\ x - y + 5z = 2 \\ 2x + 3y + 3z = 7 \end{cases}$

EXAMPLE 2   Solve the system.

$$\begin{cases} 2x - 4y + 8z = 2 & (1) \\ -x - 3y + z = 11 & (2) \\ x - 2y + 4z = 0 & (3) \end{cases}$$

Solution Add equations (2) and (3) to eliminate x, and the new equation is

$$-5y + 5z = 11 \quad (4)$$

To eliminate x again, multiply both sides of equation (2) by 2, and add the resulting equation to equation (1). Then

$$\begin{cases} 2x - 4y + 8z = 2 \\ 2(-x - 3y + z) = 2(11) \end{cases} \quad \begin{array}{l} \text{simplifies} \\ \text{to} \end{array} \quad \begin{cases} 2x - 4y + 8z = 2 \\ \underline{-2x - 6y + 2z = 22} \\ \quad\quad -10y + 10z = 24 \quad (5) \end{cases}$$

Next, solve for y and z using equations (4) and (5). Multiply both sides of equation (4) by -2, and add the resulting equation to equation (5).

$$\begin{cases} -2(-5y + 5z) = -2(11) \\ -10y + 10z = 24 \end{cases} \quad \begin{array}{l} \text{simplifies} \\ \text{to} \end{array} \quad \begin{cases} 10y - 10z = -22 \\ \underline{-10y + 10z = 24} \\ \quad\quad\quad 0 = 2 \quad \text{False} \end{cases}$$

Since the statement is false, this system is inconsistent and has no solution. The solution set is the empty set $\{\ \}$ or $\varnothing$. □

PRACTICE 2 Solve the system. $\begin{cases} 6x - 3y + 12z = 4 \\ -6x + 4y - 2z = 7 \\ -2x + y - 4z = 3 \end{cases}$

The elimination method is summarized next.

Solving a System of Three Linear Equations by the Elimination Method

STEP 1. Write each equation in standard form $Ax + By + Cz = D$.

STEP 2. Choose a pair of equations and use the equations to eliminate a variable.

STEP 3. Choose any **other** pair of equations and eliminate the **same variable** as in Step 2.

> **Helpful Hint**
> Make sure you read closely and follow Step 3.

STEP 4. Two equations in two variables should be obtained from Step 2 and Step 3. Use methods from Section 4.1 to solve this system for both variables.

STEP 5. To solve for the third variable, substitute the values of the variables found in Step 4 into any of the original equations containing the third variable.

STEP 6. Check the ordered triple solution in _all three_ original equations.

Concept Check ✓

In the system

$$\begin{cases} x + y + z = 6 & \text{Equation (1)} \\ 2x - y + z = 3 & \text{Equation (2)} \\ x + 2y + 3z = 14 & \text{Equation (3)} \end{cases}$$

equations (1) and (2) are used to eliminate y. Which action could be used to best finish solving? Why?

a. Use (1) and (2) to eliminate z.　　　　　**b.** Use (2) and (3) to eliminate y.

c. Use (1) and (3) to eliminate x.

Answer to Concept Check: b

EXAMPLE 3 Solve the system.

$$\begin{cases} 2x + 4y = 1 & (1) \\ 4x \quad\quad - 4z = -1 & (2) \\ \quad\quad y - 4z = -3 & (3) \end{cases}$$

Solution Notice that equation (2) has no term containing the variable y. Let us eliminate y using equations (1) and (3). Multiply both sides of equation (3) by -4, and add the resulting equation to equation (1). Then

$$\begin{cases} 2x + 4y = 1 \\ -4(y - 4z) = -4(-3) \end{cases} \text{ simplifies to } \begin{cases} 2x + 4y = 1 \\ \underline{\quad - 4y + 16z = 12} \\ 2x \quad\quad + 16z = 13 \quad (4) \end{cases}$$

Next, solve for z using equations (4) and (2). Multiply both sides of equation (4) by -2 and add the resulting equation to equation (2).

$$\begin{cases} -2(2x + 16z) = -2(13) \\ 4x - 4z = -1 \end{cases} \text{ simplifies to } \begin{cases} -4x - 32z = -26 \\ \underline{4x - 4z = -1} \\ -36z = -27 \\ z = \dfrac{3}{4} \end{cases}$$

Replace z with $\dfrac{3}{4}$ in equation (3) and solve for y.

$$y - 4\left(\dfrac{3}{4}\right) = -3 \quad \text{Let } z = \dfrac{3}{4} \text{ in equation (3).}$$
$$y - 3 = -3$$
$$y = 0$$

Replace y with 0 in equation (1) and solve for x.

$$2x + 4(0) = 1$$
$$2x = 1$$
$$x = \dfrac{1}{2}$$

The solution is $\left(\dfrac{1}{2}, 0, \dfrac{3}{4}\right)$. Check to see that this solution satisfies all three equations of the system. □

PRACTICE
3 Solve the system. $\begin{cases} 3x + 4y = 0 \\ 9x \quad\quad - 4z = 6 \\ \quad -2y + 7z = 1 \end{cases}$

EXAMPLE 4 Solve the system.

$$\begin{cases} x - 5y - 2z = 6 & (1) \\ -2x + 10y + 4z = -12 & (2) \\ \dfrac{1}{2}x - \dfrac{5}{2}y - z = 3 & (3) \end{cases}$$

Solution Multiply both sides of equation (3) by 2 to eliminate fractions, and multiply both sides of equation (2) by $-\dfrac{1}{2}$ so that the coefficient of x is 1. The resulting system is then

$$\begin{cases} x - 5y - 2z = 6 & (1) \\ x - 5y - 2z = 6 & \text{Multiply (2) by } -\dfrac{1}{2}. \\ x - 5y - 2z = 6 & \text{Multiply (3) by 2.} \end{cases}$$

All three equations are identical, and therefore equations (1), (2), and (3) are all equivalent. There are infinitely many solutions of this system. The equations are dependent. The solution set can be written as $\{(x, y, z) | x - 5y - 2z = 6\}$.

PRACTICE 4 Solve the system. $\begin{cases} 2x + y - 3z = 6 \\ x + \dfrac{1}{2}y - \dfrac{3}{2}z = 3 \\ -4x - 2y + 6z = -12 \end{cases}$

As mentioned earlier, we can also use the substitution method to solve a system of linear equations in three variables.

EXAMPLE 5 Solve the system:

$$\begin{cases} x - 4y - 5z = 35 & (1) \\ x - 3y = 0 & (2) \\ -y + z = -55 & (3) \end{cases}$$

Solution Notice in equations (2) and (3) that a variable is missing. Also notice that both equations contain the variable y. Let's use the substitution method by solving equation (2) for x and equation (3) for z and substituting the results in equation (1).

$$x - 3y = 0 \qquad (2)$$
$$x = 3y \qquad \text{Solve equation (2) for } x.$$
$$-y + z = -55 \qquad (3)$$
$$z = y - 55 \qquad \text{Solve equation (3) for } z.$$

Now substitute $3y$ for x and $y - 55$ for z in equation (1).

$$x - 4y - 5z = 35 \qquad (1)$$

▶ **Helpful Hint**
Do not forget to distribute.

$$3y - 4y - 5(y - 55) = 35 \qquad \text{Let } x = 3y \text{ and } z = y - 55.$$
$$3y - 4y - 5y + 275 = 35 \qquad \text{Use the distributive law and multiply.}$$
$$-6y + 275 = 35 \qquad \text{Combine like terms.}$$
$$-6y = -240 \qquad \text{Subtract 275 from both sides.}$$
$$y = 40 \qquad \text{Solve.}$$

To find x, recall that $x = 3y$ and substitute 40 for y. Then $x = 3y$ becomes $x = 3 \cdot 40 = 120$. To find z, recall that $z = y - 55$ and substitute 40 for y, also. Then $z = y - 55$ becomes $z = 40 - 55 = -15$. The solution is $(120, 40, -15)$.

PRACTICE 5 Solve the system. $\begin{cases} x + 2y + 4z = 16 \\ x + 2z = -4 \\ y - 3z = 30 \end{cases}$

4.2 | EXERCISE SET

 MyMathLab PRACTICE   WATCH   DOWNLOAD   READ   REVIEW

Solve.

1. Choose the equation(s) that has $(-1, 3, 1)$ as a solution.
 a. $x + y + z = 3$ **b.** $-x + y + z = 5$
 c. $-x + y + 2z = 0$ **d.** $x + 2y - 3z = 2$

2. Choose the equation(s) that has $(2, 1, -4)$ as a solution.
 a. $x + y + z = -1$ **b.** $x - y - z = -3$
 c. $2x - y + z = -1$ **d.** $-x - 3y - z = -1$

3. Use the result of Exercise 1 to determine whether $(-1, 3, 1)$ is a solution of the system below. Explain your answer.
$$\begin{cases} x + y + z = 3 \\ -x + y + z = 5 \\ x + 2y - 3z = 2 \end{cases}$$

4. Use the result of Exercise 2 to determine whether $(2, 1, -4)$ is a solution of the system below. Explain your answer.
$$\begin{cases} x + y + z = -1 \\ x - y - z = -3 \\ 2x - y + z = -1 \end{cases}$$

MIXED PRACTICE

Solve each system. See Examples 1 through 5.

5. $\begin{cases} x - y + z = -4 \\ 3x + 2y - z = 5 \\ -2x + 3y - z = 15 \end{cases}$ **6.** $\begin{cases} x + y - z = -1 \\ -4x - y + 2z = -7 \\ 2x - 2y - 5z = 7 \end{cases}$

7. $\begin{cases} x + y = 3 \\ 2y = 10 \\ 3x + 2y - 3z = 1 \end{cases}$ **8.** $\begin{cases} 5x = 5 \\ 2x + y = 4 \\ 3x + y - 4z = -15 \end{cases}$

9. $\begin{cases} 2x + 2y + z = 1 \\ -x + y + 2z = 3 \\ x + 2y + 4z = 0 \end{cases}$ **10.** $\begin{cases} 2x - 3y + z = 5 \\ x + y + z = 0 \\ 4x + 2y + 4z = 4 \end{cases}$

11. $\begin{cases} x - 2y + z = -5 \\ -3x + 6y - 3z = 15 \\ 2x - 4y + 2z = -10 \end{cases}$ **12.** $\begin{cases} 3x + y - 2z = 2 \\ -6x - 2y + 4z = -2 \\ 9x + 3y - 6z = 6 \end{cases}$

13. $\begin{cases} 4x - y + 2z = 5 \\ 2y + z = 4 \\ 4x + y + 3z = 10 \end{cases}$ **14.** $\begin{cases} 5y - 7z = 14 \\ 2x + y + 4z = 10 \\ 2x + 6y - 3z = 30 \end{cases}$

15. $\begin{cases} x + 5z = 0 \\ 5x + y = 0 \\ y - 3z = 0 \end{cases}$ **16.** $\begin{cases} x - 5y = 0 \\ x - z = 0 \\ -x + 5z = 0 \end{cases}$

17. $\begin{cases} 6x - 5z = 17 \\ 5x - y + 3z = -1 \\ 2x + y = -41 \end{cases}$ **18.** $\begin{cases} x + 2y = 6 \\ 7x + 3y + z = -33 \\ x - z = 16 \end{cases}$

19. $\begin{cases} x + y + z = 8 \\ 2x - y - z = 10 \\ x - 2y - 3z = 22 \end{cases}$ **20.** $\begin{cases} 5x + y + 3z = 1 \\ x - y + 3z = -7 \\ -x + y = 1 \end{cases}$

21. $\begin{cases} x + 2y - z = 5 \\ 6x + y + z = 7 \\ 2x + 4y - 2z = 5 \end{cases}$ **22.** $\begin{cases} 4x - y + 3z = 10 \\ x + y - z = 5 \\ 8x - 2y + 6z = 10 \end{cases}$

23. $\begin{cases} 2x - 3y + z = 2 \\ x - 5y + 5z = 3 \\ 3x + y - 3z = 5 \end{cases}$ **24.** $\begin{cases} 4x + y - z = 8 \\ x - y + 2z = 3 \\ 3x - y + z = 6 \end{cases}$

25. $\begin{cases} -2x - 4y + 6z = -8 \\ x + 2y - 3z = 4 \\ 4x + 8y - 12z = 16 \end{cases}$ **26.** $\begin{cases} -6x + 12y + 3z = -6 \\ 2x - 4y - z = 2 \\ -x + 2y + \dfrac{z}{2} = -1 \end{cases}$

27. $\begin{cases} 2x + 2y - 3z = 1 \\ y + 2z = -14 \\ 3x - 2y = -1 \end{cases}$ **28.** $\begin{cases} 7x + 4y = 10 \\ x - 4y + 2z = 6 \\ y - 2z = -1 \end{cases}$

29. $\begin{cases} x + 2y - z = 5 \\ -3x - 2y - 3z = 11 \\ 4x + 4y + 5z = -18 \end{cases}$ **30.** $\begin{cases} 3x - 3y + z = -1 \\ 3x - y - z = 3 \\ -6x + 2y + 2z = -6 \end{cases}$

31. $\begin{cases} \dfrac{3}{4}x - \dfrac{1}{3}y + \dfrac{1}{2}z = 9 \\ \dfrac{1}{6}x + \dfrac{1}{3}y - \dfrac{1}{2}z = 2 \\ \dfrac{1}{2}x - y + \dfrac{1}{2}z = 2 \end{cases}$ **32.** $\begin{cases} \dfrac{1}{3}x - \dfrac{1}{4}y + z = -9 \\ \dfrac{1}{2}x - \dfrac{1}{3}y - \dfrac{1}{4}z = -6 \\ x - \dfrac{1}{2}y - z = -8 \end{cases}$

REVIEW AND PREVIEW

Solve. See Section 2.2.

33. The sum of two numbers is 45 and one number is twice the other. Find the numbers.

34. The difference between two numbers is 5. Twice the smaller number added to five times the larger number is 53. Find the numbers.

Solve. See Section 2.1.

35. $2(x - 1) - 3x = x - 12$

36. $7(2x - 1) + 4 = 11(3x - 2)$

37. $-y - 5(y + 5) = 3y - 10$

38. $z - 3(z + 7) = 6(2z + 1)$

CONCEPT EXTENSIONS

39. Write a single linear equation in three variables that has $(-1, 2, -4)$ as a solution. (There are many possibilities.) Explain the process you used to write an equation.

40. Write a system of three linear equations in three variables that has $(2, 1, 5)$ as a solution. (There are many possibilities.) Explain the process you used to write an equation.

41. Write a system of linear equations in three variables that has the solution $(-1, 2, -4)$. Explain the process you used to write your system.

42. When solving a system of three equation in three unknowns, explain how to determine that a system has no solution.

43. The fraction $\dfrac{1}{24}$ can be written as the following sum:

$$\frac{1}{24} = \frac{x}{8} + \frac{y}{4} + \frac{z}{3}$$

where the numbers x, y, and z are solutions of

$$\begin{cases} x + y + z = 1 \\ 2x - y + z = 0 \\ -x + 2y + 2z = -1 \end{cases}$$

Solve the system and see that the sum of the fractions is $\dfrac{1}{24}$.

44. The fraction $\dfrac{1}{18}$ can be written as the following sum:

$$\frac{1}{18} = \frac{x}{2} + \frac{y}{3} + \frac{z}{9}$$

where the numbers x, y, and z are solutions of

$$\begin{cases} x + 3y + z = -3 \\ -x + y + 2z = -14 \\ 3x + 2y - z = 12 \end{cases}$$

Solve the system and see that the sum of the fractions is $\dfrac{1}{18}$.

Solving systems involving more than three variables can be accomplished with methods similar to those encountered in this section. Apply what you already know to solve each system of equations in four variables.

45. $\begin{cases} x + y \quad\;\; - w = 0 \\ \quad\;\; y + 2z + w = 3 \\ x \quad\quad - z \quad\;\; = 1 \\ 2x - y \quad\quad - w = -1 \end{cases}$

46. $\begin{cases} 5x + 4y \quad\quad\quad = 29 \\ \quad\quad y + z - w = -2 \\ 5x \quad\quad + z \quad\quad = 23 \\ \quad\quad y - z + w = 4 \end{cases}$

47. $\begin{cases} x + y + z + w = 5 \\ 2x + y + z + w = 6 \\ x + y + z \quad\;\; = 2 \\ x + y \quad\quad\quad = 0 \end{cases}$

48. $\begin{cases} 2x \quad\quad - z \quad\quad = -1 \\ \quad\quad y + z + w = 9 \\ \quad\quad y \quad - 2w = -6 \\ x + y \quad\quad\quad = 3 \end{cases}$

49. Write a system of three linear equations in three variables that are dependent equations.

50. What is the solution to the system in Exercise 49?

4.3 SYSTEMS OF LINEAR EQUATIONS AND PROBLEM SOLVING

OBJECTIVES

1 Solve problems that can be modeled by a system of two linear equations.

2 Solve problems with cost and revenue functions.

3 Solve problems that can be modeled by a system of three linear equations.

OBJECTIVE 1 ▶ Solving problem modeled by systems of two equations. Thus far, we have solved problems by writing one-variable equations and solving for the variable. Some of these problems can be solved, perhaps more easily, by writing a system of equations, as illustrated in this section.

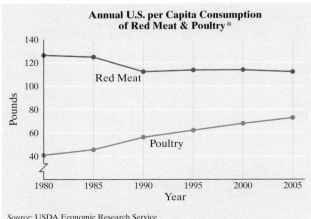

Annual U.S. per Capita Consumption of Red Meat & Poultry*

Source: USDA Economic Research Service
* Excludes shipments to Puerto Rico and other U.S. possessions

| **EXAMPLE 1** | **Predicting Equal Consumption of Red Meat and Poultry** |

America's consumption of red meat has decreased most years since 1980 while consumption of poultry has increased. The function $y = -0.59x + 124.6$ approximates the annual pounds of red meat consumed per capita, where x is the number of years since 1980. The function $y = 1.34x + 40.9$ approximates the annual pounds of poultry consumed per capita, where x is also the number of years since 1980. If this trend continues, determine the year in which the annual consumption of red meat and poultry is equal. (*Source:* Based on data from Economic Research Service, U.S. Dept. of Agriculture)

Solution

1. UNDERSTAND. Read and reread the problem and guess a year. Let's guess the year 2020. This year is 40 years since 1980, so $x = 40$. Now let $x = 40$ in each given function.

   Red meat: $y = -0.59x + 124.6 = -0.59(40) + 124.6 = 101$ pounds
   Poultry: $y = 1.34x + 40.9 \quad = 1.34(40) + 40.9 \quad = 94.5$ pounds

Since the projected pounds in 2020 for red meat and poultry are not the same, we guessed incorrectly, but we do have a better understanding of the problem. We also know that the year will be later than 2020 since projected consumption of red meat is still greater than poultry that year.

2. TRANSLATE. We are already given the system of equations.

3. SOLVE. We want to know the year x in which pounds y are the same, so we solve the system:

$$\begin{cases} y = -0.59x + 124.6 \\ y = 1.34x + 40.9 \end{cases}$$

Since both equations are solved for y, one way to solve is to use the substitution method.

$$y = -0.59x + 124.6 \quad \text{First equation}$$

$$1.34x + 40.9 = -0.59x + 124.6 \quad \text{Let } y = 1.34x + 40.9.$$

$$1.93x = 83.7$$

$$x = \frac{83.7}{1.93} \approx 43.37$$

4. INTERPRET. Since we are only asked to give the year, we need only solve for x.

Check: To check, see whether $x \approx 43.37$ gives approximately the same number of pounds of red meat and poultry.

   Red meat: $-0.59x + 124.6 = -0.59(43.37) + 124.6 = 99.01$ pounds
   Poultry: $1.34x + 40.9 = 1.34(43.37) + 40.9 = 99.02$ pounds

Since we rounded the number of years, the number of pounds do differ slightly. They differ only by 0.0041, so we can assume that we solved correctly.

State: The consumption of red meat and poultry will be the same about 43.37 years after 1980, or 2023.37. Thus, in the year 2023, we predict the consumption will be the same. □

PRACTICE

1 Read Example 1. If we use the years 1995, 2000, and 2005 only to write functions approximating the consumption of red meat and poultry, we have the following:

   Red meat: $y = -0.16x + 113.9$
   Poultry: $y = 1.06x + 62.3$

where x is the years since 1995 and y is pounds per year consumed.

a. Assuming this trend continues, predict the year in which the consumption of red meat and poultry will be the same.

b. Does your answer differ from the example? Why or why not?

Note: A similar exercise is found in Section 4.1, Exercise 85. In the example above, the data years used to generate the equations are 1980–2005. In Section 4.1, the data years used are 2000–2005. Note the differing equations and answers.

EXAMPLE 2   Finding Unknown Numbers

A first number is 4 less than a second number. Four times the first number is 6 more than twice the second. Find the numbers.

Solution

1. UNDERSTAND. Read and reread the problem and guess a solution. If a first number is 10 and this is 4 less than a second number, the second number is 14. Four times the first number is 4(10), or 40. This is not equal to 6 more than twice the second number, which is 2(14) + 6 or 34. Although we guessed incorrectly, we now have a better understanding of the problem.

Since we are looking for two numbers, we will let

$$x = \text{first number}$$
$$y = \text{second number}$$

2. TRANSLATE. Since we have assigned two variables to this problem, we will translate the given facts into two equations. For the first statement we have

In words:	the first number	is	4 less than the second number
	↓	↓	↓
Translate:	x	$=$	$y - 4$

Next we translate the second statement into an equation.

In words:	four times the first number	is	6 more than twice the second number
	↓	↓	↓
Translate:	$4x$	$=$	$2y + 6$

3. SOLVE. Here we solve the system

$$\begin{cases} x = y - 4 \\ 4x = 2y + 6 \end{cases}$$

Since the first equation expresses x in terms of y, we will use substitution. We substitute $y - 4$ for x in the second equation and solve for y.

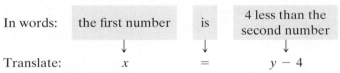

$$4x = 2y + 6 \quad \text{Second equation}$$
$$4(y - 4) = 2y + 6$$
$$4y - 16 = 2y + 6 \quad \text{Let } x = y - 4.$$
$$2y = 22$$
$$y = 11$$

Now we replace y with 11 in the equation $x = y - 4$ and solve for x. Then $x = y - 4$ becomes $x = 11 - 4 = 7$. The ordered pair solution of the system is $(7, 11)$.

4. INTERPRET. Since the solution of the system is (7, 11), then the first number we are looking for is 7 and the second number is 11.

Check: Notice that 7 *is* 4 less than 11, and 4 times 7 *is* 6 more than twice 11. The proposed numbers, 7 and 11, are correct.

State: The numbers are 7 and 11.   □

PRACTICE
2   A first number is 5 more than a second number. Twice the first number is 2 less than 3 times the second number. Find the numbers.

EXAMPLE 3   Finding the Rate of Speed

Two cars leave Indianapolis, one traveling east and the other west. After 3 hours they are 297 miles apart. If one car is traveling 5 mph faster than the other, what is the speed of each?

Solution

1. UNDERSTAND. Read and reread the problem. Let's guess a solution and use the formula $d = rt$ (distance = rate · time) to check. Suppose that one car is traveling at a rate of 55 miles per hour. This means that the other car is traveling at a rate of 50 miles per hour since we are told that one car is traveling 5 mph faster than the other. To find the distance apart after 3 hours, we will first find the distance traveled by each car. One car's distance is rate · time = 55(3) = 165 miles. The other car's distance is rate · time = 50(3) = 150 miles. Since one car is traveling east and the other west, their distance apart is the sum of their distances, or 165 miles + 150 miles = 315 miles. Although this distance apart is not the required distance of 297 miles, we now have a better understanding of the problem.

Let's model the problem with a system of equations. We will let

$$x = \text{speed of one car}$$
$$y = \text{speed of the other car}$$

We summarize the information on the following chart. Both cars have traveled 3 hours. Since distance = rate · time, their distances are $3x$ and $3y$ miles, respectively.

	Rate •	*Time* =	*Distance*
One Car	x	3	$3x$
Other Car	y	3	$3y$

2. TRANSLATE. We can now translate the stated conditions into two equations.

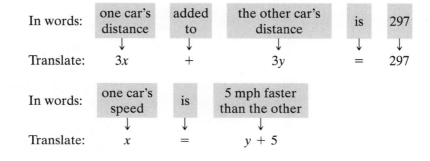

3. SOLVE. Here we solve the system

$$\begin{cases} 3x + 3y = 297 \\ x = y + 5 \end{cases}$$

Again, the substitution method is appropriate. We replace x with $y + 5$ in the first equation and solve for y.

$$3x + 3y = 297 \quad \text{First equation}$$

$$3(y + 5) + 3y = 297 \quad \text{Let } x = y + 5.$$
$$3y + 15 + 3y = 297$$
$$6y = 282$$
$$y = 47$$

To find x, we replace y with 47 in the equation $x = y + 5$. Then $x = 47 + 5 = 52$. The ordered pair solution of the system is $(52, 47)$.

4. INTERPRET. The solution $(52, 47)$ means that the cars are traveling at 52 mph and 47 mph, respectively.

Check: Notice that one car is traveling 5 mph faster than the other. Also, if one car travels 52 mph for 3 hours, the distance is $3(52) = 156$ miles. The other car traveling for 3 hours at 47 mph travels a distance of $3(47) = 141$ miles. The sum of the distances $156 + 141$ is 297 miles, the required distance.

State: The cars are traveling at 52 mph and 47 mph. □

> ▶ **Helpful Hint**
>
> Don't forget to attach units, if appropriate.

PRACTICE

3 In 2007, the French train TGV V150 became the fastest conventional rail train in the world. It broke the 1990 record of the next fastest conventional rail train, the French TGV Atlantique. Assume the V150 and the Atlantique left the same station in Paris, with one heading west and one heading east. After 2 hours, they were 2150 kilometers apart. If the V150 is 75 kph faster than the Atlantique, what is the speed of each?

EXAMPLE 4 **Mixing Solutions**

Lynn Pike, a pharmacist, needs 70 liters of a 50% alcohol solution. She has available a 30% alcohol solution and an 80% alcohol solution. How many liters of each solution should she mix to obtain 70 liters of a 50% alcohol solution?

Solution

1. UNDERSTAND. Read and reread the problem. Next, guess the solution. Suppose that we need 20 liters of the 30% solution. Then we need $70 - 20 = 50$ liters of the 80% solution. To see if this gives us 70 liters of a 50% alcohol solution, let's find the amount of pure alcohol in each solution.

number of liters	×	alcohol strength	=	amount of pure alcohol
20 liters	×	0.30	=	6 liters
50 liters	×	0.80	=	40 liters
70 liters	×	0.50	=	35 liters

Since 6 liters + 40 liters = 46 liters and not 35 liters, our guess is incorrect, but we have gained some insight as to how to model and check this problem.

We will let

$$x = \text{amount of 30\% solution, in liters}$$
$$y = \text{amount of 80\% solution, in liters}$$

and use a table to organize the given data.

	Number of Liters	Alcohol Strength	Amount of Pure Alcohol
30% Solution	x	30%	$0.30x$
80% Solution	y	80%	$0.80y$
50% Solution Needed	70	50%	$(0.50)(70)$

2. **TRANSLATE.** We translate the stated conditions into two equations.

In words: | amount of 30% solution | + | amount of 80% solution | = | 70 |

Translate: x + y =   70

In words: | amount of pure alcohol in 30% solution | + | amount of pure alcohol in 80% solution | = | amount of pure alcohol in 50% solution |

Translate: $0.30x$ + $0.80y$ = $(0.50)(70)$

3. **SOLVE.** Here we solve the system

$$\begin{cases} x + y = 70 \\ 0.30x + 0.80y = (0.50)(70) \end{cases}$$

To solve this system, we use the elimination method. We multiply both sides of the first equation by -3 and both sides of the second equation by 10. Then

$$\begin{cases} -3(x + y) = -3(70) \\ 10(0.30x + 0.80y) = 10(0.50)(70) \end{cases} \text{ simplifies to } \begin{cases} -3x - 3y = -210 \\ \underline{3x + 8y = 350} \\ 5y = 140 \\ y = 28 \end{cases}$$

Now we replace y with 28 in the equation $x + y = 70$ and find that $x + 28 = 70$, or $x = 42$.
The ordered pair solution of the system is $(42, 28)$.

4. **INTERPRET.**

Check: Check the solution in the same way that we checked our guess.

State: The pharmacist needs to mix 42 liters of 30% solution and 28 liters of 80% solution to obtain 70 liters of 50% solution.   □

PRACTICE

4   Keith Robinson is a chemistry teacher who needs 1 liter of a solution of 5% hydrochloric acid to carry out an experiment. If he only has a stock solution of 99% hydrochloric acid, how much water (0% acid) and how much stock solution (99%) of HCL must he mix to get 1 liter of 5% solution? Round answers to the nearest hundredth of a liter.

Concept Check ✓

Suppose you mix an amount of 25% acid solution with an amount of 60% acid solution. You then calculate the acid strength of the resulting acid mixture. For which of the following results should you suspect an error in your calculation? Why?

a. 14%   **b.** 32%   **c.** 55%

OBJECTIVE 2 ▶ **Solving problems with cost and revenue functions.** Recall that businesses are often computing cost and revenue functions or equations to predict sales, to determine whether prices need to be adjusted, and to see whether the company is making or losing money. Recall also that the value at which revenue equals cost is called the break-even point. When revenue is less than cost, the company is losing money; when revenue is greater than cost, the company is making money.

EXAMPLE 5   **Finding a Break-Even Point**

A manufacturing company recently purchased $3000 worth of new equipment to offer new personalized stationery to its customers. The cost of producing a package of personalized stationery is $3.00, and it is sold for $5.50. Find the number of packages that must be sold for the company to break even.

Solution

1. UNDERSTAND. Read and reread the problem. Notice that the cost to the company will include a one-time cost of $3000 for the equipment and then $3.00 per package produced. The revenue will be $5.50 per package sold.

   To model this problem, we will let

$$x = \text{number of packages of personalized stationery}$$
$$C(x) = \text{total cost for producing } x \text{ packages of stationery}$$
$$R(x) = \text{total revenue for selling } x \text{ packages of stationery}$$

2. TRANSLATE. The revenue equation is

In words:	revenue for selling x packages of stationery	=	price per package	·	number of packages
Translate:	$R(x)$	=	5.5	·	x

The cost equation is

In words:	cost for producing x packages of stationery	=	cost per package	·	number of packages	+	cost for equipment
Translate:	$C(x)$	=	3	·	x	+	3000

Since the break-even point is when $R(x) = C(x)$, we solve the equation

$$5.5x = 3x + 3000$$

3. SOLVE.

$$5.5x = 3x + 3000$$

$$2.5x = 3000 \qquad \text{Subtract } 3x \text{ from both sides.}$$

$$x = 1200 \qquad \text{Divide both sides by 2.5.}$$

4. INTERPRET.

Check: To see whether the break-even point occurs when 1200 packages are produced and sold, see if revenue equals cost when $x = 1200$. When $x = 1200$, $R(x) = 5.5x = 5.5(1200) = 6600$ and $C(x) = 3x + 3000 = 3(1200) + 3000 = 6600$. Since $R(1200) = C(1200) = 6600$, the break-even point is 1200.

State: The company must sell 1200 packages of stationery to break even. The graph of this system is shown.

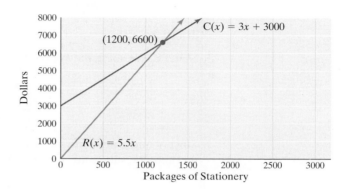

PRACTICE

5   An online-only electronics firm recently purchased $3000 worth of new equipment to create shock-proof packaging for its products. The cost of producing one shock-proof package is $2.50, and the firm charges the customer $4.50 for the packaging. Find the number of packages that must be sold for the company to break even.

OBJECTIVE 3 ▶ Solving problems modeled by systems of three equations. To introduce problem solving by writing a system of three linear equations in three variables, we solve a problem about triangles.

EXAMPLE 6   **Finding Angle Measures**

The measure of the largest angle of a triangle is 80° more than the measure of the smallest angle, and the measure of the remaining angle is 10° more than the measure of the smallest angle. Find the measure of each angle.

Solution

1. UNDERSTAND. Read and reread the problem. Recall that the sum of the measures of the angles of a triangle is 180°. Then guess a solution. If the smallest angle measures 20°, the measure of the largest angle is 80° more, or $20° + 80° = 100°$. The measure of the remaining angle is 10° more than the measure of the smallest angle, or $20° + 10° = 30°$. The sum of these three angles is $20° + 100° + 30° = 150°$, not the required 180°. We now know that the measure of the smallest angle is greater than 20°.

　　To model this problem we will let

x = degree measure of the smallest angle

y = degree measure of the largest angle

z = degree measure of the remaining angle

2. TRANSLATE. We translate the given information into three equations.

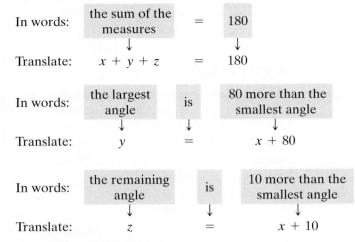

In words: | the sum of the measures | = | 180

Translate: $x + y + z = 180$

In words: | the largest angle | is | 80 more than the smallest angle

Translate: $y = x + 80$

In words: | the remaining angle | is | 10 more than the smallest angle

Translate: $z = x + 10$

3. SOLVE. We solve the system

$$\begin{cases} x + y + z = 180 \\ y = x + 80 \\ z = x + 10 \end{cases}$$

Since y and z are both expressed in terms of x, we will solve using the substitution method. We substitute $y = x + 80$ and $z = x + 10$ in the first equation. Then

$$x + y + z = 180 \quad \text{First equation}$$

$$x + (x + 80) + (x + 10) = 180 \quad \text{Let } y = x + 80 \text{ and } z = x + 10.$$

$$3x + 90 = 180$$

$$3x = 90$$

$$x = 30$$

Then $y = x + 80 = 30 + 80 = 110$, and $z = x + 10 = 30 + 10 = 40$. The ordered triple solution is $(30, 110, 40)$.

4. INTERPRET.

Check: Notice that $30° + 40° + 110° = 180°$. Also, the measure of the largest angle, $110°$, is $80°$ more than the measure of the smallest angle, $30°$. The measure of the remaining angle, $40°$, is $10°$ more than the measure of the smallest angle, $30°$. □

PRACTICE

6 The measure of the largest angle of a triangle is $40°$ more than the measure of the smallest angle, and the measure of the remaining angle is $20°$ more than the measure of the smallest angle. Find the measure of each angle.

4.3 EXERCISE SET

MyMathLab   PRACTICE WATCH DOWNLOAD READ REVIEW

MIXED PRACTICE

Solve. See Examples 1 through 4.

1. One number is two more than a second number. Twice the first is 4 less than 3 times the second. Find the numbers.

2. Three times one number minus a second is 8, and the sum of the numbers is 12. Find the numbers.

3. The United States has the world's only "large deck" aircraft carriers which can hold up to 72 aircraft. The Enterprise class carrier is longest in length while the Nimitz class carrier is the second longest. The total length of these two carriers is 2193 feet while the difference of their lengths is only 9 feet. (*Source: U.S.A. Today*)

a. Find the length of each class carrier.

b. If a football field has a length of 100 yards, determine the length of the Enterprise class carrier in terms of number of football fields.

4. The rate of growth of participation (age 7 and older) in sports featured in the X-Games has slowed in recent years, but still surpasses that for some older sports such as football. The most popular X-Game sport is inline roller skating, followed by skateboarding. In 2005, the total number of participants in both sports was 25.1 million. If the number of participants in skateboarding was 14.2 million less than twice the number of participants in inline skating, find the number of participants in each sport. (*Source:* National Sporting Goods Association)

5. A B747 aircraft flew 6 hours with the wind. The return trip took 7 hours against the wind. If the speed of the plane in still air is 13 times the speed of the wind, find the wind speed and the speed of the plane in still air.

6. During a multi-day camping trip, Terry Watkins rowed 17 hours downstream. It took 26.5 hours rowing upstream to travel the same distance. If the speed of the current is 6.8 kilometers per hour less than his rowing speed in still water, find his rowing speed and the speed of the current.

7. Find how many quarts of 4% butterfat milk and 1% butterfat milk should be mixed to yield 60 quarts of 2% butterfat milk.

8. A pharmacist needs 500 milliliters of a 20% phenobarbital solution but has only 5% and 25% phenobarbital solutions available. Find how many milliliters of each he should mix to get the desired solution.

9. In 2005, the United Kingdom was the most popular host country in which U.S. students traveling abroad studied. Italy was the second most popular destination. A total of 56,929 students visited one of the two countries. If 7213 more U.S. students studied in the United Kingdom than in Italy, find how many students studied abroad in each country. (*Source:* Institute of International Education, *Open Doors 2006*)

10. Harvard University and Cornell University are each known for their excellent libraries, and each is participating with Google to put their collections into Google's searchable database. In 2005, Harvard libraries contained 266,791 more printed volumes than twice the number of printed volumes in the libraries of Cornell. Together, these two great libraries house 23,199,904 printed volumes. Find the number of printed volumes in each library. (*Source:* Association of Research Libraries)

11. Karen Karlin bought some large frames for $15 each and some small frames for $8 each at a closeout sale. If she bought 22 frames for $239, find how many of each type she bought.

12. Hilton University Drama Club sold 311 tickets for a play. Student tickets cost 50 cents each; nonstudent tickets cost $1.50. If total receipts were $385.50, find how many tickets of each type were sold.

13. One number is two less than a second number. Twice the first is 4 more than 3 times the second. Find the numbers.

14. Twice a first number plus a second number is 42, and the first number minus the second number is -6. Find the numbers.

15. In the United States, the percent of women using the Internet is increasing faster than the percent of men. For the years 2000–2005, the function $y = 5.3x + 39.5$ can be used to estimate the percent of females using the Internet, while the function $y = 4.5x + 45.5$ can be used to estimate the percent of males. For both functions, x is the number of years since 2000. If this trend continues, predict the year in which the percent of females using the Internet equals the percent of males. (*Source:* Pew Internet & American Life Project)

16. The percent of car vehicle sales has been decreasing over a ten-year period while the percent of light truck (pickups, sport-utility vans, and minivans) vehicles has been increasing. For the years 2000–2006, the function $y = -x + 54.2$ can be used to estimate the percent of new car vehicle sales in the United States, while the function $y = x + 45.8$ can be used to estimate the percent of light truck vehicle sales. For both functions, x is the number of years since 2000. (*Source:* USA *Today,* Environmental Protection Agency, "Light-Duty Automotive Technology and fuel Economy Trends: 1975–2006")

a. Calculate the year in which the percent of new car sales equaled the percent of light truck sales.

b. Before the actual 2001 vehicle sales data was published, *USA Today* predicted that light truck sales would likely be greater than car sales in the year 2001. Does your finding in part (a) agree with this statement?

17. An office supply store in San Diego sells 7 writing tablets and 4 pens for $6.40. Also, 2 tablets and 19 pens cost $5.40. Find the price of each.

18. A Candy Barrel shop manager mixes M&M's worth $2.00 per pound with trail mix worth $1.50 per pound. Find how many pounds of each she should use to get 50 pounds of a party mix worth $1.80 per pound.

19. A Piper airplane and a B737 aircraft cross each other (at different altitudes) traveling in opposite directions. The B737 travels 5 times the speed of the Piper. If in 4 hours, they are 2160 miles apart, find the speed of each aircraft.

20. Two cyclists start at the same point and travel in opposite directions. One travels 4 mph faster than the other. In 4 hours they are 112 miles apart. Find how fast each is traveling.

21. While it is said that trains opened up the American West to settlement, U.S. railroad miles have been on the decline for decades. On the other hand, the miles of roads in the U.S. highway system have been increasing. The function $y = -1379.4x + 150,604$ represents the U.S. railroad miles, while the function $y = 478.4x + 157,838$ models the number of U.S. highway miles, where x is the number of years after 1995. For each function, x is the number of years after 1995. (*Source:* Association of American Railroads, Federal Highway Administration)

a. Explain how the decrease in railroad miles can be verified by their given function while the increase in highway miles can be verified by their given function.

b. Find the year in which it is estimated that the number of U.S. railroad miles and the number of U.S. highway miles were the same.

22. The annual U.S. per capita consumption of whole milk has decreased since 1980, while the per capita consumption of lower fat milk has increased. For the years 1980–2005, the function $y = -0.40x + 15.9$ approximates the annual U.S. per capita consumption of whole milk in gallons, and the function $y = 0.14x + 11.9$ approximates the annual U.S. per capita consumption of lower fat milk in gallons. Determine the year in which the per capita consumption of whole milk equaled the per capita consumption of lower fat milk. (*Source:* Economic Research Service: U.S.D.A.)

△ **23.** The perimeter of a triangle is 93 centimeters. If two sides are equally long and the third side is 9 centimeters longer than the others, find the lengths of the three sides.

24. Jack Reinholt, a car salesman, has a choice of two pay arrangements: a weekly salary of $200 plus 5% commission on sales, or a straight 15% commission. Find the amount of weekly sales for which Jack's earnings are the same regardless of the pay arrangement.

25. Hertz car rental agency charges $25 daily plus 10 cents per mile. Budget charges $20 daily plus 25 cents per mile. Find the daily mileage for which the Budget charge for the day is twice that of the Hertz charge for the day.

26. Carroll Blakemore, a drafting student, bought three templates and a pencil one day for $6.45. Another day he bought two pads of paper and four pencils for $7.50. If the price of a pad of paper is three times the price of a pencil, find the price of each type of item.

△ **27.** In the figure, line l and line m are parallel lines cut by transversal t. Find the values of x and y.

△ **28.** Find the values of x and y in the following isosceles triangle.

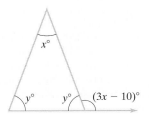

Given the cost function $C(x)$ and the revenue function $R(x)$, find the number of units x that must be sold to break even. See Example 5.

29. $C(x) = 30x + 10,000 \quad R(x) = 46x$

30. $C(x) = 12x + 15,000 \quad R(x) = 32x$

31. $C(x) = 1.2x + 1500 \quad R(x) = 1.7x$

32. $C(x) = 0.8x + 900 \quad R(x) = 2x$

33. $C(x) = 75x + 160,000 \quad R(x) = 200x$

34. $C(x) = 105x + 70,000 \quad R(x) = 245x$

35. The planning department of Abstract Office Supplies has been asked to determine whether the company should introduce a new computer desk next year. The department estimates that $6000 of new manufacturing equipment will need to be purchased and that the cost of constructing each desk will be $200. The department also estimates that the revenue from each desk will be $450.

a. Determine the revenue function $R(x)$ from the sale of x desks.

b. Determine the cost function $C(x)$ for manufacturing x desks.

c. Find the break-even point.

36. Baskets, Inc., is planning to introduce a new woven basket. The company estimates that $500 worth of new equipment will be needed to manufacture this new type of basket and that it will cost $15 per basket to manufacture. The company also estimates that the revenue from each basket will be $31.

a. Determine the revenue function $R(x)$ from the sale of x baskets.

b. Determine the cost function $C(x)$ for manufacturing x baskets.

c. Find the break-even point.

Solve. See Example 6.

37. Rabbits in a lab are to be kept on a strict daily diet that includes 30 grams of protein, 16 grams of fat, and 24 grams of carbohydrates. The scientist has only three food mixes available with the following grams of nutrients per unit.

	Protein	*Fat*	*Carbohydrate*
Mix A	4	6	3
Mix B	6	1	2
Mix C	4	1	12

Find how many units of each mix are needed daily to meet each rabbit's dietary need.

38. Gerry Gundersen mixes different solutions with concentrations of 25%, 40%, and 50% to get 200 liters of a 32% solution. If he uses twice as much of the 25% solution as of the 40% solution, find how many liters of each kind he uses.

△ **39.** The perimeter of a quadrilateral (four-sided polygon) is 29 inches. The longest side is twice as long as the shortest side. The other two sides are equally long and are 2 inches longer than the shortest side. Find the length of all four sides.

△ **40.** The measure of the largest angle of a triangle is 90° more than the measure of the smallest angle, and the measure of the remaining angle is 30° more than the measure of the smallest angle. Find the measure of each angle.

41. The sum of three numbers is 40. One number is five more than a second number. It is also twice the third. Find the numbers.

42. The sum of the digits of a three-digit number is 15. The tens-place digit is twice the hundreds-place digit, and the ones-place digit is 1 less than the hundreds-place digit. Find the three-digit number.

43. Diana Taurasi, of the Phoenix Mercury, was the WNBA's top scorer for the 2006 regular season, with a total of 860 points. The number of two-point field goals that Taurasi made was 65 less than double the number of three-point field goals she made. The number of free throws (each worth one point) she made was 34 less than the number of two-point field goals she made. Find how many free throws, two-point field goals, and three-point field goals Diana Taurasi made during the 2006 regular season. (*Source:* Women's National Basketball Association)

44. During the 2006 NBA playoffs, the top scoring player was Dwayne Wade of the Miami Heat. Wade scored a total of 654 points during the playoffs. The number of free throws (each worth one point) he made was three less than the number of two-point field goals he made. He also made 27 fewer three-point field goals than one-fifth the number of two-point

field goals. How many free throws, two-point field goals, and three-point field goals did Dwayne Wade make during the 2006 playoffs? (*Source:* National Basketball Association)

△ **45.** Find the values of x, y, and z in the following triangle.

△ **46.** The sum of the measures of the angles of a quadrilateral is 360°. Find the value of x, y, and z in the following quadrilateral.

REVIEW AND PREVIEW

Multiply both sides of equation (1) by 2, and add the resulting equation to equation (2). See Section 4.2.

47. $3x - y + z = 2$ (1)
$-x + 2y + 3z = 6$ (2)

48. $2x + y + 3z = 7$ (1)
$-4x + y + 2z = 4$ (2)

Multiply both sides of equation (1) by -3, and add the resulting equation to equation (2). See Section 4.2.

49. $x + 2y - z = 0$ (1)
$3x + y - z = 2$ (2)

50. $2x - 3y + 2z = 5$ (1)
$x - 9y + z = -1$ (2)

CONCEPT EXTENSIONS

51. The number of personal bankruptcy petitions filed in the United States was constantly increasing from the early 1980s until the bankruptcy laws were changed in 2006. In 2006, the number of petitions filed was only 25,765 more than the number of petitions filed in 1996. The total number of personal bankruptcies filed in these two years was 2,144,653. Find the number of personal bankruptcies filed in each year. (*Source: Based on data from the Administrative Office of the United States Courts*)

52. In 2006, the median weekly earnings for male postal service mail carriers in the United States was $126 more than the median weekly earnings for female mail postal service carriers. The median weekly earnings for female postal service mail carriers was 0.86 time that of their male counterparts. Also in 2006, the median weekly earnings for female lawyers in the United States was $540 less than the median weekly earnings for male lawyers. The median weekly earnings of male lawyers was 1.4 times that of their female counterparts. (*Source: Based on data from the Bureau of Labor Statistics*)

   a. Find the median weekly earnings for female postal service mail carriers in the United States in 2006.

   b. Find the median weekly earnings for female lawyers in the United States in 2006.

   c. Of the four groups of workers described in the problem, which group makes the greatest weekly earnings? Which group makes the least weekly earnings?

53. My Space and Facebook are both popular social networking Web sites. The function $f(x) = 0.85x + 41.75$ represents the My Space minutes (in thousands)/month while the function $f(x) = 1.13x + 10.49$ represents the Facebook minutes (in thousands)/month. In both of these functions $x = 1$ represents Feb. 2007, $x = 2$ represents March 2007 and so on.

   a. Solve the system formed by these functions. Round each coordinate to the nearest whole number.

   b. Use your answer to part **a** to predict the month and year in which the total pages viewed for My Space and Facebook are the same.

54. Find the values of a, b, and c such that the equation $y = ax^2 + bx + c$ has ordered pair solutions $(1, 6)$, $(-1, -2)$, and $(0, -1)$. To do so, substitute each ordered pair solution into the equation. Each time, the result is an equation in three unknowns: a, b, and c. Then solve the resulting system of three linear equations in three unknowns, a, b, and c.

55. Find the values of a, b, and c such that the equation $y = ax^2 + bx + c$ has ordered pair solutions $(1, 2)$, $(2, 3)$ and $(-1, 6)$. (*Hint:* See Exercise 53.)

56. Data (x, y) for the total number y (in thousands) of college-bound students who took the ACT assessment in the year x are $(0, 1065)$, $(1, 1070)$ and $(3, 1175)$, where $x = 0$ represents 2000 and $x = 1$ represents 2001. Find the values of a, b, and c such that the equation $y = ax^2 + bx + c$ models this data. According to your model, how many students will take the ACT in 2009? (*Source:* ACT, Inc.)

57. Monthly normal rainfall data (x, y) for Portland, Oregon, are $(4, 2.47)$, $(7, 0.6)$, $(8, 1.1)$, where x represents time in months (with $x = 1$ representing January) and y represents rainfall in inches. Find the values of a, b, and c rounded to 2 decimal places such that the equation $y = ax^2 + bx + c$ models this data. According to your model, how much rain should Portland expect during September? (*Source:* National Climatic Data Center)

INTEGRATED REVIEW SYSTEMS OF LINEAR EQUATIONS

Sections 4.1–4.3

The graphs of various systems of equations are shown. Match each graph with the solution of its corresponding system.

A

B

C

D

1. Solution: $(1, 2)$

2. Solution: $(-2, 3)$

3. No solution

4. Infinite number of solutions

Solve each system by elimination or substitution.

5. $\begin{cases} x + y = 4 \\ \quad\ y = 3x \end{cases}$

6. $\begin{cases} x - y = -4 \\ \quad\ y = 4x \end{cases}$

7. $\begin{cases} x + \ y = 1 \\ x - 2y = 4 \end{cases}$

8. $\begin{cases} 2x - \ y = 8 \\ \ x + 3y = 11 \end{cases}$

9. $\begin{cases} 2x + 5y = 8 \\ 6x + y = 10 \end{cases}$

10. $\begin{cases} \dfrac{1}{8}x - \dfrac{1}{2}y = -\dfrac{5}{8} \\ -3x - 8y = 0 \end{cases}$

11. $\begin{cases} 4x - 7y = 7 \\ 12x - 21y = 24 \end{cases}$

12. $\begin{cases} 2x - 5y = 3 \\ -4x + 10y = -6 \end{cases}$

13. $\begin{cases} y = \dfrac{1}{3}x \\ 5x - 3y = 4 \end{cases}$

14. $\begin{cases} y = \dfrac{1}{4}x \\ 2x - 4y = 3 \end{cases}$

15. $\begin{cases} x + y = 2 \\ -3y + z = -7 \\ 2x + y - z = -1 \end{cases}$

16. $\begin{cases} y + 2z = -3 \\ x - 2y = 7 \\ 2x - y + z = 5 \end{cases}$

17. $\begin{cases} 2x + 4y - 6z = 3 \\ -x + y - z = 6 \\ x + 2y - 3z = 1 \end{cases}$

18. $\begin{cases} x - y + 3z = 2 \\ -2x + 2y - 6z = -4 \\ 3x - 3y + 9z = 6 \end{cases}$

19. $\begin{cases} x + y - 4z = 5 \\ x - y + 2z = -2 \\ 3x + 2y + 4z = 18 \end{cases}$

20. $\begin{cases} 2x - y + 3z = 2 \\ x + y - 6z = 0 \\ 3x + 4y - 3z = 6 \end{cases}$

21. A first number is 8 less than a second number. Twice the first number is 11 more than the second number. Find the numbers.

△ **22.** The sum of the measures of the angles of a quadrilateral is 360°. The two smallest angles of the quadrilateral have the same measure. The third angle measures 30° more than the measure of one of the smallest angles and the fourth angle measures 50° more than the measure of one of the smallest angles. Find the measure of each angle.

▶ **Helpful Hint**

Are you preparing for your test? Don't forget to take the Chapter 4 Test on page 229. Then check your answers at the back of the text and use the Chapter Test Prep Video CD to see the fully worked-out solutions to any of the exercises you want to review.

CHAPTER 4 HIGHLIGHTS

DEFINITIONS AND CONCEPTS	EXAMPLES

SECTION 4.1   SOLVING SYSTEMS OF LINEAR EQUATIONS IN TWO VARIABLES

A **system of linear equations** consists of two or more linear equations.

$$\begin{cases} x - 3y = 6 \\ y = \dfrac{1}{2}x \end{cases} \qquad \begin{cases} x + 2y - z = 1 \\ 3x - y + 4z = 0 \\ 5y + z = 6 \end{cases}$$

A **solution** of a system of two equations in two variables is an ordered pair (x, y) that makes both equations true.

Determine whether $(2, -5)$ is a solution of the system.

$$\begin{cases} x + y = -3 \\ 2x - 3y = 19 \end{cases}$$

Replace x with 2 and y with -5 in both equations.

$$x + y = -3 \qquad\qquad 2x - 3y = 19$$
$$2 + (-5) \stackrel{?}{=} -3 \qquad 2(2) - 3(-5) \stackrel{?}{=} 19$$
$$-3 = -3 \quad \text{True} \qquad 4 + 15 \stackrel{?}{=} 19$$
$$19 = 19 \quad \text{True}$$

$(2, -5)$ is a solution of the system.

Geometrically, a solution of a system in two variables is a point of intersection of the graphs of the equations.

Solve by graphing: $\begin{cases} y = 2x - 1 \\ x + 2y = 13 \end{cases}$

DEFINITIONS AND CONCEPTS	EXAMPLES

A system of equations with at least one solution is a **consistent system.** A system that has no solution is an **inconsistent system.**

If the graphs of two linear equations are identical, the equations are **dependent.**

If their graphs are different, the equations are **independent.**

One solution:
Independent equations
Consistent system

No solution:
Independent equations
Inconsistent system

Infinite number of solutions:
Dependent equations
Consistent system

Solving a System of Linear Equations by the Substitution Method

Step 1. Solve one equation for a variable.

Step 2. Substitute the expression for the variable into the other equation.

Step 3. Solve the equation from Step 2 to find the value of one variable.

Step 4. Substitute the value from Step 3 in either original equation to find the value of the other variable.

Step 5. Check the solution in both equations.

Solve by substitution:

$$\begin{cases} y = x + 2 \\ 3x - 2y = -5 \end{cases}$$

Since the first equation is solved for y, substitute $x + 2$ for y in the second equation.

$$3x - 2y = -5 \quad \text{Second equation}$$
$$3x - 2(x + 2) = -5 \quad \text{Let } y = x + 2.$$
$$3x - 2x - 4 = -5$$
$$x - 4 = -5 \quad \text{Simplify.}$$
$$x = -1 \quad \text{Add 4.}$$

To find y, let $x = -1$ in $y = x + 2$, so $y = -1 + 2 = 1$. The solution $(-1, 1)$ checks.

Solving a System of Linear Equations by the Elimination Method

Step 1. Rewrite each equation in standard form, $Ax + By = C$.

Step 2. Multiply one or both equations by a nonzero number so that the coefficients of a variable are opposites.

Step 3. Add the equations.

Step 4. Find the value of the remaining variable by solving the resulting equation.

Step 5. Substitute the value from Step 4 into either original equation to find the value of the other variable.

Step 6. Check the solution in both equations.

Solve by elimination:

$$\begin{cases} x - 3y = -3 \\ -2x + y = 6 \end{cases}$$

Multiply both sides of the first equation by 2.

$$2x - 6y = -6$$
$$\underline{-2x + y = 6}$$
$$-5y = 0 \quad \text{Add.}$$
$$y = 0 \quad \text{Divide by } -5.$$

To find x, let $y = 0$ in an original equation.

$$x - 3y = -3$$
$$x - 3 \cdot 0 = -3$$
$$x = -3$$

The solution $(-3, 0)$ checks.

DEFINITIONS AND CONCEPTS	EXAMPLES

SECTION 4.2 SOLVING SYSTEMS OF LINEAR EQUATIONS IN THREE VARIABLES

A **solution** of an equation in three variables x, y, and z is an **ordered triple** (x, y, z) that makes the equation a true statement.

Verify that $(-2, 1, 3)$ is a solution of $2x + 3y - 2z = -7$. Replace x with -2, y with 1, and z with 3.

$$2(-2) + 3(1) - 2(3) \stackrel{?}{=} -7$$
$$-4 + 3 - 6 \stackrel{?}{=} -7$$
$$-7 = -7 \quad \text{True}$$

$(-2, 1, 3)$ is a solution.

Solving a System of Three Linear Equations by the Elimination Method

Step 1. Write each equation in standard form, $Ax + By + Cz = D$.

Step 2. Choose a pair of equations and use them to eliminate a variable.

Step 3. Choose any other pair of equations and eliminate the same variable.

Step 4. Solve the system of two equations in two variables from Steps 2 and 3.

Step 5. Solve for the third variable by substituting the values of the variables from Step 4 into any of the original equations.

Step 6. Check the solution in all three original equations.

Solve:

$$\begin{cases} 2x + y - z = 0 & (1) \\ x - y - 2z = -6 & (2) \\ -3x - 2y + 3z = -22 & (3) \end{cases}$$

1. Each equation is written in standard form.

2.
$$\begin{array}{ll} 2x + y - z = 0 & (1) \\ \underline{x - y - 2z = -6} & (2) \\ 3x \quad\quad - 3z = -6 & (4) \quad \text{Add.} \end{array}$$

3. Eliminate y from equations (1) and (3) also.

$$\begin{array}{ll} 4x + 2y - 2z = 0 & \text{Multiply equation} \\ \underline{-3x - 2y + 3z = -22} \; (3) & \text{(1) by 2.} \\ x \quad\quad + z = -22 & (5) \quad \text{Add.} \end{array}$$

4. Solve.

$$\begin{cases} 3x - 3z = -6 & (4) \\ x + z = -22 & (5) \end{cases}$$

$$\begin{array}{ll} x - z = -2 & \text{Divide equation (4) by 3.} \\ \underline{x + z = -22} & (5) \\ 2x \quad\quad = -24 \\ x \quad\quad = -12 \end{array}$$

To find z, use equation (5).

$$x + z = -22$$
$$-12 + z = -22$$
$$z = -10$$

5. To find y, use equation (1).

$$2x + y - z = 0$$
$$2(-12) + y - (-10) = 0$$
$$-24 + y + 10 = 0$$
$$y = 14$$

6. The solution $(-12, 14, -10)$ checks.

DEFINITIONS AND CONCEPTS	**EXAMPLES**

	Two numbers have a sum of 11. Twice one number is 3 less than 3 times the other. Find the numbers.
1. UNDERSTAND the problem.	**1.** Read and reread. x = one number y = other number
2. TRANSLATE.	**2.** In words: sum of numbers is 11 $\downarrow$ $\downarrow$ $\downarrow$ Translate: $x + y$ $=$ 11 In words: twice one number is 3 less than 3 times the other number $\downarrow$ $\downarrow$ $\downarrow$ Translate: $2x$ $=$ $3y - 3$
3. SOLVE.	**3.** Solve the system: $\begin{cases} x + y = 11 \\ 2x = 3y - 3 \end{cases}$ In the first equation, $x = 11 - y$. Substitute into the other equation. $$2x = 3y - 3$$ $$2(11 - y) = 3y - 3$$ $$22 - 2y = 3y - 3$$ $$-5y = -25$$ $$y = 5$$ Replace y with 5 in the equation $x = 11 - y$. Then $x = 11 - 5 = 6$. The solution is $(6, 5)$.
4. INTERPRET.	**4.** *Check:* See that $6 + 5 = 11$ is the required sum and that twice 6 is 3 times 5 less 3. *State:* The numbers are 6 and 5.

CHAPTER 4 REVIEW

(4.1) *Solve each system of equations in two variables by each method: (a) graphing, (b) substitution, and (c) elimination.*

1. $\begin{cases} 3x + 10y = 1 \\ x + 2y = -1 \end{cases}$
  2. $\begin{cases} y = \dfrac{1}{2}x + \dfrac{2}{3} \\ 4x + 6y = 4 \end{cases}$

3. $\begin{cases} 2x - 4y = 22 \\ 5x - 10y = 15 \end{cases}$
  4. $\begin{cases} 3x - 6y = 12 \\ 2y = x - 4 \end{cases}$

5. $\begin{cases} \dfrac{1}{2}x - \dfrac{3}{4}y = -\dfrac{1}{2} \\ \dfrac{1}{8}x + \dfrac{3}{4}y = \dfrac{19}{8} \end{cases}$

6. The revenue equation for a certain style of backpack is $y = 32x$, where x is the number of backpacks sold and y is the income in dollars for selling x backpacks. The cost equation for these units is $y = 15x + 25{,}500$, where x is the number of backpacks manufactured and y is the cost in dollars for manufacturing x backpacks. Find the number of units to be sold for the company to break even. (*Hint:* Solve the system of equations formed by the two given equations.)

(4.2) *Solve each system of equations in three variables.*

7. $\begin{cases} x\ \ \ \ \ + z = 4 \\ 2x - y\ \ \ \ \ = 4 \\ x + y - z = 0 \end{cases}$

8. $\begin{cases} 2x + 5y\ \ \ \ \ = 4 \\ x - 5y + z = -1 \\ 4x\ \ \ \ \ - z = 11 \end{cases}$

9. $\begin{cases} 4y + 2z = 5 \\ 2x + 8y\ \ \ \ \ = 5 \\ 6x\ \ \ \ \ + 4z = 1 \end{cases}$

10. $\begin{cases} 5x + 7y\ \ \ \ \ = 9 \\ 14y - z = 28 \\ 4x\ \ \ \ \ + 2z = -4 \end{cases}$

11. $\begin{cases} 3x - 2y + 2z = 5 \\ -x + 6y + z = 4 \\ 3x + 14y + 7z = 20 \end{cases}$

12. $\begin{cases} x + 2y + 3z = 11 \\ y + 2z = 3 \\ 2x\ \ \ \ \ + 2z = 10 \end{cases}$

13. $\begin{cases} 7x - 3y + 2z = 0 \\ 4x - 4y - z = 2 \\ 5x + 2y + 3z = 1 \end{cases}$

14. $\begin{cases} x - 3y - 5z = -5 \\ 4x - 2y + 3z = 13 \\ 5x + 3y + 4z = 22 \end{cases}$

(4.3) *Use systems of equations to solve.*

15. The sum of three numbers is 98. The sum of the first and second is two more than the third number, and the second is four times the first. Find the numbers.

16. One number is three times a second number, and twice the sum of the numbers is 168. Find the numbers.

17. Two cars leave Chicago, one traveling east and the other west. After 4 hours they are 492 miles apart. If one car is traveling 7 mph faster than the other, find the speed of each.

18. The foundation for a rectangular Hardware Warehouse has a length three times the width and is 296 feet around. Find the dimensions of the building.

19. James Callahan has available a 10% alcohol solution and a 60% alcohol solution. Find how many liters of each solution he should mix to make 50 liters of a 40% alcohol solution.

20. An employee at See's Candy Store needs a special mixture of candy. She has creme-filled chocolates that sell for $3.00 per pound, chocolate-covered nuts that sell for $2.70 per pound, and chocolate-covered raisins that sell for $2.25 per pound. She wants to have twice as many raisins as nuts in the mixture. Find how many pounds of each she should use to make 45 pounds worth $2.80 per pound.

21. Chris Kringler has $2.77 in her coin jar—all in pennies, nickels, and dimes. If she has 53 coins in all and four more nickels than dimes, find how many of each type of coin she has.

22. If $10,000 and $4000 are invested such that $1250 in interest is earned in one year, and if the rate of interest on the larger investment is 2% more than that on the smaller investment, find the rates of interest.

23. The perimeter of an isosceles (two sides equal) triangle is 73 centimeters. If the unequal side is 7 centimeters longer than the two equal sides, find the lengths of the three sides.

24. The sum of three numbers is 295. One number is five more than a second and twice the third. Find the numbers.

25. $\begin{cases} 3x + 10y = 1 \\ x + 2y = -1 \end{cases}$

26. $\begin{cases} 3x - 6y = 12 \\ 2y = x - 4 \end{cases}$

27. $\begin{cases} 3x - 2y = -8 \\ 6x + 5y = 11 \end{cases}$

CHAPTER 4 TEST TEST PREP VIDEO

Remember to use the Chapter Test Prep Video CD to see the fully worked-out solutions to any of the exercises you want to review.

Solve each system of equations graphically and then solve by the elimination method or the substitution method.

1. $\begin{cases} 2x - y = -1 \\ 5x + 4y = 17 \end{cases}$

2. $\begin{cases} 7x - 14y = 5 \\ x = 2y \end{cases}$

Solve each system.

3. $\begin{cases} 4x - 7y = 29 \\ 2x + 5y = -11 \end{cases}$

4. $\begin{cases} 15x + 6y = 15 \\ 10x + 4y = 10 \end{cases}$

5. $\begin{cases} 2x - 3y = 4 \\ 3y + 2z = 2 \\ x - z = -5 \end{cases}$

6. $\begin{cases} 3x - 2y - z = -1 \\ 2x - 2y = 4 \\ 2x - 2z = -12 \end{cases}$

7. $\begin{cases} \dfrac{x}{2} + \dfrac{y}{4} = -\dfrac{3}{4} \\ x + \dfrac{3}{4}y = -4 \end{cases}$

8. $\begin{cases} x - y = -2 \\ 3x - 3y = -6 \end{cases}$

9. $\begin{cases} x + 2y = -1 \\ 2x + 5y = -5 \end{cases}$

10. $\begin{cases} x - y - z = 0 \\ 3x - y - 5z = -2 \\ 2x + 3y = -5 \end{cases}$

11. A motel in New Orleans charges $90 per day for double occupancy and $80 per day for single occupancy. If 80 rooms are occupied for a total of $6930, how many rooms of each kind are occupied?

12. The research department of a company that manufactures children's fruit drinks is experimenting with a new flavor. A 17.5% fructose solution is needed, but only 10% and 20% solutions are available. How many gallons of a 10% fructose solution should be mixed with a 20% fructose solution to obtain 20 gallons of a 17.5% fructose solution?

13. A company that manufactures boxes recently purchased $2000 worth of new equipment to offer gift boxes to its customers. The cost of producing a package of gift boxes is $1.50 and it is sold for $4.00. Find the number of packages that must be sold for the company to break even.

14. The measure of the largest angle of a triangle is 3 less than five times the measure of the smallest angle. The measure of the remaining angle is 1 less than twice the measure of the smallest angle. Find the measure of each angle.

CHAPTER 4 CUMULATIVE REVIEW

1. Determine whether each statement is true or false.

   a. $3 \in \{x \mid x \text{ is a natural number}\}$

   b. $7 \notin \{1, 2, 3\}$

2. Determine whether each statement is true or false.

   a. $\{0, 7\} \subseteq \{0, 2, 4, 6, 8\}$

   b. $\{1, 3, 5\} \subseteq \{1, 3, 5, 7\}$

3. Simplify the following expressions.

   a. $11 + 2 - 7$

   b. $-5 - 4 + 2$

4. Subtract.

   a. $-7 - (-2)$

   b. $14 - 38$

5. Write the additive inverse, or opposite, of each.

   a. 4

   b. $\dfrac{3}{7}$

   c. -11.2

6. Write the reciprocal of each.

   a. 5   **b.** $-\dfrac{2}{3}$

7. Use the distributive property to multiply.

   a. $3(2x + y)$

   b. $-(3x - 1)$

   c. $0.7a(b - 2)$

8. Multiply.

   a. $7(3x - 2y + 4)$

   b. $-(-2s - 3t)$

9. Use the distributive property to simplify each expression.

   a. $3x - 5x + 4$

   b. $7yz + yz$

   c. $4z + 6.1$

10. Simplify.

   a. $5y^2 - 1 + 2(y^2 + 2)$

   b. $(7.8x - 1.2) - (5.6x - 2.4)$

Solve.

11. $-4x - 1 + 5x = 9x + 3 - 7x$

12. $8y - 14 = 6y - 14$

13. $0.3x + 0.1 = 0.27x - 0.02$

14. $2(m - 6) - m = 4(m - 3) - 3m$

15. A pennant in the shape of an isosceles triangle is to be constructed for the Slidell High School Athletic Club and sold at a fund-raiser. The company manufacturing the pennant charges according to perimeter, and the athletic club has determined that a perimeter of 149 centimeters should make a nice profit. If each equal side of the triangle is twice the length of the third side, increased by 12 centimeters, find the lengths of the sides of the triangular pennant.

16. A quadrilateral has 4 angles whose sum is $360°$. In a particular quadrilateral, two angles have the same measure. A third angle is $10°$ more than the measure of one of the equal angles, and the fourth angle is half the measure of one of the equal angles. Find the measures of the angles.

17. Solve: $3x + 4 \geq 2x - 6$. Graph the solution set.

18. Solve: $5(2x - 1) > -5$

19. Solve: $2 < 4 - x < 7$

20. Solve: $-1 < \dfrac{-2x - 1}{3} < 1$

21. Solve: $|2x| + 5 = 7$

22. Solve: $|x - 5| = 4$

23. Solve for m: $|m - 6| < 2$

24. $|2x + 1| > 5$

25. Plot each ordered pair on a Cartesian coordinate system and name the quadrant or axis in which the point is located.

    a. $(2, -1)$ **b.** $(0, 5)$ **c.** $(-3, 5)$

    d. $(-2, 0)$ **e.** $\left(-\dfrac{1}{2}, -4\right)$ **f.** $(1.5, 1.5)$

26. Name the quadrant or axis each point is located.

    a. $(-1, -5)$

    b. $(4, -2)$

    c. $(0, 2)$

27. Is the relation $x = y^2$ also a function?

28. Graph: $-2x + \dfrac{1}{2}y = -2$

29. If $f(x) = 7x^2 - 3x + 1$ and $g(x) = 3x - 2$, find the following.

    a. $f(1)$ **b.** $g(1)$

    c. $f(-2)$ **d.** $g(0)$

30. If $f(x) = 3x^2$, find the following.

    a. $f(5)$ **b.** $f(-2)$

31. Graph $g(x) = 2x + 1$. Compare this graph with the graph of $f(x) = 2x$.

32. Find the slope of the line containing $(-2, 6)$ and $(0, 9)$.

33. Find the slope and the y-intercept of the line $3x - 4y = 4$.

34. Find the slope and y-intercept of the line defined by $y = 2$.

35. Are the following pairs of lines parallel, perpendicular, or neither?

    a. $3x + 7y = 4$
         $6x + 14y = 7$

    b. $-x + 3y = 2$
         $2x + 6y = 5$

36. Find an equation of the line through $(0, -9)$ with slope $\dfrac{1}{5}$.

37. Find an equation of the line through points $(4, 0)$ and $(-4, -5)$. Write the equation using function notation.

38. Find an equation of the line through $(-2, 6)$ perpendicular to $f(x) = \dfrac{1}{2}x - \dfrac{1}{3}$.

39. Graph $3x \geq y$.

41. Determine whether the given ordered pair is a solution of the system.

    a. $\begin{cases} -x + y = 2 \\ 2x - y = -3 \end{cases}$ $(-1, 1)$

    b. $\begin{cases} 5x + 3y = -1 \\ x - y = 1 \end{cases}$ $(-2, 3)$

42. Solve the system:
$$\begin{cases} 5x + y = -2 \\ 4x - 2y = -10 \end{cases}$$

43. Solve the system.
$$\begin{cases} 3x - y + z = -15 \\ x + 2y - z = 1 \\ 2x + 3y - 2z = 0 \end{cases}$$

44. Solve the system:
$$\begin{cases} x - 2y + z = 0 \\ 3x - y - 2z = -15 \\ 2x - 3y + 3z = 7 \end{cases}$$

46. Solve the system:
$$\begin{cases} -6x + 8y = 0 \\ 9x - 12y = 2 \end{cases}$$

5

Exponents, Polynomials, and Polynomial Functions

To remember the Great Lakes, remember the word "**HOMES.**"

H = Huron
O = Ontario
M = Michigan
E = Erie
S = Superior

The Great Lakes are a group of five lakes in North America on or near the United States-Canada border. They were formed at the end of the last ice age, about 10,000 years ago.

The Great Lakes are the largest freshwater lake group on this Earth. They contain about 84% of North America's surface fresh water and 21% of the world's supply. The total surface area of the Great Lakes is about the size of Texas. Lake Superior alone is larger than the state of South Carolina. In Section 5.2, Exercise 99, page 246, we will explore the mass of the water in Lake Superior.

Linear equations are important for solving problems. They are not sufficient, however, to solve all problems. Many real-world phenomena are modeled by polynomials. We begin this chapter by reviewing exponents. We will then study operations on polynomials and how polynomials can be used in problem solving.

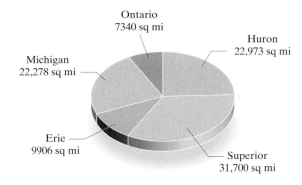

Surface Areas of Great Lakes

5.1 EXPONENTS AND SCIENTIFIC NOTATION

OBJECTIVES

1 Use the product rule for exponents.

2 Evaluate expressions raised to the 0 power.

3 Use the quotient rule for exponents.

4 Evaluate expressions raised to the negative *n*th power.

5 Convert between scientific notation and standard notation.

OBJECTIVE 1 ▶ Using the product rule. Recall that exponents may be used to write repeated factors in a more compact form. As we have seen in the previous chapters, exponents can be used when the repeated factor is a number or a variable. For example,

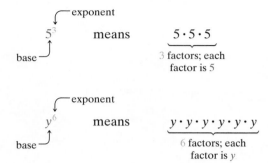

Expressions such as 5^3 and y^6 that contain exponents are called **exponential expressions.**

Exponential expressions can be multiplied, divided, added, subtracted, and themselves raised to powers. In this section, we review operations on exponential expressions.

We review multiplication first. To multiply x^2 by x^3, use the definition of an exponent.

$$x^2 \cdot x^3 = \underbrace{(x \cdot x)(x \cdot x \cdot x)}_{x \text{ is a factor 5 times}}$$
$$= x^5$$

Notice that the result is exactly the same if we add the exponents.

$$x^2 \cdot x^3 = x^{2+3} = x^5$$

This suggests the following.

Product Rule for Exponents

If m and n are positive integers and a is a real number, then

$$a^m \cdot a^n = a^{m+n}$$

In other words, the *product* of exponential expressions with a common base is the common base raised to a power equal to the *sum* of the exponents of the factors.

EXAMPLE 1   Use the product rule to simplify.

a. $2^2 \cdot 2^5$ **b.** $x^7 x^3$ **c.** $y \cdot y^2 \cdot y^4$

Solution

a. $2^2 \cdot 2^5 = 2^{2+5} = 2^7$
b. $x^7 x^3 = x^{7+3} = x^{10}$
c. $y \cdot y^2 \cdot y^4 = (y^1 \cdot y^2) \cdot y^4$
$= y^3 \cdot y^4$
$= y^7$

PRACTICE
1   Use the product rule to simplify.

a. $3^4 \cdot 3^2$ **b.** $x^5 \cdot x^2$ **c.** $y \cdot y^3 \cdot y^5$

EXAMPLE 2   Use the product rule to simplify.

a. $(3x^6)(5x)$ **b.** $(-2.4x^3p^2)(4xp^{10})$

Solution   Here, we use properties of multiplication to group together like bases.

a. $(3x^6)(5x) = 3(5)x^6x^1 = 15x^7$

b. $(-2.4x^3p^2)(4xp^{10}) = -2.4(4)x^3x^1p^2p^{10} = -9.6x^4p^{12}$

PRACTICE
2   Use the product rule to simplify.

a. $(5z^3)(7z)$ **b.** $(-4.1t^5q^3)(5tq^5)$

OBJECTIVE 2 ▶ Evaluating expressions raised to the 0 power. The definition of a^n does not include the possibility that n might be 0. But if it did, then, by the product rule,

$$\underbrace{a^0 \cdot a^n} = a^{0+n} = a^n = \underbrace{1 \cdot a^n}$$

From this, we reasonably define that $a^0 = 1$, as long as a does not equal 0.

> **Zero Exponent**
> If a does not equal 0, then $a^0 = 1$.

EXAMPLE 3   Evaluate the following.

a. 7^0 **b.** -7^0 **c.** $(2x + 5)^0$ **d.** $2x^0$

Solution

a. $7^0 = 1$

b. Without parentheses, only 7 is raised to the 0 power.
$$-7^0 = -(7^0) = -(1) = -1$$

c. $(2x + 5)^0 = 1$

d. $2x^0 = 2(1) = 2$

PRACTICE
3   Evaluate the following.

a. 5^0 **b.** -5^0 **c.** $(3x - 8)^0$ **d.** $3x^0$

OBJECTIVE 3 ▶ Using the quotient rule. To find quotients of exponential expressions, we again begin with the definition of a^n to simplify $\dfrac{x^9}{x^2}$. For example,

$$\frac{x^9}{x^2} = \frac{x \cdot x \cdot x \cdot x \cdot x \cdot x \cdot x \cdot x \cdot x}{x \cdot x} = x^7$$

(Assume for the next two sections that denominators containing variables are not 0.) Notice that the result is exactly the same if we subtract the exponents.

$$\frac{x^9}{x^2} = x^{9-2} = x^7$$

This suggests the following.

Quotient Rule for Exponents

If a is a nonzero real number and n and m are integers, then

$$\frac{a^m}{a^n} = a^{m-n}$$

In other words, the *quotient* of exponential expressions with a common base is the common base raised to a power equal to the *difference* of the exponents.

EXAMPLE 4 Use the quotient rule to simplify.

a. $\dfrac{x^7}{x^4}$ **b.** $\dfrac{5^8}{5^2}$ **c.** $\dfrac{20x^6}{4x^5}$ **d.** $\dfrac{12y^{10}z^7}{14y^8z^7}$

Solution

a. $\dfrac{x^7}{x^4} = x^{7-4} = x^3$

b. $\dfrac{5^8}{5^2} = 5^{8-2} = 5^6$

c. $\dfrac{20x^6}{4x^5} = 5x^{6-5} = 5x^1,$ or $5x$

d. $\dfrac{12y^{10}z^7}{14y^8z^7} = \dfrac{6}{7}y^{10-8} \cdot z^{7-7} = \dfrac{6}{7}y^2z^0 = \dfrac{6}{7}y^2,$ or $\dfrac{6y^2}{7}$

PRACTICE
4   Use the quotient rule to simplify.

a. $\dfrac{z^8}{z^3}$ **b.** $\dfrac{3^9}{3^3}$ **c.** $\dfrac{45x^7}{5x^3}$ **d.** $\dfrac{24a^{14}b^6}{18a^7b^6}$

OBJECTIVE 4 ▶ Evaluating exponents raised to the negative *n*th power. When the exponent of the denominator is larger than the exponent of the numerator, applying the quotient rule yields a negative exponent. For example,

$$\frac{x^3}{x^5} = x^{3-5} = x^{-2}$$

Using the definition of a^n, though, gives us

$$\frac{x^3}{x^5} = \frac{x \cdot x \cdot x}{x \cdot x \cdot x \cdot x \cdot x} = \frac{1}{x^2}$$

From this, we reasonably define $x^{-2} = \dfrac{1}{x^2}$ or, in general, $a^{-n} = \dfrac{1}{a^n}$.

Negative Exponents

If a is a real number other than 0 and n is a positive integer, then

$$a^{-n} = \frac{1}{a^n}$$

EXAMPLE 5   Simplify and write with positive exponents only.

a. 5^{-2} **b.** $(-4)^{-4}$ **c.** $2x^{-3}$ **d.** $(3x)^{-1}$

e. $\dfrac{m^5}{m^{15}}$ **f.** $\dfrac{3^3}{3^6}$ **g.** $2^{-1} + 3^{-2}$ **h.** $\dfrac{1}{t^{-5}}$

Solution

a. $5^{-2} = \dfrac{1}{5^2} = \dfrac{1}{25}$

b. $(-4)^{-4} = \dfrac{1}{(-4)^4} = \dfrac{1}{256}$

c. $2x^{-3} = 2 \cdot \dfrac{1}{x^3} = \dfrac{2}{x^3}$ Without parentheses, only x is raised to the -3 power.

d. $(3x)^{-1} = \dfrac{1}{(3x)^1} = \dfrac{1}{3x}$ With parentheses, both 3 and x are raised to the -1 power.

e. $\dfrac{m^5}{m^{15}} = m^{5-15} = m^{-10} = \dfrac{1}{m^{10}}$

f. $\dfrac{3^3}{3^6} = 3^{3-6} = 3^{-3} = \dfrac{1}{3^3} = \dfrac{1}{27}$

g. $2^{-1} + 3^{-2} = \dfrac{1}{2^1} + \dfrac{1}{3^2} = \dfrac{1}{2} + \dfrac{1}{9} = \dfrac{9}{18} + \dfrac{2}{18} = \dfrac{11}{18}$

h. $\dfrac{1}{t^{-5}} = \dfrac{1}{\frac{1}{t^5}} = 1 \div \dfrac{1}{t^5} = 1 \cdot \dfrac{t^5}{1} = t^5$

PRACTICE
5   Simplify and write with positive exponents only.

a. 6^{-2} **b.** $(-2)^{-6}$ **c.** $3x^{-5}$ **d.** $(5y)^{-1}$ **e.** $\dfrac{k^4}{k^{11}}$

f. $\dfrac{5^3}{5^5}$ **g.** $5^{-1} + 2^{-2}$ **h.** $\dfrac{1}{z^{-8}}$

> ▶ **Helpful Hint**
> Notice that when a factor containing an exponent is moved from the numerator to the denominator or from the denominator to the numerator, the sign of its exponent changes.
>
> $$x^{-3} = \dfrac{1}{x^3}, \qquad 5^{-2} = \dfrac{1}{5^2} = \dfrac{1}{25}$$
>
> $$\dfrac{1}{y^{-4}} = y^4, \qquad \dfrac{1}{2^{-3}} = 2^3 = 8$$

EXAMPLE 6   Simplify and write with positive exponents only.

a. $\dfrac{x^{-9}}{x^2}$ **b.** $\dfrac{5p^4}{p^{-3}}$ **c.** $\dfrac{2^{-3}}{2^{-1}}$ **d.** $\dfrac{2x^{-7}y^2}{10xy^{-5}}$ **e.** $\dfrac{(3x^{-3})(x^2)}{x^6}$

Solution

a. $\dfrac{x^{-9}}{x^2} = x^{-9-2} = x^{-11} = \dfrac{1}{x^{11}}$

b. $\dfrac{5p^4}{p^{-3}} = 5 \cdot p^{4-(-3)} = 5p^7$

c. $\dfrac{2^{-3}}{2^{-1}} = 2^{-3-(-1)} = 2^{-2} = \dfrac{1}{2^2} = \dfrac{1}{4}$

d. $\dfrac{2x^{-7}y^2}{10xy^{-5}} = \dfrac{x^{-7-1} \cdot y^{2-(-5)}}{5} = \dfrac{x^{-8}y^7}{5} = \dfrac{y^7}{5x^8}$

e. Simplify the numerator first.

$$\dfrac{(3x^{-3})(x^2)}{x^6} = \dfrac{3x^{-3+2}}{x^6} = \dfrac{3x^{-1}}{x^6} = 3x^{-1-6} = 3x^{-7} = \dfrac{3}{x^7}$$

PRACTICE

6 Simplify and write with positive exponents only.

a. $\dfrac{z^{-8}}{z^3}$　　**b.** $\dfrac{7t^3}{t^{-5}}$　　**c.** $\dfrac{3^{-2}}{3^{-4}}$　　**d.** $\dfrac{5a^{-5}b^3}{15a^2b^{-4}}$　　**e.** $\dfrac{(2x^{-5})(x^6)}{x^5}$

Concept Check ✓

Find and correct the error in the following:

$$\dfrac{y^{-6}}{y^{-2}} = y^{-6-2} = y^{-8} = \dfrac{1}{y^8}$$

EXAMPLE 7 Simplify. Assume that a and t are nonzero integers and that x is not 0.

a. $x^{2a} \cdot x^3$　　　　**b.** $\dfrac{x^{2t-1}}{x^{t-5}}$

Solution

a. $x^{2a} \cdot x^3 = x^{2a+3}$　　　　Use the product rule.

b. $\dfrac{x^{2t-1}}{x^{t-5}} = x^{(2t-1)-(t-5)}$　　　　Use the quotient rule.

$\qquad\qquad = x^{2t-1-t+5} = x^{t+4}$

PRACTICE

7 Simplify. Assume that a and t are nonzero integers and that x is not 0.

a. $x^{3a} \cdot x^4$　　　　**b.** $\dfrac{x^{3t-2}}{x^{t-3}}$

OBJECTIVE 5 ▶ Converting between scientific notation and standard notation. Very large and very small numbers occur frequently in nature. For example, the distance between the Earth and the Sun is approximately 150,000,000 kilometers. A helium atom has a diameter of 0.000 000 022 centimeters. It can be tedious to write these very large and very small numbers in standard notation like this. **Scientific notation** is a convenient shorthand notation for writing very large and very small numbers.

Helium atom

0.000000022
centimeters

150,000,000 km

Scientific Notation

A positive number is written in **scientific notation** if it is written as the product of a number a, where $1 \le a < 10$ and an integer power r of 10:

$$a \times 10^r$$

The following are examples of numbers written in scientific notation.

diameter of helium atom : $\quad 2.2 \times 10^{-8}$ cm; 1.5×10^8 km $\quad \leftarrow$ approximate distance between Earth and Sun

---

Writing a Number in Scientific Notation

STEP 1. Move the decimal point in the original number until the new number has a value between 1 and 10.

STEP 2. Count the number of decimal places the decimal point was moved in Step 1. If the original number is 10 or greater, the count is positive. If the original number is less than 1, the count is negative.

STEP 3. Write the product of the new number in Step 1 by 10 raised to an exponent equal to the count found in Step 2.

EXAMPLE 8   Write each number in scientific notation.

a. 730,000   **b.** 0.00000104

Solution

a. STEP 1. Move the decimal point until the number is between 1 and 10.

$$730{,}000.$$

STEP 2. The decimal point is moved 5 places and the original number is 10 or greater, so the count is positive 5.

STEP 3. $730{,}000 = 7.3 \times 10^5$.

b. STEP 1. Move the decimal point until the number is between 1 and 10.

$$0.00000104$$

STEP 2. The decimal point is moved 6 places and the original number is less then 1, so the count is -6.

STEP 3. $0.00000104 = 1.04 \times 10^{-6}$. $\quad\square$

PRACTICE
8   Write each number in scientific notation.

a. 65,000   **b.** 0.000038

To write a scientific notation number in standard form, we reverse the preceding steps.

Writing a Scientific Notation Number in Standard Notation

Move the decimal point in the number the same number of places as the exponent on 10. If the exponent is positive, move the decimal point to the right. If the exponent is negative, move the decimal point to the left.

EXAMPLE 9 Write each number in standard notation.

a. 7.7×10^8 **b.** 1.025×10^{-3}

Solution

a. $7.7 \times 10^8 = 770{,}000{,}000$ Since the exponent is positive, move the decimal point 8 places to the right. Add zeros as needed.

b. $1.025 \times 10^{-3} = 0.001025$ Since the exponent is negative, move the decimal point 3 places to the left. Add zeros as needed.

PRACTICE
9   Write each number in standard notation.

a. 6.2×10^5 **b.** 3.109×10^{-2}

Concept Check

Which of the following numbers have values that are less than 1?

a. 3.5×10^{-5} **b.** 3.5×10^5 **c.** -3.5×10^5 **d.** -3.5×10^{-5}

Answers to Concept Check:
a, c, d

Scientific Calculator Explorations

Multiply 5,000,000 by 700,000 on your calculator. The display should read ⟨ 3.5   12 ⟩ or ⟨ 3.5 E 12 ⟩, which is the product written in scientific notation. Both these notations mean 3.5×10^{12}.

   To enter a number written in scientific notation on a calculator, find the key marked ⟨ EE ⟩. (On some calculators, this key may be marked ⟨ EXP ⟩.)
To enter 7.26×10^{13}, press the keys

$$\boxed{7.26} \quad \boxed{\text{EE}} \quad \boxed{13}$$

The display will read ⟨ 7.26   13 ⟩ or ⟨ 7.26 E 13 ⟩.

Use your calculator to perform each operation indicated.

1. Multiply 3×10^{11} and 2×10^{32}.

2. Divide 6×10^{14} by 3×10^9.

3. Multiply 5.2×10^{23} and 7.3×10^4.

4. Divide 4.38×10^{41} by 3×10^{17}.

VOCABULARY & READINESS CHECK

State the base of the exponent 5 in each expression.

1. $9x^5$ **2.** yz^5 **3.** -3^5 **4.** $(-3)^5$ **5.** $(y^7)^5$ **6.** $9 \cdot 2^5$

Write each expression with positive exponents.

7. $5x^{-1}y^{-2}$ **8.** $7xy^{-4}$ **9.** $a^2b^{-1}c^{-5}$ **10.** $a^{-4}b^2c^{-6}$ **11.** $\dfrac{y^{-2}}{x^{-4}}$ **12.** $\dfrac{x^{-7}}{z^{-3}}$

5.1 | EXERCISE SET

Use the product rule to simplify each expression. See Examples 1 and 2.

1. $4^2 \cdot 4^3$

2. $3^3 \cdot 3^5$

3. $x^5 \cdot x^3$

4. $a^2 \cdot a^9$

5. $m \cdot m^7 \cdot m^6$

6. $n \cdot n^{10} \cdot n^{12}$

7. $(4xy)(-5x)$

8. $(-7xy)(7y)$

9. $(-4x^3 p^2)(4y^3 x^3)$

10. $(-6a^2 b^3)(-3ab^3)$

Evaluate each expression. See Example 3.

11. -8^0

12. $(-9)^0$

13. $(4x + 5)^0$

14. $(3x - 1)^0$

15. $-x^0$

16. $-5x^0$

17. $4x^0 + 5$

18. $8x^0 + 1$

Use the quotient rule to simplify. See Example 4.

19. $\dfrac{a^5}{a^2}$

20. $\dfrac{x^9}{x^4}$

21. $-\dfrac{26z^{11}}{2z^7}$

22. $-\dfrac{16x^5}{8x}$

23. $\dfrac{x^9 y^6}{x^8 y^6}$

24. $\dfrac{a^{12} b^2}{a^9 b}$

25. $\dfrac{12x^4 y^7}{9xy^5}$

26. $\dfrac{24a^{10} b^{11}}{10ab^3}$

27. $\dfrac{-36a^5 b^7 c^{10}}{6ab^3 c^4}$

28. $\dfrac{49a^3 bc^{14}}{-7abc^8}$

Simplify and write using positive exponents only. See Examples 5 and 6.

29. 4^{-2}

30. 2^{-3}

31. $(-3)^{-3}$

32. $(-6)^{-2}$

33. $\dfrac{x^7}{x^{15}}$

34. $\dfrac{z}{z^3}$

35. $5a^{-4}$

36. $10b^{-1}$

37. $\dfrac{x^{-7}}{y^{-2}}$

38. $\dfrac{p^{-13}}{q^{-3}}$

39. $\dfrac{x^{-2}}{x^5}$

40. $\dfrac{z^{-12}}{z^{10}}$

41. $\dfrac{8r^4}{2r^{-4}}$

42. $\dfrac{3s^3}{15s^{-3}}$

43. $\dfrac{x^{-9} x^4}{x^{-5}}$

44. $\dfrac{y^{-7} y}{y^8}$

45. $\dfrac{2a^{-6} b^2}{18ab^{-5}}$

46. $\dfrac{18ab^{-6}}{3a^{-3} b^6}$

47. $\dfrac{(24x^8)(x)}{20x^{-7}}$

48. $\dfrac{(30z^2)(z^5)}{55z^{-4}}$

MIXED PRACTICE

Simplify and write using positive exponents only. See Examples 1 through 6.

49. $-7x^3 \cdot 20x^9$

50. $-3y \cdot -9y^4$

51. $x^7 \cdot x^8 \cdot x$

52. $y^6 \cdot y \cdot y^9$

53. $2x^3 \cdot 5x^7$

54. $-3z^4 \cdot 10z^7$

55. $(5x)^0 + 5x^0$

56. $4y^0 - (4y)^0$

57. $\dfrac{z^{12}}{z^{15}}$

58. $\dfrac{x^{11}}{x^{20}}$

59. $3^0 - 3t^0$

60. $4^0 + 4x^0$

61. $\dfrac{y^{-3}}{y^{-7}}$

62. $\dfrac{y^{-6}}{y^{-9}}$

63. $4^{-1} + 3^{-2}$

64. $1^{-3} - 4^{-2}$

65. $3x^{-1}$

66. $(4x)^{-1}$

67. $\dfrac{r^4}{r^{-4}}$

68. $\dfrac{x^{-5}}{x^3}$

69. $\dfrac{x^{-7} y^{-2}}{x^2 y^2}$

70. $\dfrac{a^{-5} b^7}{a^{-2} b^{-3}}$

71. $(-4x^2 y)(3x^4)(-2xy^5)$

72. $(-6a^4 b)(2b^3)(-3ab^6)$

73. $2^{-4} \cdot x$

74. $5^{-2} \cdot y$

75. $\dfrac{5^{17}}{5^{13}}$

76. $\dfrac{10^{25}}{10^{23}}$

77. $\dfrac{8^{-7}}{8^{-6}}$

78. $\dfrac{13^{-10}}{13^{-9}}$

79. $\dfrac{9^{-5} a^4}{9^{-3} a^{-1}}$

80. $\dfrac{11^{-9} b^3}{11^{-7} b^{-4}}$

81. $\dfrac{14x^{-2} yz^{-4}}{2xyz}$

82. $\dfrac{30x^{-7} yz^{-14}}{3xyz}$

Simplify. Assume that variables in the exponents represent nonzero integers and that x, y, and z are not 0. See Example 7.

83. $x^5 \cdot x^{7a}$

84. $y^{2p} \cdot y^{9p}$

85. $\dfrac{x^{3t-1}}{x^t}$

86. $\dfrac{y^{4p-2}}{y^{3p}}$

87. $x^{4a} \cdot x^7$

88. $x^{9y} \cdot x^{-7y}$

89. $\dfrac{z^{6x}}{z^7}$

90. $\dfrac{y^6}{y^{4z}}$

91. $\dfrac{x^{3t} \cdot x^{4t-1}}{x^t}$

92. $\dfrac{z^{5x} \cdot z^{x-7}}{z^x}$

Write each number in scientific notation. See Example 8.

93. 31,250,000

94. 678,000

95. 0.016

96. 0.007613

97. 67,413

98. 36,800,000

99. 0.0125

100. 0.00084

101. 0.000053

102. 98,700,000,000

Write each number in scientific notation.

103. Total revenues for Wal-Mart in fiscal year ending January 2007 were $344,992,000,000. (*Source:* Wal-Mart Stores, Inc.)

104. The University of Texas system has more than 170,000 students statewide. (*Source:* University of Texas)

105. On a recent day, the Apple iTunes Store featured more than 3,500,000 songs to buy for $0.99 each.

106. In 2006, approximately 61,049,000 passengers passed through the Los Angeles International Airport. (*Source:* Los Angeles International Airport)

107. Lake Mead, created from the Colorado River by the Hoover Dam, has a capacity of 124,000,000,000 cubic feet of water. (*Source:* U.S. Bureau of Reclamation)

108. The temperature of the core of the sun is about 27,000,000°F.

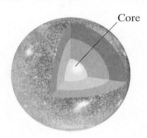

Core

109. A pulsar is a rotating neutron star that gives off sharp, regular pulses of radio waves. For one particular pulsar, the rate of pulses is every 0.001 second.

110. To convert from cubic inches to cubic meters, multiply by 0.0000164.

Write each number in standard notation, without exponents. See Example 9.

111. 3.6×10^{-9}

112. 2.7×10^{-5}

113. 9.3×10^{7}

114. 6.378×10^{8}

115. 1.278×10^{6}

116. 7.6×10^{4}

117. 7.35×10^{12}

118. 1.66×10^{-5}

119. 4.03×10^{-7}

120. 8.007×10^{8}

Write each number in standard notation.

121. The estimated world population in 1 A.D. was 3.0×10^{8}. (*Source:* World Almanac and Book of Facts)

122. There are 3.949×10^{6} miles of highways, roads, and streets in the United States. (*Source:* Bureau of Transportation Statistics)

123. In 2006, teenagers had an estimated spending power of 1.53×10^{11} dollars. (*Source:* A. C. Neilson Research)

124. Each day, an estimated 1.2×10^{9} beverages consumed throughout the world are Coca Cola products. (*Source:* Coca-Cola)

REVIEW AND PREVIEW

Evaluate. See Sections 1.3 and 5.1.

125. $(5 \cdot 2)^{2}$

126. $5^{2} \cdot 2^{2}$

127. $\left(\dfrac{3}{4}\right)^{3}$

128. $\dfrac{3^{3}}{4^{3}}$

129. $(2^{3})^{2}$

130. $(2^{2})^{3}$

CONCEPT EXTENSIONS

131. Explain how to convert a number from standard notation to scientific notation.

132. Explain how to convert a number from scientific notation to standard notation.

133. Explain why $(-5)^{0}$ simplifies to 1 but -5^{0} simplifies to -1.

134. Explain why both $4x^{0} - 3y^{0}$ and $(4x - 3y)^{0}$ simplify to 1.

135. Simplify where possible.

   a. $x^{a} \cdot x^{a}$ **b.** $x^{a} + x^{a}$

   c. $\dfrac{x^{a}}{x^{b}}$ **d.** $x^{a} \cdot x^{b}$

   e. $x^{a} + x^{b}$

136. Which numbers are equal to 36,000? Of these, which is written in scientific notation?

   a. 36×10^{3} **b.** 360×10^{2}

   c. 0.36×10^{5} **d.** 3.6×10^{4}

Without calculating, determine which number is larger.

137. 7^{11} or 7^{13}

138. 5^{10} or 5^{9}

139. 7^{-11} or 7^{-13}

140. 5^{-10} or 5^{-9}

What to Do the Day of an Exam?

Your first exam may be soon. On the day of an exam, don't forget to try the following:

- Allow yourself plenty of time to arrive.
- Read the directions on the test carefully.
- Read each problem carefully as you take your test. Make sure that you answer the question asked.
- Watch your time and pace yourself so that you may attempt each problem on your test.
- Check your work and answers.
- **Do not turn your test in early.** If you have extra time, spend it double-checking your work.

Good luck!

Answer the following questions based on your most recent mathematics exam, whenever that was.

1. How soon before class did you arrive?
2. Did you read the directions on the test carefully?
3. Did you make sure you answered the question asked for each problem on the exam?
4. Were you able to attempt each problem on your exam?
5. If your answer to question 4 is no, list reasons why.
6. Did you have extra time on your exam?
7. If your answer to question 6 is yes, describe how you spent that extra time.

5.2 MORE WORK WITH EXPONENTS AND SCIENTIFIC NOTATION

OBJECTIVES

1. Use the power rules for exponents.
2. Use exponent rules and definitions to simplify exponential expressions.
3. Compute, using scientific notation.

OBJECTIVE 1 ▶ Using the power rules. The volume of the cube shown whose side measures x^2 units is $(x^2)^3$ cubic units. To simplify an expression such as $(x^2)^3$, we use the definition of a^n. Then

$$(x^2)^3 = \underbrace{(x^2)(x^2)(x^2)}_{x^2 \text{ is a factor 3 times}} = x^{2+2+2} = x^6$$

Notice that the result is exactly the same if the exponents are multiplied.

$$(x^2)^3 = x^{2 \cdot 3} = x^6$$

This suggests that the power of an exponential expression raised to a power is the product of the exponents. Two additional rules for exponents are given in the following box.

x^2 units

The Power Rule and Power of a Product or Quotient Rules for Exponents

If a and b are real numbers and m and n are integers, then

$$(a^m)^n = a^{m \cdot n} \qquad \text{Power rule}$$
$$(ab)^m = a^m b^m \qquad \text{Power of a product}$$
$$\left(\frac{a}{b}\right)^n = \frac{a^n}{b^n}(b \neq 0) \qquad \text{Power of a quotient}$$

EXAMPLE 1 Use the power rule to simplify the following expressions. Use positive exponents to write all results.

a. $(x^5)^7$ 　　　 b. $(2^2)^3$ 　　　 c. $(5^{-1})^2$ 　　　 d. $(y^{-3})^{-4}$

Solution

a. $(x^5)^7 = x^{5 \cdot 7} = x^{35}$ 　　　 b. $(2^2)^3 = 2^{2 \cdot 3} = 2^6 = 64$

c. $(5^{-1})^2 = 5^{-1 \cdot 2} = 5^{-2} = \dfrac{1}{5^2} = \dfrac{1}{25}$ 　 d. $(y^{-3})^{-4} = y^{-3(-4)} = y^{12}$

1 Use the power rule to simplify the following expressions. Use positive exponents to write all results.

a. $(z^3)^5$ **b.** $(5^2)^2$ **c.** $(3^{-1})^3$ **d.** $(x^{-4})^{-6}$

EXAMPLE 2 Use the power rules to simplify the following. Use positive exponents to write all results.

a. $(5x^2)^3$ **b.** $\left(\dfrac{2}{3}\right)^3$ **c.** $\left(\dfrac{3p^4}{q^5}\right)^2$ **d.** $\left(\dfrac{2^{-3}}{y}\right)^{-2}$ **e.** $(x^{-5}y^2z^{-1})^7$

Solution

a. $(5x^2)^3 = 5^3 \cdot (x^2)^3 = 5^3 \cdot x^{2\cdot3} = 125x^6$

b. $\left(\dfrac{2}{3}\right)^3 = \dfrac{2^3}{3^3} = \dfrac{8}{27}$

c. $\left(\dfrac{3p^4}{q^5}\right)^2 = \dfrac{(3p^4)^2}{(q^5)^2} = \dfrac{3^2 \cdot (p^4)^2}{(q^5)^2} = \dfrac{9p^8}{q^{10}}$

d. $\left(\dfrac{2^{-3}}{y}\right)^{-2} = \dfrac{(2^{-3})^{-2}}{y^{-2}}$

$= \dfrac{2^6}{y^{-2}} = 64y^2$ Use the negative exponent rule.

e. $(x^{-5}y^2z^{-1})^7 = (x^{-5})^7 \cdot (y^2)^7 \cdot (z^{-1})^7$

$= x^{-35}y^{14}z^{-7} = \dfrac{y^{14}}{x^{35}z^7}$

2 Use the power rules to simplify the following. Use positive exponents to write all results.

a. $(2x^3)^5$ **b.** $\left(\dfrac{3}{5}\right)^2$ **c.** $\left(\dfrac{2a^5}{b^7}\right)^4$ **d.** $\left(\dfrac{3^{-2}}{x}\right)^{-1}$ **e.** $(a^{-2}b^{-5}c^4)^{-2}$

OBJECTIVE 2 ▶ Using exponent rules and definitions to simplify. In the next few examples, we practice the use of several of the rules and definitions for exponents. The following is a summary of these rules and definitions.

Summary of Rules for Exponents

If a and b are real numbers and m and n are integers, then

Product rule	$a^m \cdot a^n = a^{m+n}$	
Zero exponent	$a^0 = 1$	$(a \neq 0)$
Negative exponent	$a^{-n} = \dfrac{1}{a^n}$	$(a \neq 0)$
Quotient rule	$\dfrac{a^m}{a^n} = a^{m-n}$	$(a \neq 0)$
Power rule	$(a^m)^n = a^{m \cdot n}$	
Power of a product	$(ab)^m = a^m \cdot b^m$	
Power of a quotient	$\left(\dfrac{a}{b}\right)^m = \dfrac{a^m}{b^m}$	$(b \neq 0)$

EXAMPLE 3   Simplify each expression. Use positive exponents to write the answers.

a. $(2x^0y^{-3})^{-2}$ **b.** $\left(\dfrac{x^{-5}}{x^{-2}}\right)^{-3}$ **c.** $\left(\dfrac{2}{7}\right)^{-2}$ **d.** $\dfrac{5^{-2}x^{-3}y^{11}}{x^2y^{-5}}$

Solution

a. $(2x^0y^{-3})^{-2} = 2^{-2}(x^0)^{-2}(y^{-3})^{-2}$

$= 2^{-2}x^0y^6$

$= \dfrac{1(y^6)}{2^2}$ Write x^0 as 1.

$= \dfrac{y^6}{4}$

b. $\left(\dfrac{x^{-5}}{x^{-2}}\right)^{-3} = \dfrac{(x^{-5})^{-3}}{(x^{-2})^{-3}} = \dfrac{x^{15}}{x^6} = x^{15-6} = x^9$

c. $\left(\dfrac{2}{7}\right)^{-2} = \dfrac{2^{-2}}{7^{-2}} = \dfrac{7^2}{2^2} = \dfrac{49}{4}$

d. $\dfrac{5^{-2}x^{-3}y^{11}}{x^2y^{-5}} = (5^{-2})\left(\dfrac{x^{-3}}{x^2}\right)\left(\dfrac{y^{11}}{y^{-5}}\right) = 5^{-2}x^{-3-2}y^{11-(-5)} = 5^{-2}x^{-5}y^{16}$

$= \dfrac{y^{16}}{5^2x^5} = \dfrac{y^{16}}{25x^5}$

PRACTICE

3   Simplify each expression. Use positive exponents to write the answer.

a. $(3ab^{-5})^{-3}$ **b.** $\left(\dfrac{y^{-7}}{y^{-4}}\right)^{-5}$ **c.** $\left(\dfrac{3}{8}\right)^{-2}$ **d.** $\dfrac{9^{-2}a^{-4}b^3}{a^2b^{-5}}$

EXAMPLE 4   Simplify each expression. Use positive exponents to write the answers.

a. $\left(\dfrac{3x^2y}{y^{-9}z}\right)^{-2}$ **b.** $\left(\dfrac{3a^2}{2x^{-1}}\right)^3\left(\dfrac{x^{-3}}{4a^{-2}}\right)^{-1}$

Solution   There is often more than one way to simplify exponential expressions. Here, we will simplify inside the parentheses if possible before we apply the power rules for exponents.

a. $\left(\dfrac{3x^2y}{y^{-9}z}\right)^{-2} = \left(\dfrac{3x^2y^{10}}{z}\right)^{-2} = \dfrac{3^{-2}x^{-4}y^{-20}}{z^{-2}} = \dfrac{z^2}{3^2x^4y^{20}} = \dfrac{z^2}{9x^4y^{20}}$

b. $\left(\dfrac{3a^2}{2x^{-1}}\right)^3\left(\dfrac{x^{-3}}{4a^{-2}}\right)^{-1} = \dfrac{27a^6}{8x^{-3}}\cdot\dfrac{x^3}{4^{-1}a^2}$

$= \dfrac{27\cdot 4\cdot a^6x^3x^3}{8\cdot a^2} = \dfrac{27a^4x^6}{2}$

PRACTICE

4   Simplify each expression. Use positive exponents to write the answers.

a. $\left(\dfrac{5a^4b}{a^{-8}c}\right)^{-3}$ **b.** $\left(\dfrac{2x^4}{5y^{-2}}\right)^3\left(\dfrac{x^{-4}}{10y^{-2}}\right)^{-1}$

EXAMPLE 5 Simplify each expression. Assume that a and b are integers and that x and y are not 0.

a. $x^{-b}(2x^b)^2$

b. $\dfrac{(y^{3a})^2}{y^{a-6}}$

Solution

a. $x^{-b}(2x^b)^2 = x^{-b}2^2x^{2b} = 4x^{-b+2b} = 4x^b$

b. $\dfrac{(y^{3a})^2}{y^{a-6}} = \dfrac{y^{6a}}{y^{a-6}} = y^{6a-(a-6)} = y^{6a-a+6} = y^{5a+6}$

PRACTICE
5 Simplify each expression. Assume that a and b are integers and that x and y are not 0.

a. $x^{-2a}(3x^a)^3$

b. $\dfrac{(y^{3b})^3}{y^{4b-3}}$

OBJECTIVE 3 ▶ Computing, using scientific notation. To perform operations on numbers written in scientific notation, we use properties of exponents.

EXAMPLE 6 Perform the indicated operations. Write each result in scientific notation.

a. $(8.1 \times 10^5)(5 \times 10^{-7})$

b. $\dfrac{1.2 \times 10^4}{3 \times 10^{-2}}$

Solution

a. $(8.1 \times 10^5)(5 \times 10^{-7}) = 8.1 \times 5 \times 10^5 \times 10^{-7}$

$= 40.5 \times 10^{-2}$ Not in scientific notation because 40.5 is not between 1 and 10.

$= (4.05 \times 10^1) \times 10^{-2}$

$= 4.05 \times 10^{-1}$

b. $\dfrac{1.2 \times 10^4}{3 \times 10^{-2}} = \left(\dfrac{1.2}{3}\right)\left(\dfrac{10^4}{10^{-2}}\right) = 0.4 \times 10^{4-(-2)}$

$= 0.4 \times 10^6 = (4 \times 10^{-1}) \times 10^6 = 4 \times 10^5$

PRACTICE
6 Perform the indicated operations. Write each result in scientific notation.

a. $(3.4 \times 10^4)(5 \times 10^{-7})$

b. $\dfrac{5.6 \times 10^8}{4 \times 10^{-2}}$

EXAMPLE 7 Use scientific notation to simplify $\dfrac{2000 \times 0.000021}{700}$. Write the result in scientific notation.

Solution $\dfrac{2000 \times 0.000021}{700} = \dfrac{(2 \times 10^3)(2.1 \times 10^{-5})}{7 \times 10^2} = \dfrac{2(2.1)}{7} \cdot \dfrac{10^3 \cdot 10^{-5}}{10^2}$

$= 0.6 \times 10^{-4}$

$= (6 \times 10^{-1}) \times 10^{-4}$

$= 6 \times 10^{-5}$

PRACTICE
7 Use scientific notation to simplify $\dfrac{2400 \times 0.0000014}{800}$. Write the result in scientific notation.

VOCABULARY & READINESS CHECK

Simplify. See Examples 1 through 4.

1. $(x^4)^5$

2. $(5^6)^2$

3. $x^4 \cdot x^5$

4. $x^7 \cdot x^8$

5. $(y^6)^7$

6. $(x^3)^4$

7. $(z^4)^9$

8. $(z^3)^7$

9. $(z^{-6})^{-3}$

10. $(y^{-4})^{-2}$

5.2 | EXERCISE SET

   PRACTICE   WATCH   DOWNLOAD   READ   REVIEW

Simplify. Write each answer using positive exponents only. See Examples 1 and 2.

1. $(3^{-1})^2$

2. $(2^{-2})^2$

3. $(x^4)^{-9}$

4. $(y^7)^{-3}$

5. $(y)^{-5}$

6. $(z^{-1})^{10}$

7. $(3x^2y^3)^2$

8. $(4x^3yz)^2$

9. $\left(\dfrac{2x^5}{y^{-3}}\right)^4$

10. $\left(\dfrac{3a^{-4}}{b^7}\right)^3$

11. $(a^2bc^{-3})^{-6}$

12. $(6x^{-6}y^7z^0)^{-2}$

13. $\left(\dfrac{x^7y^{-3}}{z^{-4}}\right)^{-5}$

14. $\left(\dfrac{a^{-2}b^{-5}}{c^{-11}}\right)^{-6}$

15. $(5^{-1})^3$

Simplify. Write each answer using positive exponents only. See Examples 3 and 4.

16. $\left(\dfrac{a^{-4}}{a^{-5}}\right)^{-2}$

17. $\left(\dfrac{x^{-9}}{x^{-4}}\right)^{-3}$

18. $\left(\dfrac{2a^{-2}b^5}{4a^2b^7}\right)^{-2}$

19. $\left(\dfrac{5x^7y^4}{10x^3y^{-2}}\right)^{-3}$

20. $\dfrac{4^{-1}x^2yz}{x^{-2}yz^3}$

21. $\dfrac{8^{-2}x^{-3}y^{11}}{x^2y^{-5}}$

22. $\left(\dfrac{6p^6}{p^{12}}\right)^2$

23. $\left(\dfrac{4p^6}{p^9}\right)^3$

24. $(-8y^3xa^{-2})^{-3}$

25. $(-xy^0x^2a^3)^{-3}$

26. $\left(\dfrac{x^{-2}y^{-2}}{a^{-3}}\right)^{-7}$

27. $\left(\dfrac{x^{-1}y^{-2}}{5^{-3}}\right)^{-5}$

MIXED PRACTICE

Simplify. Write each answer using positive exponents.

28. $(8^2)^{-1}$

29. $(x^7)^{-9}$

30. $(y^{-4})^5$

31. $\left(\dfrac{7}{8}\right)^3$

32. $\left(\dfrac{4}{3}\right)^2$

33. $(4x^2)^2$

34. $(-8x^3)^2$

35. $(-2^{-2}y)^3$

36. $(-4^{-6}y^{-6})^{-4}$

37. $\left(\dfrac{4^{-4}}{y^3x}\right)^{-2}$

38. $\left(\dfrac{7^{-3}}{ab^2}\right)^{-2}$

39. $\left(\dfrac{1}{4}\right)^{-3}$

40. $\left(\dfrac{1}{8}\right)^{-2}$

41. $\left(\dfrac{3x^5}{6x^4}\right)^4$

42. $\left(\dfrac{8^{-3}}{y^2}\right)^{-2}$

43. $\dfrac{(y^3)^{-4}}{y^3}$

44. $\dfrac{2(y^3)^{-3}}{y^{-3}}$

45. $\left(\dfrac{2x^{-3}}{y^{-1}}\right)^{-3}$

46. $\left(\dfrac{n^5}{2m^{-2}}\right)^{-4}$

47. $\dfrac{3^{-2}a^{-5}b^6}{4^{-2}a^{-7}b^{-3}}$

48. $\dfrac{2^{-3}m^{-4}n^{-5}}{5^{-2}m^{-5}n}$

49. $(4x^6y^5)^{-2}(6x^4y^3)$

50. $(5xy)^3(z^{-2})^{-3}$

51. $x^6(x^6bc)^{-6}$

52. $2(y^2b)^{-4}$

53. $\dfrac{2^{-3}x^2y^{-5}}{5^{-2}x^7y^{-1}}$

54. $\dfrac{7^{-1}a^{-3}b^5}{a^2b^{-2}}$

55. $\left(\dfrac{2x^2}{y^4}\right)^3\left(\dfrac{2x^5}{y}\right)^{-2}$

56. $\left(\dfrac{3z^{-2}}{y}\right)^2\left(\dfrac{9y^{-4}}{z^{-3}}\right)^{-1}$

Simplify the following. Assume that variables in the exponents represent integers and that all other variables are not 0. See Example 5.

57. $(x^{3a+6})^3$

58. $(x^{2b+7})^2$

59. $\dfrac{x^{4a}(x^{4a})^3}{x^{4a-2}}$

60. $\dfrac{x^{-5y+2}x^{2y}}{x}$

61. $(b^{5x-2})^2$

62. $(c^{2a+3})^3$

63. $\dfrac{(y^{2a})^8}{y^{a-3}}$

64. $\dfrac{(y^{4a})^7}{y^{2a-1}}$

65. $\left(\dfrac{2x^{3t}}{x^{2t-1}}\right)^4$

66. $\left(\dfrac{3y^{5a}}{y^{-a+1}}\right)^2$

67. $\dfrac{25x^{2a+1}y^{a-1}}{5x^{3a+1}y^{2a-3}}$

68. $\dfrac{16x^{-5-3a}y^{-2a-b}}{2x^{-5+3b}y^{-2b-a}}$

Perform each indicated operation. Write each answer in scientific notation. See Examples 6 and 7.

69. $(5 \times 10^{11})(2.9 \times 10^{-3})$

70. $(3.6 \times 10^{-12})(6 \times 10^9)$

71. $(2 \times 10^5)^3$

72. $(3 \times 10^{-7})^3$

73. $\dfrac{3.6 \times 10^{-4}}{9 \times 10^2}$

74. $\dfrac{1.2 \times 10^9}{2 \times 10^{-5}}$

75. $\dfrac{0.0069}{0.023}$

76. $\dfrac{0.00048}{0.0016}$

77. $\dfrac{18{,}200 \times 100}{91{,}000}$

78. $\dfrac{0.0003 \times 0.0024}{0.0006 \times 20}$

79. $\dfrac{6000 \times 0.006}{0.009 \times 400}$

80. $\dfrac{0.00016 \times 300}{0.064 \times 100}$

81. $\dfrac{0.00064 \times 2000}{16{,}000}$

82. $\dfrac{0.00072 \times 0.003}{0.00024}$

83. $\dfrac{66{,}000 \times 0.001}{0.002 \times 0.003}$

84. $\dfrac{0.0007 \times 11{,}000}{0.001 \times 0.0001}$

85. $\dfrac{9.24 \times 10^{15}}{(2.2 \times 10^{-2})(1.2 \times 10^{-5})}$

86. $\dfrac{(2.6 \times 10^{-3})(4.8 \times 10^{-4})}{1.3 \times 10^{-12}}$

Solve.

87. A computer can add two numbers in about 10^{-8} second. Express in scientific notation how long it would take this computer to do this task 200,000 times.

88. To convert from square inches to square meters, multiply by 6.452×10^{-4}. The area of the following square is 4×10^{-2} square inches. Convert this area to square meters.

4×10^{-2} sq in.

89. To convert from cubic inches to cubic meters, multiply by 1.64×10^{-5}. A grain of salt is in the shape of a cube. If an average size of a grain of salt is 3.8×10^{-6} cubic inches, convert this volume to cubic meters.

REVIEW AND PREVIEW

Simplify each expression. See Section 1.4.

90. $-5y + 4y - 18 - y$

91. $12m - 14 - 15m - 1$

92. $-3x - (4x - 2)$

93. $-9y - (5 - 6y)$

94. $3(z - 4) - 2(3z + 1)$

95. $5(x - 3) - 4(2x - 5)$

CONCEPT EXTENSIONS

96. Each side of the cube shown is $\dfrac{2x^{-2}}{y}$ meters. Find its volume.

$\dfrac{2x^{-2}}{y}$ m

97. The lot shown is in the shape of a parallelogram with base $\dfrac{3x^{-1}}{y^{-3}}$ feet and height $5x^{-7}$ feet. Find its area.

$5x^{-7}$ ft

$\dfrac{3x^{-1}}{y^{-3}}$ ft

98. The density D of an object is equivalent to the quotient of its mass M and volume V. Thus $D = \dfrac{M}{V}$. Express in scientific notation the density of an object whose mass is 500,000 pounds and whose volume is 250 cubic feet.

99. The density of ordinary water is 3.12×10^{-2} tons per cubic foot. The volume of water in the largest of the Great Lakes, Lake Superior, is 4.269×10^{14} cubic feet. Use the formula $D = \dfrac{M}{V}$ (see Exercise 98) to find the mass (in tons) of the water in Lake Superior. Express your answer in scientific notation. (*Source:* National Ocean Service)

100. Is there a number a such that $a^{-1} = a^{1}$? If so, give the value of a.

101. Is there a number a such that a^{-2} is a negative number? If so, give the value of a.

102. Explain whether 0.4×10^{-5} is written in scientific notation.

103. The estimated population of the United States in 2007 was 3.016×10^{8}. The land area of the United States is 3.536×10^{6} square miles. Find the population density (number of people per square mile) for the United States in 2007. Round to the nearest whole number. (*Source:* U.S. Census Bureau)

104. In 2006, the value of goods imported into the United States was $\$1.855 \times 10^{12}$. The estimated population of the United States in 2006 was 2.98×10^{8}. Find the average value of imports per person in the United States for 2006. Round to the nearest dollar. (*Sources:* U.S. Census Bureau, Bureau of Economic Analysis)

105. The largest subway system in the world (based on passenger volume) is in Tokyo, Japan, with an estimated 2.82×10^9 riders per year. The subway system in Toronto boasts an estimated 4.44×10^8 riders per year. How many times greater is the Tokyo subway volume than the Toronto subway volume? Round to the nearest tenth. (*Source:* Tokyo and Toronto Transit Authorities)

106. Explain whether 0.4×10^{-5} is written in scientific notation.

107. In 2006, the population of Beijing was approximately 15.38×10^6. To prepare for the 2008 Summer Olympic Games, the Chinese put forth a massive effort to increase the numbers of their population who speak a foreign language. By the end of 2006, about 4.87×10^6 people in Beijing could boast that they speak a foreign language. What percent of the residents of Beijing could speak a foreign language at the end of 2006? Round to the nearest tenth of a percent. (*Source: China Daily*)

108. In 2006, downtown office space in downtown New York City was estimated to be 4.21×10^8 sq ft, while office space in downtown Dallas was 4.8×10^7 sq feet. How many times greater is the square footage of office space in New York City than Dallas? Round to the nearest tenth. (*Source: National Center for Real Estate Research*)

5.3 POLYNOMIALS AND POLYNOMIAL FUNCTIONS

OBJECTIVES

1 Identify term, constant, polynomial, monomial, binomial, trinomial, and the degree of a term and of a polynomial.

2 Define polynomial functions.

3 Review combining like terms.

4 Add polynomials.

5 Subtract polynomials.

6 Recognize the graph of a polynomial function from the degree of the polynomial.

OBJECTIVE 1 ▶ Identifing polynomial terms and degrees of terms and polynomials. A **term** is a number or the product of a number and one or more variables raised to powers. The **numerical coefficient,** or simply the **coefficient,** is the numerical factor of a term.

Term	*Numerical Coefficient of Term*
$-1.2x^5$	-1.2
$x^3 y$	1
$-z$	-1
2	2
$\dfrac{x^9}{7}\left(\text{or } \dfrac{1}{7}x^9\right)$	$\dfrac{1}{7}$

If a term contains only a number, it is called a **constant term,** or simply a **constant.** A **polynomial** is a finite sum of terms in which all variables are raised to nonnegative integer powers and no variables appear in any denominator.

Polynomials	*Not Polynomials*	
$4x^5 y + 7xz$	$5x^{-3} + 2x$	Negative integer exponent
$-5x^3 + 2x + \dfrac{2}{3}$	$\dfrac{6}{x^2} - 5x + 1$	Variable in denominator

A polynomial that contains only one variable is called a **polynomial in one variable.** For example, $3x^2 - 2x + 7$ is a **polynomial in x.** This polynomial in x is written in *descending order* since the terms are listed in descending order of the variable's exponents. (The term 7 can be thought of as $7x^0$.) The following examples are polynomials in one variable written in **descending order.**

$$4x^3 - 7x^2 + 5 \qquad y^2 - 4 \qquad 8a^4 - 7a^2 + 4a$$

A **monomial** is a polynomial consisting of one term. A **binomial** is a polynomial consisting of two terms. A **trinomial** is a polynomial consisting of three terms.

Monomials	Binomials	Trinomials
ax^2	$x + y$	$x^2 + 4xy + y^2$
$-3x$	$6y^2 - 2$	$-x^4 + 3x^3 + 1$
4	$\dfrac{5}{7}z^3 - 2z$	$8y^2 - 2y - 10$

By definition, all monomials, binomials, and trinomials are also polynomials.

Each term of a polynomial has a **degree.**

> **Degree of a Term**
> The **degree of a term** is the sum of the exponents on the *variables* contained in the term.

EXAMPLE 1   Find the degree of each term.

a. $3x^2$ **b.** -2^3x^5 **c.** y **d.** $12x^2yz^3$ **e.** 5.27

Solution

a. The exponent on x is 2, so the degree of the term is 2.

b. The exponent on x is 5, so the degree of the term is 5. (Recall that the degree is the sum of the exponents on only the *variables.*)

c. The degree of y, or y^1, is 1.

d. The degree is the sum of the exponents on the variables, or $2 + 1 + 3 = 6$.

e. The degree of 5.27, which can be written as $5.27x^0$, is 0.   □

PRACTICE

1   Find the degree of each term.

a. $4x^5$ **b.** -4^3y^3 **c.** z **d.** $65a^3b^7c$ **e.** 36

From the preceding example, we can say that the degree of a constant is 0. Also, the term 0 has no degree.

Each polynomial also has a degree.

> **Degree of a Polynomial**
> The **degree of a polynomial** is the largest degree of all its terms.

EXAMPLE 2   Find the degree of each polynomial and indicate whether the polynomial is also a monomial, binomial, or trinomial.

	Polynomial	Degree	Classification
a.	$7x^3 - \dfrac{3}{4}x + 2$	3	Trinomial
b.	$-xyz$	$1 + 1 + 1 = 3$	Monomial
c.	$x^4 - 16.5$	4	Binomial

□

PRACTICE
2   Find the degree of each polynomial and indicate whether the polynomial is also a monomial, binomial, or trinomial.

	Polynomial	Degree	Classification
a.	$3x^4 + 2x^2 - 3$		
b.	$9abc^3$		
c.	$8x^5 + 5x^3$		

EXAMPLE 3   Find the degree of the polynomial
$$3xy + x^2y^2 - 5x^2 - 6.7$$

Solution   The degree of each term is

$$3xy + x^2y^2 - 5x^2 - 6.7$$

Degree: 2   4   2   0

The largest degree of any term is 4, so the degree of this polynomial is 4.   □

PRACTICE
3   Find the degree of the polynomial $2x^3y - 3x^3y^2 - 9y^5 + 9.6$.

OBJECTIVE 2 ▶ Defining polynomial functions. At times, it is convenient to use function notation to represent polynomials. For example, we may write $P(x)$ to represent the polynomial $3x^2 - 2x - 5$. In symbols, this is

$$P(x) = 3x^2 - 2x - 5$$

This function is called a **polynomial function** because the expression $3x^2 - 2x - 5$ is a polynomial.

> **▶ Helpful Hint**
> Recall that the symbol $P(x)$ **does not mean** P times x. It is a special symbol used to denote a function.

EXAMPLE 4   If $P(x) = 3x^2 - 2x - 5$, find the following.

a. $P(1)$ **b.** $P(-2)$

Solution

a. Substitute 1 for x in $P(x) = 3x^2 - 2x - 5$ and simplify.
$$P(x) = 3x^2 - 2x - 5$$
$$P(1) = 3(1)^2 - 2(1) - 5 = -4$$

b. Substitute -2 for x in $P(x) = 3x^2 - 2x - 5$ and simplify.
$$P(x) = 3x^2 - 2x - 5$$
$$P(-2) = 3(-2)^2 - 2(-2) - 5 = 11$$ □

PRACTICE
4   If $P(x) = -5x^2 + 2x - 8$, find the following.

a. $P(-1)$ **b.** $P(3)$

Many real-world phenomena are modeled by polynomial functions. If the polynomial function model is given, we can often find the solution of a problem by evaluating the function at a certain value.

EXAMPLE 5   Finding the Height of an Object

The world's highest bridge, the Millau Viaduct in France, is 1125 feet above the River Tarn. An object is dropped from the top of this bridge. Neglecting air resistance, the height of the object at time t seconds is given by the polynomial function $P(t) = -16t^2 + 1125$. Find the height of the object when $t = 1$ second and when $t = 8$ seconds.

 Solution   To find the height of the object at 1 second, we find $P(1)$.

$$P(t) = -16t^2 + 1125$$
$$P(1) = -16(1)^2 + 1125$$
$$P(1) = 1109$$

When $t = 1$ second, the height of the object is 1109 feet.
To find the height of the object at 8 seconds, we find $P(8)$.

$$P(t) = -16t^2 + 1125$$
$$P(8) = -16(8)^2 + 1125$$
$$P(8) = 101$$

When $t = 8$ seconds, the height of the object is 101 feet. Notice that as time t increases, the height of the object decreases. □

PRACTICE
5   The largest natural bridge is in the canyons at the base of Navajo Mountain, Utah. From the base to the top of the arch, it measures 290 feet. Neglecting air resistance, the height of an object dropped off the bridge is given by the polynomial function $P(t) = -16t^2 + 290$ at time t seconds. Find the height of the object at time $t = 0$ second and $t = 2$ seconds.

OBJECTIVE 3 ▶ Combining like terms review. Before we add polynomials, recall that terms are considered to be **like terms** if they contain exactly the same variables raised to exactly the same powers.

Like Terms	Unlike Terms
$-5x^2, -x^2$	$4x^2, 3x$
$7xy^3z, -2xzy^3$	$12x^2y^3, -2xy^3$

To simplify a polynomial, **combine like terms** by using the distributive property. For example, by the distributive property,

$$5x + 7x = (5 + 7)x = 12x$$

EXAMPLE 6   Simplify by combining like terms.

a. $-12x^2 + 7x^2 - 6x$ **b.** $3xy - 2x + 5xy - x$

Solution   By the distributive property,

a. $-12x^2 + 7x^2 - 6x = (-12 + 7)x^2 - 6x = -5x^2 - 6x$

b. Use the associative and commutative properties to group together like terms; then combine.

$$3xy - 2x + 5xy - x = 3xy + 5xy - 2x - x$$
$$= (3 + 5)xy + (-2 - 1)x$$
$$= \underbrace{8xy} - \underbrace{3x}$$

> ▶ **Helpful Hint**
>
> These two terms are unlike terms. They cannot be combined.

PRACTICE
6 Simplify by combining like terms.

a. $8x^4 - 5x^4 - 5x$ **b.** $4ab - 5b + 3ab + 2b$

OBJECTIVE 4 ▶ Adding polynomials. Now we have reviewed the necessary skills to add polynomials.

> **Adding Polynomials**
> To add polynomials, combine all like terms.

EXAMPLE 7 Add.

a. $(7x^3y - xy^3 + 11) + (6x^3y - 4)$ **b.** $(3a^3 - b + 2a - 5) + (a + b + 5)$

Solution

a. To add, remove the parentheses and group like terms.

$$(7x^3y - xy^3 + 11) + (6x^3y - 4)$$
$$= 7x^3y - xy^3 + 11 + 6x^3y - 4$$
$$= 7x^3y + 6x^3y - xy^3 + 11 - 4 \quad \text{Group like terms.}$$
$$= 13x^3y - xy^3 + 7 \quad \text{Combine like terms.}$$

b.
$$(3a^3 - b + 2a - 5) + (a + b + 5)$$
$$= 3a^3 - b + 2a - 5 + a + b + 5$$
$$= 3a^3 - b + b + 2a + a - 5 + 5 \quad \text{Group like terms.}$$
$$= 3a^3 + 3a \quad \text{Combine like terms.}$$

PRACTICE
7 Add.

a. $(3a^4b - 5ab^2 + 7) + (9ab^2 - 12)$ **b.** $(2x^5 - 3y + x - 6) + (4y - 2x - 3)$

EXAMPLE 8 Add $11x^3 - 12x^2 + x - 3$ and $x^3 - 10x + 5$.

Solution
$$(11x^3 - 12x^2 + x - 3) + (x^3 - 10x + 5)$$
$$= 11x^3 + x^3 - 12x^2 + x - 10x - 3 + 5 \quad \text{Group like terms.}$$
$$= 12x^3 - 12x^2 - 9x + 2 \quad \text{Combine like terms.}$$

PRACTICE
8 Add $5x^3 - 3x^2 - 9x - 8$ and $x^3 + 9x^2 + 2x$.

Sometimes it is more convenient to add polynomials vertically. To do this, line up like terms beneath one another and add like terms.

OBJECTIVE 5 ▶ Subtracting polynomials. The definition of subtraction of real numbers can be extended to apply to polynomials. To subtract a number, we add its opposite.

$$a - b = a + (-b)$$

Likewise, to subtract a polynomial, we add its opposite. In other words, if P and Q are polynomials, then

$$P - Q = P + (-Q)$$

The polynomial $-Q$ is the **opposite,** or **additive inverse,** of the polynomial Q. We can find $-Q$ by writing the opposite of each term of Q.

> **Subtracting Polynomials**
> To subtract a polynomial, add its opposite.

For example,

To subtract, change the signs; then add.

$$(3x^2 + 4x - 7) - (3x^2 - 2x - 5) = (3x^2 + 4x - 7) + (-3x^2 + 2x + 5)$$
$$= 3x^2 + 4x - 7 - 3x^2 + 2x + 5$$
$$= 6x - 2 \qquad \text{Combine like terms.}$$

Concept Check ✓

Which polynomial is the opposite of $16x^3 - 5x + 7$?

a. $-16x^3 - 5x + 7$ **b.** $-16x^3 + 5x - 7$

c. $16x^3 + 5x + 7$ **d.** $-16x^3 + 5x + 7$

EXAMPLE 9   Subtract: $(12z^5 - 12z^3 + z) - (-3z^4 + z^3 + 12z)$

Solution   To subtract, add the opposite of the second polynomial to the first polynomial.

$$(12z^5 - 12z^3 + z) - (-3z^4 + z^3 + 12z)$$
$$= 12z^5 - 12z^3 + z + 3z^4 - z^3 - 12z) \qquad \text{Add the opposite of the polynomial being subtracted.}$$
$$= 12z^5 + 3z^4 - 12z^3 - z^3 + z - 12z \qquad \text{Group like terms.}$$
$$= 12z^5 + 3z^4 - 13z^3 - 11z \qquad \text{Combine like terms.} \qquad \square$$

PRACTICE
9   Subtract: $(13a^4 - 7a^3 - 9) - (-2a^4 + 8a^3 - 12)$.

Concept Check ✓

Why is the following subtraction incorrect?

$$(7z - 5) - (3z - 4)$$
$$= 7z - 5 - 3z - 4$$
$$= 4z - 9$$

Answers to Concept Check:
b;

With parentheses removed, the expression should be

$$7z - 5 - 3z + 4 = 4z - 1$$

EXAMPLE 10   Subtract $4x^3y^2 - 3x^2y^2 + 2y^2$ from $10x^3y^2 - 7x^2y^2$.

Solution   If we subtract 2 from 8, the difference is $8 - 2 = 6$. Notice the order of the numbers, and then write "Subtract $4x^3y^2 - 3x^2y^2 + 2y^2$ from $10x^3y^2 - 7x^2y^2$" as a mathematical expression.

$$(10x^3y^2 - 7x^2y^2) - (4x^3y^2 - 3x^2y^2 + 2y^2)$$
$$= 10x^3y^2 - 7x^2y^2 - 4x^3y^2 + 3x^2y^2 - 2y^2 \quad \text{Remove parentheses.}$$
$$= 6x^3y^2 - 4x^2y^2 - 2y^2 \quad \text{Combine like terms.} \qquad \square$$

PRACTICE
10   Subtract $5x^2y^2 - 3xy^2 + 5y^3$ from $11x^2y^2 - 7xy^2$.

To add or subtract polynomials vertically, just remember to line up like terms. For example, perform the subtraction $(10x^3y^2 - 7x^2y^2) - (4x^3y^2 - 3x^2y^2 + 2y^2)$ vertically.

Add the opposite of the second polynomial.

$$\begin{array}{r} 10x^3y^2 - 7x^2y^2 \\ -(4x^3y^2 - 3x^2y^2 + 2y^2) \end{array} \quad \text{is equivalent to} \quad \begin{array}{r} 10x^3y^2 - 7x^2y^2 \\ -4x^3y^2 + 3x^2y^2 - 2y^2 \\ \hline 6x^3y^2 - 4x^2y^2 - 2y^2 \end{array}$$

Polynomial functions, like polynomials, can be added, subtracted, multiplied, and divided. For example, if

$$P(x) = x^2 + x + 1$$

then

$$2P(x) = 2(x^2 + x + 1) = 2x^2 + 2x + 2 \quad \text{Use the distributive property.}$$

Also, if $Q(x) = 5x^2 - 1$, then $P(x) + Q(x) = (x^2 + x + 1) + (5x^2 - 1) = 6x^2 + x$.

A useful business and economics application of subtracting polynomial functions is finding the profit function $P(x)$ when given a revenue function $R(x)$ and a cost function $C(x)$. In business, it is true that

$$\text{profit} = \text{revenue} - \text{cost, or}$$
$$P(x) = R(x) - C(x)$$

For example, if the revenue function is $R(x) = 7x$ and the cost function is $C(x) = 2x + 5000$, then the profit function is

$$P(x) = R(x) - C(x)$$

or

$$P(x) = 7x - (2x + 5000) \quad \text{Substitute } R(x) = 7x$$
$$P(x) = 5x - 5000 \quad\quad\quad \text{and } C(x) = 2x + 5000.$$

Problem-solving exercises involving profit are in the exercise set.

OBJECTIVE 6 ▶ **Recognizing graphs of polynomial functions from their degree.** In this section, we reviewed how to find the degree of a polynomial. Knowing the degree of a polynomial can help us recognize the graph of the related polynomial function. For example, we know from Section 3.1 that the graph of the polynomial function $f(x) = x^2$ is a parabola as shown to the left.

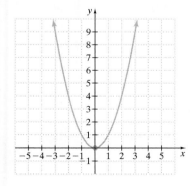

The polynomial x^2 has degree 2. The graphs of all polynomial functions of degree 2 will have this same general shape—opening upward, as shown, or downward. Graphs of polynomial functions of degree 2 or 3 will, in general, resemble one of the graphs shown next.

General Shapes of Graphs of Polynomial Functions

Degree 2

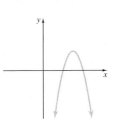

Coefficient of x^2
is a positive number.

Coefficient of x^2
is a negative number.

Degree 3

 or   or

Coefficient of x^3
is a positive number.

Coefficient of x^3
is a negative number.

EXAMPLE 11 Determine which of the following graphs most closely resembles the graph of $f(x) = 5x^3 - 6x^2 + 2x + 3$

A   B   C   D

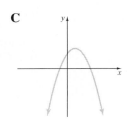

Solution The degree of $f(x)$ is 3, which means that its graph has the shape of B or D. The coefficient of x^3 is 5, a positive number, so the graph has the shape of B.   □

PRACTICE

11 Determine which of the following graphs most closely resembles the graph of $f(x) = x^3 - 3$.

A   B   C   D

Graphing Calculator Explorations

A graphing calculator may be used to visualize addition and subtraction of polynomials in one variable. For example, to visualize the following polynomial subtraction statement

$$(3x^2 - 6x + 9) - (x^2 - 5x + 6) = 2x^2 - x + 3$$

graph both

$$Y_1 = (3x^2 - 6x + 9) - (x^2 - 5x + 6) \quad \text{Left side of equation}$$

and

$$Y_2 = 2x^2 - x + 3 \quad \text{Right side of equation}$$

on the same screen and see that their graphs coincide. (*Note:* If the graphs do not coincide, we can be sure that a mistake has been made in combining polynomials or in calculator keystrokes. If the graphs appear to coincide, we cannot be sure that our work is correct. This is because it is possible for the graphs to differ so slightly that we do not notice it.)

The graphs of Y_1 and Y_2 are shown. The graphs appear to coincide, so the subtraction statement

$$(3x^2 - 6x + 9) - (x^2 - 5x + 6) = 2x^2 - x + 3$$

appears to be correct.

Perform the indicated operations. Then visualize by using the procedure described above.

1. $(2x^2 + 7x + 6) + (x^3 - 6x^2 - 14)$
2. $(-14x^3 - x + 2) + (-x^3 + 3x^2 + 4x)$
3. $(1.8x^2 - 6.8x - 1.7) - (3.9x^2 - 3.6x)$
4. $(-4.8x^2 + 12.5x - 7.8) - (3.1x^2 - 7.8x)$
5. $(1.29x - 5.68) + (7.69x^2 - 2.55x + 10.98)$
6. $(-0.98x^2 - 1.56x + 5.57) + (4.36x - 3.71)$

VOCABULARY & READINESS CHECK

Use the choices below to fill in each blank. Not all choices will be used.

monomial	trinomial	like	degree	coefficient
binomial	polynomial	unlike	variables	term

1. The numerical factor of a term is the _____ .

2. A _____ is a finite sum of terms in which all variables are raised to nonnegative integer powers and no variables appear in any denominator.

3. A _____ is a polynomial with 2 terms.

4. A _____ is a polynomial with 1 term.

5. A _____ is a polynomial with 3 terms.

6. The degree of a term is the sum of the exponents on the _____ in the term.

7. The _____ of a polynomial is the largest degree of all its terms.

8. _____ terms contain the same variables raised to the same powers.

Add or subtract, if possible.

9. $5x + x$ 10. $5x - x$ 11. $y + y$ 12. $z^2 + z^2$ 13. $7xy^2 - y^2$ 14. $x^3 - 9x^3$

5.3 EXERCISE SET

MyMathLab PRACTICE WATCH DOWNLOAD READ REVIEW

Find the degree of each term. See Example 1.

1. 4

2. 7

3. $5x^2$

4. $-z^3$

5. $-3xy^2$

6. $12x^3z$

7. -8^7y^3

8. $-9^{11}y^5$

9. $3.78ab^3c^5$

10. $9.11r^2st^{12}$

Find the degree of each polynomial and indicate whether the polynomial is a monomial, binomial, trinomial, or none of these. See Examples 2 and 3.

11. $6x + 0.3$

12. $7x - 0.8$

13. $3x^2 - 2x + 5$

14. $5x^2 - 3x - 2$

15. -3^4xy^2

16. -7^5abc

17. $x^2y - 4xy^2 + 5x + y^4$

18. $-2x^2y - 3y^2 + 4x + y^5$

If $P(x) = x^2 + x + 1$ and $Q(x) = 5x^2 - 1$, find the following. See Example 4.

19. $P(7)$

20. $Q(4)$

21. $Q(-10)$

22. $P(-4)$

23. $Q\left(\dfrac{1}{4}\right)$

24. $P\left(\dfrac{1}{2}\right)$

Refer to Example 5 for Exercises 25 through 28.

25. Find the height of the object at $t = 2$ seconds.

26. Find the height of the object at $t = 4$ seconds.

27. Find the height of the object at $t = 6$ seconds.

28. Approximate (to the nearest second) how long it takes before the object hits the ground. (*Hint:* The object hits the ground when $P(x) = 0$.)

Simplify by combining like terms. See Example 6.

29. $5y + y$

30. $-x + 3x$

31. $4x + 7x - 3$

32. $-8y + 9y + 4y^2$

33. $4xy + 2x - 3xy - 1$

34. $-8xy^2 + 4x - x + 2xy^2$

35. $7x^2 - 2xy + 5y^2 - x^2 + xy + 11y^2$

36. $-a^2 + 18ab - 2b^2 + 14a^2 - 12ab - b^2$

MIXED PRACTICE

Perform the indicated operations. See Examples 7 through 10.

37. $(9y^2 - 8) + (9y^2 - 9)$

38. $(x^2 + 4x - 7) + (8x^2 + 9x - 7)$

39. Add $(x^2 + xy - y^2)$ and $(2x^2 - 4xy + 7y^2)$.

40. Add $(4x^3 - 6x^2 + 5x + 7)$ and $(2x^2 + 6x - 3)$.

41. $\begin{array}{r} x^2 - 6x + 3 \\ + \quad (2x + 5) \\ \hline \end{array}$

42. $\begin{array}{r} -2x^2 + 3x - 9 \\ + \quad (2x - 3) \\ \hline \end{array}$

43. $(9y^2 - 7y + 5) - (8y^2 - 7y + 2)$

44. $(2x^2 + 3x + 12) - (5x - 7)$

45. Subtract $(6x^2 - 3x)$ from $(4x^2 + 2x)$.

46. Subtract $(xy + x - y)$ from $(xy + x - 3)$.

47. $\begin{array}{r} 3x^2 - 4x + 8 \\ - \quad (5x^2 - 7) \\ \hline \end{array}$

48. $\begin{array}{r} -3x^2 - 4x + 8 \\ - \quad (5x + 12) \\ \hline \end{array}$

49. $(5x - 11) + (-x - 2)$

50. $(3x^2 - 2x) + (5x^2 - 9x)$

51. $(7x^2 + x + 1) - (6x^2 + x - 1)$

52. $(4x - 4) - (-x - 4)$

53. $(7x^3 - 4x + 8) + (5x^3 + 4x + 8x)$

54. $(9xyz + 4x - y) + (-9xyz - 3x + y + 2)$

55. $(9x^3 - 2x^2 + 4x - 7) - (2x^3 - 6x^2 - 4x + 3)$

56. $(3x^2 + 6xy + 3y^2) - (8x^2 - 6xy - y^2)$

57. Add $(y^2 + 4yx + 7)$ and $(-19y^2 + 7yx + 7)$.

58. Subtract $(x - 4)$ from $(3x^2 - 4x + 5)$.

59. $(3x^3 - b + 2a - 6) + (-4x^3 + b + 6a - 6)$

60. $(5x^2 - 6) + (2x^2 - 4x + 8)$

61. $(4x^2 - 6x + 2) - (-x^2 + 3x + 5)$

62. $(5x^2 + x + 9) - (2x^2 - 9)$

63. $(-3x + 8) + (-3x^2 + 3x - 5)$

64. $(5y^2 - 2y + 4) + (3y + 7)$

65. $(-3 + 4x^2 + 7xy^2) + (2x^3 - x^2 + xy^2)$

66. $(-3x^2y + 4) - (-7x^2y - 8y)$

67. $\begin{array}{r} 6y^2 - 6y + 4 \\ -(-y^2 - 6y + 7) \\ \hline \end{array}$

68. $\begin{array}{r} -4x^3 + 4x^2 - 4x \\ -(2x^3 - 2x^2 + 3x) \\ \hline \end{array}$

69. $\begin{array}{r} 3x^2 + 15x + 8 \\ +(2x^2 + 7x + 8) \\ \hline \end{array}$

70. $\begin{array}{r} 9x^2 + 9x - 4 \\ +(7x^2 - 3x - 4) \\ \hline \end{array}$

71. $\left(\dfrac{1}{2}x^2 - \dfrac{1}{3}x^2y + 2y^3\right) + \left(\dfrac{1}{4}x^2 - \dfrac{8}{3}x^2y^2 - \dfrac{1}{2}y^3\right)$

72. $\left(\dfrac{2}{5}a^2 - ab + \dfrac{4}{3}b^2\right) + \left(\dfrac{1}{5}a^2b - ab + \dfrac{5}{6}b^2\right)$

73. Find the sum of $(5q^4 - 2q^2 - 3q)$ and $(-6q^4 + 3q^2 + 5)$.

74. Find the sum of $(5y^4 - 7y^2 + x^2 - 3)$ and $(-3y^4 + 2y^2 + 4)$.

75. Subtract $(3x + 7)$ from the sum of $(7x^2 + 4x + 9)$ and $(8x^2 + 7x - 8)$.

76. Subtract $(9x + 8)$ from the sum of $(3x^2 - 2x - x^3 + 2)$ and $(5x^2 - 8x - x^3 + 4)$.

77. Find the sum of $(4x^4 - 7x^2 + 3)$ and $(2 - 3x^4)$.

78. Find the sum of $(8x^4 - 14x^2 + 6)$ and $(-12x^6 - 21x^4 - 9x^2)$.

79. $\left(\dfrac{2}{3}x^2 - \dfrac{1}{6}x + \dfrac{5}{6}\right) - \left(\dfrac{1}{3}x^2 + \dfrac{5}{6}x - \dfrac{1}{6}\right)$

80. $\left(\dfrac{3}{16}x^2 + \dfrac{5}{8}x - \dfrac{1}{4}\right) - \left(\dfrac{5}{16}x^2 - \dfrac{3}{8}x + \dfrac{3}{4}\right)$

Solve. See Example 5.

The surface area of a rectangular box is given by the polynomial function

$$f(x) = 2HL + 2LW + 2HW$$

and is measured in square units. In business, surface area is often calculated to help determine cost of materials.

81. A rectangular box is to be constructed to hold a new camcorder. The box is to have dimensions 5 inches by 4 inches by 9 inches. Find the surface area of the box.

82. Suppose it has been determined that a box of dimensions 4 inches by 4 inches by 8.5 inches can be used to contain the camcorder in Exercise 81. Find the surface area of this box and calculate the square inches of material saved by using this box instead of the box in Exercise 81.

83. A projectile is fired upward from the ground with an initial velocity of 300 feet per second. Neglecting air resistance, the height of the projectile at any time t can be described by the polynomial function $P(t) = -16t^2 + 300t$. Find the height of the projectile at each given time.

    a. $t = 1$ second   **b.** $t = 2$ seconds

    c. $t = 3$ seconds   **d.** $t = 4$ seconds

    e. Explain why the height increases and then decreases as time passes.

    f. Approximate (to the nearest second) how long before the object hits the ground.

84. An object is thrown upward with an initial velocity of 25 feet per second from the top of the 984-foot-high Eiffel Tower in Paris, France. The height of the object at any time t can be described by the polynomial function $P(t) = -16t^2 + 25t + 984$. Find the height of the projectile at each given time. (*Source:* Council on Tall Buildings and Urban Habitat, Lehigh University)

    a. $t = 1$ second

    b. $t = 3$ seconds

    c. $t = 5$ seconds

    d. Approximate (to the nearest second) how long before the object hits the ground.

85. The polynomial function $P(x) = 45x - 100,000$ models the relationship between the number of computer briefcases x that a company sells and the profit the company makes, $P(x)$. Find $P(4000)$, the profit from selling 4000 computer briefcases.

86. The total cost (in dollars) for MCD, Inc., Manufacturing Company to produce x blank audiocassette tapes per week is given by the polynomial function $C(x) = 0.8x + 10,000$. Find the total cost of producing 20,000 tapes per week.

87. The total revenues (in dollars) for MCD, Inc., Manufacturing Company to sell x blank audiocassette tapes per week is given by the polynomial function $R(x) = 2x$. Find the total revenue from selling 20,000 tapes per week.

88. In business, profit equals revenue minus cost, or $P(x) = R(x) - C(x)$. Find the profit function for MCD, Inc. by subtracting the given functions in Exercises 86 and 87.

Match each equation with its graph. See Example 11.

89. $f(x) = 3x^2 - 2$

90. $h(x) = 5x^3 - 6x + 2$

91. $g(x) = -2x^3 - 3x^2 + 3x - 2$

92. $F(x) = -2x^2 - 6x + 2$

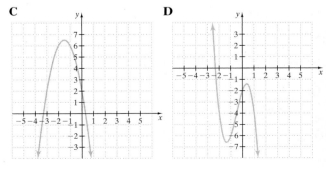

REVIEW AND PREVIEW

Multiply. See Section 1.4.

93. $5(3x - 2)$

94. $-7(2z - 6y)$

95. $-2(x^2 - 5x + 6)$

96. $5(-3y^2 - 2y + 7)$

CONCEPT EXTENSIONS

Solve. See the Concept Checks in this section.

97. Which polynomial(s) is the opposite of $8x - 6$?

   a. $-(8x - 6)$ **b.** $8x + 6$

   c. $-8x + 6$ **d.** $-8x - 6$

98. Which polynomial(s) is the opposite of $-y^5 + 10y^3 - 2.3$?

   a. $y^5 + 10y^3 + 2.3$ **b.** $-y^5 - 10y^3 - 2.3$

   c. $y^5 + 10y^3 - 2.3$ **d.** $y^5 - 10y^3 + 2.3$

99. Correct the subtraction.

$$(12x - 1.7) - (15x + 6.2) = 12x - 1.7 - 15x + 6.2$$
$$= -3x + 4.5$$

100. Correct the addition.

$$(12x - 1.7) + (15x + 6.2) = 12x - 1.7 + 15x + 6.2$$
$$= 27x + 7.9$$

101. Write a function, $P(x)$, so that $P(0) = 7$.

102. Write a function, $R(x)$, so that $R(1) = 2$.

103. In your own words, describe how to find the degree of a term.

104. In your own words, describe how to find the degree of a polynomial.

Perform the indicated operations.

105. $(4x^{2a} - 3x^a + 0.5) - (x^{2a} - 5x^a - 0.2)$

106. $(9y^{5a} - 4y^{3a} + 1.5y) - (6y^{5a} - y^{3a} + 4.7y)$

107. $(8x^{2y} - 7x^y + 3) + (-4x^{2y} + 9x^y - 14)$

108. $(14z^{5x} + 3z^{2x} + z) - (2z^{5x} - 10z^{2x} + 3z)$

Find each perimeter.

109.

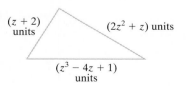

$(x + 5y)$ units

$(3x^2 - x + 2y)$ units

110.

$(z + 2)$ units $(2z^2 + z)$ units

$(z^3 - 4z + 1)$ units

If $P(x) = 3x + 3$, $Q(x) = 4x^2 - 6x + 3$, and $R(x) = 5x^2 - 7$, find the following.

111. $P(x) + Q(x)$

112. $R(x) + P(x)$

113. $Q(x) - R(x)$

114. $P(x) - Q(x)$

115. $2[Q(x)] - R(x)$

116. $-5[P(x)] - Q(x)$

117. $3[R(x)] + 4[P(x)]$

118. $2[Q(x)] + 7[R(x)]$

*If $P(x)$ is the polynomial given, find **a.** $P(a)$, **b.** $P(-x)$, and **c.** $P(x + h)$.*

119. $P(x) = 2x - 3$

120. $P(x) = 8x + 3$

121. $P(x) = 4x$

122. $P(x) = -4x$

123. $P(x) = 4x - 1$

124. $P(x) = 3x - 2$

125. The function $f(x) = 0.07x^2 - 0.8x + 3.6$ can be used to approximate the amazing growth of the number of Web logs (Blogs) appearing on the Internet from January 2004 to October 2006, where January, 2004 = 1 for x, February 2004 = 2 for x, and so on, and y is the number of blogs (in millions). Round answers to the nearest tenth of a million. (Note: This is one company's tracking of the cumulative number of blogs. These numbers vary greatly according to source and activity of blog.) (*Source:* Technorati)

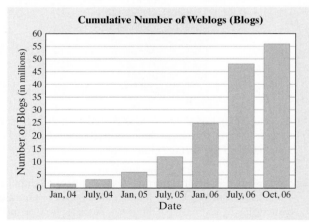

Cumulative Number of Weblogs (Blogs)

   Number of Blogs (in millions) vs *Date* (Jan, 04; July, 04; Jan, 05; July, 05; Jan, 06; July, 06; Oct, 06)

   a. Approximate the number of Web logs on the Internet in January 2004.

   b. Approximate the number of Web logs on the Internet in October 2006.

   c. Use this function to approximate the number of Web logs on the Internet in May 2009. (65 months)

   d. From parts (a), (b), and (c), determine whether the number of Web logs on the Internet is increasing at a steady rate. Explain why or why not.

126. The function $f(x) = -61x^2 - 5530x + 585,753$ can be used to approximate the number of international students studying in the United States during the academic years 2002 through 2006, where x is the number of years after 2002 and $f(x)$ is the number of international students.

(*Source:* Institute of International Education: *Open Doors 2006*)

a. Approximate the number of international students studying in the United States in 2003.

b. Approximate the number of international students studying in the United States in 2005.

c. Use the function to predict the number of international students studying in the United States in 2008.

127. The function $f(x) = -0.39x^2 + 2.49x + 38.7$ can be used to approximate the number of Americans under age 65 without health insurance during the period 1999–2005, where x is the number of years after 1999 and $f(x)$ is the number in millions of Americans. Round answers to the nearest tenth of a million. (*Source:* National Center for Health Statistics)

a. Approximate the number of Americans under 65 without health insurance in 2003.

b. Use the function to predict the number of Americans under 65 without health insurance in 2008.

128. University libraries need to continue to grow to meet the educational needs of their students. The function $f(x) = -14x^2 + 269.2x + 7414.2$ approximates the number of written volumes (in thousands) to be found in the University of California, Los Angeles, libraries for the years from 2002 to 2005, where x is the number of years after 2002. (*Source:* Association of Research Libraries)

a. Approximate the number of volumes in 2004.

b. Use the function to estimate the number of volumes at UCLA libraries in 2008.

129. Sport utility vehicle (SUV) sales in the United States have increased since 1995. The function $f(x) = -0.005x^2 + 0.377x + 1.71$ can be used to approximate the number of SUV sales during the years 1995–2004, where x is the number of years after 1995 and $f(x)$ is the SUV sales (in millions). Round answers to the nearest tenth of a million. (*Source:* Bureau of Transportation Statistics)

a. Approximate the number of SUVs sold in 2003.

b. Use the function to predict the number of SUVs sold in 2010.

130. The function $f(x) = 873x^2 - 4104x + 40{,}263$ can be used to approximate the number of AIDS cases diagnosed in the United States from 2001 to 2005, where x is the number of years since 2001. (*Source:* Based on data from the U.S. Centers for Disease Control and Prevention)

a. Approximate the number of AIDS cases diagnosed in the United States in 2001.

b. Approximate the number of AIDS cases diagnosed in the United States in 2003.

c. Approximate the number of AIDS cases diagnosed in the United States in 2005.

d. Describe the trend in the number of AIDS cases diagnosed during the period covered by this model.

5.4 | MULTIPLYING POLYNOMIALS

OBJECTIVES

1 Multiply two polynomials.

2 Multiply binomials.

3 Square binomials.

4 Multiply the sum and difference of two terms.

5 Multiply three or more polynomials.

6 Evaluate polynomial functions.

OBJECTIVE 1 ▶ Multiplying two polynomials. Properties of real numbers and exponents are used continually in the process of multiplying polynomials. To multiply monomials, for example, we apply the commutative and associative properties of real numbers and the product rule for *exponents*.

EXAMPLE 1   Multiply.

a. $(2x^3)(5x^6)$ 　　　　b. $(7y^4z^4)(-xy^{11}z^5)$

Solution   Group like bases and apply the product rule for exponents.

a. $(2x^3)(5x^6) = 2(5)(x^3)(x^6) = 10x^9$

b. $(7y^4z^4)(-xy^{11}z^5) = 7(-1)x(y^4y^{11})(z^4z^5) = -7xy^{15}z^9$

PRACTICE
1　Multiply.

a. $(3x^4)(2x^2)$ 　　　　b. $(-5m^4np^3)(-8mnp^5)$

To multiply a monomial by a polynomial other than a monomial, we use an expanded form of the distributive property.

$$a(b + c + d + \cdots + z) = ab + ac + ad + \cdots + az$$

Notice that the monomial a is multiplied by each term of the polynomial.

▶ Helpful Hint

See Sections 5.1 and 5.2 to review exponential expressions further.

EXAMPLE 2 Multiply.

a. $2x(5x - 4)$ **b.** $-3x^2(4x^2 - 6x + 1)$ **c.** $-xy(7x^2y + 3xy - 11)$

Solution Apply the distributive property.

a. $2x(5x - 4) = 2x(5x) + 2x(-4)$ Use the distributive property.
$$= 10x^2 - 8x \qquad \text{Multiply.}$$

b. $-3x^2(4x^2 - 6x + 1) = -3x^2(4x^2) + (-3x^2)(-6x) + (-3x^2)(1)$
$$= -12x^4 + 18x^3 - 3x^2$$

c. $-xy(7x^2y + 3xy - 11) = -xy(7x^2y) + (-xy)(3xy) + (-xy)(-11)$
$$= -7x^3y^2 - 3x^2y^2 + 11xy \qquad \square$$

PRACTICE

2 Multiply.

a. $3x(7x - 1)$ **b.** $-5a^2(3a^2 - 6a + 5)$ **c.** $-mn^3(5m^2n^2 + 2mn - 5m)$

To multiply any two polynomials, we can use the following.

> **Multiplying Two Polynomials**
> To multiply any two polynomials, use the distributive property and multiply each term of one polynomial by each term of the other polynomial. Then combine any like terms.

Concept Check ☑

Find the error:

$$4x(x - 5) + 2x$$
$$= 4x(x) + 4x(-5) + 4x(2x)$$
$$= 4x^2 - 20x + 8x^2$$
$$= 12x^2 - 20x$$

EXAMPLE 3 Multiply and simplify the product if possible.

a. $(x + 3)(2x + 5)$ **b.** $(2x - 3)(5x^2 - 6x + 7)$

Solution

a. Multiply each term of $(x + 3)$ by $(2x + 5)$.

$$(x + 3)(2x + 5) = x(2x + 5) + 3(2x + 5) \quad \text{Apply the distributive property.}$$
$$= 2x^2 + 5x + 6x + 15 \quad \text{Apply the distributive property again.}$$
$$= 2x^2 + 11x + 15 \quad \text{Combine like terms.}$$

b. Multiply each term of $(2x - 3)$ by each term of $(5x^2 - 6x + 7)$.

$$(2x - 3)(5x^2 - 6x + 7) = 2x(5x^2 - 6x + 7) + (-3)(5x^2 - 6x + 7)$$
$$= 10x^3 - 12x^2 + 14x - 15x^2 + 18x - 21$$
$$= 10x^3 - 27x^2 + 32x - 21 \quad \text{Combine like terms.} \quad \square$$

Answer to Concept Check:
$4x(x - 5) + 2x$
$= 4x(x) + 4x(-5) + 2x$
$= 4x^2 - 20x + 2x$
$= 4x^2 - 18x$

PRACTICE

3 Multiply and simplify the product if possible.

a. $(x + 5)(2x + 3)$ **b.** $(3x - 1)(x^2 - 6x + 2)$

Sometimes polynomials are easier to multiply vertically, in the same way we multiply real numbers. When multiplying vertically, we line up like terms in the **partial products** vertically. This makes combining like terms easier.

EXAMPLE 4   Multiply vertically $(4x^2 + 7)(x^2 + 2x + 8)$.

Solution

$$
\begin{array}{r}
x^2 + 2x + 8 \\
4x^2 + 7 \\
\hline
7x^2 + 14x + 56 \\
4x^4 + 8x^3 + 32x^2 \\
\hline
4x^4 + 8x^3 + 39x^2 + 14x + 56
\end{array}
$$

$7(x^2 + 2x + 8)$
$4x^2(x^2 + 2x + 8)$
Combine like terms.   □

PRACTICE
4   Multiply vertically: $(3x^2 + 2)(x^2 - 4x - 5)$.

OBJECTIVE 2 ▸ Multiplying binomials.   When multiplying a binomial by a binomial, we can use a special order of multiplying terms, called the **FOIL** order. The letters of FOIL stand for "**F**irst-**O**uter-**I**nner-**L**ast." To illustrate this method, let's multiply $(2x - 3)$ by $(3x + 1)$.

Multiply the **F**irst terms of each binomial. $(2x - 3)(3x + 1)$ $\quad$ F $\quad 2x(3x) = 6x^2$

Multiply the **O**uter terms of each binomial. $(2x - 3)(3x + 1)$ $\quad$ O $\quad 2x(1) = 2x$

Multiply the **I**nner terms of each binomial. $(2x - 3)(3x + 1)$ $\quad$ I $\quad -3(3x) = -9x$

Multiply the **L**ast terms of each binomial. $(2x - 3)(3x + 1)$ $\quad$ L $\quad -3(1) = -3$
Combine like terms.

$$6x^2 + 2x - 9x - 3 = 6x^2 - 7x - 3$$

EXAMPLE 5   Use the FOIL order to multiply $(x - 1)(x + 2)$.

Solution

$$
\begin{array}{cccc}
\text{First} & \text{Outer} & \text{Inner} & \text{Last}
\end{array}
$$

$$(x - 1)(x + 2) = x \cdot x \ + \ 2 \cdot x \ + \ (-1)x \ + \ (-1)(2)$$
$$= x^2 + 2x - x - 2$$
$$= x^2 + x - 2 \quad \text{Combine like terms.} \quad □$$

PRACTICE
5   Use the FOIL order to multiply $(x - 5)(x + 3)$.

EXAMPLE 6   Multiply.

a. $(2x - 7)(3x - 4)$ $\qquad$ **b.** $(3x^2 + y)(5x^2 - 2y)$

Solution

$$
\begin{array}{cccc}
\text{First} & \text{Outer} & \text{Inner} & \text{Last}
\end{array}
$$

a. $(2x - 7)(3x - 4) = 2x(3x) + 2x(-4) + (-7)(3x) + (-7)(-4)$
$$= 6x^2 - 8x - 21x + 28$$
$$= 6x^2 - 29x + 28$$

$$\begin{array}{cccc} \text{F} & \text{O} & \text{I} & \text{L} \\ \downarrow & \downarrow & \downarrow & \downarrow \end{array}$$

b. $(3x^2 + y)(5x^2 - 2y) = 15x^4 - 6x^2y + 5x^2y - 2y^2$
$$= 15x^4 - x^2y - 2y^2$$

PRACTICE
6 Multiply.

a. $(3x - 5)(2x - 7)$　　　　　　**b.** $(2x^2 - 3y)(4x^2 + y)$

OBJECTIVE 3 ▶ Squaring binomials. The **square of a binomial** is a special case of the product of two binomials. By the FOIL order for multiplying two binomials, we have

$$(a + b)^2 = (a + b)(a + b)$$

$$\begin{array}{cccc} \text{F} & \text{O} & \text{I} & \text{L} \\ \downarrow & \downarrow & \downarrow & \downarrow \end{array}$$

$$= a^2 + ab + ba + b^2$$
$$= a^2 + 2ab + b^2$$

This product can be visualized geometrically by analyzing areas.

Area of larger square: $(a + b)^2$

Sum of areas of smaller rectangles: $a^2 + 2ab + b^2$

Thus, $(a + b)^2 = a^2 + 2ab + b^2$

The same pattern occurs for the square of a difference. In general,

Square of a Binomial
$$(a + b)^2 = a^2 + 2ab + b^2 \qquad (a - b)^2 = a^2 - 2ab + b^2$$

In other words, a binomial squared is the sum of the first term squared, twice the product of both terms, and the second term squared.

EXAMPLE 7 Multiply.

a. $(x + 5)^2$　　　**b.** $(x - 9)^2$　　　**c.** $(3x + 2z)^2$　　　**d.** $(4m^2 - 3n)^2$

Solution

$$(a + b)^2 = a^2 + 2 \cdot a \cdot b + b^2$$

a. $\quad\downarrow\quad\downarrow\quad\quad\downarrow\quad\downarrow\ \downarrow\ \downarrow\quad\ \downarrow$
$$(x + 5)^2 = x^2 + 2 \cdot x \cdot 5 + 5^2 = x^2 + 10x + 25$$

b. $(x - 9)^2 = x^2 - 2 \cdot x \cdot 9 + 9^2 = x^2 - 18x + 81$

c. $(3x + 2z)^2 = (3x)^2 + 2(3x)(2z) + (2z)^2 = 9x^2 + 12xz + 4z^2$

d. $(4m^2 - 3n)^2 = (4m^2)^2 - 2(4m^2)(3n) + (3n)^2 = 16m^4 - 24m^2n + 9n^2$

PRACTICE
7 Multiply.

a. $(x + 6)^2$　　　**b.** $(x - 2)^2$　　　**c.** $(3x + 5y)^2$　　　**d.** $(3x^2 - 8b)^2$

▶ Helpful Hint
Note that $(a + b)^2 = a^2 + 2ab + b^2$, **not** $a^2 + b^2$. Also,
$$(a - b)^2 = a^2 - 2ab + b^2, \quad \textbf{not} \quad a^2 - b^2.$$

OBJECTIVE 4 ▶ Multiplying the sum and difference of two terms. Another special product applies to the sum and difference of the same two terms. Multiply $(a + b)(a - b)$ to see a pattern.

$$(a + b)(a - b) = a^2 - ab + ba - b^2$$
$$= a^2 - b^2$$

Product of the Sum and Difference of Two Terms

$$(a + b)(a - b) = a^2 - b^2$$

The product of the sum and difference of the same two terms is the difference of the first term squared and the second term squared.

EXAMPLE 8   Multiply.

a. $(x - 3)(x + 3)$

b. $(4y + 1)(4y - 1)$

c. $(x^2 + 2y)(x^2 - 2y)$

d. $\left(3m^2 - \dfrac{1}{2}\right)\left(3m^2 + \dfrac{1}{2}\right)$

Solution

$$(a + b)(a - b) = a^2 - b^2$$

a. $\quad\downarrow\quad\downarrow\quad\downarrow\quad\downarrow\qquad\downarrow\qquad\downarrow$
$$(x + 3)(x - 3) = x^2 - 3^2 = x^2 - 9$$

b. $(4y + 1)(4y - 1) = (4y)^2 - 1^2 = 16y^2 - 1$

c. $(x^2 + 2y)(x^2 - 2y) = (x^2)^2 - (2y)^2 = x^4 - 4y^2$

d. $\left(3m^2 - \dfrac{1}{2}\right)\left(3m^2 + \dfrac{1}{2}\right) = (3m^2)^2 - \left(\dfrac{1}{2}\right)^2 = 9m^4 - \dfrac{1}{4}$

PRACTICE
8   Multiply.

a. $(x - 7)(x + 7)$

b. $(2a + 5)(2a - 5)$

c. $\left(5x^2 + \dfrac{1}{4}\right)\left(5x^2 - \dfrac{1}{4}\right)$

d. $(a^3 - 4b^2)(a^3 + 4b^2)$

EXAMPLE 9   Multiply $[3 + (2a + b)]^2$.

Solution   Think of 3 as the first term and $(2a + b)$ as the second term, and apply the method for squaring a binomial.

$$[a + b]^2 = a^2 + 2(a) \cdot b + b^2$$
$$[3 + \overbrace{(2a + b)}]^2 = 3^2 + 2(3)\overbrace{(2a + b)} + \overbrace{(2a + b)}^2$$
$$= 9 + 6(2a + b) + (2a + b)^2$$
$$= 9 + 12a + 6b + (2a)^2 + 2(2a)(b) + b^2 \quad \text{Square } (2a + b).$$
$$= 9 + 12a + 6b + 4a^2 + 4ab + b^2$$

PRACTICE
9   Multiply $[2 + (3x - y)]^2$.

EXAMPLE 10 Multiply $[(5x - 2y) - 1][(5x - 2y) + 1]$.

Solution Think of $(5x - 2y)$ as the first term and 1 as the second term, and apply the method for the product of the sum and difference of two terms.

$$\overset{(a \quad - b)}{\overbrace{[(5x - 2y)} - 1]}\overset{(a \quad + b)}{\overbrace{[(5x - 2y)} + 1]} = \overset{a^2 \quad - b^2}{\overbrace{(5x - 2y)}^2 - 1^2}$$

$$= (5x)^2 - 2(5x)(2y) + (2y)^2 - 1 \quad \text{Square } (5x - 2y).$$

$$= 25x^2 - 20xy + 4y^2 - 1 \qquad \square$$

PRACTICE
10 Multiply $[(3x - y) - 5][(3x - y) + 5]$.

OBJECTIVE 5 ▶ Multiplying three or more polynomials. To multiply three or more polynomials, more than one method may be needed.

EXAMPLE 11 Multiply: $(x - 3)(x + 3)(x^2 - 9)$

Solution We multiply the first two binomials, the sum and difference of two terms. Then we multiply the resulting two binomials, the square of a binomial.

$$(x - 3)(x + 3)(x^2 - 9) = (x^2 - 9)(x^2 - 9) \quad \text{Multiply } (x - 3)(x + 3).$$

$$= (x^2 - 9)^2$$

$$= x^4 - 18x^2 + 81 \quad \text{Square } (x^2 - 9). \qquad \square$$

PRACTICE
11 Multiply $(x + 4)(x - 4)(x^2 - 16)$.

OBJECTIVE 6 ▶ Evaluating polynomial functions. Our work in multiplying polynomials is often useful in evaluating polynomial functions.

EXAMPLE 12 If $f(x) = x^2 + 5x - 2$, find $f(a + 1)$.

Solution To find $f(a + 1)$, replace x with the expression $a + 1$ in the polynomial function $f(x)$.

$$f(x) = x^2 + 5x - 2$$

$$f(a + 1) = (a + 1)^2 + 5(a + 1) - 2$$

$$= a^2 + 2a + 1 + 5a + 5 - 2$$

$$= a^2 + 7a + 4 \qquad \square$$

PRACTICE
12 If $f(x) = x^2 - 3x + 5$, find $f(h + 1)$.

Graphing Calculator Explorations

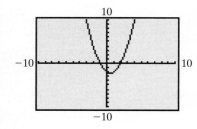

In the previous section, we used a graphing calculator to visualize addition and subtraction of polynomials in one variable. In this section, the same method is used to visualize multiplication of polynomials in one variable. For example, to see that

$$(x - 2)(x + 1) = x^2 - x - 2,$$

graph both $Y_1 = (x - 2)(x + 1)$ and $Y_2 = x^2 - x - 2$ on the same screen and see whether their graphs coincide.

By tracing along both graphs, we see that the graphs of Y_1 and Y_2 appear to coincide, and thus $(x - 2)(x + 1) = x^2 - x - 2$ appears to be correct.

Multiply. Then use a graphing calculator to visualize the results.

1. $(x + 4)(x - 4)$

2. $(x + 3)(x + 3)$

3. $(3x - 7)^2$

4. $(5x - 2)^2$

5. $(5x + 1)(x^2 - 3x - 2)$

6. $(7x + 4)(2x^2 + 3x - 5)$

VOCABULARY & READINESS CHECK

Use the choices to fill in each blank.

1. $(6x^3)\left(\dfrac{1}{2}x^3\right) =$ _____

   a. $3x^3$ **b.** $3x^6$ **c.** $10x^6$ **d.** $\dfrac{13}{2}x^6$

2. $(x + 7)^2 =$ _____

   a. $x^2 + 49$ **b.** $x^2 - 49$ **c.** $x^2 + 14x + 49$ **d.** $x^2 + 7x + 49$

3. $(x + 7)(x - 7) =$ _____

   a. $x^2 + 49$ **b.** $x^2 - 49$ **c.** $x^2 + 14x - 49$ **d.** $x^2 + 7x - 49$

4. The product of $(3x - 1)(4x^2 - 2x + 1)$ is a polynomial of degree _____.

   a. 3   **b.** 12   **c.** $12x^3$ **d.** 2

5. If $f(x) = x^2 + 1$ then $f(a + 1) =$ _____

   a. $(a + 1)^2$ **b.** $a + 1$ **c.** $(a + 1)^2 + (a + 1)$ **d.** $(a + 1)^2 + 1$

6. $[x + (2y + 1)]^2 =$ _____

   a. $[x + (2y + 1)][x - (2y + 1)]$ **b.** $[x + (2y + 1)][x + (2y + 1)]$ **c.** $[x + (2y + 1)][x + (2y - 1)]$

5.4 | EXERCISE SET

Multiply. See Examples 1 through 4.

1. $(-4x^3)(3x^2)$

2. $(-6a)(4a)$

3. $3x(4x + 7)$

4. $5x(6x - 4)$

5. $-6xy(4x + y)$

6. $-8y(6xy + 4x)$

7. $-4ab(xa^2 + ya^2 - 3)$

8. $-6b^2z(z^2a + baz - 3b)$

9. $(x - 3)(2x + 4)$

10. $(y + 5)(3y - 2)$

11. $(2x + 3)(x^3 - x + 2)$

12. $(a + 2)(3a^2 - a + 5)$

13. $3x - 2$
       $\times\ 5x + 1$

14. $2z - 4$
       $\times\ 6z - 2$

15. $3m^2 + 2m - 1$
       $\times\ \quad\quad 5m + 2$

16. $2x^2 - 3x - 4$
       $\times\ \quad\quad x + 5$

Multiply the binomials. See Examples 5 and 6.

17. $(x - 3)(x + 4)$

18. $(c - 3)(c + 1)$

19. $(5x + 8y)(2x - y)$

20. $(2n - 9m)(n - 7m)$

21. $(3x - 1)(x + 3)$

22. $(5d - 3)(d + 6)$

23. $\left(3x + \dfrac{1}{2}\right)\left(3x - \dfrac{1}{2}\right)$

24. $\left(2x - \dfrac{1}{3}\right)\left(2x + \dfrac{1}{3}\right)$

25. $(5x^2 - 2y^2)(x^2 - 3y^2)$

26. $(4x^2 - 5y^2)(x^2 - 2y^2)$

Multiply, using special product methods. See Examples 7 and 8.

27. $(x + 4)^2$

28. $(x - 5)^2$

29. $(6y - 1)(6y + 1)$

30. $(7x - 9)(7x + 9)$

31. $(3x - y)^2$

32. $(4x - z)^2$

33. $(5b - 6y)(5b + 6y)$

34. $(2x - 4y)(2x + 4y)$

Multiply, using special product methods. See Examples 9 and 10.

35. $[3 + (4b + 1)]^2$

36. $[5 - (3b - 3)]^2$

37. $[(2s - 3) - 1][(2s - 3) + 1]$

38. $[(2y + 5) + 6][(2y + 5) - 6]$

39. $[(xy + 4) - 6]^2$

40. $[(2a^2 + 4a) + 1]^2$

41. Explain when the FOIL method can be used to multiply polynomials.

42. Explain why the product of $(a + b)$ and $(a - b)$ is not a trinomial.

Multiply. See Example 11.

43. $(x + y)(x - y)(x^2 - y^2)$

44. $(z - y)(z + y)(z^2 - y^2)$

45. $(x - 2)^4$

46. $(x - 1)^4$

47. $(x - 5)(x + 5)(x^2 + 25)$

48. $(x + 3)(x - 3)(x^2 + 9)$

MIXED PRACTICE

Multiply.

49. $(3x + 1)(3x + 5)$

50. $(4x - 5)(5x + 6)$

51. $(2x^3 + 5)(5x^2 + 4x + 1)$

52. $(3y^3 - 1)(3y^3 - 6y + 1)$

53. $(7x - 3)(7x + 3)$

54. $(4x + 1)(4x - 1)$

55. $\begin{array}{r} 3x^2 + 4x - 4 \\ \times \quad\quad 3x + 6 \end{array}$

56. $\begin{array}{r} 6x^2 + 2x - 1 \\ \times \quad\quad 3x - 6 \end{array}$

57. $\left(4x + \dfrac{1}{3}\right)\left(4x - \dfrac{1}{2}\right)$

58. $\left(4y - \dfrac{1}{3}\right)\left(3y - \dfrac{1}{8}\right)$

59. $(6x + 1)^2$

60. $(4x + 7)^2$

61. $(x^2 + 2y)(x^2 - 2y)$

62. $(3x + 2y)(3x - 2y)$

63. $-6a^2b^2[5a^2b^2 - 6a - 6b]$

64. $7x^2y^3(-3ax - 4xy + z)$

65. $(a - 4)(2a - 4)$

66. $(2x - 3)(x + 1)$

67. $(7ab + 3c)(7ab - 3c)$

68. $(3xy - 2b)(3xy + 2b)$

69. $(m - 4)^2$

70. $(x + 2)^2$

71. $(3x + 1)^2$

72. $(4x + 6)^2$

73. $(y - 4)(y - 3)$

74. $(c - 8)(c + 2)$

75. $(x + y)(2x - 1)(x + 1)$

76. $(z + 2)(z - 3)(2z + 1)$

77. $(3x^2 + 2x - 1)^2$

78. $(4x^2 + 4x - 4)^2$

79. $(3x + 1)(4x^2 - 2x + 5)$

80. $(2x - 1)(5x^2 - x - 2)$

If $f(x) = x^2 - 3x$, find the following. See Example 12.

81. $f(a)$

82. $f(c)$

83. $f(a + h)$

84. $f(a + 5)$

85. $f(b - 2)$

86. $f(a - b)$

REVIEW AND PREVIEW

Use the slope-intercept form of a line, $y = mx + b$, to find the slope of each line. See Section 3.4.

87. $y = -2x + 7$

88. $y = \dfrac{3}{2}x - 1$

89. $3x - 5y = 14$

90. $x + 7y = 2$

Use the vertical line test to determine which of the following are graphs of functions. See Section 3.2.

91.

92.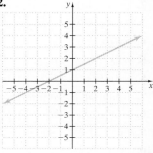

CONCEPT EXTENSIONS

Solve. See the Concept Check in this section.

93. Find the error: $7y(3z - 2) + 1$
$$= 21yz - 14y + 7y$$
$$= 21yz - 7y$$

94. Find the error: $2x + 3x(12 - x)$

$$= 5x(2 - x)$$
$$= 60x - 5x^2$$

95. Explain how to multiply a polynomial by a polynomial.

96. Explain why $(3x + 2)^2$ does not equal $9x^2 + 4$.

97. If $F(x) = x^2 + 3x + 2$, find
   a. $F(a + h)$
   b. $F(a)$
   c. $F(a + h) - F(a)$

98. If $g(x) = x^2 + 2x + 1$, find
   a. $g(a + h)$
   b. $g(a)$
   c. $g(a + h) - g(a)$

Multiply. Assume that variables represent positive integers.

99. $5x^2y^n(6y^{n+1} - 2)$

100. $-3yz^n(2y^3z^{2n} - 1)$

101. $(x^a + 5)(x^{2a} - 3)$

102. $(x^a + y^{2b})(x^a - y^{2b})$

For Exercises 103 through 106, write the result as a simplified polynomial.

103. Find the area of the circle. Do not approximate π.

(5x − 2) km

104. Find the volume of the cylinder. Do not approximate π.

(y − 3) cm

7y cm

Find the area of each shaded region.

105.

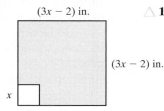

(3x − 2) in.

(3x − 2) in.

x

x

106.

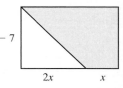

x − 7

2x   x

107. Perform each indicated operation. Explain the difference between the two problems.
   a. $(3x + 5) + (3x + 7)$
   b. $(3x + 5)(3x + 7)$

108. Explain when the FOIL method can be used to multiply polynomials.

If $R(x) = x + 5$, $Q(x) = x^2 - 2$, and $P(x) = 5x$, find the following.

109. $P(x) \cdot R(x)$

110. $P(x) \cdot Q(x)$

111. $[Q(x)]^2$

112. $[R(x)]^2$

113. $R(x) \cdot Q(x)$

114. $P(x) \cdot R(x) \cdot Q(x)$

📖 STUDY SKILLS BUILDER

Are You Getting All the Mathematics Help That You Need?

Remember that, in addition to your instructor, there are many places to get help with your mathematics course. For example,

- This text has an accompanying video lesson for every section and worked out solutions to every Chapter Test exercise on video.
- The back of the book contains answers to odd-numbered exercises and selected solutions.
- A *student Solutions Manual* is available that contains worked-out solutions to odd-numbered exercises as well as solutions to every exercise in the Integrated Reviews, Chapter Reviews, Chapter Tests, and Cumulative Reviews.

- Don't forget to check with your instructor for other local resources available to you, such as a tutor center.

Exercises

1. List items you find helpful in the text and all student supplements to this text.

2. List all the campus help that is available to you for this course.

3. List any help (besides the textbook) from Exercises 1 and 2 above that you are using.

4. List any help (besides the textbook) that you feel you should try.

5. Write a goal for yourself that includes trying anything you listed in Exercise 4 during the next week.

5.5 THE GREATEST COMMON FACTOR AND FACTORING BY GROUPING

OBJECTIVE 1 ▶ Identifying the GCF. Factoring is the reverse process of multiplying. It is the process of writing a polynomial as a product.

$$6x^2 + 13x - 5 = (3x - 1)(2x + 5)$$

factoring

multiplying

In the next few sections, we review techniques for factoring polynomials. These techniques are used at the end of this chapter to solve polynomial equations.

To factor a polynomial, we first factor out the greatest common factor (GCF) of its terms, using the distributive property. The GCF of a list of terms or monomials is the product of the GCF of the numerical coefficients and each GCF of the powers of a common variable.

> **Finding the GCF of a List of Monomials**
>
> **STEP 1.** Find the GCF of the numerical coefficients.
>
> **STEP 2.** Find the GCF of the variable factors.
>
> **STEP 3.** The product of the factors found in Steps 1 and 2 is the GCF of the monomials.

EXAMPLE 1 Find the GCF of $20x^3y$, $10x^2y^2$, and $35x^3$.

Solution The GCF of the numerical coefficients 20, 10, and 35 is 5, the largest integer that is a factor of each integer. The GCF of the variable factors x^3, x^2, and x^3 is x^2 because x^2 is the largest factor common to all three powers of x. The variable y is not a common factor because it does not appear in all three monomials. The GCF is thus

$$5 \cdot x^2, \quad \text{or} \quad 5x^2$$

To see this in factored form,

$$20x^3y = 2 \cdot 2 \cdot 5 \cdot x^2 \cdot x \cdot y$$
$$10x^2y^2 = 2 \cdot 5 \cdot x^2 \cdot y$$
$$35x^3 = 3 \cdot 5 \cdot x^2 \cdot x$$
$$\text{GCF} = 5 \cdot x^2$$

PRACTICE

1 Find the GCF of $32x^4y^2$, $48x^3y$, $24y^2$.

OBJECTIVE 2 ▶ Factoring out the GCF of a polynomial's terms. A first step in factoring polynomials is to use the distributive property and write the polynomial as a product of the GCF of its monomial terms and a simpler polynomial. This is called **factoring out the GCF.**

EXAMPLE 2 Factor.

a. $8x^2 + 4$ **b.** $5y - 2z^4$ **c.** $6x^2 - 3x^3 + 12x^4$

Solution

a. The GCF of terms $8x^2$ and 4 is 4.

$$8x^2 + 4 = 4 \cdot 2x^2 + 4 \cdot 1 \quad \text{Factor out 4 from each term.}$$
$$= 4(2x^2 + 1) \quad \text{Apply the distributive property.}$$

The factored form of $8x^2 + 4$ is $4(2x^2 + 1)$. To check, multiply $4(2x^2 + 1)$ to see that the product is $8x^2 + 4$.

b. There is no common factor of the terms $5y$ and $-2z^4$ other than 1 (or -1).

c. The greatest common factor of $6x^2$, $-3x^3$, and $12x^4$ is $3x^2$. Thus,

$$6x^2 - 3x^3 + 12x^4 = 3x^2 \cdot 2 - 3x^2 \cdot x + 3x^2 \cdot 4x^2$$
$$= 3x^2(2 - x + 4x^2)$$

PRACTICE

2   Factor.

a. $6x^2 + 9 + 15x$ **b.** $3x - 8y^3$ **c.** $8a^4 - 2a^3$

▶ **Helpful Hint**

To verify that the GCF has been factored out correctly, multiply the factors together and see that their product is the original polynomial.

EXAMPLE 3   Factor $17x^3y^2 - 34x^4y^2$.

Solution   The GCF of the two terms is $17x^3y^2$, which we factor out of each term.

$$17x^3y^2 - 34x^4y^2 = 17x^3y^2 \cdot 1 - 17x^3y^2 \cdot 2x$$
$$= 17x^3y^2(1 - 2x)$$

PRACTICE

3   Factor $64x^5y^2 - 8x^3y^2$.

▶ **Helpful Hint**

If the GCF happens to be one of the terms in the polynomial, a factor of 1 will remain for this term when the GCF is factored out. For example, in the polynomial $21x^2 + 7x$, the GCF of $21x^2$ and $7x$ is $7x$, so

$$21x^2 + 7x = 7x \cdot 3x + 7x \cdot 1 = 7x(3x + 1)$$

Concept Check ☑

Which factorization of $12x^2 + 9x - 3$ is correct?

a. $3(4x^2 + 3x + 1)$ **b.** $3(4x^2 + 3x - 1)$ **c.** $3(4x^2 + 3x - 3)$ **d.** $3(4x^2 + 3x)$

EXAMPLE 4   Factor $-3x^3y + 2x^2y - 5xy$.

Solution   Two possibilities are shown for factoring this polynomial. First, the common factor xy is factored out.

$$-3x^3y + 2x^2y - 5xy = xy(-3x^2 + 2x - 5)$$

Also, the common factor $-xy$ can be factored out as shown.

$$-3x^3y + 2x^2y - 5xy = -xy(3x^2) + (-xy)(-2x) + (-xy)(5)$$
$$= -xy(3x^2 - 2x + 5)$$

Both of these alternatives are correct.

PRACTICE

4   Factor $-9x^4y^2 + 5x^2y^2 + 7xy^2$.

EXAMPLE 5   Factor $2(x - 5) + 3a(x - 5)$.

Solution   The greatest common factor is the binomial factor $(x - 5)$.

$$2(x - 5) + 3a(x - 5) = (x - 5)(2 + 3a)$$ □

PRACTICE
5   Factor $3(x + 4) + 5b(x + 4)$.

EXAMPLE 6   Factor $7x(x^2 + 5y) - (x^2 + 5y)$.

Solution $7x(x^2 + 5y) - (x^2 + 5y) = 7x(x^2 + 5y) - 1(x^2 + 5y)$

$$= (x^2 + 5y)(7x - 1)$$ □

> **Helpful Hint**
> Notice that we wrote $-(x^2 + 5y)$ as $-1(x^2 + 5y)$ to aid in factoring.

PRACTICE
6   Factor $8b(a^3 + 2y) - (a^3 + 2y)$.

OBJECTIVE 3 ▶ Factoring polynomials by grouping. Sometimes it is possible to factor a polynomial by grouping the terms of the polynomial and looking for common factors in each group. This method of factoring is called **factoring by grouping.**

EXAMPLE 7   Factor $ab - 6a + 2b - 12$.

Solution   First look for the GCF of all four terms. The GCF of all four terms is 1. Next group the first two terms and the last two terms and factor out common factors from each group.

$$ab - 6a + 2b - 12 = (ab - 6a) + (2b - 12)$$

Factor a from the first group and 2 from the second group.

$$= a(b - 6) + 2(b - 6)$$

Now we see a GCF of $(b - 6)$. Factor out $(b - 6)$ to get

$$a(b - 6) + 2(b - 6) = (b - 6)(a + 2)$$

Check: To check, multiply $(b - 6)$ and $(a + 2)$ to see that the product is $ab - 6a + 2b - 12$.   □

PRACTICE
7   Factor $xy + 2y - 10 - 5x$.

> **Helpful Hint**
> Notice that the polynomial $a(b - 6) + 2(b - 6)$ is *not* in factored form. It is a *sum*, not a *product*. The factored form is $(b - 6)(a + 2)$.

EXAMPLE 8   Factor $x^3 + 5x^2 + 3x + 15$.

Solution $x^3 + 5x^2 + 3x + 15 = (x^3 + 5x^2) + (3x + 15)$ Group pairs of terms.

$$= x^2(x + 5) + 3(x + 5)$$ Factor each binomial.

$$= (x + 5)(x^2 + 3)$$ Factor out the common factor, $(x + 5)$.   □

PRACTICE
8   Factor $a^3 + 2a^2 + 5a + 10$.

EXAMPLE 9   Factor $m^2n^2 + m^2 - 2n^2 - 2$.

Solution $m^2n^2 + m^2 - 2n^2 - 2 = (m^2n^2 + m^2) + (-2n^2 - 2)$ Group pairs of terms.

$$= m^2(n^2 + 1) - 2(n^2 + 1)$$ Factor each binomial.

$$= (n^2 + 1)(m^2 - 2)$$ Factor out the common factor, $(n^2 + 1)$. □

PRACTICE
9   Factor $x^2y^2 + 3y^2 - 5x^2 - 15$.

EXAMPLE 10   Factor $xy + 2x - y - 2$.

Solution $xy + 2x - y - 2 = (xy + 2x) + (-y - 2)$ Group pairs of terms.

$$= x(y + 2) - 1(y + 2)$$ Factor each binomial.

$$= (y + 2)(x - 1)$$ Factor out the common factor $(y + 2)$. □

PRACTICE
10   Factor $pq + 3p - q - 3$.

VOCABULARY & READINESS CHECK

Use the choices below to fill in each blank. Some choices will be used more than once and some not at all.

least   greatest   sum   product   factoring x^3 x^7 true   false

1. The reverse process of multiplying is _____.
2. The greatest common factor (GCF) of x^7, x^3, x^5 is ____.
3. In general, the GCF of a list of common variables raised to powers is the _____ exponent in the list.
4. Factoring means writing as a _____.
5. True or false: A factored form of $2xy^3 + 10xy$ is $2xy \cdot y^2 + 2xy \cdot 5$. _____
6. True or false: A factored form of $x^3 - 6x^2 + x$ is $x(x^2 - 6x)$. _____
7. True or false: A factored form of $5x - 5y + x^3 - x^2y$ is $5(x - y) + x^2(x - y)$. _____
8. True or false: A factored form of $5x - 5y + x^3 - x^2y$ is $(x - y)(5 + x^2)$. _____

Find the GCF of each list of monomials.

9. $6, 12$ **10.** $9, 27$ **11.** $15x, 10$ **12.** $9x, 12$
13. $13x, 2x$ **14.** $4y, 5y$ **15.** $7x, 14x$ **16.** $8z, 4z$

5.5 EXERCISE SET

PRACTICE   WATCH   DOWNLOAD   READ   REVIEW

Find the GCF of each list of monomials. See Example 1.

1. a^8, a^5, a^3
2. b^9, b^2, b^5
3. $x^2y^3z^3, y^2z^3, xy^2z^2$
4. $xy^2z^3, x^2y^2z^2, x^2y^3$
5. $6x^3y, 9x^2y^2, 12x^2y$
6. $4xy^2, 16xy^3, 8x^2y^2$
7. $10x^3yz^3, 20x^2z^5, 45xz^3$
8. $12y^2z^4, 9xy^3z^4, 15x^2y^2z^3$

Factor out the GCF in each polynomial. See Examples 2 through 6.

9. $18x - 12$
10. $21x + 14$
11. $4y^2 - 16xy^3$
12. $3z - 21xz^4$
13. $6x^5 - 8x^4 + 2x^3$

14. $9x + 3x^2 - 6x^3$
15. $8a^3b^3 - 4a^2b^2 + 4ab + 16ab^2$
16. $12a^3b - 6ab + 18ab^2 - 18a^2b$
17. $6(x + 3) + 5a(x + 3)$
18. $2(x - 4) + 3y(x - 4)$
19. $2x(z + 7) + (z + 7)$
20. $x(y - 2) + (y - 2)$
21. $3x(x^2 + 5) - 2(x^2 + 5)$
22. $4x(2y + 3) - 5(2y + 3)$
23. When $3x^2 - 9x + 3$ is factored, the result is $3(x^2 - 3x + 1)$. Explain why it is necessary to include the term 1 in this factored form.

24. Construct a trinomial whose GCF is $5x^2y^3$.

Factor each polynomial by grouping. See Examples 7 through 10.

25. $ab + 3a + 2b + 6$

26. $ab + 2a + 5b + 10$

27. $ac + 4a - 2c - 8$

28. $bc + 8b - 3c - 24$

29. $2xy - 3x - 4y + 6$

30. $12xy - 18x - 10y + 15$

31. $12xy - 8x - 3y + 2$

32. $20xy - 15x - 4y + 3$

MIXED PRACTICE

Factor each polynomial

33. $6x^3 + 9$

34. $6x^2 - 8$

35. $x^3 + 3x^2$

36. $x^4 - 4x^3$

37. $8a^3 - 4a$

38. $12b^4 + 3b^2$

39. $-20x^2y + 16xy^3$

40. $-18xy^3 + 27x^4y$

41. $10a^2b^3 + 5ab^2 - 15ab^3$

42. $10ef - 20e^2f^3 + 30e^3f$

43. $9abc^2 + 6a^2bc - 6ab + 3bc$

44. $4a^2b^2c - 6ab^2c - 4ac + 8a$

45. $4x(y - 2) - 3(y - 2)$

46. $8y(z + 8) - 3(z + 8)$

47. $6xy + 10x + 9y + 15$

48. $15xy + 20x + 6y + 8$

49. $xy + 3y - 5x - 15$

50. $xy + 4y - 3x - 12$

51. $6ab - 2a - 9b + 3$

52. $16ab - 8a - 6b + 3$

53. $12xy + 18x + 2y + 3$

54. $20xy + 8x + 5y + 2$

55. $2m(n - 8) - (n - 8)$

56. $3a(b - 4) - (b - 4)$

57. $15x^3y^2 - 18x^2y^2$

58. $12x^4y^2 - 16x^3y^3$

59. $2x^2 + 3xy + 4x + 6y$

60. $3x^2 + 12x + 4xy + 16y$

61. $5x^2 + 5xy - 3x - 3y$

62. $4x^2 + 2xy - 10x - 5y$

63. $x^3 + 3x^2 + 4x + 12$

64. $x^3 + 4x^2 + 3x + 12$

65. $x^3 - x^2 - 2x + 2$

66. $x^3 - 2x^2 - 3x + 6$

REVIEW AND PREVIEW

Simplify the following. See Section 5.1.

67. $(5x^2)(11x^5)$

68. $(7y)(-2y^3)$

69. $(5x^2)^3$

70. $(-2y^3)^4$

Find each product by using the FOIL order of multiplying binomials. See Section 5.4.

71. $(x + 2)(x - 5)$

72. $(x - 7)(x - 1)$

73. $(x + 3)(x + 2)$

74. $(x - 4)(x + 2)$

75. $(y - 3)(y - 1)$

76. $(s + 8)(s + 10)$

CONCEPT EXTENSIONS

Solve. See the Concept Check in this section.

77. Which factorization of $10x^2 - 2x - 2$ is correct?

a. $2(5x^2 - x + 1)$ **b.** $2(5x^2 - x)$

c. $2(5x^2 - x - 2)$ **d.** $2(5x^2 - x - 1)$

78. Which factorization of $x^4 + 5x^3 - x^2$ is correct?

a. $-1(x^4 + 5x^3 + x^2)$ **b.** $x^2(x^2 + 5x^3 - x^2)$

c. $x^2(x^2 + 5x - 1)$ **d.** $5x^2(x^2 + 5x - 5)$

Solve.

79. The area of the material needed to manufacture a tin can is given by the polynomial $2\pi r^2 + 2\pi rh$, where the radius is r and height is h. Factor this expression.

80. To estimate the cost of a new product, one expression used by the production department is $4\pi r^2 + \frac{4}{3}\pi r^3$. Write an equivalent expression by factoring $4\pi r^2$ from both terms.

81. At the end of T years, the amount of money A in a savings account earning simple interest from an initial investment of $5600 at rate r is given by the formula $A = 5600 + 5600rt$. Write an equivalent equation by factoring the expression $5600 + 5600rt$.

82. An open-topped box has a square base and a height of 10 inches. If each of the bottom edges of the box has length x inches, find the amount of material needed to construct the box. Write the answer in factored form.

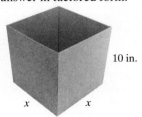

10 in.

83. Explain why $9(5 - x) + y(5 - x)$ is not a factored form of $45 - 9x + 5y - xy$.

84. Construct a 4-term polynomial whose greatest common factor is $2a^3b^4$.

85. A factored polynomial can be in many forms. For example, a factored form of $xy - 3x - 2y + 6$ is $(x - 2)(y - 3)$. Which of the following is not a factored form of $xy - 3x - 2y + 6$?

   a. $(2 - x)(3 - y)$ **b.** $(-2 + x)(-3 + y)$

   c. $(y - 3)(x - 2)$ **d.** $(-x + 2)(-y + 3)$

86. Consider the following sequence of algebraic steps:

$$x^3 - 6x^2 + 2x - 10 = (x^3 - 6x^2) + (2x - 10)$$
$$= x^2(x - 6) + 2(x - 5)$$

Explain whether the final result is the factored form of the original polynomial.

87. Which factorization of $12x^2 + 9x + 3$ is correct?

   a. $3(4x^2 + 3x + 1)$ **b.** $3(4x^2 + 3x - 1)$

   c. $3(4x^2 + 3x - 3)$ **d.** $3(4x^2 + 3x)$

88. The amount E of voltage in an electrical circuit is given by the formula

$$IR_1 + IR_2 = E$$

Write an equivalent equation by factoring the expression $IR_1 + IR_2$.

89. At the end of T years, the amount of money A in a savings account earning simple interest from an initial investment of P dollars at rate R is given by the formula

$$A = P + PRT$$

Write an equivalent equation by factoring the expression $P + PRT$.

Factor out the greatest common factor. Assume that variables used as exponents represent positive integers.

90. $x^{3n} - 2x^{2n} + 5x^n$

91. $3y^n + 3y^{2n} + 5y^{8n}$

92. $6x^{8a} - 2x^{5a} - 4x^{3a}$

93. $3x^{5a} - 6x^{3a} + 9x^{2a}$

94. An object is thrown upward from the ground with an initial velocity of 64 feet per second. The height $h(t)$ in feet of the object after t seconds is given by the polynomial function

$$h(t) = -16t^2 + 64t$$

   a. Write an equivalent factored expression for the function $h(t)$ by factoring $-16t^2 + 64t$.

   b. Find $h(1)$ by using

$$h(t) = -16t^2 + 64t$$

   and then by using the factored form of $h(t)$.

   c. Explain why the values found in part (b) are the same.

95. An object is dropped from the gondola of a hot-air balloon at a height of 224 feet. The height $h(t)$ of the object after t seconds is given by the polynomial function

$$h(t) = -16t^2 + 224$$

224 ft

   a. Write an equivalent factored expression for the function $h(t)$ by factoring $-16t^2 + 224$.

   b. Find $h(2)$ by using $h(t) = -16t^2 + 224$ and then by using the factored form of the function.

   c. Explain why the values found in part **b** are the same.

5.6 FACTORING TRINOMIALS

OBJECTIVES

1 Factor trinomials of the form $x^2 + bx + c$.

2 Factor trinomials of the form $ax^2 + bx + c$.
   a. Method 1—Trial and Check
   b. Method 2—Grouping

3 Factor by substitution.

OBJECTIVE 1 ▶ Factoring trinomials of the form $x^2 + bx + c$. In the previous section, we used factoring by grouping to factor four-term polynomials. In this section, we present techniques for factoring trinomials. Since $(x - 2)(x + 5) = x^2 + 3x - 10$, we say that $(x - 2)(x + 5)$ is a factored form of $x^2 + 3x - 10$. Taking a close look at how $(x - 2)$ and $(x + 5)$ are multiplied suggests a pattern for factoring trinomials of the form

$$x^2 + bx + c$$

$$(x - 2)(x + 5) = x^2 + 3x - 10$$

The pattern for factoring is summarized next.

> **Factoring a Trinomial of the Form $x^2 + bx + c$**
>
> Find two numbers whose product is c and whose sum is b. The factored form of $x^2 + bx + c$ is
>
> $$(x + \text{one number})(x + \text{other number})$$

EXAMPLE 1   Factor $x^2 + 10x + 16$.

Solution   We look for two integers whose product is 16 and whose sum is 10. Since our integers must have a positive product and a positive sum, we look at only positive factors of 16.

Positive Factors of 16	*Sum of Factors*	
1, 16	$1 + 16 = 17$	
4, 4	$4 + 4 = 8$	
2, 8	$2 + 8 = 10$	Correct pair

The correct pair of numbers is 2 and 8 because their product is 16 and their sum is 10. Thus,

$$x^2 + 10x + 16 = (x + 2)(x + 8)$$

Check: To check, see that $(x + 2)(x + 8) = x^2 + 10x + 16$.   ☐

PRACTICE
1   Factor $x^2 + 5x + 6$.

EXAMPLE 2   Factor $x^2 - 12x + 35$.

Solution   We need to find two integers whose product is 35 and whose sum is -12. Since our integers must have a positive product and a negative sum, we consider only negative factors of 35.

Negative Factors of 35	*Sum of Factors*	
$-1, -35$	$-1 + (-35) = -36$	
$-5, -7$	$-5 + (-7) = -12$	Correct pair

The numbers are -5 and -7.

$$x^2 - 12x + 35 = [x + (-5)][x + (-7)]$$
$$= (x - 5)(x - 7)$$

Check: To check, see that $(x - 5)(x - 7) = x^2 - 12x + 35$.   ☐

PRACTICE
2   Factor $x^2 - 11x + 24$.

EXAMPLE 3   Factor $5x^3 - 30x^2 - 35x$.

Solution   First we factor out the greatest common factor, $5x$.

$$5x^3 - 30x^2 - 35x = 5x(x^2 - 6x - 7)$$

Next we try to factor $x^2 - 6x - 7$ by finding two numbers whose product is -7 and whose sum is -6. The numbers are 1 and -7.

$$5x^3 - 30x^2 - 35x = 5x(x^2 - 6x - 7)$$
$$= 5x(x + 1)(x - 7)$$ ☐

PRACTICE
3   Factor $3x^3 - 9x^2 - 30x$.

> ▶ **Helpful Hint**
>
> If the polynomial to be factored contains a common factor that is factored out, don't forget to include that common factor in the final factored form of the original polynomial.

EXAMPLE 4   Factor $2n^2 - 38n + 80$.

Solution   The terms of this polynomial have a greatest common factor of 2, which we factor out first.

$$2n^2 - 38n + 80 = 2(n^2 - 19n + 40)$$

Next we factor $n^2 - 19n + 40$ by finding two numbers whose product is 40 and whose sum is -19. Both numbers must be negative since their sum is -19. Possibilities are

$$-1 \text{ and } -40, \qquad -2 \text{ and } -20, \qquad -4 \text{ and } -10, \qquad -5 \text{ and } -8$$

None of the pairs has a sum of -19, so no further factoring with integers is possible. The factored form of $2n^2 - 38n + 80$ is

$$2n^2 - 38n + 80 = 2(n^2 - 19n + 40)$$ □

PRACTICE
   4   Factor $2b^2 - 18b - 22$.

We call a polynomial such as $n^2 - 19n + 40$ that cannot be factored further, a **prime polynomial.**

OBJECTIVE 2 ▶ **Factoring trinomials of the form $ax^2 + bx + c$.** Next, we factor trinomials of the form $ax^2 + bx + c$, where the coefficient a of x^2 is not 1. Don't forget that the first step in factoring any polynomial is to factor out the greatest common factor of its terms. We will review two methods here. The first method we'll call trial and check.

EXAMPLE 5   **Method 1—Trial and Check**

Factor $2x^2 + 11x + 15$.

Solution   Factors of $2x^2$ are $2x$ and x. Let's try these factors as first terms of the binomials.

$$2x^2 + 11x + 15 = (2x + \quad)(x + \quad)$$

Next we try combinations of factors of 15 until the correct middle term, $11x$, is obtained. We will try only positive factors of 15 since the coefficient of the middle term, 11, is positive. Positive factors of 15 are 1 and 15 and 3 and 5.

$(2x + 1)(x + 15)$

$1x$

$30x$
———   Incorrect middle term
$31x$

$(2x + 15)(x + 1)$

$15x$

$2x$
———   Incorrect middle term
$17x$

$(2x + 3)(x + 5)$

$3x$

$10x$
———   Incorrect middle term
$13x$

$(2x + 5)(x + 3)$

$5x$

$6x$
———   Correct middle term
$11x$

Thus, the factored form of $2x^2 + 11x + 15$ is $(2x + 5)(x + 3)$.   □

PRACTICE
   5   Factor $2x^2 + 13x + 6$.

Factoring a Trinomial of the Form $ax^2 + bx + c$

STEP 1. Write all pairs of factors of ax^2.

STEP 2. Write all pairs of factors of c, the constant term.

STEP 3. Try various combinations of these factors until the correct middle term bx is found.

STEP 4. If no combination exists, the polynomial is **prime.**

EXAMPLE 6   Factor $3x^2 - x - 4$.

Solution   Factors of $3x^2$: $3x \cdot x$
Factors of -4: $-1 \cdot 4$, $1 \cdot -4$, $-2 \cdot 2$, $2 \cdot -2$

Let's try possible combinations of these factors.

$$(3x - 1)(x + 4)$$
$$-1x$$
$$12x$$
$$\overline{11x}$$ Incorrect middle term

$$(3x + 4)(x - 1)$$
$$4x$$
$$-3x$$
$$\overline{1x}$$ Incorrect middle term

$$(3x - 4)(x + 1)$$
$$-4x$$
$$3x$$
$$\overline{-1x}$$ Correct middle term

Thus, $3x^2 - x - 4 = (3x - 4)(x + 1)$.

PRACTICE
6   Factor $4x^2 + 5x - 6$.

▶ **Helpful Hint—Sign Patterns**
A positive constant in a trinomial tells us to look for two numbers with the same sign. The sign of the coefficient of the middle term tells us whether the signs are both positive or both negative.

both positive   same sign   both negative   same sign

$$2x^2 + 7x + 3 = (2x + 1)(x + 3) \qquad 2x^2 - 7x + 3 = (2x - 1)(x - 3)$$

A negative constant in a trinomial tells us to look for two numbers with opposite signs.

opposite signs   opposite signs

$$2x^2 - 5x - 3 = (2x + 1)(x - 3) \qquad 2x^2 + 5x - 3 = (2x - 1)(x + 3)$$

EXAMPLE 7   Factor $12x^3y - 22x^2y + 8xy$.

Solution   First we factor out the greatest common factor of the terms of this trinomial, $2xy$.

$$12x^3y - 22x^2y + 8xy = 2xy(6x^2 - 11x + 4)$$

Now we try to factor the trinomial $6x^2 - 11x + 4$.
Factors of $6x^2$: $2x \cdot 3x$, $6x \cdot x$

Let's try $2x$ and $3x$.

$$2xy(6x^2 - 11x + 4) = 2xy(2x + \quad)(3x + \quad)$$

The constant term, 4, is positive and the coefficient of the middle term, -11, is negative, so we factor 4 into negative factors only.

Negative factors of 4: $-4(-1)$, $\quad -2(-2)$

Let's try -4 and -1.

$$2xy(2x - 4)(3x - 1)$$

$$\begin{array}{r} -12x \\ -2x \\ \hline -14x \end{array} \quad \text{Incorrect middle term}$$

This combination cannot be correct, because one of the factors, $(2x - 4)$, has a common factor of 2. This cannot happen if the polynomial $6x^2 - 11x + 4$ has no common factors.

Now let's try -1 and -4.

$$2xy(2x - 1)(3x - 4)$$

$$\begin{array}{r} -3x \\ -8x \\ \hline -11x \end{array} \quad \text{Correct middle term}$$

Thus,

$$12x^3y - 22x^2y + 8xy = 2xy(2x - 1)(3x - 4)$$

If this combination had not worked, we would have tried -2 and -2 as factors of 4 and then $6x$ and x as factors of $6x^2$. □

PRACTICE
7 Factor $18b^4 - 57b^3 + 30b^2$.

▶ **Helpful Hint**

If a trinomial has no common factor (other than 1), then none of its binomial factors will contain a common factor (other than 1).

EXAMPLE 8 Factor $16x^2 + 24xy + 9y^2$.

Solution No greatest common factor can be factored out of this trinomial.

Factors of $16x^2$: $16x \cdot x$, $\quad 8x \cdot 2x$, $\quad 4x \cdot 4x$

Factors of $9y^2$: $y \cdot 9y$, $\quad 3y \cdot 3y$

We try possible combinations until the correct factorization is found.

$$16x^2 + 24xy + 9y^2 = (4x + 3y)(4x + 3y) \quad \text{or} \quad (4x + 3y)^2 \qquad □$$

PRACTICE
8 Factor $25x^2 + 20xy + 4y^2$.

The trinomial $16x^2 + 24xy + 9y^2$ in Example 8 is an example of a **perfect square trinomial** since its factors are two identical binomials. In the next section, we examine a special method for factoring perfect square trinomials.

Method 2—Grouping

There is another method we can use when factoring trinomials of the form $ax^2 + bx + c$: Write the trinomial as a four-term polynomial, and then factor by grouping.

Factoring a Trinomial of the Form $ax^2 + bx + c$ by Grouping

STEP 1. Find two numbers whose product is $a \cdot c$ and whose sum is b.

STEP 2. Write the term bx as a sum by using the factors found in Step 1.

STEP 3. Factor by grouping.

EXAMPLE 9   Factor $6x^2 + 13x + 6$.

Solution   In this trinomial, $a = 6$, $b = 13$, and $c = 6$.

STEP 1. Find two numbers whose product is $a \cdot c$, or $6 \cdot 6 = 36$, and whose sum is b, 13. The two numbers are 4 and 9.

STEP 2. Write the middle term, $13x$, as the sum $4x + 9x$.

$$6x^2 + 13x + 6 = 6x^2 + 4x + 9x + 6$$

STEP 3. Factor $6x^2 + 4x + 9x + 6$ by grouping.

$$(6x^2 + 4x) + (9x + 6) = 2x(3x + 2) + 3(3x + 2)$$
$$= (3x + 2)(2x + 3)$$

PRACTICE
9   Factor $20x^2 + 23x + 6$.

Concept Check ☑

Name one way that a factorization can be checked.

EXAMPLE 10   Factor $18x^2 - 9x - 2$.

Solution   In this trinomial, $a = 18$, $b = -9$, and $c = -2$.

STEP 1. Find two numbers whose product is $a \cdot c$ or $18(-2) = -36$ and whose sum is b, -9. The two numbers are -12 and 3.

STEP 2. Write the middle term, $-9x$, as the sum $-12x + 3x$.

$$18x^2 - 9x - 2 = 18x^2 - 12x + 3x - 2$$

STEP 3. Factor by grouping.

$$(18x^2 - 12x) + (3x - 2) = 6x(3x - 2) + 1(3x - 2)$$
$$= (3x - 2)(6x + 1).$$

PRACTICE
10   Factor $15x^2 + 4x - 3$.

Answer to Concept Check:
Answers may vary. A sample is: By multiplying the factors to see that the product is the original polynomial.

OBJECTIVE 3 ▶ Factoring by substitution. A complicated looking polynomial may be a simpler trinomial "in disguise." Revealing the simpler trinomial is possible by substitution.

EXAMPLE 11   Factor $2(a + 3)^2 - 5(a + 3) - 7$.

Solution   The quantity $(a + 3)$ is in two of the terms of this polynomial. **Substitute** x for $(a + 3)$, and the result is the following simpler trinomial.

$$2(a + 3)^2 - 5(a + 3) - 7 \quad \text{Original trinomial.}$$
$$= 2(x)^2 \quad - \quad 5(x) - 7 \quad \text{Substitute } x \text{ for } (a + 3).$$

Now factor $2x^2 - 5x - 7$.

$$2x^2 - 5x - 7 = (2x - 7)(x + 1)$$

But the quantity in the original polynomial was $(a + 3)$, not x. Thus, we need to reverse the substitution and replace x with $(a + 3)$.

$$(2x - 7)(x + 1) \quad \text{Factored expression.}$$
$$= [2(a + 3) - 7][(a + 3) + 1] \quad \text{Substitute } (a + 3) \text{ for } x.$$
$$= (2a + 6 - 7)(a + 3 + 1) \quad \text{Remove inside parentheses.}$$
$$= (2a - 1)(a + 4) \quad \text{Simplify.}$$

Thus, $2(a + 3)^2 - 5(a + 3) - 7 = (2a - 1)(a + 4)$. □

PRACTICE
11   Factor $3(x + 1)^2 - 7(x + 1) - 20$.

EXAMPLE 12   Factor $5x^4 + 29x^2 - 42$.

Solution   Again, substitution may help us factor this polynomial more easily. Since this polynomial contains the variable x, we will choose a different substitution variable. Let $y = x^2$, so $y^2 = (x^2)^2$, or x^4. Then

$$5x^4 + 29x^2 - 42$$

becomes

$$5y^2 + 29y - 42$$

which factors as

$$5y^2 + 29y - 42 = (5y - 6)(y + 7)$$

Next, replace y with x^2 to get

$$(5x^2 - 6)(x^2 + 7)$$ □

PRACTICE
12   Factor $6x^4 - 11x^2 - 10$.

VOCABULARY & READINESS CHECK

1. Find two numbers whose product is 10 and whose sum is 7.
2. Find two numbers whose product is 12 and whose sum is 8.
3. Find two numbers whose product is 24 and whose sum is 11.
4. Find two numbers whose product is 30 and whose sum is 13.

5.6 | EXERCISE SET

Factor each trinomial. See Examples 1 through 4.

1. $x^2 + 9x + 18$

2. $x^2 + 9x + 20$

3. $x^2 - 12x + 32$

4. $x^2 - 12x + 27$

5. $x^2 + 10x - 24$

6. $x^2 + 3x - 54$

7. $x^2 - 2x - 24$

8. $x^2 - 9x - 36$

9. $3x^2 - 18x + 24$

10. $x^2y^2 + 4xy^2 + 3y^2$

11. $4x^2z + 28xz + 40z$

12. $5x^2 - 45x + 70$

13. $2x^2 - 24x - 64$

14. $3n^2 - 6n - 51$

Factor each trinomial. See Examples 5 through 10.

15. $5x^2 + 16x + 3$

16. $3x^2 + 8x + 4$

17. $2x^2 - 11x + 12$

18. $3x^2 - 19x + 20$

19. $2x^2 + 25x - 20$

20. $6x^2 + 13x + 8$

21. $4x^2 - 12x + 9$

22. $25x^2 - 30x + 9$

23. $12x^2 + 10x - 50$

24. $12y^2 - 48y + 45$

25. $3y^4 - y^3 - 10y^2$

26. $2x^2z + 5xz - 12z$

27. $6x^3 + 8x^2 + 24x$

28. $18y^3 + 12y^2 + 2y$

29. $2x^2 - 5xy - 3y^2$

30. $6x^2 + 11xy + 4y^2$

31. $28y^2 + 22y + 4$

32. $24y^3 - 2y^2 - y$

33. $2x^2 + 15x - 27$

34. $3x^2 + 14x + 15$

Use substitution to factor each polynomial completely. See Examples 11 and 12.

35. $x^4 + x^2 - 6$

36. $x^4 - x^2 - 20$

37. $(5x + 1)^2 + 8(5x + 1) + 7$

38. $(3x - 1)^2 + 5(3x - 1) + 6$

39. $x^6 - 7x^3 + 12$

40. $x^6 - 4x^3 - 12$

41. $(a + 5)^2 - 5(a + 5) - 24$

42. $(3c + 6)^2 + 12(3c + 6) - 28$

MIXED PRACTICE

Factor each polynomial completely. See Examples 1 through 12.

43. $x^2 - 24x - 81$

44. $x^2 - 48x - 100$

45. $x^2 - 15x - 54$

46. $x^2 - 15x + 54$

47. $3x^2 - 6x + 3$

48. $8x^2 - 8x + 2$

49. $3x^2 - 5x - 2$

50. $5x^2 - 14x - 3$

51. $8x^2 - 26x + 15$

52. $12x^2 - 17x + 6$

53. $18x^4 + 21x^3 + 6x^2$

54. $20x^5 + 54x^4 + 10x^3$

55. $x^2 + 8xz + 7z^2$

56. $a^2 - 2ab - 15b^2$

57. $x^2 - x - 12$

58. $x^2 + 4x - 5$

59. $3a^2 + 12ab + 12b^2$

60. $2x^2 + 16xy + 32y^2$

61. $x^2 + 4x + 5$

62. $x^2 + 6x + 8$

63. $2(x + 4)^2 + 3(x + 4) - 5$

64. $3(x + 3)^2 + 2(x + 3) - 5$

65. $6x^2 - 49x + 30$

66. $4x^2 - 39x + 27$

67. $x^4 - 5x^2 - 6$

68. $x^4 - 5x^2 + 6$

69. $6x^3 - x^2 - x$

70. $12x^3 + x^2 - x$

71. $12a^2 - 29ab + 15b^2$

72. $16y^2 + 6yx - 27x^2$

73. $9x^2 + 30x + 25$

74. $4x^2 + 6x + 9$

75. $3x^2y - 11xy + 8y$

76. $5xy^2 - 9xy + 4x$

77. $2x^2 + 2x - 12$

78. $3x^2 + 6x - 45$

79. $(x - 4)^2 + 3(x - 4) - 18$

80. $(x - 3)^2 - 2(x - 3) - 8$

81. $2x^6 + 3x^3 - 9$

82. $3x^6 - 14x^3 + 8$

83. $72xy^4 - 24xy^2z + 2xz^2$

84. $36xy^2 - 48xyz^2 + 16xz^4$

85. $2x^3y + 2x^2y - 12xy$

86. $3x^2y^3 + 6x^2y^2 - 45x^2y$

87. $x^2 + 6xy + 5y^2$

88. $x^2 + 6xy + 8y^2$

REVIEW AND PREVIEW

Multiply. See Section 5.4.

89. $(x - 3)(x + 3)$

90. $(x - 4)(x + 4)$

91. $(2x + 1)^2$

92. $(3x + 5)^2$

93. $(x - 2)(x^2 + 2x + 4)$

94. $(y + 1)(y^2 - y + 1)$

CONCEPT EXTENSIONS

95. Find all positive and negative integers b such that $x^2 + bx + 6$ is factorable.

96. Find all positive and negative integers b such that $x^2 + bx - 10$ is factorable.

97. The volume $V(x)$ of a box in terms of its height x is given by the function $V(x) = x^3 + 2x^2 - 8x$. Factor this expression for $V(x)$.

98. Based on your results from Exercise 97, find the length and width of the box if the height is 5 inches and the dimensions of the box are whole numbers.

99. Suppose that a movie is being filmed in New York City. An action shot requires an object to be thrown upward with an initial velocity of 80 feet per second off the top of 1 Madison Square Plaza, a height of 576 feet. The height $h(t)$ in feet of the object after t seconds is given by the function $h(t) = -16t^2 + 80t + 576$. (*Source: The World Almanac*)

a. Find the height of the object at $t = 0$ seconds, $t = 2$ seconds, $t = 4$ seconds, and $t = 6$ seconds.

b. Explain why the height of the object increases and then decreases as time passes.

576 ft

c. Factor the polynomial $-16t^2 + 80t + 576$.

100. Suppose that an object is thrown upward with an initial velocity of 64 feet per second off the edge of a 960-foot cliff. The height $h(t)$ in feet of the object after t seconds is given by the function

$$h(t) = -16t^2 + 64t + 960$$

a. Find the height of the object at $t = 0$ seconds, $t = 3$ seconds, $t = 6$ seconds, and $t = 9$ seconds.

b. Explain why the height of the object increases and then decreases as time passes.

c. Factor the polynomial $-16t^2 + 64t + 960$.

Factor. Assume that variables used as exponents represent positive integers.

101. $x^{2n} + 10x^n + 16$

102. $x^{2n} - 7x^n + 12$

103. $x^{2n} - 3x^n - 18$

104. $x^{2n} + 7x^n - 18$

105. $2x^{2n} + 11x^n + 5$

106. $3x^{2n} - 8x^n + 4$

107. $4x^{2n} - 12x^n + 9$

108. $9x^{2n} + 24x^n + 16$

Recall that a graphing calculator may be used to check addition, subtraction, and multiplication of polynomials. In the same manner, a graphing calculator may be used to check factoring of polynomials in one variable. For example, to see that

$$2x^3 - 9x^2 - 5x = x(2x + 1)(x - 5)$$

graph $Y_1 = 2x^3 - 9x^2 - 5x$ *and* $Y_2 = x(2x + 1)(x - 5)$. *Then trace along both graphs to see that they coincide. Factor the following and use this method to check your results.*

109. $x^4 + 6x^3 + 5x^2$

110. $x^3 + 6x^2 + 8x$

111. $30x^3 + 9x^2 - 3x$

112. $-6x^4 + 10x^3 - 4x^2$

STUDY SKILLS BUILDER

Is Your Notebook Still Organized?

It's never too late to organize your material in a course. Let's see how you are doing.

1. Are all your graded papers in one place in your math notebook or binder?

2. Flip through the pages of your notebook. Are your notes neat and readable?

3. Are your notes complete with no sections missing?

4. Are important notes marked in some way (like an exclamation point) so that you will know to review them before a quiz or test?

5. Are your assignments complete?

6. Do exercises that have given you trouble have a mark (like a question mark) so that you will remember to talk to your instructor or a tutor about them?

7. Describe your attitude toward this course.

8. List ways your attitude can improve and make a commitment to work on at least one of these during the next week.

5.7 FACTORING BY SPECIAL PRODUCTS

OBJECTIVES

1 Factor a perfect square trinomial.

2 Factor the difference of two squares.

3 Factor the sum or difference of two cubes.

OBJECTIVE 1 ▶ Factoring a perfect square trinomial. In the previous section, we considered a variety of ways to factor trinomials of the form $ax^2 + bx + c$. In one particular example, we factored $16x^2 + 24xy + 9y^2$ as

$$16x^2 + 24xy + 9y^2 = (4x + 3y)^2$$

Recall that $16x^2 + 24xy + 9y^2$ is a perfect square trinomial because its factors are two identical binomials. A perfect square trinomial can be factored quickly if you recognize the trinomial as a perfect square.

A trinomial is a perfect square trinomial if it can be written so that its first term is the square of some quantity a, its last term is the square of some quantity b, and its middle term is twice the product of the quantities a and b. The following special formulas can be used to factor perfect square trinomials.

Perfect Square Trinomials

$$a^2 + 2ab + b^2 = (a + b)^2$$
$$a^2 - 2ab + b^2 = (a - b)^2$$

Notice that these formulas above are the same special products from Section 5.4 for the square of a binomial.

From

$$a^2 + 2ab + b^2 = (a + b)^2,$$

we see that

$$16x^2 + 24xy + 9y^2 = (4x)^2 + 2(4x)(3y) + (3y)^2 = (4x + 3y)^2$$

EXAMPLE 1   Factor $m^2 + 10m + 25$.

Solution   Notice that the first term is a square: $m^2 = (m)^2$, the last term is a square: $25 = 5^2$; and $10m = 2 \cdot 5 \cdot m$.

Thus,

$$m^2 + 10m + 25 = m^2 + 2(m)(5) + 5^2 = (m + 5)^2 \qquad \square$$

PRACTICE
1   Factor $b^2 + 16b + 64$.

EXAMPLE 2 Factor $3a^2x - 12abx + 12b^2x$.

Solution The terms of this trinomial have a GCF of $3x$, which we factor out first.

$$3a^2x - 12abx + 12b^2x = 3x(a^2 - 4ab + 4b^2)$$

Now, the polynomial $a^2 - 4ab + 4b^2$ is a perfect square trinomial. Notice that the first term is a square: $a^2 = (a)^2$; the last term is a square: $4b^2 = (2b)^2$; and $4ab = 2(a)(2b)$. The factoring can now be completed as

$$3x(a^2 - 4ab + 4b^2) = 3x(a - 2b)^2$$ □

PRACTICE

2 Factor $45x^2b - 30xb + 5b$.

▶ **Helpful Hint**

If you recognize a trinomial as a perfect square trinomial, use the special formulas to factor. However, methods for factoring trinomials in general from Section 5.6 will also result in the correct factored form.

OBJECTIVE 2 ▶ **Factoring the difference of two squares.** We now factor special types of binomials, beginning with the **difference of two squares.** The special product pattern presented in Section 5.4 for the product of a sum and a difference of two terms is used again here. However, the emphasis is now on factoring rather than on multiplying.

Difference of Two Squares

$$a^2 - b^2 = (a + b)(a - b)$$

Notice that a binomial is a difference of two squares when it is the difference of the square of some quantity a and the square of some quantity b.

EXAMPLE 3 Factor the following.

a. $x^2 - 9$ **b.** $16y^2 - 9$ **c.** $50 - 8y^2$ **d.** $x^2 - \dfrac{1}{4}$

Solution

a. $x^2 - 9 = x^2 - 3^2$ **b.** $16y^2 - 9 = (4y)^2 - 3^2$
$\qquad = (x + 3)(x - 3)$ $\qquad\qquad\quad = (4y + 3)(4y - 3)$

c. First factor out the common factor of 2.
$\quad 50 - 8y^2 = 2(25 - 4y^2)$
$\qquad\qquad\quad = 2(5 + 2y)(5 - 2y)$

d. $x^2 - \dfrac{1}{4} = x^2 - \left(\dfrac{1}{2}\right)^2 = \left(x + \dfrac{1}{2}\right)\left(x - \dfrac{1}{2}\right)$ □

PRACTICE

3 Factor the following.

a. $x^2 - 16$

b. $25b^2 - 49$

c. $45 - 20x^2$

d. $y^2 - \dfrac{1}{81}$

The binomial $x^2 + 9$ is a **sum of two squares** and cannot be factored by using real numbers. **In general, except for factoring out a GCF, the sum of two squares usually cannot be factored by using real numbers.**

> ▶ **Helpful Hint**
>
> The sum of two squares whose GCF is 1 usually cannot be factored by using real numbers. For example, $x^2 + 9$ is called a prime polynomial.

EXAMPLE 4   Factor the following.

a. $p^4 - 16$ **b.** $(x + 3)^2 - 36$

Solution

a. $p^4 - 16 = (p^2)^2 - 4^2$
$= (p^2 + 4)(p^2 - 4)$

The binomial factor $p^2 + 4$ cannot be factored by using real numbers, but the binomial factor $p^2 - 4$ is a difference of squares.

$$(p^2 + 4)(p^2 - 4) = (p^2 + 4)(p + 2)(p - 2)$$

b. Factor $(x + 3)^2 - 36$ as the difference of squares.

$(x + 3)^2 - 36 = (x + 3)^2 - 6^2$
$= [(x + 3) + 6][(x + 3) - 6]$ Factor.
$= [x + 3 + 6][x + 3 - 6]$ Remove parentheses.
$= (x + 9)(x - 3)$ Simplify.   □

PRACTICE
4   Factor the following.

a. $x^4 - 10000$ **b.** $(x + 2)^2 - 49$

Concept Check ☑

Is $(x - 4)(y^2 - 9)$ completely factored? Why or why not?

EXAMPLE 5   Factor $x^2 + 4x + 4 - y^2$.

Solution   Factoring by grouping comes to mind since the sum of the first three terms of this polynomial is a perfect square trinomial.

$x^2 + 4x + 4 - y^2 = (x^2 + 4x + 4) - y^2$ Group the first three terms.
$= (x + 2)^2 - y^2$ Factor the perfect square trinomial.

This is not factored yet since we have a *difference*, not a *product*. Since $(x + 2)^2 - y^2$ is a difference of squares, we have

$(x + 2)^2 - y^2 = [(x + 2) + y][(x + 2) - y]$
$= (x + 2 + y)(x + 2 - y)$ □

Answer to Concept Check:
no; $(y^2 - 9)$ can be factored

PRACTICE
5   Factor $m^2 + 6m + 9 - n^2$.

OBJECTIVE 3 ▶ Factoring the sum or difference of two cubes. Although the sum of two squares usually cannot be factored, the sum of two cubes, as well as the difference of two cubes, can be factored as follows.

> **Sum and Difference of Two Cubes**
> $$a^3 + b^3 = (a + b)(a^2 - ab + b^2)$$
> $$a^3 - b^3 = (a - b)(a^2 + ab + b^2)$$

To check the first pattern, let's find the product of $(a + b)$ and $(a^2 - ab + b^2)$.

$$(a + b)(a^2 - ab + b^2) = a(a^2 - ab + b^2) + b(a^2 - ab + b^2)$$
$$= a^3 - a^2b + ab^2 + a^2b - ab^2 + b^3$$
$$= a^3 + b^3$$

EXAMPLE 6   Factor $x^3 + 8$.

Solution   First we write the binomial in the form $a^3 + b^3$. Then we use the formula

$$a^3 + b^3 = (a + b)(a^2 - a \cdot b + b^2), \quad \text{where } a \text{ is } x \text{ and } b \text{ is } 2.$$

$$x^3 + 8 = x^3 + 2^3 = (x + 2)(x^2 - x \cdot 2 + 2^2)$$

Thus, $x^3 + 8 = (x + 2)(x^2 - 2x + 4)$ ☐

PRACTICE
6   Factor $x^3 + 64$.

EXAMPLE 7   Factor $p^3 + 27q^3$.

Solution
$$p^3 + 27q^3 = p^3 + (3q)^3$$
$$= (p + 3q)[p^2 - (p)(3q) + (3q)^2]$$
$$= (p + 3q)(p^2 - 3pq + 9q^2)$$ ☐

PRACTICE
7   Factor $a^3 + 8b^3$.

EXAMPLE 8   Factor $y^3 - 64$.

Solution   This is a difference of cubes since $y^3 - 64 = y^3 - 4^3$.

From

$$a^3 - b^3 = (a - b)(a^2 + a \cdot b + b^2)$$

$$y^3 - 4^3 = (y - 4)(y^2 + y \cdot 4 + 4^2)$$

$$= (y - 4)(y^2 + 4y + 16)$$ ☐

PRACTICE
8   Factor $27 - y^3$.

> ▶ **Helpful Hint**
> When factoring sums or differences of cubes, be sure to notice the sign patterns.
>
> Same sign
>
> $$x^3 + y^3 = (x + y)(x^2 - xy + y^2)$$
>
> Opposite sign
>
> Always positive
>
> Same sign
>
> $$x^3 - y^3 = (x - y)(x^2 + xy + y^2)$$
>
> Opposite sign

EXAMPLE 9 Factor $125q^2 - n^3q^2$.

Solution First we factor out a common factor of q^2.

$$125q^2 - n^3q^2 = q^2(125 - n^3)$$
$$= q^2(5^3 - n^3)$$

Opposite sign   Positive

$$= q^2(5 - n)[5^2 + (5)(n) + (n^2)]$$
$$= q^2(5 - n)(25 + 5n + n^2)$$

Thus, $125q^2 - n^3q^2 = q^2(5 - n)(25 + 5n + n^2)$. The trinomial $25 + 5n + n^2$ cannot be factored further. ☐

PRACTICE
9 Factor $b^3x^2 - 8x^2$.

VOCABULARY & READINESS CHECK

Write each term as a square. For example $25x^2$ as a square is $(5x)^2$.

1. $81y^2$ **2.** $4z^2$ **3.** $64x^6$ **4.** $49y^6$

Write each number or term as a cube.

5. 125 **6.** 216 **7.** $8x^3$ **8.** $27y^3$ **9.** $64x^6$ **10.** x^3y^6

5.7 EXERCISE SET

Factor the following. See Examples 1 and 2.

1. $x^2 + 6x + 9$

2. $x^2 - 10x + 25$

3. $4x^2 - 12x + 9$

4. $25x^2 + 10x + 1$

5. $3x^2 - 24x + 48$

6. $x^3 + 14x^2 + 49x$

7. $9y^2x^2 + 12yx^2 + 4x^2$

8. $32x^2 - 16xy + 2y^2$

Factor the following. See Examples 3 through 5.

9. $x^2 - 25$

10. $y^2 - 100$

11. $9 - 4z^2$

12. $16x^2 - y^2$

13. $(y + 2)^2 - 49$

14. $(x - 1)^2 - z^2$

15. $64x^2 - 100$

16. $4x^2 - 36$

Factor the following. See Examples 6 through 9.

17. $x^3 + 27$

18. $y^3 + 1$

19. $z^3 - 1$

20. $x^3 - 8$

21. $m^3 + n^3$

22. $r^3 + 125$

23. $x^3 y^2 - 27 y^2$

24. $64 - p^3$

25. $a^3 b + 8 b^4$

26. $8ab^3 + 27a^4$

27. $125 y^3 - 8 x^3$

28. $54 y^3 - 128$

Factor the following. See Example 5.

29. $x^2 + 6x + 9 - y^2$

30. $x^2 + 12x + 36 - y^2$

31. $x^2 - 10x + 25 - y^2$

32. $x^2 - 18x + 81 - y^2$

33. $4x^2 + 4x + 1 - z^2$

34. $9y^2 + 12y + 4 - x^2$

MIXED PRACTICE

Factor each polynomial completely.

35. $9x^2 - 49$

36. $25x^2 - 4$

37. $x^2 - 12x + 36$

38. $x^2 - 18x + 81$

39. $x^4 - 81$

40. $x^4 - 256$

41. $x^2 + 8x + 16 - 4y^2$

42. $x^2 + 14x + 49 - 9y^2$

43. $(x + 2y)^2 - 9$

44. $(3x + y)^2 - 25$

45. $x^3 - 216$

46. $8 - a^3$

47. $x^3 + 125$

48. $x^3 + 216$

49. $4x^2 + 25$

50. $16x^2 + 25$

51. $4a^2 + 12a + 9$

52. $9a^2 - 30a + 25$

53. $18x^2 y - 2y$

54. $12xy^2 - 108x$

55. $8x^3 + y^3$

56. $27x^3 - y^3$

57. $x^6 - y^3$

58. $x^3 - y^6$

59. $x^2 + 16x + 64 - x^4$

60. $x^2 + 20x + 100 - x^4$

61. $3x^6 y^2 + 81 y^2$

62. $x^2 y^9 + x^2 y^3$

63. $(x + y)^3 + 125$

64. $(x + y)^3 + 27$

65. $(2x + 3)^3 - 64$

66. $(4x + 2)^3 - 125$

REVIEW AND PREVIEW

Solve the following equations. See Section 2.1.

67. $x - 5 = 0$

68. $x + 7 = 0$

69. $3x + 1 = 0$

70. $5x - 15 = 0$

71. $-2x = 0$

72. $3x = 0$

73. $-5x + 25 = 0$

74. $-4x - 16 = 0$

CONCEPT EXTENSIONS

Determine whether each polynomial is factored completely or not. See the Concept Check in this section.

75. $5x(x^2 - 4)$

76. $x^2 y^2 (x^3 - y^3)$

77. $7y(a^2 + a + 1)$

78. $9z(x^2 + 4)$

79. A manufacturer of metal washers needs to determine the cross-sectional area of each washer. If the outer radius of the washer is R and the radius of the hole is r, express the area of the washer as a polynomial. Factor this polynomial completely.

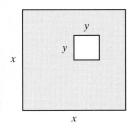

80. Express the area of the shaded region as a polynomial. Factor the polynomial completely.

Express the volume of each solid as a polynomial. To do so, subtract the volume of the "hole" from the volume of the larger solid. Then factor the resulting polynomial.

△ **81.**

△ **82.**

Find the value of c that makes each trinomial a perfect square trinomial.

83. $x^2 + 6x + c$

84. $y^2 + 10y + c$

85. $m^2 - 14m + c$

86. $n^2 - 2n + c$

87. $x^2 + cx + 16$

88. $x^2 + cx + 36$

89. Factor $x^6 - 1$ completely, using the following methods from this chapter.

a. Factor the expression by treating it as the difference of two squares, $(x^3)^2 - 1^2$.

b. Factor the expression treating it as the difference of two cubes, $(x^2)^3 - 1^3$.

c. Are the answers to parts **a** and **b** the same? Why or why not?

Factor. Assume that variables used as exponents represent positive integers.

90. $x^{2n} - 25$

91. $x^{2n} - 36$

92. $36x^{2n} - 49$

93. $25x^{2n} - 81$

94. $x^{4n} - 16$

95. $x^{4n} - 625$

INTEGRATED REVIEW OPERATIONS ON POLYNOMIALS AND FACTORING STRATEGIES

Sections 5.1–5.7

OPERATIONS ON POLYNOMIALS

Perform each indicated operation.

1. $(-y^2 + 6y - 1) + (3y^2 - 4y - 10)$

2. $(5z^4 - 6z^2 + z + 1) - (7z^4 - 2z + 1)$

3. Subtract $(x - 5)$ from $(x^2 - 6x + 2)$.

4. $(2x^2 + 6x - 5) + (5x^2 - 10x)$

5. $(5x - 3)^2$

6. $(5x^2 - 14x - 3) \div (5x + 1)$

7. $(2x^4 - 3x^2 + 5x - 2) \div (x + 2)$

8. $(4x - 1)(x^2 - 3x - 2)$

FACTORING STRATEGIES

The key to proficiency in factoring polynomials is to practice until you are comfortable with each technique. A strategy for factoring polynomials completely is given next.

Factoring a Polynomial

STEP 1. Are there any common factors? If so, factor out the greatest common factor.

STEP 2. How many terms are in the polynomial?

a. If there are *two* terms, decide if one of the following formulas may be applied:

i. Difference of two squares: $a^2 - b^2 = (a - b)(a + b)$

ii. Difference of two cubes: $a^3 - b^3 = (a - b)(a^2 + ab + b^2)$

iii. Sum of two cubes: $a^3 + b^3 = (a + b)(a^2 - ab + b^2)$

b. If there are *three* terms, try one of the following:

i. Perfect square trinomial: $a^2 + 2ab + b^2 = (a + b)^2$
$$a^2 - 2ab + b^2 = (a - b)^2$$

ii. If not a perfect square trinomial, factor by using the methods presented in Section 5.5.

c. If there are *four* or more terms, try factoring by grouping.

STEP 3. See whether any factors in the factored polynomial can be factored further.

A few examples are worked for you below.

EXAMPLE 1   Factor each polynomial completely.

a. $8a^2b - 4ab$ **b.** $36x^2 - 9$ **c.** $2x^2 - 5x - 7$

d. $5p^2 + 5 + qp^2 + q$ **e.** $9x^2 + 24x + 16$ **f.** $y^2 + 25$

Solution

a. STEP 1.   The terms have a common factor of $4ab$, which we factor out.

$$8a^2b - 4ab = 4ab(2a - 1)$$

     STEP 2.   There are two terms, but the binomial $2a - 1$ is not the difference of two squares or the sum or difference of two cubes.

     STEP 3.   The factor $2a - 1$ cannot be factored further.

b. STEP 1.   Factor out a common factor of 9.

$$36x^2 - 9 = 9(4x^2 - 1)$$

     STEP 2.   The factor $4x^2 - 1$ has two terms, and it is the difference of two squares.

$$9(4x^2 - 1) = 9(2x + 1)(2x - 1)$$

     STEP 3.   No factor with more than one term can be factored further.

c. STEP 1.   The terms of $2x^2 - 5x - 7$ contain no common factor other than 1 or -1.

     STEP 2.   There are three terms. The trinomial is not a perfect square, so we factor by methods from Section 5.6.

$$2x^2 - 5x - 7 = (2x - 7)(x + 1)$$

     STEP 3.   No factor with more than one term can be factored further.

d. STEP 1.   There is no common factor of all terms of $5p^2 + 5 + qp^2 + q$.

     STEP 2.   The polynomial has four terms, so try factoring by grouping.

$$
\begin{aligned}
5p^2 + 5 + qp^2 + q &= (5p^2 + 5) + (qp^2 + q) \quad \text{Group the terms.} \\
&= 5(p^2 + 1) + q(p^2 + 1) \\
&= (p^2 + 1)(5 + q)
\end{aligned}
$$

     STEP 3.   No factor can be factored further.

e. STEP 1.   The terms of $9x^2 + 24x + 16$ contain no common factor other than 1 or -1.

     STEP 2.   The trinomial $9x^2 + 24x + 16$ is a perfect square trinomial, and $9x^2 + 24x + 16 = (3x + 4)^2$.

     STEP 3.   No factor can be factored further.

f. STEP 1.   There is no common factor of $y^2 + 25$ other than 1.

     STEP 2.   This binomial is the sum of two squares and is prime.

     STEP 3.   The binomial $y^2 + 25$ cannot be factored further.   □

PRACTICE

1   Factor each polynomial completely.

a. $12x^2y - 3xy$ **b.** $49x^2 - 4$

c. $5x^2 + 2x - 3$ **d.** $3x^2 + 6 + x^3 + 2x$

e. $4x^2 + 20x + 25$ **f.** $b^2 + 100$

EXAMPLE 2 Factor each completely.

a. $27a^3 - b^3$ b. $3n^2m^4 - 48m^6$ c. $2x^2 - 12x + 18 - 2z^2$
d. $8x^4y^2 + 125xy^2$ e. $(x - 5)^2 - 49y^2$

Solution

a. This binomial is the difference of two cubes.

$$27a^3 - b^3 = (3a)^3 - b^3$$
$$= (3a - b)[(3a)^2 + (3a)(b) + b^2]$$
$$= (3a - b)(9a^2 + 3ab + b^2)$$

b. $3n^2m^4 - 48m^6 = 3m^4(n^2 - 16m^2)$ Factor out the GCF, $3m^4$.
$$= 3m^4(n + 4m)(n - 4m)$$ Factor the difference of squares.

c. $2x^2 - 12x + 18 - 2z^2 = 2(x^2 - 6x + 9 - z^2)$ The GCF is 2.
$$= 2[(x^2 - 6x + 9) - z^2]$$ Group the first three terms together.
$$= 2[(x - 3)^2 - z^2]$$ Factor the perfect square trinomial.
$$= 2[(x - 3) + z][(x - 3) - z]$$ Factor the difference of squares.
$$= 2(x - 3 + z)(x - 3 - z)$$

d. $8x^4y^2 + 125xy^2 = xy^2(8x^3 + 125)$ The GCF is xy^2.
$$= xy^2[(2x)^3 + 5^3]$$
$$= xy^2(2x + 5)[(2x)^2 - (2x)(5) + 5^2]$$ Factor the sum of cubes.
$$= xy^2(2x + 5)(4x^2 - 10x + 25)$$

e. This binomial is the difference of squares.

$$(x - 5)^2 - 49y^2 = (x - 5)^2 - (7y)^2$$
$$= [(x - 5) + 7y][(x - 5) - 7y]$$
$$= (x - 5 + 7y)(x - 5 - 7y)$$ □

PRACTICE
2   Factor each polynomial completely.

a. $64x^3 + y^3$
b. $7x^2y^2 - 63y^4$
c. $3x^2 + 12x + 12 - 3b^2$
d. $x^5y^4 + 27x^2y$
e. $(x + 7)^2 - 81y^2$

Factor completely.

9. $x^2 - 8x + 16 - y^2$ **10.** $12x^2 - 22x - 20$

11. $x^4 - x$ **12.** $(2x + 1)^2 - 3(2x + 1) + 2$

13. $14x^2y - 2xy$ **14.** $24ab^2 - 6ab$

15. $4x^2 - 16$ **16.** $9x^2 - 81$

17. $3x^2 - 8x - 11$

18. $5x^2 - 2x - 3$

19. $4x^2 + 8x - 12$

20. $6x^2 - 6x - 12$

21. $4x^2 + 36x + 81$

22. $25x^2 + 40x + 16$

23. $8x^3 + 125y^3$

24. $27x^3 - 64y^3$

25. $64x^2y^3 - 8x^2$

26. $27x^5y^4 - 216x^2y$

27. $(x + 5)^3 + y^3$

28. $(y - 1)^3 + 27x^3$

29. $(5a - 3)^2 - 6(5a - 3) + 9$

30. $(4r + 1)^2 + 8(4r + 1) + 16$

31. $7x^2 - 63x$

32. $20x^2 + 23x + 6$

33. $ab - 6a + 7b - 42$

34. $20x^2 - 220x + 600$

35. $x^4 - 1$

36. $15x^2 - 20x$

37. $10x^2 - 7x - 33$

38. $45m^3n^3 - 27m^2n^2$

39. $5a^3b^3 - 50a^3b$

40. $x^4 + x$

41. $16x^2 + 25$

42. $20x^3 + 20y^3$

43. $10x^3 - 210x^2 + 1100x$

44. $9y^2 - 42y + 49$

45. $64a^3b^4 - 27a^3b$

46. $y^4 - 16$

47. $2x^3 - 54$

48. $2sr + 10s - r - 5$

49. $3y^5 - 5y^4 + 6y - 10$

50. $64a^2 + b^2$

51. $100z^3 + 100$

52. $250x^4 - 16x$

53. $4b^2 - 36b + 81$

54. $2a^5 - a^4 + 6a - 3$

55. $(y - 6)^2 + 3(y - 6) + 2$

56. $(c + 2)^2 - 6(c + 2) + 5$

△ **57.** Express the area of the shaded region as a polynomial. Factor the polynomial completely.

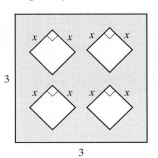

5.8 SOLVING EQUATIONS BY FACTORING AND PROBLEM SOLVING

OBJECTIVE 1 ▶ Solving polynomial equations by factoring. In this section, your efforts to learn factoring start to pay off. We use factoring to solve polynomial equations, which in turn helps us solve problems that can be modeled by polynomial equations and also helps us sketch the graph of polynomial functions.

A **polynomial equation** is the result of setting two polynomials equal to each other. Examples of polynomial equations are

$$3x^3 - 2x^2 = x^2 + 2x - 1 \qquad 2.6x + 7 = -1.3 \qquad -5x^2 - 5 = -9x^2 - 2x + 1$$

A polynomial equation is in **standard form** if one side of the equation is 0. In standard form the polynomial equations above are

$$3x^3 - 3x^2 - 2x + 1 = 0 \qquad 2.6x + 8.3 = 0 \qquad 4x^2 + 2x - 6 = 0$$

The degree of a simplified polynomial equation in standard form is the same as the highest degree of any of its terms. A polynomial equation of degree 2 is also called a **quadratic equation.**

A solution of a polynomial equation in one variable is a value of the variable that makes the equation true. The method presented in this section for solving polynomial equations is called the **factoring method.** This method is based on the **zero-factor property.**

Zero-Factor Property

If a and b are real numbers and $a \cdot b = 0$, then $a = 0$ or $b = 0$. This property is true for three or more factors also.

In other words, if the product of two or more real numbers is zero, then at least one number must be zero.

EXAMPLE 1 Solve: $(x + 2)(x - 6) = 0$.

Solution By the zero-factor property, $(x + 2)(x - 6) = 0$ only if $x + 2 = 0$ or $x - 6 = 0$.

$$x + 2 = 0 \quad \text{or} \quad x - 6 = 0 \quad \text{Apply the zero-factor property.}$$
$$x = -2 \quad \text{or} \qquad x = 6 \quad \text{Solve each linear equation.}$$

To check, let $x = -2$ and then let $x = 6$ in the original equation.

Let $x = -2$.	Let $x = 6$.
Then $(x + 2)(x - 6) = 0$	Then $(x + 2)(x - 6) = 0$
becomes $(-2 + 2)(-2 - 6) \stackrel{?}{=} 0$	becomes $(6 + 2)(6 - 6) \stackrel{?}{=} 0$
$(0)(-8) \stackrel{?}{=} 0$	$(8)(0) \stackrel{?}{=} 0$
$0 = 0 \quad$ True	$0 = 0 \quad$ True

Both -2 and 6 check, so they are both solutions. The solution set is $\{-2, 6\}$. □

PRACTICE

1 Solve: $(x + 8)(x - 5) = 0$.

EXAMPLE 2   Solve: $2x^2 + 9x - 5 = 0$.

Solution   To use the zero-factor property, one side of the equation must be 0, and the other side must be in factored form.

$$2x^2 + 9x - 5 = 0$$
$$(2x - 1)(x + 5) = 0 \qquad \text{Factor.}$$
$$2x - 1 = 0 \quad \text{or} \quad x + 5 = 0 \quad \text{Set each factor equal to zero.}$$
$$2x = 1$$
$$x = \frac{1}{2} \quad \text{or} \qquad x = -5 \quad \text{Solve each linear equation.}$$

The solutions are -5 and $\frac{1}{2}$. To check, let $x = \frac{1}{2}$ in the original equation; then let $x = -5$ in the original equation. The solution set is $\left\{ -5, \frac{1}{2} \right\}$.   ☐

PRACTICE
2   Solve: $3x^2 + 10x - 8 = 0$.

Solving Polynomial Equations by Factoring

STEP 1. Write the equation in standard form so that one side of the equation is 0.

STEP 2. Factor the polynomial completely.

STEP 3. Set each factor containing a variable equal to 0.

STEP 4. Solve the resulting equations.

STEP 5. Check each solution in the original equation.

Since it is not always possible to factor a polynomial, not all polynomial equations can be solved by factoring. Other methods of solving polynomial equations are presented in Chapter 8.

EXAMPLE 3   Solve: $x(2x - 7) = 4$.

Solution   First, write the equation in standard form; then, factor.

$$x(2x - 7) = 4$$
$$2x^2 - 7x = 4 \qquad \text{Multiply.}$$
$$2x^2 - 7x - 4 = 0 \qquad \text{Write in standard form.}$$
$$(2x + 1)(x - 4) = 0 \qquad \text{Factor.}$$
$$2x + 1 = 0 \quad \text{or} \quad x - 4 = 0 \quad \text{Set each factor equal to zero.}$$
$$2x = -1 \qquad \text{Solve.}$$
$$x = -\frac{1}{2} \quad \text{or} \qquad x = 4$$

The solutions are $-\frac{1}{2}$ and 4. Check both solutions in the original equation.   ☐

PRACTICE
3   Solve: $x(3x + 14) = -8$.

▶ **Helpful Hint**

To apply the zero-factor property, one side of the equation must be 0, and the other side of the equation must be factored. To solve the equation $x(2x - 7) = 4$, for example, you may **not** set each factor equal to 4.

EXAMPLE 4 Solve: $3(x^2 + 4) + 5 = -6(x^2 + 2x) + 13$.

Solution Rewrite the equation so that one side is 0.

$$3(x^2 + 4) + 5 = -6(x^2 + 2x) + 13.$$
$$3x^2 + 12 + 5 = -6x^2 - 12x + 13 \qquad \text{Apply the distributive property.}$$
$$9x^2 + 12x + 4 = 0 \qquad \text{Rewrite the equation so that one side is 0.}$$
$$(3x + 2)(3x + 2) = 0 \qquad \text{Factor.}$$
$$3x + 2 = 0 \quad \text{or} \quad 3x + 2 = 0 \qquad \text{Set each factor equal to 0.}$$
$$3x = -2 \quad \text{or} \qquad 3x = -2$$
$$x = -\frac{2}{3} \quad \text{or} \qquad x = -\frac{2}{3} \qquad \text{Solve each equation.}$$

The solution is $-\frac{2}{3}$. Check by substituting $-\frac{2}{3}$ into the original equation. □

PRACTICE
4 Solve: $8(x^2 + 3) + 4 = -8x(x + 3) + 19$.

If the equation contains fractions, we clear the equation of fractions as a first step.

EXAMPLE 5 Solve: $2x^2 = \frac{17}{3}x + 1$.

Solution
$$2x^2 = \frac{17}{3}x + 1$$
$$3(2x^2) = 3\left(\frac{17}{3}x + 1\right) \qquad \text{Clear the equation of fractions.}$$
$$6x^2 = 17x + 3 \qquad \text{Apply the distributive property.}$$
$$6x^2 - 17x - 3 = 0 \qquad \text{Rewrite the equation in standard form.}$$
$$(6x + 1)(x - 3) = 0 \qquad \text{Factor.}$$
$$6x + 1 = 0 \quad \text{or} \quad x - 3 = 0 \qquad \text{Set each factor equal to zero.}$$
$$6x = -1$$
$$x = -\frac{1}{6} \quad \text{or} \qquad x = 3 \qquad \text{Solve each equation.}$$

The solutions are $-\frac{1}{6}$ and 3. □

PRACTICE
5 Solve: $4x^2 = \frac{15}{2}x + 1$.

EXAMPLE 6 Solve: $x^3 = 4x$.

Solution
$$x^3 = 4x$$
$$x^3 - 4x = 0 \qquad \text{Rewrite the equation so that one side is 0.}$$
$$x(x^2 - 4) = 0 \qquad \text{Factor out the GCF, } x.$$
$$x(x + 2)(x - 2) = 0 \qquad \text{Factor the difference of squares.}$$
$$x = 0 \quad \text{or} \quad x + 2 = 0 \quad \text{or} \quad x - 2 = 0 \qquad \text{Set each factor equal to 0.}$$
$$x = 0 \quad \text{or} \qquad x = -2 \quad \text{or} \qquad x = 2 \qquad \text{Solve each equation.}$$

The solutions are -2, 0, and 2. Check by substituting into the original equation. □

PRACTICE
6 Solve: $x^3 = 2x^2 + 3x$.

Notice that the *third*-degree equation of Example 6 yielded *three* solutions.

EXAMPLE 7   Solve: $x^3 + 5x^2 = x + 5$.

Solution   First, write the equation so that one side is 0.

$$x^3 + 5x^2 - x - 5 = 0$$
$$(x^3 - x) + (5x^2 - 5) = 0 \qquad \text{Factor by grouping.}$$
$$x(x^2 - 1) + 5(x^2 - 1) = 0$$
$$(x^2 - 1)(x + 5) = 0$$
$$(x + 1)(x - 1)(x + 5) = 0 \qquad \text{Factor the difference of squares.}$$
$$x + 1 = 0 \quad \text{or} \quad x - 1 = 0 \quad \text{or} \quad x + 5 = 0 \qquad \text{Set each factor equal to 0.}$$
$$x = -1 \quad \text{or} \qquad x = 1 \quad \text{or} \qquad x = -5 \quad \text{Solve each equation.}$$

The solutions are -5, -1, and 1. Check in the original equation.   □

PRACTICE
7   Solve: $x^3 - 9x = 18 - 2x^2$.

Concept Check ✓

Which solution strategies are incorrect? Why?

a. Solve $(y - 2)(y + 2) = 4$ by setting each factor equal to 4.
b. Solve $(x + 1)(x + 3) = 0$ by setting each factor equal to 0.
c. Solve $z^2 + 5z + 6 = 0$ by factoring $z^2 + 5z + 6$ and setting each factor equal to 0.
d. Solve $x^2 + 6x + 8 = 10$ by factoring $x^2 + 6x + 8$ and setting each factor equal to 0.

OBJECTIVE 2 ▶ Solving problems modeled by polynomial equations. Some problems may be modeled by polynomial equations. To solve these problems, we use the same problem-solving steps that were introduced in Section 2.2. When solving these problems, keep in mind that a solution of an equation that models a problem is not always a solution to the problem. For example, a person's weight or the length of a side of a geometric figure is always a positive number. Discard solutions that do not make sense as solutions of the problem.

EXAMPLE 8   **Finding the Return Time of a Rocket**

An Alpha III model rocket is launched from the ground with an A8–3 engine. Without a parachute, the height of the rocket h at time t seconds is approximated by the equation,

$$h = -16t^2 + 144t$$

Find how long it takes the rocket to return to the ground.

Solution

1. UNDERSTAND. Read and reread the problem. The equation $h = -16t^2 + 144t$ models the height of the rocket. Familiarize yourself with this equation by finding a few values.

When $t = 1$ second, the height of the rocket is

$$h = -16(1)^2 + 144(1) = 128 \text{ feet}$$

When $t = 2$ seconds, the height of the rocket is

$$h = -16(2)^2 + 144(2) = 224 \text{ feet}$$

2. TRANSLATE. To find how long it takes the rocket to return to the ground, we want to know what value of t makes the height h equal to 0. That is, we want to solve $h = 0$.

$$-16t^2 + 144t = 0$$

Answer to Concept Check:
a and d; the zero-factor property
works only if one side of the
equation is 0

3. SOLVE the quadratic equation by factoring.

$$-16t^2 + 144t = 0$$
$$-16t(t - 9) = 0$$
$$-16t = 0 \quad \text{or} \quad t - 9 = 0$$
$$t = 0 \qquad\qquad t = 9$$

4. INTERPRET. The height h is 0 feet at time 0 seconds (when the rocket is launched) and at time 9 seconds.

Check: See that the height of the rocket at 9 seconds equals 0.

$$h = -16(9)^2 + 144(9) = -1296 + 1296 = 0$$

State: The rocket returns to the ground 9 seconds after it is launched. ☐

PRACTICE

8 A model rocket is launched from the ground. Its height h in feet at time t seconds is approximated by the equation $h = -16t^2 + 96t$. Find how long it takes the rocket to return to the ground.

Some of the exercises at the end of this section make use of the **Pythagorean theorem.** Before we review this theorem, recall that a **right triangle** is a triangle that contains a 90° angle, or right angle. The **hypotenuse** of a right triangle is the side opposite the right angle and is the longest side of the triangle. The **legs** of a right triangle are the other sides of the triangle.

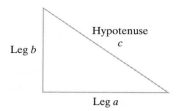

Hypotenuse
c

Leg b

Leg a

> **Pythagorean Theorem**
> In a right triangle, the sum of the squares of the lengths of the two legs is equal to the square of the length of the hypotenuse.
>
> $$(\text{leg})^2 + (\text{leg})^2 = (\text{hypotenuse})^2 \quad \text{or} \quad a^2 + b^2 = c^2$$

EXAMPLE 9 Using the Pythagorean Theorem

While framing an addition to an existing home, Kim Menzies, a carpenter, used the Pythagorean theorem to determine whether a wall was "square"—that is, whether the wall formed a right angle with the floor. He used a triangle whose sides are three consecutive integers. Find a right triangle whose sides are three consecutive integers.

Solution

1. UNDERSTAND. Read and reread the problem.

   Let x, $x + 1$, and $x + 2$ be three consecutive integers. Since these integers represent lengths of the sides of a right triangle, we have

   $$x = \text{one leg}$$
   $$x + 1 = \text{other leg}$$
   $$x + 2 = \text{hypotenuse (longest side)}$$

2. TRANSLATE. By the Pythagorean theorem, we have

In words:	$(\text{leg})^2$	$+$	$(\text{leg})^2$	$=$	$(\text{hypotenuse})^2$
	$\downarrow$		$\downarrow$		$\downarrow$
Translate:	$(x)^2$	$+$	$(x + 1)^2$	$=$	$(x + 2)^2$

3. SOLVE the equation.

   $$x^2 + (x + 1)^2 = (x + 2)^2$$
   $$x^2 + x^2 + 2x + 1 = x^2 + 4x + 4 \qquad \text{Multiply.}$$
   $$2x^2 + 2x + 1 = x^2 + 4x + 4$$
   $$x^2 - 2x - 3 = 0 \qquad \text{Write in standard form.}$$
   $$(x - 3)(x + 1) = 0$$
   $$x - 3 = 0 \quad \text{or} \quad x + 1 = 0$$
   $$x = 3 \qquad\qquad x = -1$$

4. INTERPRET. Discard $x = -1$ since length cannot be negative. If $x = 3$, then $x + 1 = 4$ and $x + 2 = 5$.

   Check: To check, see that $(\text{leg})^2 + (\text{leg})^2 = (\text{hypotenuse})^2$

   $$3^2 + 4^2 = 5^2$$
   $$9 + 16 = 25 \quad \text{True}$$

   State: The lengths of the sides of the right triangle are 3, 4, and 5 units. Kim used this information, for example, by marking off lengths of 3 and 4 feet on the floor and framing respectively. If the diagonal length between these marks was 5 feet, the wall was "square." If not, adjustments were made. □

PRACTICE

9 Find a right triangle whose sides are consecutive even integers.

OBJECTIVE 3 ▶ Finding the *x*-intercepts of polynomial functions. Recall that to find the *x*-intercepts of the graph of a function, let or and solve for *x*. This fact gives us a visual interpretation of the results of this section.

From Example 1, we know that the solutions of the equation $(x + 2)(x - 6) = 0$ are -2 and 6. These solutions give us important information about the related polynomial function $p(x) = (x + 2)(x - 6)$. We know that when *x* is -2 or when *x* is 6, the value of $p(x)$ is 0.

$$p(x) = (x + 2)(x - 6)$$
$$p(-2) = (-2 + 2)(-2 - 6) = (0)(-8) = 0$$
$$p(6) = (6 + 2)(6 - 6) = (8)(0) = 0$$

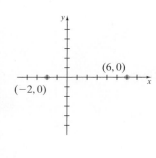

Thus, we know that $(-2, 0)$ and $(6, 0)$ are the *x*-intercepts of the graph of $p(x)$.

We also know that the graph of $p(x)$ does not cross the *x*-axis at any other point. For this reason, and the fact that $p(x) = (x + 2)(x - 6) = x^2 - 4x - 12$ has degree 2, we conclude that the graph of *p* must look something like one of these two graphs:

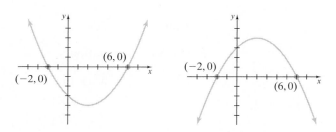

In a later chapter, we explore these graphs more fully. For the moment, know that the solutions of a polynomial equation are the *x*-intercepts of the graph of the related function and that the *x*-intercepts of the graph of a polynomial function are the solutions of the related polynomial equation. These values are also called **roots,** or **zeros,** of a polynomial function.

EXAMPLE 10   **Match Each Function with Its Graph**

$$f(x) = (x - 3)(x + 2) \quad g(x) = x(x + 2)(x - 2) \quad h(x) = (x - 2)(x + 2)(x - 1)$$

A   **B**   **C**

Solution   The graph of the function $f(x) = (x - 3)(x + 2)$ has two *x*-intercepts, $(3, 0)$ and $(-2, 0)$, because the equation $0 = (x - 3)(x + 2)$ has two solutions, 3 and -2.

The graph of $f(x)$ is graph B.

The graph of the function $g(x) = x(x + 2)(x - 2)$ has three *x*-intercepts $(0, 0)$, $(-2, 0)$, and $(2, 0)$, because the equation $0 = x(x + 2)(x - 2)$ has three solutions, 0, -2, and 2.

The graph of $g(x)$ is graph C.

The graph of the function $h(x) = (x - 2)(x + 2)(x - 1)$ has three x-intercepts, $(-2, 0)$, $(1, 0)$, and $(2, 0)$, because the equation $0 = (x - 2)(x + 2)(x - 1)$ has three solutions, -2, 1, and 2.

The graph of $h(x)$ is graph A.

PRACTICE
10   Match each function with its graph.

$$f(x) = (x - 1)(x + 3) \qquad g(x) = x(x + 3)(x - 2) \qquad h(x) = (x - 3)(x + 2)(x - 2)$$

A **B** **C**

Graphing Calculator Explorations

We can use a graphing calculator to approximate real number solutions of any quadratic equation in standard form, whether the associated polynomial is factorable or not. For example, let's solve the quadratic equation $x^2 - 2x - 4 = 0$. The solutions of this equation will be the x-intercepts of the graph of the function $f(x) = x^2 - 2x - 4$. (Recall that to find x-intercepts, we let $f(x) = 0$, or $y = 0$.) When we use a standard window, the graph of this function looks like this.

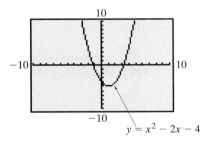

$$y = x^2 - 2x - 4$$

The graph appears to have one x-intercept between -2 and -1 and one between 3 and 4. To find the x-intercept between 3 and 4 to the nearest hundredth, we can use a zero feature, a Zoom feature, which magnifies a portion of the graph around the cursor, or we can redefine our window. If we redefine our window to

$$\text{Xmin} = 2 \qquad\qquad \text{Ymin} = -1$$
$$\text{Xmax} = 5 \qquad\qquad \text{Ymax} = 1$$
$$\text{Xscl} = 1 \qquad\qquad \text{Yscl} = 1$$

the resulting screen is

By using the Trace feature, we can now see that one of the intercepts is between 3.21 and 3.25. To approximate to the nearest hundredth, Zoom again or redefine the window to

$$Xmin = 3.2 \qquad Ymin = -0.1$$
$$Xmax = 3.3 \qquad Ymax = 0.1$$
$$Xscl = 1 \qquad Yscl = 1$$

If we use the Trace feature again, we see that, to the nearest hundredth, the x-intercept is 3.24. By repeating this process, we can approximate the other x-intercept to be -1.24.

To check, find $f(3.24)$ and $f(-1.24)$. Both of these values should be close to 0. (They will not be exactly 0 since we approximated these solutions.)

$$f(3.24) = 0.0176 \quad \text{and} \quad f(-1.24) = 0.0176$$

Solve each of these quadratic equations by graphing a related function and approximating the x-intercepts to the nearest thousandth.

1. $x^2 + 3x - 2 = 0$

2. $5x^2 - 7x + 1 = 0$

3. $2.3x^2 - 4.4x - 5.6 = 0$

4. $0.2x^2 + 6.2x + 2.1 = 0$

5. $0.09x^2 - 0.13x - 0.08 = 0$

6. $x^2 + 0.08x - 0.01 = 0$

VOCABULARY & READINESS CHECK

Solve each equation for the variable. See Example 1.

1. $(x - 3)(x + 5) = 0$

2. $(y + 5)(y + 3) = 0$

3. $(z - 3)(z + 7) = 0$

4. $(c - 2)(c - 4) = 0$

5. $x(x - 9) = 0$

6. $w(w + 7) = 0$

5.8 EXERCISE SET

MyMathLab PRACTICE | WATCH | DOWNLOAD | READ | REVIEW

Solve each equation. See Example 1.

1. $(x + 3)(3x - 4) = 0$

2. $(5x + 1)(x - 2) = 0$

3. $3(2x - 5)(4x + 3) = 0$

4. $8(3x - 4)(2x - 7) = 0$

Solve each equation. See Examples 2 through 5.

5. $x^2 + 11x + 24 = 0$

6. $y^2 - 10y + 24 = 0$

7. $12x^2 + 5x - 2 = 0$

8. $3y^2 - y - 14 = 0$

9. $z^2 + 9 = 10z$

10. $n^2 + n = 72$

11. $x(5x + 2) = 3$

12. $n(2n - 3) = 2$

13. $x^2 - 6x = x(8 + x)$

14. $n(3 + n) = n^2 + 4n$

15. $\dfrac{z^2}{6} - \dfrac{z}{2} - 3 = 0$

16. $\dfrac{c^2}{20} - \dfrac{c}{4} + \dfrac{1}{5} = 0$

17. $\dfrac{x^2}{2} + \dfrac{x}{20} = \dfrac{1}{10}$

18. $\dfrac{y^2}{30} = \dfrac{y}{15} + \dfrac{1}{2}$

19. $\dfrac{4t^2}{5} = \dfrac{t}{5} + \dfrac{3}{10}$

20. $\dfrac{5x^2}{6} - \dfrac{7x}{2} + \dfrac{2}{3} = 0$

Solve each equation. See Examples 6 and 7.

21. $(x + 2)(x - 7)(3x - 8) = 0$

22. $(4x + 9)(x - 4)(x + 1) = 0$

23. $y^3 = 9y$

24. $n^3 = 16n$

25. $x^3 - x = 2x^2 - 2$

26. $m^3 = m^2 + 12m$

27. Explain how solving $2(x - 3)(x - 1) = 0$ differs from solving $2x(x - 3)(x - 1) = 0$.

28. Explain why the zero-factor property works for more than two numbers whose product is 0.

MIXED PRACTICE

Solve each equation.

29. $(2x + 7)(x - 10) = 0$

30. $(x + 4)(5x - 1) = 0$

31. $3x(x - 5) = 0$

32. $4x(2x + 3) = 0$

33. $x^2 - 2x - 15 = 0$

34. $x^2 + 6x - 7 = 0$

35. $12x^2 + 2x - 2 = 0$

36. $8x^2 + 13x + 5 = 0$

37. $w^2 - 5w = 36$

38. $x^2 + 32 = 12x$

39. $25x^2 - 40x + 16 = 0$

40. $9n^2 + 30n + 25 = 0$

41. $2r^3 + 6r^2 = 20r$

42. $-2t^3 = 108t - 30t^2$

43. $z(5z - 4)(z + 3) = 0$

44. $2r(r + 3)(5r - 4) = 0$

45. $2z(z + 6) = 2z^2 + 12z - 8$

46. $3c^2 - 8c + 2 = c(3c - 8)$

47. $(x - 1)(x + 4) = 24$

48. $(2x - 1)(x + 2) = -3$

49. $\dfrac{x^2}{4} - \dfrac{5}{2}x + 6 = 0$

50. $\dfrac{x^2}{18} + \dfrac{x}{2} + 1 = 0$

51. $y^2 + \dfrac{1}{4} = -y$

52. $\dfrac{x^2}{10} + \dfrac{5}{2} = x$

53. $y^3 + 4y^2 = 9y + 36$

54. $x^3 + 5x^2 = x + 5$

55. $2x^3 = 50x$

56. $m^5 = 36m^3$

57. $x^2 + (x + 1)^2 = 61$

58. $y^2 + (y + 2)^2 = 34$

59. $m^2(3m - 2) = m$

60. $x^2(5x + 3) = 26x$

61. $3x^2 = -x$

62. $y^2 = -5y$

63. $x(x - 3) = x^2 + 5x + 7$

64. $z^2 - 4z + 10 = z(z - 5)$

65. $3(t - 8) + 2t = 7 + t$

66. $7c - 2(3c + 1) = 5(4 - 2c)$

67. $-3(x - 4) + x = 5(3 - x)$

68. $-4(a + 1) - 3a = -7(2a - 3)$

69. Which solution strategies are incorrect? Why?

    a. Solve $(y - 2)(y + 2) = 4$ by setting each factor equal to 4.

    b. Solve $(x + 1)(x + 3) = 0$ by setting each factor equal to 0.

    c. Solve $z^2 + 5z + 6 = 0$ by factoring $z^2 + 5z + 6$ and setting each factor equal to 0.

    d. Solve $x^2 + 6x + 8 = 10$ by factoring $x^2 + 6x + 8$ and setting each factor equal to 0.

70. Describe two ways a linear equation differs from a quadratic equation.

Solve. See Examples 8 and 9.

71. One number exceeds another by five, and their product is 66. Find the numbers.

72. If the sum of two numbers is 4 and their product is $\dfrac{15}{4}$, find the numbers.

73. An electrician needs to run a cable from the top of a 60-foot tower to a transmitter box located 45 feet away from the base of the tower. Find how long he should make the cable.

Tower Rewiring Plan

transmitter box

60 feet

45 feet

74. A stereo system installer needs to run speaker wire along the two diagonals of a rectangular room whose dimensions are 40 feet by 75 feet. Find how much speaker wire she needs.

75 ft

40 ft

75. If the cost, $C(x)$, for manufacturing x units of a certain product is given by $C(x) = x^2 - 15x + 50$, find the number of units manufactured at a cost of \$9500.

76. Determine whether any three consecutive integers represent the lengths of the sides of a right triangle.

77. The shorter leg of a right triangle is 3 centimeters less than the other leg. Find the length of the two legs if the hypotenuse is 15 centimeters.

78. The longer leg of a right triangle is 4 feet longer than the other leg. Find the length of the two legs if the hypotenuse is 20 feet.

79. Marie Mulroney has a rectangular board 12 inches by 16 inches around which she wants to put a uniform border of shells. If she has enough shells for a border whose area is 128 square inches, determine the width of the border.

12 in.

16 in.

x

x

80. A gardener has a rose garden that measures 30 feet by 20 feet. He wants to put a uniform border of pine bark around the outside of the garden. Find how wide the border should be if he has enough pine bark to cover 336 square feet.

x

x

20 ft

30 ft

81. While hovering near the top of Ribbon Falls in Yosemite National Park at 1600 feet, a helicopter pilot accidentally drops his sunglasses. The height $h(t)$ of the sunglasses after *t* seconds is given by the polynomial function

$$h(t) = -16t^2 + 1600$$

When will the sunglasses hit the ground?

82. After *t* seconds, the height *h*(*t*) of a model rocket launched from the ground into the air is given by the function

$$h(t) = -16t^2 + 80t$$

Find how long it takes the rocket to reach a height of 96 feet.

△ **83.** The floor of a shed has an area of 90 square feet. The floor is in the shape of a rectangle whose length is 3 feet less than twice the width. Find the length and the width of the floor of the shed.

△ **84.** A vegetable garden with an area of 200 square feet is to be fertilized. If the length of the garden is 1 foot less than three times the width, find the dimensions of the garden.

85. The function $W(x) = 0.5x^2$ gives the number of servings of wedding cake that can be obtained from a two-layer *x*-inch square wedding cake tier. What size square wedding cake tier is needed to serve 50 people? (*Source:* Based on data from the *Wilton 2000 Yearbook of Cake Decorating*)

86. Use the function in Exercise 85 to determine what size square wedding cake tier is needed to serve 200 people.

87. Suppose that a movie is being filmed in New York City. An action shot requires an object to be thrown upward with an initial velocity of 80 feet per second off the top of 1 Madison Square Plaza, a height of 576 feet. The height *h*(*t*) in feet of the object after *t* seconds is given by the function

$$h(t) = -16t^2 + 80t + 576.$$

Determine how long before the object strikes the ground. (See Exercise 99, Section 5.6) (*Source: The World Almanac*)

576 ft

88. Suppose that an object is thrown upward with an initial velocity of 64 feet per second off the edge of a 960-foot-cliff. The height *h*(*t*) in feet of the object after t seconds is given by the function

$$h(t) = -16t^2 + 64t + 960$$

Determine how long before the object strikes the ground. (See Exercise 100, Section 5.6)

Match each polynomial function with its graph (A–F). See Example 10.

89. $f(x) = (x - 2)(x + 5)$

90. $g(x) = (x + 1)(x - 6)$

91. $h(x) = x(x + 3)(x - 3)$

92. $F(x) = (x + 1)(x - 2)(x + 5)$

93. $G(x) = 2x^2 + 9x + 4$

94. $H(x) = 2x^2 - 7x - 4$

A

B

C

D

E

F

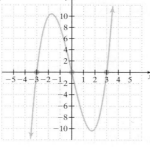

REVIEW AND PREVIEW

Write the x- and y-intercepts for each graph and determine whether the graph is the graph of a function. See Sections 3.1 and 3.2.

95.

96.

97.

98.

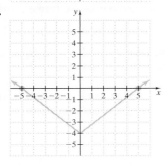

99. Draw a function with intercepts $(-3, 0)$, $(5, 0)$, and $(0, 4)$.

100. Draw a function with intercepts $(-7, 0)$, $\left(-\frac{1}{2}, 0\right)$, $(4, 0)$, and $(0, -1)$.

CONCEPT EXTENSIONS

Each exercise contains an error. Find and correct the error. See the Concept Check in the section.

101. $(x - 5)(x + 2) = 0$
$$x - 5 = 0 \quad \text{or} \quad x + 2 = 0$$
$$x = -5 \quad \text{or} \quad x = -2$$

102. $(4x - 5)(x + 7) = 0$
$$4x - 5 = 0 \quad \text{or} \quad x + 7 = 0$$
$$x = \frac{4}{5} \quad \text{or} \quad x = -7$$

103. $y(y - 5) = -6$
$$y = -6 \quad \text{or} \quad y - 5 = -5$$
$$y = -7 \quad \text{or} \quad y = 0$$

104. $3x^2 - 19x = 14$
$$-16x = 14$$
$$x = -\frac{14}{16}$$
$$x = -\frac{7}{8}$$

Solve.

105. $(x^2 + x - 6)(3x^2 - 14x - 5) = 0$

106. $(x^2 - 9)(x^2 + 8x + 16) = 0$

107. Is the following step correct? Why or why not?
$$x(x - 3) = 5$$
$$x = 5 \quad \text{or} \quad x - 3 = 5$$

Write a quadratic equation that has the given numbers as solutions.

108. $5, 3$

109. $6, 7$

110. $-1, 2$

111. $4, -3$

THE BIGGER PICTURE   SOLVING EQUATIONS AND INEQUALITIES

Continue the outline started in Section 2.4 and continued in Sections 2.5 and 2.7. Write how to recognize and how to solve quadratic equations by factoring.

Solving Equations and Inequalities

I. Equations

   A. Linear equations (Sec. 2.1)

   B. Absolute value equations (Sec. 2.6)

   C. Quadratic equations: Equation can be written in the standard form $ax^2 + bx + c = 0$, with $a \neq 0$.

   Solve: $2x^2 - 7x = 9$

$2x^2 - 7x - 9 = 0$	Write in standard form so that equation is equal to 0.
$(2x - 9)(x + 1) = 0$	Factor.
$2x - 9 = 0$ or $x + 1 = 0$	Set each factor equal to 0.
$x = \dfrac{9}{2}$ or $x = -1$	Solve.

II. Inequalities

   A. Linear inequalities (Sec. 2.4)

   B. Compound inequalities (Sec. 2.5)

   C. Absolute value inequalities (Sec. 2.7)

Solve. If an inequality write your answer in interval notation.

1. $|7x - 3| = |5x + 9|$

2. $\left|\dfrac{x + 2}{5}\right| < 1$

3. $3(x - 6) + 2 = 9 + 5(3x - 1)$

4. $(x - 6)(2x + 3) = 0$

5. $|-3x + 10| \geq -2$

6. $|-2x - 5| = 11$

7. $x(x - 7) = 30$

8. $8x - 4 \geq 15x - 4$

CHAPTER 5 GROUP ACTIVITY

Finding the Largest Area

This activity may be completed by working in groups or individually.

A picture framer has a piece of wood that measures 1 inch wide by 50 inches long. She would like to make a picture frame with the largest possible interior area. Complete the following activity to help her determine the dimensions of the frame that she should use to achieve her goal.

1. Use the situation shown in the figure to write an equation in *x* and *y* for the *outer* perimeter of the frame. (Remember that the outer perimeter will equal 50 inches.)

2. Use your equation from Question 1 to help you find the value of *y* for each value of *x* given in the table. Complete the *y* column of the table. (*Note:* The first two columns of the table give possible combinations for the outer dimensions of the frame.)

3. How is the interior width of the frame related to the exterior width of the frame? How is the interior height of the frame related to the exterior height of the frame? Use these relationships to complete the two columns of the table labeled "Interior Width" and "Interior Height."

4. Complete the last column of the table labeled "Interior Area" by using the columns of dimensions for the interior width and height.

5. From the table, what appears to be the largest interior area of the frame? Which exterior dimensions of the frame provide this area?

6. Use the patterns in the table to write an algebraic expression in terms of *x* for the interior width of the frame.

7. Use the patterns in the table to write an algebraic expression in terms of *y* for the interior height of the frame.

8. Use the perimeter equation from Question 1 to rewrite the algebraic expression for the interior height of the frame in terms of x.

Frame's Interior Dimensions				
x	y	Interior Width	Interior Height	Interior Area
2.0				
2.5				
3.0				
3.5				
4.0				
4.5				
5.0				
5.5				
6.0				
6.5				
7.0				
7.5				
8.0				
8.5				

Frame's Interior Dimensions				
x	y	Interior Width	Interior Height	Interior Area
9.0				
9.5				
10.0				
10.5				
11.0				
11.5				
12.0				
12.5				
13.0				
13.5				
14.0				
14.5				
15.0				

9. Find a function A that gives the interior area of the frame in terms of its exterior width x. (*Hint:* Study the patterns in the table. How could the expressions from Questions 6 and 8 be used to write this function?)

10. Graph the function A. Locate and label the point from the table that represents the maximum interior area. Describe the location of the point in relation to the rest of the graph.

CHAPTER 5 VOCABULARY CHECK

Fill in each blank with one of the words or phrases listed below.

| quadratic equation | scientific notation | polynomial | exponents | 1 | 0 | monomial |
| binomial | trinomial | degree of a polynomial | degree of a term | | | factoring |

1. A _____ is a finite sum of terms in which all variables are raised to nonnegative integer powers and no variables appear in any denominator.

2. _____ is the process of writing a polynomial as a product.

3. _____ are used to write repeated factors in a more compact form.

4. The _____ is the sum of the exponents on the variables contained in the term.

5. A _____ is a polynomial with one term.

6. If a is not 0, $a^0 =$ _____.

7. A _____ is a polynomial with three terms.

8. A polynomial equation of degree 2 is also called a _____.

9. A positive number is written in _____ if it is written as the product of a number a, such that $1 \leq a < 10$ and a power of 10.

10. The _____ is the largest degree of all of its terms.

11. A _____ is a polynomial with two terms.

12. If a and b are real numbers and $a \cdot b =$ _____, then $a = 0$ or $b = 0$.

▶ **Helpful Hint**

Are you preparing for your test? Don't forget to take the Chapter 5 Test on page 311. Then check your answers at the back of the text and use the Chapter Test Prep Video CD to see the fully worked-out solutions to any of the exercises you want to review.

CHAPTER 5 HIGHLIGHTS

DEFINITIONS AND CONCEPTS	EXAMPLES

SECTION 5.1   EXPONENTS AND SCIENTIFIC NOTATION

Product rule: $a^m \cdot a^n = a^{m+n}$

Zero exponent: $a^0 = 1, a \neq 0$

Quotient rule: $\dfrac{a^m}{a^n} = a^{m-n}, a \neq 0$

Negative exponent: $a^{-n} = \dfrac{1}{a^n}, a \neq 0$

A positive number is written in **scientific notation** if it is written as the product of a number a, where $1 \leq a < 10$, and an integer power of 10: $a \times 10^r$.

$x^2 \cdot x^3 = x^5$

$7^0 = 1, (-10)^0 = 1$

$\dfrac{y^{10}}{y^4} = y^{10-4} = y^6$

$3^{-2} = \dfrac{1}{3^2} = \dfrac{1}{9}, \dfrac{x^{-5}}{x^{-7}} = x^{-5-(-7)} = x^2$

Numbers written in scientific notation

$$568,000 = 5.68 \times 10^5$$
$$0.0002117 = 2.117 \times 10^{-4}$$

SECTION 5.2   MORE WORK WITH EXPONENTS AND SCIENTIFIC NOTATION

Power rules:

$$(a^m)^n = a^{m \cdot n}$$
$$(ab)^m = a^m b^m$$
$$\left(\frac{a}{b}\right)^n = \frac{a^n}{b^n}, b \neq 0$$

$$(7^8)^2 = 7^{16}$$
$$(2y)^3 = 2^3 y^3 = 8y^3$$
$$\left(\frac{5x^{-3}}{x^2}\right)^{-2} = \frac{5^{-2}x^6}{x^{-4}}$$
$$= 5^{-2} \cdot x^{6-(-4)}$$
$$= \frac{x^{10}}{5^2}, \quad \text{or} \quad \frac{x^{10}}{25}$$

SECTION 5.3   POLYNOMIALS AND POLYNOMIAL FUNCTIONS

A **polynomial** is a finite sum of terms in which all variables have exponents raised to nonnegative integer powers and no variables appear in the denominator.

Polynomials

$$1.3x^2 \quad \text{(monomial)}$$
$$-\frac{1}{3}y + 5 \quad \text{(binomial)}$$
$$6z^2 - 5z + 7 \quad \text{(trinomial)}$$

A function P is a **polynomial function** if $P(x)$ is a polynomial.

For the polynomial function
$$P(x) = -x^2 + 6x - 12, \text{ find } P(-2)$$
$$P(-2) = -(-2)^2 + 6(-2) - 12 = -28.$$

To add polynomials, combine all like terms.

Add

$$(3y^2x - 2yx + 11) + (-5y^2x - 7)$$
$$= -2y^2x - 2yx + 4$$

To subtract polynomials, change the signs of the terms of the polynomial being subtracted, then add.

Subtract

$$(-2z^3 - z + 1) - (3z^3 + z - 6)$$
$$= -2z^3 - z + 1 - 3z^3 - z + 6$$
$$= -5z^3 - 2z + 7$$

DEFINITIONS AND CONCEPTS	EXAMPLES

SECTION 5.4   MULTIPLYING POLYNOMIALS

To multiply two polynomials, use the distributive property and multiply each term of one polynomial by each term of the other polynomial; then combine like terms.

Special products

$$(a + b)^2 = a^2 + 2ab + b^2$$
$$(a - b)^2 = a^2 - 2ab + b^2$$
$$(a + b)(a - b) = a^2 - b^2$$

Multiply

$$(x^2 - 2x)(3x^2 - 5x + 1)$$
$$= 3x^4 - 5x^3 + x^2 - 6x^3 + 10x^2 - 2x$$
$$= 3x^4 - 11x^3 + 11x^2 - 2x$$
$$(3m + 2n)^2 = 9m^2 + 12mn + 4n^2$$
$$(z^2 - 5)^2 = z^4 - 10z^2 + 25$$
$$(7y + 1)(7y - 1) = 49y^2 - 1$$

The FOIL method may be used when multiplying two binomials.

Multiply

$$(x^2 + 5)(2x^2 - 9)$$
$$\begin{array}{cccc} F & O & I & L \end{array}$$
$$= x^2(2x^2) + x^2(-9) + 5(2x^2) + 5(-9)$$
$$= 2x^4 - 9x^2 + 10x^2 - 45$$
$$= 2x^4 + x^2 - 45$$

SECTION 5.5   THE GREATEST COMMON FACTOR AND FACTORING BY GROUPING

The greatest common factor (GCF) of the terms of a polynomial is the product of the GCF of the numerical coefficients and the GCF of the variable factors.

Factor: $14xy^3 - 2xy^2 = 2 \cdot 7 \cdot x \cdot y^3 - 2 \cdot x \cdot y^2$.

The GCF is $2 \cdot x \cdot y^2$, or $2xy^2$.

$$14xy^3 - 2xy^2 = 2xy^2(7y - 1)$$

To factor a polynomial by grouping, group the terms so that each group has a common factor. Factor out these common factors. Then see if the new groups have a common factor.

Factor $x^4y - 5x^3 + 2xy - 10$.

$$x^4y - 5x^3 + 2xy - 10 = x^3(xy - 5) + 2(xy - 5)$$
$$= (xy - 5)(x^3 + 2)$$

SECTION 5.6   FACTORING TRINOMIALS

To factor $ax^2 + bx + c$, by trial and check,

Step 1. Write all pairs of factors of ax^2.

Step 2. Write all pairs of factors of c.

Step 3. Try combinations of these factors until the middle term bx is found.

Factor $28x^2 - 27x - 10$.

Factors of $28x^2$: $28x$ and x, $2x$ and $14x$, $4x$ and $7x$.

Factors of -10: -2 and 5, 2 and -5, -10 and 1, 10 and -1.

$$28x^2 - 27x - 10 = (7x + 2)(4x - 5)$$

To factor $ax^2 + bx + c$ by grouping,

Find two numbers whose product is $a \cdot c$ and whose sum is b, write the term bx using the two numbers found, and then factor by grouping.

$$2x^2 - 3x - 5 = 2x^2 - 5x + 2x - 5$$
$$= x(2x - 5) + 1(2x - 5)$$
$$= (2x - 5)(x + 1)$$

DEFINITIONS AND CONCEPTS	EXAMPLES

SECTION 5.7   FACTORING BY SPECIAL PRODUCTS

Perfect square trinomial

$$a^2 + 2ab + b^2 = (a + b)^2$$
$$a^2 - 2ab + b^2 = (a - b)^2$$

Difference of two squares

$$a^2 - b^2 = (a + b)(a - b)$$

Sum and difference of two cubes

$$a^3 + b^3 = (a + b)(a^2 - ab + b^2)$$
$$a^3 - b^3 = (a - b)(a^2 + ab + b^2)$$

To factor a polynomial

Step 1. Factor out the GCF.

Step 2. If the polynomial is a binomial, see if it is a difference of two squares or a sum or difference of two cubes. If it is a trinomial, see if it is a perfect square trinomial. If not, try factoring by methods of Section 5.6. If it is a polynomial with 4 or more terms, try factoring by grouping.

Step 3. See if any factors can be factored further.

Factor

$$25x^2 + 30x + 9 = (5x + 3)^2$$
$$49z^2 - 28z + 4 = (7z - 2)^2$$

$$36x^2 - y^2 = (6x + y)(6x - y)$$
$$8y^3 + 1 = (2y + 1)(4y^2 - 2y + 1)$$
$$27p^3 - 64q^3 = (3p - 4q)(9p^2 + 12pq + 16q^2)$$

Factor $10x^4y + 5x^2y - 15y$.

$$10x^4y + 5x^2y - 15y = 5y(2x^4 + x^2 - 3)$$
$$= 5y(2x^2 + 3)(x^2 - 1)$$
$$= 5y(2x^2 + 3)(x + 1)(x - 1)$$

SECTION 5.8   SOLVING EQUATIONS BY FACTORING AND PROBLEM SOLVING

To solve polynomial equations by factoring:

Step 1. Write the equation so that one side is 0.

Step 2. Factor the polynomial completely.

Step 3. Set each factor equal to 0.

Step 4. Solve the resulting equations.

Step 5. Check each solution.

Solve

$$2x^3 - 5x^2 = 3x$$
$$2x^3 - 5x^2 - 3x = 0$$
$$x(2x + 1)(x - 3) = 0$$
$$x = 0 \quad \text{or} \quad 2x + 1 = 0 \quad \text{or} \quad x - 3 = 0$$
$$x = 0 \quad \text{or} \quad x = -\frac{1}{2} \quad \text{or} \quad x = 3$$

The solutions are $0, -\frac{1}{2}$, and 3.

CHAPTER 5 REVIEW

(5.1) *Evaluate.*

1. $(-2)^2$

2. $(-3)^4$

3. -2^2

4. -3^4

5. 8^0

6. -9^0

7. -4^{-2}

8. $(-4)^{-2}$

Simplify each expression. Use only positive exponents.

9. $-xy^2 \cdot y^3 \cdot xy^2z$

10. $(-4xy)(-3xy^2b)$

11. $a^{-14} \cdot a^5$

12. $\dfrac{a^{16}}{a^{17}}$

13. $\dfrac{x^{-7}}{x^4}$

14. $\dfrac{9a(a^{-3})}{18a^{15}}$

15. $\dfrac{y^{6p-3}}{y^{6p+2}}$

Write in scientific notation.

16. 36,890,000

17. -0.000362

Write each number without exponents.

18. 1.678×10^{-6}

19. 4.1×10^5

(5.2) *Simplify. Use only positive exponents.*

20. $(8^5)^3$

21. $\left(\dfrac{a}{4}\right)^2$

22. $(3x)^3$

23. $(-4x)^{-2}$

24. $\left(\dfrac{6x}{5}\right)^2$

25. $(8^6)^{-3}$

26. $\left(\dfrac{4}{3}\right)^{-2}$

27. $(-2x^3)^{-3}$

28. $\left(\dfrac{8p^6}{4p^4}\right)^{-2}$

29. $(-3x^{-2}y^2)^3$

30. $\left(\dfrac{x^{-5}y^{-3}}{z^3}\right)^{-5}$

31. $\dfrac{4^{-1}x^3yz}{x^{-2}yx^4}$

32. $(5xyz)^{-4}(x^{-2})^{-3}$

33. $\dfrac{2(3yz)^{-3}}{y^{-3}}$

Simplify each expression.

34. $x^{4a}(3x^{5a})^3$

35. $\dfrac{4y^{3x-3}}{2y^{2x+4}}$

Use scientific notation to find the quotient. Express each quotient in scientific notation.

36. $\dfrac{(0.00012)(144{,}000)}{0.0003}$

37. $\dfrac{(-0.00017)(0.00039)}{3000}$

Simplify. Use only positive exponents.

38. $\dfrac{27x^{-5}y^5}{18x^{-6}y^2}\cdot\dfrac{x^4y^{-2}}{x^{-2}y^3}$

39. $\dfrac{3x^5}{y^{-4}}\cdot\dfrac{(3xy^{-3})^{-2}}{(z^{-3})^{-4}}$

40. $\dfrac{(x^w)^2}{(x^{w-4})^{-2}}$

(5.3) *Find the degree of each polynomial.*

41. $x^2y - 3xy^3z + 5x + 7y$

42. $3x + 2$

Simplify by combining like terms.

43. $4x + 8x - 6x^2 - 6x^2y$

44. $-8xy^3 + 4xy^3 - 3x^3y$

Add or subtract as indicated.

45. $(3x + 7y) + (4x^2 - 3x + 7) + (y - 1)$

46. $(4x^2 - 6xy + 9y^2) - (8x^2 - 6xy - y^2)$

47. $(3x^2 - 4b + 28) + (9x^2 - 30) - (4x^2 - 6b + 20)$

48. Add $(9xy + 4x^2 + 18)$ and $(7xy - 4x^3 - 9x)$.

49. Subtract $(x - 7)$ from the sum of $(3x^2y - 7xy - 4)$ and $(9x^2y + x)$.

50. $\begin{array}{r} x^2 - 5x + 7 \\ -(x + 4) \\ \hline \end{array}$

51. $\begin{array}{r} x^3\ \ \ \ + 2xy^2 - y \\ + (x - 4xy^2\ \ -7) \\ \hline \end{array}$

If $P(x) = 9x^2 - 7x + 8$, find the following.

52. $P(6)$

53. $P(-2)$

54. $P(-3)$

If $P(x) = 2x - 1$ and $Q(x) = x^2 + 2x - 5$, find the following.

55. $P(x) + Q(x)$

56. $2[P(x)] - Q(x)$

△ **57.** Find the perimeter of the rectangle.

$x^2y + 5$ cm

$2x^2y - 6x + 1$ cm

(5.4) *Multiply.*

58. $-6x(4x^2 - 6x + 1)$

59. $-4ab^2(3ab^3 + 7ab + 1)$

60. $(x - 4)(2x + 9)$

61. $(-3xa + 4b)^2$

62. $(9x^2 + 4x + 1)(4x - 3)$

63. $(5x - 9y)(3x + 9y)$

64. $\left(x - \dfrac{1}{3}\right)\left(x + \dfrac{2}{3}\right)$

65. $(x^2 + 9x + 1)^2$

Multiply, using special products.

66. $(3x - y)^2$

67. $(4x + 9)^2$

68. $(x + 3y)(x - 3y)$

69. $[4 + (3a - b)][4 - (3a - b)]$

70. If $P(x) = 2x - 1$ and $Q(x) = x^2 + 2x - 5$, find $P(x) \cdot Q(x)$.

△ **71.** Find the area of the rectangle.

$3y - 7z$ units

$3y + 7z$ units

Multiply. Assume that all variable exponents represent integers.

72. $4a^b(3a^{b+2} - 7)$

73. $(4xy^z - b)^2$

74. $(3x^a - 4)(3x^a + 4)$

(5.5) Factor out the greatest common factor.

75. $16x^3 - 24x^2$

76. $36y - 24y^2$

77. $6ab^2 + 8ab - 4a^2b^2$

78. $14a^2b^2 - 21ab^2 + 7ab$

79. $6a(a + 3b) - 5(a + 3b)$

80. $4x(x - 2y) - 5(x - 2y)$

81. $xy - 6y + 3x - 18$

82. $ab - 8b + 4a - 32$

83. $pq - 3p - 5q + 15$

84. $x^3 - x^2 - 2x + 2$

△ **85.** A smaller square is cut from a larger rectangle. Write the area of the shaded region as a factored polynomial.

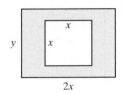

(5.6) Completely factor each polynomial.

86. $x^2 - 14x - 72$

87. $x^2 + 16x - 80$

88. $2x^2 - 18x + 28$

89. $3x^2 + 33x + 54$

90. $2x^3 - 7x^2 - 9x$

91. $3x^2 + 2x - 16$

92. $6x^2 + 17x + 10$

93. $15x^2 - 91x + 6$

94. $4x^2 + 2x - 12$

95. $9x^2 - 12x - 12$

96. $y^2(x + 6)^2 - 2y(x + 6)^2 - 3(x + 6)^2$

97. $(x + 5)^2 + 6(x + 5) + 8$

98. $x^4 - 6x^2 - 16$

99. $x^4 + 8x^2 - 20$

(5.7) Factor each polynomial completely.

100. $x^2 - 100$

101. $x^2 - 81$

102. $2x^2 - 32$

103. $6x^2 - 54$

104. $81 - x^4$

105. $16 - y^4$

106. $(y + 2)^2 - 25$

107. $(x - 3)^2 - 16$

108. $x^3 + 216$

109. $y^3 + 512$

110. $8 - 27y^3$

111. $1 - 64y^3$

112. $6x^4y + 48xy$

113. $2x^5 + 16x^2y^3$

114. $x^2 - 2x + 1 - y^2$

115. $x^2 - 6x + 9 - 4y^2$

116. $4x^2 + 12x + 9$

117. $16a^2 - 40ab + 25b^2$

△ **118.** The volume of the cylindrical shell is $\pi R^2 h - \pi r^2 h$ cubic units. Write this volume as a factored expression.

(5.8) Solve each polynomial equation for the variable.

119. $(3x - 1)(x + 7) = 0$

120. $3(x + 5)(8x - 3) = 0$

121. $5x(x - 4)(2x - 9) = 0$

122. $6(x + 3)(x - 4)(5x + 1) = 0$

123. $2x^2 = 12x$

124. $4x^3 - 36x = 0$

125. $(1 - x)(3x + 2) = -4x$

126. $2x(x - 12) = -40$

127. $3x^2 + 2x = 12 - 7x$

128. $2x^2 + 3x = 35$

129. $x^3 - 18x = 3x^2$

130. $19x^2 - 42x = -x^3$

131. $12x = 6x^3 + 6x^2$

132. $8x^3 + 10x^2 = 3x$

133. The sum of a number and twice its square is 105. Find the number.

△ **134.** The length of a rectangular piece of carpet is 5 meters less than twice its width. Find the dimensions of the carpet if its area is 33 square meters.

135. A scene from an adventure film calls for a stunt dummy to be dropped from above the second-story platform of the

Eiffel Tower, a distance of 400 feet. Its height $h(t)$ at time t seconds is given by

$$h(t) = -16t^2 + 400$$

Determine when the stunt dummy will reach the ground.

400 ft

MIXED REVIEW

136. The Royal Gorge suspension bridge in Colorado is 1053 feet above the Arkansas River. Neglecting air resistance, the height of an object dropped off the bridge is given by the polynomial function $P(t) = -16t^2 + 1053$ after time t seconds. Find the height of the object when $t = 1$ second and when $t = 8$ seconds.

Perform the indicated operation.

137. $(x + 5)(3x^2 - 2x + 1)$

138. $(3x^2 + 4x - 1.2) - (5x^2 - x + 5.7)$

139. $(3x^2 + 4x - 1.2) + (5x^2 - x + 5.7)$

140. $\left(7ab - \dfrac{1}{2}\right)^2$

If $P(x) = -x^2 + x - 4$, find

141. $P(5)$ **142.** $P(-2)$

Factor each polynomial completely.

143. $12y^5 - 6y^4$

144. $x^2y + 4x^2 - 3y - 12$

145. $6x^2 - 34x - 12$

146. $y^2(4x + 3)^2 - 19y(4x + 3)^2 - 20(4x + 3)^2$

147. $4z^7 - 49z^5$

148. $5x^4 + 4x^2 - 9$

Solve each equation.

149. $8x^2 = 24x$ **150.** $x(x - 11) = 26$

CHAPTER 5 TEST TEST PREP VIDEO

Remember to use the Chapter Test Prep Video CD to see the fully worked-out solutions to any of the exercises you want to review.

Simplify. Use positive exponents to write the answers.

1. $(-9x)^{-2}$ **2.** $-3xy^{-2}(4xy^2)z$

3. $\dfrac{6^{-1}a^2b^{-3}}{3^{-2}a^{-5}b^2}$ **4.** $\left(\dfrac{-xy^{-5}z}{xy^3}\right)^{-5}$

Write Exercises 5 and 6 in scientific notation.

5. 630,000,000   **6.** 0.01200

7. Write 5×10^{-6} without exponents.

8. Use scientific notation to find the quotient.

$$\dfrac{(0.0024)(0.00012)}{0.00032}$$

Perform the indicated operations.

9. $(4x^3y - 3x - 4) - (9x^3y + 8x + 5)$

10. $-3xy(4x + y)$

11. $(3x + 4)(4x - 7)$

12. $(5a - 2b)(5a + 2b)$

13. $(6m + n)^2$

14. $(2x - 1)(x^2 - 6x + 4)$

Factor each polynomial completely.

15. $16x^3y - 12x^2y^4$

16. $x^2 - 13x - 30$

17. $4y^2 + 20y + 25$

18. $6x^2 - 15x - 9$

19. $4x^2 - 25$

20. $x^3 + 64$

21. $3x^2y - 27y^3$

22. $6x^2 + 24$

23. $16y^3 - 2$

24. $x^2y - 9y - 3x^2 + 27$

Solve the equation for the variable.

25. $3n(7n - 20) = 96$

26. $(x + 2)(x - 2) = 5(x + 4)$

27. $2x^3 + 5x^2 = 8x + 20$

△ **28.** Write the area of the shaded region as a factored polynomial.

29. A pebble is hurled upward from the top of the Canada Trust Tower, which is 880 feet tall, with an initial velocity of 96 feet per second. Neglecting air resistance, the height $h(t)$ of the pebble after t seconds is given by the polynomial function

$$h(t) = -16t^2 + 96t + 880$$

a. Find the height of the pebble when $t = 1$.

b. Find the height of the pebble when $t = 5.1$.

c. When will the pebble hit the ground?

CHAPTER 5 CUMULATIVE REVIEW

1. Find the roots.

a. $\sqrt[3]{27}$

b. $\sqrt[5]{1}$

c. $\sqrt[4]{16}$

2. Find the roots.

a. $\sqrt[3]{64}$

b. $\sqrt[4]{81}$

c. $\sqrt[5]{32}$

3. Solve: $2(x - 3) = 5x - 9$.

4. Solve: $0.3y + 2.4 = 0.1y + 4$

5. Karen Estes just received an inheritance of $10,000 and plans to place all the money in a savings account that pays 5% compounded quarterly to help her son go to college in 3 years. How much money will be in the account in 3 years?

6. A gallon of latex paint can cover 400 square feet. How many gallon containers of paint should be bought to paint two coats on each wall of a rectangular room whose dimensions are 14 feet by 18 feet? (Assume 8-foot ceilings).

7. Solve and graph the solution set.

a. $\frac{1}{4}x \leq \frac{3}{8}$

b. $-2.3x < 6.9$

8. Solve. Graph the solution set and write it in interval notation.

$$x + 2 \leq \frac{1}{4}(x - 7)$$

Solve.

9. $-1 \leq \frac{2x}{3} + 5 \leq 2$

10. Solve: $-\frac{1}{3} < \frac{3x + 1}{6} \leq \frac{1}{3}$

11. $|y| = 0$

12. Solve: $8 + |4c| = 24$

13. $\left|2x - \frac{1}{10}\right| < -13$

14. Solve: $|5x - 1| + 9 > 5$

15. Graph the linear equation $y = \frac{1}{3}x$.

16. Graph the linear equation $y = 3x$.

17. Evaluate $f(2)$, $f(-6)$, and $f(0)$ for the function

$$f(x) = \begin{cases} 2x + 3 & \text{if } x \leq 0 \\ -x - 1 & \text{if } x > 0 \end{cases}$$

Write your results in ordered-pair form.

18. If $f(x) = 3x^2 + 2x + 3$, find $f(-3)$.

19. Graph $x = 2$.

20. Graph $y - 5 = 0$.

21. Find the slope of the line $y = 2$.

22. Find the slope of the line, $f(x) = -2x - 3$.

23. Find an equation of the horizontal line containing the point $(2, 3)$.

24. Find the equation of the vertical line containing the point $(-3, 2)$.

25. Graph the union of $x + \frac{1}{2}y \geq -4$ or $y \leq -2$.

26. Find the equation of the line containing the point $(-2, 3)$ and slope of 0.

27. Use the substitution method to solve the system.
$$\begin{cases} 2x + 4y = -6 \\ x = 2y - 5 \end{cases}$$

28. Use the substitution method to solve the system.
$$\begin{cases} 4x - 2y = 8 \\ y = 3x - 6 \end{cases}$$

29. Solve the system. $\begin{cases} 2x + 4y = 1 \\ 4x - 4z = -1 \\ y - 4z = -3 \end{cases}$

30. Solve the system. $\begin{cases} x + y - \frac{3}{2}z = \frac{1}{2} \\ -y - 2z = 14 \\ x - \frac{2}{3}y = -\frac{1}{3} \end{cases}$

31. A first number is 4 less than a second number. Four times the first number is 6 more than twice the second. Find the numbers.

32. One solution contains 20% acid and a second solution contains 60% acid. How many ounces of each solution should be mixed in order to have 50 ounces of a 30% acid solution?

33. Use matrices to solve the system. $\begin{cases} 2x - y = 3 \\ 4x - 2y = 5 \end{cases}$

34. Use matrices to solve the system. $\begin{cases} 4y = 8 \\ x + y = 7 \end{cases}$

35. The measure of the largest angle of a triangle is 80° more than the measure of the smallest angle, and the measure of the remaining angle is 10° more than the measure of the smallest angle. Find the measure of each angle.

36. Find the equation of the line with slope $\frac{1}{2}$, through the point $(0, 5)$. Write the equation using function notation.

37. Write each number in scientific notation.
   a. 730,000
   b. 0.00000104

38. Write each number in scientific notation.
   a. 8,250,000
   b. 0.0000346

39. Simplify each expression. Use positive exponents to write the answers.

   a. $(2x^0 y^{-3})^{-2}$ **b.** $\left(\dfrac{x^{-5}}{x^{-2}}\right)^{-3}$

   c. $\left(\dfrac{2}{7}\right)^{-2}$ **d.** $\dfrac{5^{-2}x^{-3}y^{11}}{x^2 y^{-5}}$

40. Simplify each expression. Use positive exponents to write the answers.

   a. $(4a^{-1}b^0)^{-3}$ **b.** $\left(\dfrac{a^{-6}}{a^{-8}}\right)^{-2}$

   c. $\left(\dfrac{2}{3}\right)^{-3}$ **d.** $\dfrac{3^{-2}a^{-2}b^{12}}{a^4 b^{-5}}$

41. Find the degree of the polynomial $3xy + x^2 y^2 - 5x^2 - 6$.

42. Subtract $(5x^2 + 3x)$ from $(3x^2 - 2x)$.

43. Multiply.
   a. $(2x^3)(5x^6)$
   b. $(7y^4 z^4)(-xy^{11}z^5)$

44. Multiply.
   a. $(3y^6)(4y^2)$
   b. $(6a^3 b^2)(-a^2 bc^4)$

Factor.

45. $17x^3 y^2 - 34x^4 y^2$

46. Factor completely $12x^3 y - 3xy^3$

47. $x^2 + 10x + 16$

48. Factor $5a^2 + 14a - 3$

49. Solve $2x^2 + 9x - 5 = 0$.

50. Solve $3x^2 - 10x - 8 = 0$

Rational Expressions

Movies still attract more people (1,448 million annually) than either theme parks (341 million) or major professional league sports (137 million) combined. U.S. theater admissions grew 3.3% in 2006 and movie advertising is changing, with advertising on TV or in the newspaper decreasing and online advertising increasing.

The graph below shows yearly rating changes for top grossing films. In Section 6.6, Exercises 60 and 61, page 368, you will have the opportunity to solve applications about movie ratings and costs to make a movie.

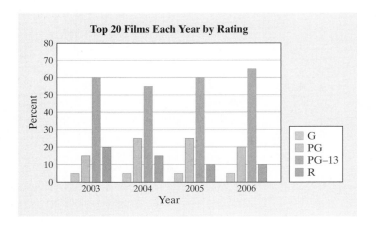

Polynomials are to algebra what integers are to arithmetic. We have added, subtracted, multiplied, and raised polynomials to powers, each operation yielding another polynomial, just as these operations on integers yield another integer. But when we divide one integer by another, the result may or may not be another integer. Likewise, when we divide one polynomial by another, we may or may not get a polynomial in return. The quotient $x \div (x + 1)$ is not a polynomial; it is a *rational expression* that can be written as

$$\frac{x}{x + 1}.$$

In this chapter, we study these new algebraic forms known as rational expressions and the *rational functions* they generate.

6.1 RATIONAL FUNCTIONS AND MULTIPLYING AND DIVIDING RATIONAL EXPRESSIONS

OBJECTIVES

1. Find the domain of a rational expression.

2. Simplify rational expressions.

3. Multiply rational expressions.

4. Divide rational expressions.

5. Use rational functions in applications.

Recall that a *rational number,* or *fraction,* is a number that can be written as the quotient $\frac{p}{q}$ of two integers p and q as long as q is not 0. A **rational expression** is an expression that can be written as the quotient $\frac{P}{Q}$ of two polynomials P and Q as long as Q is not 0.

Examples of Rational Expressions

$$\frac{3x + 7}{2} \qquad \frac{5x^2 - 3}{x - 1} \qquad \frac{7x - 2}{2x^2 + 7x + 6}$$

Rational expressions are sometimes used to describe functions. For example, we call the function $f(x) = \frac{x^2 + 2}{x - 3}$ a **rational function** since $\frac{x^2 + 2}{x - 3}$ is a rational expression.

OBJECTIVE 1 ▶ Finding the domain of a rational expression. As with fractions, a rational expression is **undefined** if the denominator is 0. If a variable in a rational expression is replaced with a number that makes the denominator 0, we say that the rational expression is **undefined** for this value of the variable. For example, the rational expression $\frac{x^2 + 2}{x - 3}$ is undefined when x is 3, because replacing x with 3 results in a denominator of 0. For this reason, we must exclude 3 from the domain of the function $f(x) = \frac{x^2 + 2}{x - 3}$.

The domain of f is then

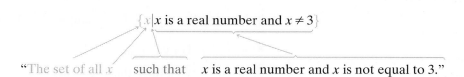

$$\{x \mid x \text{ is a real number and } x \neq 3\}$$

"The set of all x such that x is a real number and x is not equal to 3."

In this section, we will use this set builder notations to write domains. Unless told otherwise, we assume that the domain of a function described by an equation is the set of all real numbers for which the equation is defined.

EXAMPLE 1   Find the domain of each rational function.

a. $f(x) = \dfrac{8x^3 + 7x^2 + 20}{2}$ **b.** $g(x) = \dfrac{5x^2 - 3}{x - 1}$ **c.** $f(x) = \dfrac{7x - 2}{x^2 - 2x - 15}$

Solution   The domain of each function will contain all real numbers except those values that make the denominator 0.

a. No matter what the value of x, the denominator of $f(x) = \dfrac{8x^3 + 7x^2 + 20}{2}$ is never 0, so the domain of f is $\{x \mid x \text{ is a real number}\}$.

b. To find the values of x that make the denominator of $g(x)$ equal to 0, we solve the equation "denominator = 0":

$$x - 1 = 0, \quad \text{or} \quad x = 1$$

The domain must exclude 1 since the rational expression is undefined when x is 1. The domain of g is $\{x \mid x \text{ is a real number and } x \neq 1\}$.

c. We find the domain by setting the denominator equal to 0.

$$x^2 - 2x - 15 = 0 \quad \text{Set the denominator equal to 0 and solve.}$$
$$(x - 5)(x + 3) = 0$$
$$x - 5 = 0 \quad \text{or} \quad x + 3 = 0$$
$$x = 5 \quad \text{or} \quad x = -3$$

If x is replaced with 5 or with -3, the rational expression is undefined.

The domain of f is $\{x \mid x \text{ is a real number and } x \neq 5, x \neq -3\}$.

PRACTICE

1 Find the domain of each rational function.

a. $f(x) = \dfrac{4x^5 - 3x^2 + 2}{-6}$ **b.** $g(x) = \dfrac{6x^2 + 1}{x + 3}$ **c.** $h(x) = \dfrac{8x - 3}{x^2 - 5x + 6}$

Concept Check ✓

For which of these values (if any) is the rational expression $\dfrac{x - 3}{x^2 + 2}$ undefined?

a. 2   **b.** 3   **c.** -2 **d.** 0   **e.** None of these

OBJECTIVE 2 ▶ Simplifying rational expressions. Recall that a fraction is in lowest terms or simplest form if the numerator and denominator have no common factors other than 1 (or -1). For example, $\dfrac{3}{13}$ is in lowest terms since 3 and 13 have no common factors other than 1 (or -1).

To **simplify** a rational expression, or to write it in lowest terms, we use a method similar to simplifying a fraction.

Recall that to simplify a fraction, we essentially "remove factors of 1." Our ability to do this comes from these facts:

- If $c \neq 0$, then $\dfrac{c}{c} = 1$. For example, $\dfrac{7}{7} = 1$ and $\dfrac{-8.65}{-8.65} = 1$.

- $n \cdot 1 = n$. For example, $-5 \cdot 1 = -5$, $126.8 \cdot 1 = 126.8$, and $\dfrac{a}{b} \cdot 1 = \dfrac{a}{b}, b \neq 0$.

In other words, we have the following:

$$\frac{a \cdot c}{b \cdot c} = \frac{a}{b} \cdot \frac{c}{c} = \frac{a}{b}$$

$$\text{Since } \tfrac{a}{b} \cdot 1 = \tfrac{a}{b}$$

Let's practice simplifying a fraction by simplifying $\dfrac{15}{65}$.

$$\frac{15}{65} = \frac{3 \cdot 5}{13 \cdot 5} = \frac{3}{13} \cdot \frac{5}{5} = \frac{3}{13} \cdot 1 = \frac{3}{13}$$

Let's use the same technique and simplify the rational expression $\dfrac{(x + 2)^2}{x^2 - 4}$.

$$\frac{(x + 2)^2}{x^2 - 4} = \frac{(x + 2)(x + 2)}{(x - 2)(x + 2)}$$

$$= \frac{(x + 2)}{(x - 2)} \cdot \frac{x + 2}{x + 2}$$

$$= \frac{x + 2}{x - 2} \cdot 1$$

$$= \frac{x + 2}{x - 2}$$

This means that the rational expression $\dfrac{(x+2)^2}{x^2-4}$ has the same value as the rational expression $\dfrac{x+2}{x-2}$ for all values of x except 2 and -2. (Remember that when x is 2, the denominators of both rational expressions are 0 and that when x is -2, the original rational expression has a denominator of 0.)

As we simplify rational expressions, we will assume that the simplified rational expression is equivalent to the original rational expression for all real numbers except those for which either denominator is 0.

Just as for numerical fractions, we can use a shortcut notation. Remember that as long as exact factors in both the numerator and denominator are divided out, we are "removing a factor of 1." We can use the following notation:

$$\frac{(x+2)^2}{x^2-4} = \frac{(x+2)\,(x+2)}{(x-2)\,(x+2)} \qquad \text{A factor of 1 is identified by the shading.}$$

$$= \frac{x+2}{x-2} \qquad \text{"Remove" the factor of 1.}$$

This "removing a factor of 1" is stated in the principle below:

Fundamental Principle of Rational Expressions

For any rational expression $\dfrac{P}{Q}$ and any polynomial R, where $R \neq 0$,

$$\frac{PR}{QR} = \frac{P}{Q} \cdot \frac{R}{R} = \frac{P}{Q} \cdot 1 = \frac{P}{Q}$$

or, simply,

$$\frac{PR}{QR} = \frac{P}{Q}$$

In general, the following steps may be used to simplify rational expressions or to write a rational expression in lowest terms.

Simplifying or Writing a Rational Expression in Lowest Terms

STEP 1. Completely factor the numerator and denominator of the rational expression.

STEP 2. Divide out factors common to the numerator and denominator. (This is the same as "removing a factor of 1.")

For now, we assume that variables in a rational expression do not represent values that make the denominator 0.

EXAMPLE 2 Simplify each rational expression.

a. $\dfrac{2x^2}{10x^3 - 2x^2}$ **b.** $\dfrac{9x^2 + 13x + 4}{8x^2 + x - 7}$

Solution

a. $\dfrac{2x^2}{10x^3 - 2x^2} = \dfrac{2x^2 \cdot 1}{2x^2\,(5x-1)} = 1 \cdot \dfrac{1}{5x-1} = \dfrac{1}{5x-1}$

b. $\dfrac{9x^2 + 13x + 4}{8x^2 + x - 7} = \dfrac{(9x + 4)\,(x + 1)}{(8x - 7)\,(x + 1)}$ Factor the numerator and denominator.

$\qquad\qquad\qquad = \dfrac{9x + 4}{8x - 7} \cdot 1$ Since $\dfrac{x + 1}{x + 1} = 1$

$\qquad\qquad\qquad = \dfrac{9x + 4}{8x - 7}$ Simplest form

PRACTICE
2   Simplify each rational expressions.

a. $\dfrac{5z^4}{10z^5 - 5z^4}$ **b.** $\dfrac{5x^2 + 13x + 6}{6x^2 + 7x - 10}$

EXAMPLE 3   Simplify each rational expression.

a. $\dfrac{2 + x}{x + 2}$ **b.** $\dfrac{2 - x}{x - 2}$

Solution

a. $\dfrac{2 + x}{x + 2} = \dfrac{x + 2}{x + 2} = 1$ By the commutative property of addition, $2 + x = x + 2$.

b. $\dfrac{2 - x}{x - 2}$

The terms in the numerator of $\dfrac{2 - x}{x - 2}$ differ by sign from the terms of the denominator, so the polynomials are opposites of each other and the expression simplifies to -1. To see this, we factor out -1 from the numerator or the denominator. If -1 is factored from the numerator, then

$$\dfrac{2 - x}{x - 2} = \dfrac{-1(-2 + x)}{x - 2} = \dfrac{-1\,(x - 2)}{x - 2} = \dfrac{-1}{1} = -1$$

If -1 is factored from the denominator, the result is the same.

$$\dfrac{2 - x}{x - 2} = \dfrac{2 - x}{-1(-x + 2)} = \dfrac{2 - x}{-1\,(2 - x)} = \dfrac{1}{-1} = -1$$

> ▶ **Helpful Hint**
>
> When the numerator and the denominator of a rational expression are opposites of each other, the expression simplifies to -1.

PRACTICE
3   Simplify each rational expression.

a. $\dfrac{x + 3}{3 + x}$ **b.** $\dfrac{3 - x}{x - 3}$

EXAMPLE 4   Simplify $\dfrac{18 - 2x^2}{x^2 - 2x - 3}$.

Solution $\dfrac{18 - 2x^2}{x^2 - 2x - 3} = \dfrac{2(9 - x^2)}{(x + 1)(x - 3)}$ Factor.

$\qquad\qquad\qquad\qquad = \dfrac{2(3 + x)(3 - x)}{(x + 1)(x - 3)}$ Factor completely.

$\qquad\qquad\qquad\qquad = \dfrac{2(3 + x) \cdot -1\,(x - 3)}{(x + 1)\,(x - 3)}$ Notice the opposites $3 - x$ and $x - 3$. Write $3 - x$ as $-1(x - 3)$ and simplify.

$\qquad\qquad\qquad\qquad = -\dfrac{2(3 + x)}{x + 1}$

PRACTICE
4   Simplify $\dfrac{20 - 5x^2}{x^2 + x - 6}$.

> ▶ **Helpful Hint**
>
> Recall that for a fraction $\dfrac{a}{b}$,
>
> $$\frac{a}{-b} = \frac{-a}{b} = -\frac{a}{b}$$
>
> For example
>
> $$\frac{-(x+1)}{(x+2)} = \frac{(x+1)}{-(x+2)} = -\frac{x+1}{x+2}$$

Concept Check ☑

Which of the following expressions are equivalent to $\dfrac{x}{8-x}$?

a. $\dfrac{-x}{x-8}$ b. $\dfrac{-x}{8-x}$ c. $\dfrac{x}{x-8}$ d. $\dfrac{-x}{-8+x}$

EXAMPLE 5   Simplify each rational expression.

a. $\dfrac{x^3+8}{2+x}$ b. $\dfrac{2y^2+2}{y^3-5y^2+y-5}$

Solution

a. $\dfrac{x^3+8}{2+x} = \dfrac{(x+2)(x^2-2x+4)}{x+2}$ Factor the sum of the two cubes.

$\qquad\qquad = x^2 - 2x + 4$ Divide out common factors.

b. $\dfrac{2y^2+2}{y^3-5y^2+y-5} = \dfrac{2(y^2+1)}{(y^3-5y^2)+(y-5)}$ Factor the numerator.

$\qquad\qquad = \dfrac{2(y^2+1)}{y^2(y-5)+1(y-5)}$ Factor the denominator by grouping.

$\qquad\qquad = \dfrac{2(y^2+1)}{(y-5)(y^2+1)}$

$\qquad\qquad = \dfrac{2}{y-5}$ Divide out common factors.   □

PRACTICE
5   Simplify each rational expression.

a. $\dfrac{x^3+64}{4+x}$ b. $\dfrac{5z^2+10}{z^3-3z^2+2z-6}$

Concept Check ☑

Does $\dfrac{n}{n+2}$ simplify to $\dfrac{1}{2}$? Why or why not?

OBJECTIVE 3 ▶ **Multiplying rational expressions.** Arithmetic operations on rational expressions are performed in the same way as they are on rational numbers.

> **Multiplying Rational Expressions**
>
> The rule for multiplying rational expressions is
>
> $$\frac{P}{Q} \cdot \frac{R}{S} = \frac{PR}{QS} \quad \text{as long as } Q \neq 0 \text{ and } S \neq 0.$$
>
> To multiply rational expressions, you may use these steps:
>
> **STEP 1.** Completely factor each numerator and denominator.
>
> **STEP 2.** Use the rule above and multiply the numerators and the denominators.
>
> **STEP 3.** Simplify the product by dividing the numerator and denominator by their common factors.

When we multiply rational expressions, notice that we factor each numerator and denominator first. This helps when we apply the fundamental principle to write the product in simplest form.

EXAMPLE 6 Multiply.

a. $\dfrac{1 + 3n}{2n} \cdot \dfrac{2n - 4}{3n^2 - 2n - 1}$
 b. $\dfrac{x^3 - 1}{-3x + 3} \cdot \dfrac{15x^2}{x^2 + x + 1}$

Solution

a. $\dfrac{1 + 3n}{2n} \cdot \dfrac{2n - 4}{3n^2 - 2n - 1} = \dfrac{1 + 3n}{2n} \cdot \dfrac{2(n - 2)}{(3n + 1)(n - 1)}$ Factor.

$\qquad\qquad\qquad\qquad = \dfrac{(1 + 3n) \cdot 2(n - 2)}{2n(3n + 1)(n - 1)}$ Multiply.

$\qquad\qquad\qquad\qquad = \dfrac{n - 2}{n(n - 1)}$ Divide out common factors.

b. $\dfrac{x^3 - 1}{-3x + 3} \cdot \dfrac{15x^2}{x^2 + x + 1} = \dfrac{(x - 1)(x^2 + x + 1)}{-3(x - 1)} \cdot \dfrac{15x^2}{x^2 + x + 1}$ Factor.

$\qquad\qquad\qquad\qquad = \dfrac{(x - 1)(x^2 + x + 1) \cdot 3 \cdot 5x^2}{-1 \cdot 3(x - 1)(x^2 + x + 1)}$ Factor.

$\qquad\qquad\qquad\qquad = \dfrac{5x^2}{-1} = -5x^2$ Simplest form   □

PRACTICE
6 Multiply.

a. $\dfrac{2 + 5n}{3n} \cdot \dfrac{6n + 3}{5n^2 - 3n - 2}$
 b. $\dfrac{x^3 - 8}{-6x + 12} \cdot \dfrac{6x^2}{x^2 + 2x + 4}$

OBJECTIVE 4 ▶ Dividing rational expressions. Recall that two numbers are reciprocals of each other if their product is 1. Similarly, if $\dfrac{P}{Q}$ is a rational expression, then $\dfrac{Q}{P}$ is its **reciprocal,** since

$$\frac{P}{Q} \cdot \frac{Q}{P} = \frac{P \cdot Q}{Q \cdot P} = 1$$

The following are examples of expressions and their reciprocals.

Expression	*Reciprocal*
$\dfrac{3}{x}$	$\dfrac{x}{3}$
$\dfrac{2 + x^2}{4x - 3}$	$\dfrac{4x - 3}{2 + x^2}$
x^3	$\dfrac{1}{x^3}$
0	no reciprocal

Dividing Rational Expressions

The rule for dividing rational expressions is

$$\frac{P}{Q} \div \frac{R}{S} = \frac{P}{Q} \cdot \frac{S}{R} = \frac{PS}{QR} \quad \text{as long as } Q \neq 0, S \neq 0, \text{ and } R \neq 0.$$

To divide by a rational expression, use the rule above and multiply by its reciprocal. Then simplify if possible.

Notice that division of rational expressions is the same as for rational numbers.

EXAMPLE 7   Divide.

a. $\dfrac{8m^2}{3m^2 - 12} \div \dfrac{40}{2 - m}$

b. $\dfrac{18y^2 + 9y - 2}{24y^2 - 10y + 1} \div \dfrac{3y^2 + 17y + 10}{8y^2 + 18y - 5}$

Solution

a.
$$\frac{8m^2}{3m^2 - 12} \div \frac{40}{2 - m} = \frac{8m^2}{3m^2 - 12} \cdot \frac{2 - m}{40} \qquad \text{Multiply by the reciprocal of the divisor.}$$

$$= \frac{8m^2(2 - m)}{3(m + 2)(m - 2) \cdot 40} \qquad \text{Factor and multiply.}$$

$$= \frac{8m^2 \cdot -1\,(m - 2)}{3(m + 2)\,(m - 2)\, \cdot 8 \cdot 5} \qquad \text{Write } (2 - m) \text{ as } -1(m - 2).$$

$$= -\frac{m^2}{15(m + 2)} \qquad \text{Simplify.}$$

b.
$$\frac{18y^2 + 9y - 2}{24y^2 - 10y + 1} \div \frac{3y^2 + 17y + 10}{8y^2 + 18y - 5}$$

$$= \frac{18y^2 + 9y - 2}{24y^2 - 10y + 1} \cdot \frac{8y^2 + 18y - 5}{3y^2 + 17y + 10} \qquad \text{Multiply by the reciprocal.}$$

$$= \frac{(6y - 1)(3y + 2)}{(6y - 1)(4y - 1)} \cdot \frac{(4y - 1)(2y + 5)}{(3y + 2)(y + 5)} \qquad \text{Factor.}$$

$$= \frac{2y + 5}{y + 5} \qquad \text{Simplest form}$$

PRACTICE

7   Divide.

a. $\dfrac{6y^3}{3y^2 - 27} \div \dfrac{42}{3 - y}$

b. $\dfrac{10x^2 + 23x - 5}{5x^2 - 51x + 10} \div \dfrac{2x^2 + 9x + 10}{7x^2 - 68x - 20}$

> ▶ **Helpful Hint**
>
> When dividing rational expressions, do not divide out common factors until the division problem is rewritten as a multiplication problem.

EXAMPLE 8   Perform each indicated operation.

$$\frac{x^2 - 25}{(x + 5)^2} \cdot \frac{3x + 15}{4x} \div \frac{x^2 - 3x - 10}{x}$$

Solution $\dfrac{x^2 - 25}{(x + 5)^2} \cdot \dfrac{3x + 15}{4x} \div \dfrac{x^2 - 3x - 10}{x}$

$$= \frac{x^2 - 25}{(x + 5)^2} \cdot \frac{3x + 15}{4x} \cdot \frac{x}{x^2 - 3x - 10} \qquad \text{To divide, multiply by the reciprocal}$$

$$= \frac{(x + 5)(x - 5)}{(x + 5)(x + 5)} \cdot \frac{3\,(x + 5)}{4\,x} \cdot \frac{x}{(x - 5)\,(x + 2)}$$

$$= \frac{3}{4(x + 2)} \qquad\qquad\qquad \square$$

PRACTICE
8   Perform each indicated operation.

$$\frac{x^2 - 16}{(x - 4)^2} \cdot \frac{5x - 20}{3x} \div \frac{x^2 + x - 12}{x}$$

OBJECTIVE 5 ▶ Using rational functions in applications. Rational functions occur often in real-life situations.

EXAMPLE 9   **Cost for Pressing Compact Discs**

For the ICL Production Company, the rational function $C(x) = \dfrac{2.6x + 10,000}{x}$ describes the company's cost per disc of pressing x compact discs. Find the cost per disc for pressing:

a. 100 compact discs
b. 1000 compact discs

Solution

a. $C(100) = \dfrac{2.6(100) + 10,000}{100} = \dfrac{10,260}{100} = 102.6$

The cost per disc for pressing 100 compact discs is $102.60.

b. $C(1000) = \dfrac{2.6(1000) + 10,000}{1000} = \dfrac{12,600}{1000} = 12.6$

The cost per disc for pressing 1000 compact discs is $12.60. Notice that as more compact discs are produced, the cost per disc decreases.   □

PRACTICE
9   A company's cost per tee shirt for silk screening x tee shirts is given by the rational function $C(x) = \dfrac{3.2x + 400}{x}$. Find the cost per tee shirt for printing:

a. 100 tee shirts   **b.** 1000 tee shirts

Graphing Calculator Explorations

Recall that since the rational expression $\dfrac{7x - 2}{(x - 2)(x + 5)}$ is not defined when $x = 2$ or when $x = -5$, we say that the domain of the rational function $f(x) = \dfrac{7x - 2}{(x - 2)(x + 5)}$ is all real numbers except 2 and -5. This domain can be written as $\{x \mid x$ is a real number and $x \neq 2, x \neq -5\}$. This means that the graph of $f(x)$ should not cross the vertical lines $x = 2$ and $x = -5$. The graph of $f(x)$ in *connected* mode is to the left. In connected mode the graphing calculator tries to connect all dots of the graph so that the result is a smooth curve. This is what has happened in the graph. Notice that the graph appears to contain vertical lines at $x = 2$ and at $x = -5$. We know that this cannot happen because the function is not defined at $x = 2$ and at $x = -5$. We also know that this cannot happen because the graph of this function would not pass the vertical line test.

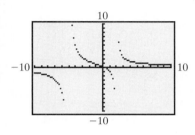

The graph of $f(x)$ in *dot* mode, is to the left. In dot mode the graphing calculator will not connect dots with a smooth curve. Notice that the vertical lines have disappeared, and we have a better picture of the graph. The graph, however, actually appears more like the hand-drawn graph below. By using a Table feature, a Calculate Value feature, or by tracing, we can see that the function is not defined at $x = 2$ and at $x = -5$.

Find the domain of each rational function. Then graph each rational function and use the graph to confirm the domain.

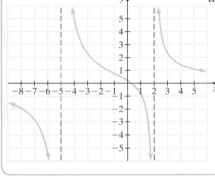

1. $f(x) = \dfrac{x + 1}{x^2 - 4}$

2. $g(x) = \dfrac{5x}{x^2 - 9}$

3. $h(x) = \dfrac{x^2}{2x^2 + 7x - 4}$

4. $f(x) = \dfrac{3x + 2}{4x^2 - 19x - 5}$

VOCABULARY & READINESS CHECK

Use the choices below to fill in each blank. Some choices may not be used.

1	true	rational	simplified	$\dfrac{-a}{-b}$	$\dfrac{-a}{b}$	$\dfrac{a}{-b}$
-1	false	domain	0			

1. A _____ expression is an expression that can be written as the quotient $\dfrac{P}{Q}$ of two polynomials P and Q as long as $Q \neq 0$.

2. A rational expression is undefined if the denominator is _____.

3. The _____ of the rational function $f(x) = \dfrac{2}{x}$ is $\{x \mid x$ is a real number and $x \neq 0\}$.

4. A rational expression is _____ if the numerator and denominator have no common factors other than 1 or -1.

5. The expression $\dfrac{x^2 + 2}{2 + x^2}$ simplifies to _____.

6. The expression $\dfrac{y - z}{z - y}$ simplifies to _____.

7. For a rational expression, $-\dfrac{a}{b} = $ _____ $ = $ _____ .

8. True or false: $\dfrac{a-6}{a+2} = \dfrac{-(a-6)}{-(a+2)} = \dfrac{-a+6}{-a-2}.$ _____

Multiply.

9. $\dfrac{x}{5} \cdot \dfrac{y}{2}$

10. $\dfrac{y}{6} \cdot \dfrac{z}{5}$

11. $\dfrac{2}{x} \cdot \dfrac{y}{3}$

12. $\dfrac{a}{5} \cdot \dfrac{7}{b}$

13. $\dfrac{m}{6} \cdot \dfrac{m}{6}$

14. $\dfrac{9}{x} \cdot \dfrac{8}{x}$

6.1 EXERCISE SET

MyMathLab

Find the domain of each rational expression. See Example 1.

1. $f(x) = \dfrac{5x - 7}{4}$

2. $g(x) = \dfrac{4 - 3x}{2}$

3. $s(t) = \dfrac{t^2 + 1}{2t}$

4. $v(t) = -\dfrac{5t + t^2}{3t}$

5. $f(x) = \dfrac{3x}{7 - x}$

6. $f(x) = \dfrac{-4x}{-2 + x}$

7. $f(x) = \dfrac{x}{3x - 1}$

8. $g(x) = \dfrac{-2}{2x + 5}$

9. $R(x) = \dfrac{3 + 2x}{x^3 + x^2 - 2x}$

10. $h(x) = \dfrac{5 - 3x}{2x^2 - 14x + 20}$

11. $C(x) = \dfrac{x + 3}{x^2 - 4}$

12. $R(x) = \dfrac{5}{x^2 - 7x}$

Simplify each rational expression. See Examples 2 through 5.

13. $\dfrac{8x - 16x^2}{8x}$

14. $\dfrac{3x - 6x^2}{3x}$

15. $\dfrac{x^2 - 9}{3 + x}$

16. $\dfrac{x^2 - 25}{5 + x}$

17. $\dfrac{9y - 18}{7y - 14}$

18. $\dfrac{6y - 18}{2y - 6}$

19. $\dfrac{x^2 + 6x - 40}{x + 10}$

20. $\dfrac{x^2 - 8x + 16}{x - 4}$

21. $\dfrac{x - 9}{9 - x}$

22. $\dfrac{x - 4}{4 - x}$

23. $\dfrac{x^2 - 49}{7 - x}$

24. $\dfrac{x^2 - y^2}{y - x}$

25. $\dfrac{2x^2 - 7x - 4}{x^2 - 5x + 4}$

26. $\dfrac{3x^2 - 11x + 10}{x^2 - 7x + 10}$

27. $\dfrac{x^3 - 125}{2x - 10}$

28. $\dfrac{4x + 4}{x^3 + 1}$

29. $\dfrac{3x^2 - 5x - 2}{6x^3 + 2x^2 + 3x + 1}$

30. $\dfrac{2x^2 - x - 3}{2x^3 - 3x^2 + 2x - 3}$

31. $\dfrac{9x^2 - 15x + 25}{27x^3 + 125}$

32. $\dfrac{8x^3 - 27}{4x^2 + 6x + 9}$

Multiply and simplify. See Example 6.

33. $\dfrac{2x - 4}{15} \cdot \dfrac{6}{2 - x}$

34. $\dfrac{10 - 2x}{7} \cdot \dfrac{14}{5x - 25}$

35. $\dfrac{18a - 12a^2}{4a^2 + 4a + 1} \cdot \dfrac{4a^2 + 8a + 3}{4a^2 - 9}$

36. $\dfrac{a - 5b}{a^2 + ab} \cdot \dfrac{b^2 - a^2}{10b - 2a}$

37. $\dfrac{9x + 9}{4x + 8} \cdot \dfrac{2x + 4}{3x^2 - 3}$

38. $\dfrac{2x^2 - 2}{10x + 30} \cdot \dfrac{12x + 36}{3x - 3}$

39. $\dfrac{2x^3 - 16}{6x^2 + 6x - 36} \cdot \dfrac{9x + 18}{3x^2 + 6x + 12}$

40. $\dfrac{x^2 - 3x + 9}{5x^2 - 20x - 105} \cdot \dfrac{x^2 - 49}{x^3 + 27}$

41. $\dfrac{a^3 + a^2b + a + b}{5a^3 + 5a} \cdot \dfrac{6a^2}{2a^2 - 2b^2}$

42. $\dfrac{4a^2 - 8a}{ab - 2b + 3a - 6} \cdot \dfrac{8b + 24}{3a + 6}$

43. $\dfrac{x^2 - 6x - 16}{2x^2 - 128} \cdot \dfrac{x^2 + 16x + 64}{3x^2 + 30x + 48}$

44. $\dfrac{2x^2 + 12x - 32}{x^2 + 16x + 64} \cdot \dfrac{x^2 + 10x + 16}{x^2 - 3x - 10}$

Divide and simplify. See Example 7.

45. $\dfrac{2x}{5} \div \dfrac{6x + 12}{5x + 10}$

46. $\dfrac{7}{3x} \div \dfrac{14 - 7x}{18 - 9x}$

47. $\dfrac{a + b}{ab} \div \dfrac{a^2 - b^2}{4a^3b}$

48. $\dfrac{6a^2b^2}{a^2 - 4} \div \dfrac{3ab^2}{a - 2}$

49. $\dfrac{x^2 - 6x + 9}{x^2 - x - 6} \div \dfrac{x^2 - 9}{4}$

50. $\dfrac{x^2 - 4}{3x + 6} \div \dfrac{2x^2 - 8x + 8}{x^2 + 4x + 4}$

51. $\dfrac{x^2 - 6x - 16}{2x^2 - 128} \div \dfrac{x^2 + 10x + 16}{x^2 + 16x + 64}$

52. $\dfrac{a^2 - a - 6}{a^2 - 81} \div \dfrac{a^2 - 7a - 18}{4a + 36}$

53. $\dfrac{3x - x^2}{x^3 - 27} \div \dfrac{x}{x^2 + 3x + 9}$

54. $\dfrac{x^2 - 3x}{x^3 - 27} \div \dfrac{2x}{2x^2 + 6x + 18}$

55. $\dfrac{8b + 24}{3a + 6} \div \dfrac{ab - 2b + 3a - 6}{a^2 - 4a + 4}$

56. $\dfrac{2a^2 - 2b^2}{a^3 + a^2b + a + b} \div \dfrac{6a^2}{a^3 + a}$

MIXED PRACTICE

Perform each indicated operation. See Examples 2 through 8.

57. $\dfrac{x^2 - 9}{4} \cdot \dfrac{x^2 - x - 6}{x^2 - 6x + 9}$

58. $\dfrac{x^2 - 4}{9} \cdot \dfrac{x^2 - 6x + 9}{x^2 - 5x + 6}$

59. $\dfrac{2x^2 - 4x - 30}{5x^2 - 40x - 75} \div \dfrac{x^2 - 8x + 15}{x^2 - 6x + 9}$

60. $\dfrac{4a + 36}{a^2 - 7a - 18} \div \dfrac{a^2 - a - 6}{a^2 - 81}$

61. Simplify: $\dfrac{r^3 + s^3}{r + s}$

62. Simplify: $\dfrac{m^3 - n^3}{m - n}$

63. $\dfrac{4}{x} \div \dfrac{3xy}{x^2} \cdot \dfrac{6x^2}{x^4}$

64. $\dfrac{4}{x} \cdot \dfrac{3xy}{x^2} \div \dfrac{6x^2}{x^4}$

65. $\dfrac{3x^2 - 5x - 2}{y^2 + y - 2} \cdot \dfrac{y^2 + 4y - 5}{12x^2 + 7x + 1} \div \dfrac{5x^2 - 9x - 2}{8x^2 - 2x - 1}$

66. $\dfrac{x^2 + x - 2}{3y^2 - 5y - 2} \cdot \dfrac{12y^2 + y - 1}{x^2 + 4x - 5} \div \dfrac{8y^2 - 6y + 1}{5y^2 - 9y - 2}$

67. $\dfrac{5a^2 - 20}{3a^2 - 12a} \div \dfrac{a^3 + 2a^2}{2a^2 - 8a} \cdot \dfrac{9a^3 + 6a^2}{2a^2 - 4a}$

68. $\dfrac{5a^2 - 20}{3a^2 - 12a} \div \left(\dfrac{a^3 + 2a^2}{2a^2 - 8a} \cdot \dfrac{9a^3 + 6a^2}{2a^2 - 4a} \right)$

69. $\dfrac{5x^4 + 3x^2 - 2}{x - 1} \cdot \dfrac{x + 1}{x^4 - 1}$

70. $\dfrac{3x^4 - 10x^2 - 8}{x - 2} \cdot \dfrac{3x + 6}{15x^2 + 10}$

Find each function value. See Example 9.

71. If $f(x) = \dfrac{x + 8}{2x - 1}$, find $f(2), f(0),$ and $f(-1)$.

72. If $f(x) = \dfrac{x - 2}{-5 + x}$, find $f(-5), f(0),$ and $f(10)$.

73. If $g(x) = \dfrac{x^2 + 8}{x^3 - 25x}$, find $g(3), g(-2),$ and $g(1)$.

74. If $s(t) = \dfrac{t^3 + 1}{t^2 + 1}$, find $s(-1), s(1),$ and $s(2)$.

75. The total revenue from the sale of a popular book is approximated by the rational function $R(x) = \dfrac{1000x^2}{x^2 + 4}$, where x is the number of years since publication and $R(x)$ is the total revenue in millions of dollars.

   a. Find the total revenue at the end of the first year.

   b. Find the total revenue at the end of the second year.

   c. Find the revenue during the second year only.

   d. Find the domain of function R.

76. The function $f(x) = \dfrac{100,000x}{100 - x}$ models the cost in dollars for removing x percent of the pollutants from a bayou in which a nearby company dumped creosol.

   a. Find the cost of removing 20% of the pollutants from the bayou. [*Hint:* Find $f(20)$.]

   b. Find the cost of removing 60% of the pollutants and then 80% of the pollutants.

   c. Find $f(90)$, then $f(95)$, and then $f(99)$. What happens to the cost as x approaches 100%?

   d. Find the domain of function f.

REVIEW AND PREVIEW

Perform each indicated operation. See Section 1.3.

77. $\dfrac{4}{5} + \dfrac{3}{5}$

78. $\dfrac{4}{10} - \dfrac{7}{10}$

79. $\dfrac{5}{28} - \dfrac{2}{21}$

80. $\dfrac{5}{13} + \dfrac{2}{7}$

81. $\dfrac{3}{8} + \dfrac{1}{2} - \dfrac{3}{16}$

82. $\dfrac{2}{9} - \dfrac{1}{6} + \dfrac{2}{3}$

CONCEPT EXTENSIONS

Solve. For Exercises 83 and 84, see the first Concept Check in this section; for Exercises 85 and 86, see the second Concept Check.

83. Which of the expressions are equivalent to $\dfrac{x}{5 - x}$?

   a. $\dfrac{-x}{5 - x}$

   b. $\dfrac{-x}{-5 + x}$

   c. $\dfrac{x}{x - 5}$

   d. $\dfrac{-x}{x - 5}$

84. Which of the expressions are equivalent to $\dfrac{-2 + x}{x}$?

   a. $\dfrac{2 - x}{-x}$

   b. $-\dfrac{2 - x}{x}$

   c. $\dfrac{x - 2}{x}$

   d. $\dfrac{x - 2}{-x}$

85. Does $\dfrac{x}{x+5}$ simplify to $\dfrac{1}{5}$? Why or why not?

86. Does $\dfrac{x+7}{x}$ simplify to 7? Why or why not?

87. Find the area of the rectangle.

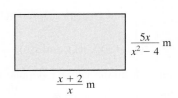

88. Find the area of the triangle.

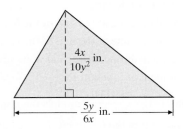

89. A parallelogram has an area of $\dfrac{x^2 + x - 2}{x^3}$ square feet and a height of $\dfrac{x^2}{x-1}$ feet. Express the length of its base as a rational expression in x. (*Hint:* Since $A = b \cdot h$, then $b = \dfrac{A}{h}$ or $b = A \div h$.)

90. A lottery prize of $\dfrac{15x^3}{y^2}$ dollars is to be divided among $5x$ people. Express the amount of money each person is to receive as a rational expression in x and y.

91. In your own words explain how to simplify a rational expression.

92. In your own words, explain the difference between multiplying rational expressions and dividing rational expressions.

93. Decide whether each rational expression equals 1, -1, or neither.

a. $\dfrac{x+5}{5+x}$ b. $\dfrac{x-5}{5-x}$

c. $\dfrac{x+5}{x-5}$ d. $\dfrac{-x-5}{x+5}$

e. $\dfrac{x-5}{-x+5}$ f. $\dfrac{-5+x}{x-5}$

94. In our definition of division for

$$\frac{P}{Q} \div \frac{R}{S}$$

we stated that $Q \neq 0$, $S \neq 0$, and $R \neq 0$. Explain why R cannot equal 0.

95. Find the polynomial in the second numerator such that the following statement is true.

$$\frac{x^2 - 4}{x^2 - 7x + 10} \cdot \frac{?}{2x^2 + 11x + 14} = 1$$

96. In your own words, explain how to find the domain of a rational function.

97. Graph a portion of the function $f(x) = \dfrac{20x}{100 - x}$. To do so, complete the given table, plot the points, and then connect the plotted points with a smooth curve.

x	0	10	30	50	70	90	95	99
y or $f(x)$								

98. The domain of the function $f(x) = \dfrac{1}{x}$ is all real numbers except 0. This means that the graph of this function will be in two pieces: one piece corresponding to x values less than 0 and one piece corresponding to x values greater than 0. Graph the function by completing the following tables, separately plotting the points, and connecting each set of plotted points with a smooth curve.

x	$\frac{1}{4}$	$\frac{1}{2}$	1	2	4
y or $f(x)$					

x	-4	-2	-1	$-\frac{1}{2}$	$-\frac{1}{4}$
y or $f(x)$					

Perform the indicated operation. Write all answers in lowest terms.

99. $\dfrac{x^{2n} - 4}{7x} \cdot \dfrac{14x^3}{x^n - 2}$

100. $\dfrac{x^{2n} + 4x^n + 4}{4x - 3} \cdot \dfrac{8x^2 - 6x}{x^n + 2}$

101. $\dfrac{y^{2n} + 9}{10y} \cdot \dfrac{y^n - 3}{y^{4n} - 81}$

102. $\dfrac{y^{4n} - 16}{y^{2n} + 4} \cdot \dfrac{6y}{y^n + 2}$

103. $\dfrac{y^{2n} - y^n - 2}{2y^n - 4} \div \dfrac{y^{2n} - 1}{1 + y^n}$

104. $\dfrac{y^{2n} + 7y^n + 10}{10} \div \dfrac{y^{2n} + 4y^n + 4}{5y^n + 25}$

STUDY SKILLS BUILDER

Are You Satisfied with Your Performance in this Course thus Far?

To see if there is room for improvement, answer these questions:

1. Am I attending all classes and arriving on time?
2. Am I working and checking my homework assignments on time?
3. Am I getting help (from my instructor or a campus learning resource lab) when I need it?

4. In addition to my instructor, am I using the text supplements that might help me?
5. Am I satisfied with my performance on quizzes and exams?

If you answered no to any of these questions, read or reread Section 1.1 for suggestions in these areas. Also, you might want to contact your instructor for additional feedback.

6.2 ADDING AND SUBTRACTING RATIONAL EXPRESSIONS

OBJECTIVES

1. Add or subtract rational expressions with common denominators.
2. Identify the least common denominator of two or more rational expressions.
3. Add or subtract rational expressions with unlike denominators.

OBJECTIVE 1 ▶ Adding or subtracting rational expressions with common denominators. Rational expressions, like rational numbers, can be added or subtracted. We add or subtract rational expressions in the same way that we add or subtract rational numbers (fractions).

Adding or Subtracting Rational Expressions with Common Denominators

If $\dfrac{P}{Q}$ and $\dfrac{R}{Q}$ are rational expressions, then

$$\frac{P}{Q} + \frac{R}{Q} = \frac{P + R}{Q} \quad \text{and} \quad \frac{P}{Q} - \frac{R}{Q} = \frac{P - R}{Q}$$

To add or subtract rational expressions with common denominators, add or subtract the numerators and write the sum or difference over the common denominator.

EXAMPLE 1   Add or subtract.

a. $\dfrac{x}{4} + \dfrac{5x}{4}$ b. $\dfrac{5}{7z^2} + \dfrac{x}{7z^2}$ c. $\dfrac{x^2}{x+7} - \dfrac{49}{x+7}$ d. $\dfrac{x}{3y^2} - \dfrac{x+1}{3y^2}$

Solution   The rational expressions have common denominators, so add or subtract their numerators and place the sum or difference over their common denominator.

a. $\dfrac{x}{4} + \dfrac{5x}{4} = \dfrac{x + 5x}{4} = \dfrac{6x}{4} = \dfrac{3x}{2}$ Add the numerators and write the result over the common denominator.

b. $\dfrac{5}{7z^2} + \dfrac{x}{7z^2} = \dfrac{5 + x}{7z^2}$

c. $\dfrac{x^2}{x+7} - \dfrac{49}{x+7} = \dfrac{x^2 - 49}{x+7}$ Subtract the numerators and write the result over the common denominator.

$\qquad = \dfrac{(x+7)(x-7)}{x+7}$ Factor the numerator.

$\qquad = x - 7$ Simplify.

d. $\dfrac{x}{3y^2} - \dfrac{x+1}{3y^2} = \dfrac{x-(x+1)}{3y^2}$ Subtract the numerators.

$= \dfrac{x-x-1}{3y^2}$ Use the distributive property.

$= -\dfrac{1}{3y^2}$ Simplify. □

PRACTICE
1   Add or subtract.

a. $\dfrac{9}{11z^2} + \dfrac{x}{11z^2}$ **b.** $\dfrac{x}{8} + \dfrac{5x}{8}$ **c.** $\dfrac{x^2}{x+4} - \dfrac{16}{x+4}$ **d.** $\dfrac{z}{2a^2} - \dfrac{z+3}{2a^2}$

Concept Check ☑

Find and correct the error.

$$\dfrac{3+2y}{y^2-1} - \dfrac{y+3}{y^2-1} = \dfrac{3+2y-y+3}{y^2-1}$$

$$= \dfrac{y+6}{y^2-1}$$

OBJECTIVE 2 ▶ Identifying the least common denominator of rational expressions.
To add or subtract rational expressions with unlike denominators, first write the rational expressions as equivalent rational expressions with common denominators.

The **least common denominator (LCD)** is usually the easiest common denominator to work with. The LCD of a list of rational expressions is a polynomial of least degree whose factors include the denominator factors in the list.

Use the following steps to find the LCD.

Finding the Least Common Denominator (LCD)

STEP 1. Factor each denominator completely.

STEP 2. The LCD is the product of all unique factors each raised to a power equal to the greatest number of times that the factor appears in any factored denominator.

EXAMPLE 2   Find the LCD of the rational expressions in each list.

a. $\dfrac{2}{3x^5y^2}, \dfrac{3z}{5xy^3}$

b. $\dfrac{7}{z+1}, \dfrac{z}{z-1}$

c. $\dfrac{m-1}{m^2-25}, \dfrac{2m}{2m^2-9m-5}, \dfrac{7}{m^2-10m+25}$

d. $\dfrac{x}{x^2-4}, \dfrac{11}{6-3x}$

Solution

a. First we factor each denominator.

$$3x^5y^2 = 3 \cdot x^5 \cdot y^2$$
$$5xy^3 = 5 \cdot x \cdot y^3$$
$$\text{LCD} = 3 \cdot 5 \cdot x^5 \cdot y^3 = 15x^5y^3$$

b. The denominators $z + 1$ and $z - 1$ do not factor further. Thus,

$$\text{LCD} = (z + 1)(z - 1)$$

c. We first factor each denominator.

$$m^2 - 25 = (m + 5)(m - 5)$$
$$2m^2 - 9m - 5 = (2m + 1)(m - 5)$$
$$m^2 - 10m + 25 = (m - 5)(m - 5)$$
$$\text{LCD} = (m + 5)(2m + 1)(m - 5)^2$$

d. Factor each denominator.

> **▶ Helpful Hint**
>
> $(x - 2)$ and $(2 - x)$ are opposite factors. Notice that -1 was factored from $(2 - x)$ so that the factors are identical.

$$x^2 - 4 = (x + 2)(x - 2)$$
$$6 - 3x = 3(2 - x) = 3(-1)(x - 2)$$
$$\text{LCD} = 3(-1)(x + 2)(x - 2)$$
$$= -3(x + 2)(x - 2)$$

> **▶ Helpful Hint**
>
> If opposite factors occur, do not use both in the LCD. Instead, factor -1 from one of the opposite factors so that the factors are then identical.

PRACTICE

2 Find the LCD of the rational expression in each list.

a. $\dfrac{7}{6x^3y^5}, \dfrac{2}{9x^2y^4}$

b. $\dfrac{11}{x - 2}, \dfrac{x}{x + 3}$

c. $\dfrac{b + 2}{b^2 - 16}, \dfrac{8}{b^2 - 8b + 16}, \dfrac{5b}{2b^2 - 5b - 12}$

d. $\dfrac{y}{y^2 - 9}, \dfrac{3}{12 - 4y}$

OBJECTIVE 3 ▶ Adding or subtracting rational expressions with unlike denominators.
To add or subtract rational expressions with unlike denominators, we write each rational expression as an equivalent rational expression so that their denominators are alike.

> **Adding or Subtracting Rational Expressions with Unlike Denominators**
>
> **STEP 1.** Find the LCD of the rational expressions.
>
> **STEP 2.** Write each rational expression as an equivalent rational expression whose denominator is the LCD found in Step 1.
>
> **STEP 3.** Add or subtract numerators, and write the result over the common denominator.
>
> **STEP 4.** Simplify the resulting rational expression.

EXAMPLE 3 Perform the indicated operation.

a. $\dfrac{2}{x^2y} + \dfrac{5}{3x^3y}$

b. $\dfrac{3}{x + 2} + \dfrac{2x}{x - 2}$

c. $\dfrac{2x - 6}{x - 1} - \dfrac{4}{1 - x}$

Solution

a. The LCD is $3x^3y$. Write each fraction as an equivalent fraction with denominator $3x^3y$. To do this, we multiply both the numerator and denominator of each fraction by the factors needed to obtain the LCD as denominator.

The first fraction is multiplied by $\dfrac{3x}{3x}$ so that the new denominator is the LCD.

$$\frac{2}{x^2y} + \frac{5}{3x^3y} = \frac{2 \cdot 3x}{x^2y \cdot 3x} + \frac{5}{3x^3y} \qquad \text{The second expression already}$$
$$\text{has a denominator of } 3x^3y.$$

$$= \frac{6x}{3x^3y} + \frac{5}{3x^3y}$$

$$= \frac{6x + 5}{3x^3y} \qquad \text{Add the numerators.}$$

b. The LCD is the product of the two denominators: $(x + 2)(x - 2)$.

$$\frac{3}{x + 2} + \frac{2x}{x - 2} = \frac{3 \cdot (x - 2)}{(x + 2) \cdot (x - 2)} + \frac{2x \cdot (x + 2)}{(x - 2) \cdot (x + 2)} \qquad \text{Write equivalent rational expressions.}$$

$$= \frac{3x - 6}{(x + 2)(x - 2)} + \frac{2x^2 + 4x}{(x + 2)(x - 2)} \qquad \text{Multiply in the numerators.}$$

$$= \frac{3x - 6 + 2x^2 + 4x}{(x + 2)(x - 2)} \qquad \text{Add the numerators.}$$

$$= \frac{2x^2 + 7x - 6}{(x + 2)(x - 2)} \qquad \text{Simplify the numerator.}$$

c. The LCD is either $x - 1$ or $1 - x$. To get a common denominator of $x - 1$, we factor -1 from the denominator of the second rational expression.

$$\frac{2x - 6}{x - 1} - \frac{4}{1 - x} = \frac{2x - 6}{x - 1} - \frac{4}{-1(x - 1)} \qquad \text{Write } 1 - x \text{ as } -1(x - 1).$$

$$= \frac{2x - 6}{x - 1} - \frac{-1 \cdot 4}{x - 1} \qquad \text{Write } \frac{4}{-1(x - 1)} \text{ as } \frac{-1 \cdot 4}{x - 1}.$$

$$= \frac{2x - 6 - (-4)}{x - 1} \qquad \text{Combine the numerators.}$$

$$= \frac{2x - 6 + 4}{x - 1} \qquad \text{Simplify.}$$

$$= \frac{2x - 2}{x - 1}$$

$$= \frac{2(x - 1)}{x - 1} \qquad \text{Factor.}$$

$$= 2 \qquad \text{Simplest form} \qquad \square$$

PRACTICE

3 Perform the indicated operation.

a. $\dfrac{4}{p^3q} + \dfrac{3}{5p^4q}$ **b.** $\dfrac{4}{y + 3} + \dfrac{5y}{y - 3}$ **c.** $\dfrac{3z - 18}{z - 5} - \dfrac{3}{5 - z}$

EXAMPLE 4   Subtract $\dfrac{5k}{k^2 - 4} - \dfrac{2}{k^2 + k - 2}$.

Solution $\dfrac{5k}{k^2 - 4} - \dfrac{2}{k^2 + k - 2} = \dfrac{5k}{(k + 2)(k - 2)} - \dfrac{2}{(k + 2)(k - 1)}$ Factor each denominator to find the LCD.

The LCD is $(k + 2)(k - 2)(k - 1)$. We write equivalent rational expressions with the LCD as denominators.

$$\frac{5k}{(k + 2)(k - 2)} - \frac{2}{(k + 2)(k - 1)}$$

$$= \frac{5k \cdot (k - 1)}{(k + 2)(k - 2) \cdot (k - 1)} - \frac{2 \cdot (k - 2)}{(k + 2)(k - 1) \cdot (k - 2)}$$ Write equivalent rational expressions.

$$= \frac{5k^2 - 5k}{(k + 2)(k - 2)(k - 1)} - \frac{2k - 4}{(k + 2)(k - 2)(k - 1)}$$ Multiply in the numerators.

$$= \frac{5k^2 - 5k - 2k + 4}{(k + 2)(k - 2)(k - 1)}$$ Subtract the numerators.

$$= \frac{5k^2 - 7k + 4}{(k + 2)(k - 2)(k - 1)}$$ Simplify.   □

> ▶ **Helpful Hint**
>
> **Very Important:** Because we are subtracting; notice the sign change on 4.

PRACTICE
4   Subtract $\dfrac{t}{t^2 - 25} - \dfrac{3}{t^2 - 3t - 10}$.

EXAMPLE 5   Add $\dfrac{2x - 1}{2x^2 - 9x - 5} + \dfrac{x + 3}{6x^2 - x - 2}$.

Solution

$$\frac{2x - 1}{2x^2 - 9x - 5} + \frac{x + 3}{6x^2 - x - 2} = \frac{2x - 1}{(2x + 1)(x - 5)} + \frac{x + 3}{(2x + 1)(3x - 2)}$$ Factor the denominators.

The LCD is $(2x + 1)(x - 5)(3x - 2)$.

$$= \frac{(2x - 1) \cdot (3x - 2)}{(2x + 1)(x - 5) \cdot (3x - 2)} + \frac{(x + 3) \cdot (x - 5)}{(2x + 1)(3x - 2) \cdot (x - 5)}$$

$$= \frac{6x^2 - 7x + 2}{(2x + 1)(x - 5)(3x - 2)} + \frac{x^2 - 2x - 15}{(2x + 1)(x - 5)(3x - 2)}$$ Multiply in the numerators.

$$= \frac{6x^2 - 7x + 2 + x^2 - 2x - 15}{(2x + 1)(x - 5)(3x - 2)}$$ Add the numerators.

$$= \frac{7x^2 - 9x - 13}{(2x + 1)(x - 5)(3x - 2)}$$ Simplify.   □

PRACTICE
5   Add $\dfrac{2x + 3}{3x^2 - 5x - 2} + \dfrac{x - 6}{6x^2 - 13x - 5}$.

EXAMPLE 6   Perform each indicated operation.

$$\frac{7}{x - 1} + \frac{10x}{x^2 - 1} - \frac{5}{x + 1}$$

Solution $\dfrac{7}{x - 1} + \dfrac{10x}{x^2 - 1} - \dfrac{5}{x + 1} = \dfrac{7}{x - 1} + \dfrac{10x}{(x - 1)(x + 1)} - \dfrac{5}{x + 1}$ Factor the denominators.

The LCD is $(x - 1)(x + 1)$.

$$= \frac{7 \cdot (x + 1)}{(x - 1) \cdot (x + 1)} + \frac{10x}{(x - 1)(x + 1)} - \frac{5 \cdot (x - 1)}{(x + 1) \cdot (x - 1)}$$

$$= \frac{7x + 7}{(x - 1)(x + 1)} + \frac{10x}{(x - 1)(x + 1)} - \frac{5x - 5}{(x + 1)(x - 1)} \quad \text{Multiply in the numerators.}$$

$$= \frac{7x + 7 + 10x - 5x + 5}{(x - 1)(x + 1)} \quad \text{Add and subtract the numerators.}$$

$$= \frac{12x + 12}{(x - 1)(x + 1)} \quad \text{Simplify.}$$

$$= \frac{12 \, (x + 1)}{(x - 1) \, (x + 1)} \quad \text{Factor the numerator.}$$

$$= \frac{12}{x - 1} \quad \text{Divide out common factors.}$$

PRACTICE
6 Perform each indicated operation.

$$\frac{2}{x - 2} + \frac{3x}{x^2 - x - 2} - \frac{1}{x + 1}$$

Graphing Calculator Explorations

A graphing calculator can be used to support the results of operations on rational expressions. For example, to verify the result of Example 3b, graph

$$Y_1 = \frac{3}{x + 2} + \frac{2x}{x - 2} \quad \text{and} \quad Y_2 = \frac{2x^2 + 7x - 6}{(x + 2)(x - 2)}$$

on the same set of axes. The graphs should be the same. Use a Table feature or a Trace feature to see that this is true.

VOCABULARY & READINESS CHECK

Name the operation(s) below that make each statement true.

    a. Addition   **b.** Subtraction   **c.** Multiplication   **d.** Division

1. The denominators must be the same before performing the operation. _____

2. To perform this operation, you multiply the first rational expression by the reciprocal of the second rational expression. ___

3. Numerator times numerator all over denominator times denominator. _____

4. These operations are commutative (order doesn't matter.) _____

For the rational expressions $\frac{5}{y}$ and $\frac{7}{y}$, perform each operation mentally.

5. Addition _____   **6.** Subtraction _____   **7.** Multiplication _____   **8.** Division _____

Be careful when subtracting! For example, $\dfrac{8}{x+1} - \dfrac{x+5}{x+1} = \dfrac{8-(x+5)}{x+1} = \dfrac{3-x}{x+1}$ *or* $\dfrac{-x+3}{x+1}$.

Use this example to help you perform the subtractions.

9. $\dfrac{5}{2x} - \dfrac{x+1}{2x} =$ _____

10. $\dfrac{9}{5x} - \dfrac{6-x}{5x} =$ _____

11. $\dfrac{y+11}{y-2} - \dfrac{y-5}{y-2} =$ _____

12. $\dfrac{z-1}{z+6} - \dfrac{z+4}{z+6} =$ _____

6.2 EXERCISE SET

MyMathLab
PRACTICE WATCH DOWNLOAD READ REVIEW

Add or subtract as indicated. Simplify each answer. See Example 1.

1. $\dfrac{2}{xz^2} - \dfrac{5}{xz^2}$

2. $\dfrac{4}{x^2 y} - \dfrac{2}{x^2 y}$

3. $\dfrac{2}{x-2} + \dfrac{x}{x-2}$

4. $\dfrac{x}{5-x} + \dfrac{7}{5-x}$

5. $\dfrac{x^2}{x+2} - \dfrac{4}{x+2}$

6. $\dfrac{x^2}{x+6} - \dfrac{36}{x+6}$

7. $\dfrac{2x-6}{x^2+x-6} + \dfrac{3-3x}{x^2+x-6}$

8. $\dfrac{5x+2}{x^2+2x-8} + \dfrac{2-4x}{x^2+2x-8}$

9. $\dfrac{x-5}{2x} - \dfrac{x+5}{2x}$

10. $\dfrac{x+4}{4x} - \dfrac{x-4}{4x}$

Find the LCD of the rational expressions in each list. See Example 2.

11. $\dfrac{2}{7}, \dfrac{3}{5x}$

12. $\dfrac{4}{5y}, \dfrac{3}{4y^2}$

13. $\dfrac{3}{x}, \dfrac{2}{x+1}$

14. $\dfrac{5}{2x}, \dfrac{7}{2+x}$

15. $\dfrac{12}{x+7}, \dfrac{8}{x-7}$

16. $\dfrac{1}{2x-1}, \dfrac{8}{2x+1}$

17. $\dfrac{5}{3x+6}, \dfrac{2x}{2x-4}$

18. $\dfrac{2}{3a+9}, \dfrac{5}{5a-15}$

19. $\dfrac{2a}{a^2-b^2}, \dfrac{1}{a^2-2ab+b^2}$

20. $\dfrac{2a}{a^2+8a+16}, \dfrac{7a}{a^2+a-12}$

21. $\dfrac{x}{x^2-9}, \dfrac{5}{x}, \dfrac{7}{12-4x}$

22. $\dfrac{9}{x^2-25}, \dfrac{1}{50-10x}, \dfrac{6}{x}$

Add or subtract as indicated. Simplify each answer. See Examples 3a and 3b.

23. $\dfrac{4}{3x} + \dfrac{3}{2x}$

24. $\dfrac{10}{7x} + \dfrac{5}{2x}$

25. $\dfrac{5}{2y^2} - \dfrac{2}{7y}$

26. $\dfrac{4}{11x^4} - \dfrac{1}{4x^2}$

27. $\dfrac{x-3}{x+4} - \dfrac{x+2}{x-4}$

28. $\dfrac{x-1}{x-5} - \dfrac{x+2}{x+5}$

29. $\dfrac{1}{x-5} - \dfrac{19-2x}{(x-5)(x+4)}$

30. $\dfrac{4x-2}{(x-5)(x+4)} - \dfrac{2}{x+4}$

Perform the indicated operation. If possible, simplify your answer. See Example 3c.

31. $\dfrac{1}{a-b} + \dfrac{1}{b-a}$

32. $\dfrac{1}{a-3} - \dfrac{1}{3-a}$

33. $\dfrac{x+1}{1-x} + \dfrac{1}{x-1}$

34. $\dfrac{5}{1-x} - \dfrac{1}{x-1}$

35. $\dfrac{5}{x-2} + \dfrac{x+4}{2-x}$

36. $\dfrac{3}{5-x} + \dfrac{x+2}{x-5}$

Perform each indicated operation. If possible, simplify your answer. See Examples 4 through 6.

37. $\dfrac{y+1}{y^2-6y+8} - \dfrac{3}{y^2-16}$

38. $\dfrac{x+2}{x^2-36} - \dfrac{x}{x^2+9x+18}$

39. $\dfrac{x+4}{3x^2+11x+6} + \dfrac{x}{2x^2+x-15}$

40. $\dfrac{x+3}{5x^2+12x+4} + \dfrac{6}{x^2-x-6}$

41. $\dfrac{7}{x^2-x-2} - \dfrac{x-1}{x^2+4x+3}$

42. $\dfrac{a}{a^2+10a+25} - \dfrac{4-a}{a^2+6a+5}$

43. $\dfrac{x}{x^2-8x+7} - \dfrac{x+2}{2x^2-9x-35}$

44. $\dfrac{x}{x^2-7x+6} - \dfrac{x+4}{3x^2-2x-1}$

45. $\dfrac{2}{a^2+2a+1} + \dfrac{3}{a^2-1}$

46. $\dfrac{9x+2}{3x^2-2x-8} + \dfrac{7}{3x^2+x-4}$

MIXED PRACTICE

Add or subtract as indicated. If possible, simplify your answer. See Examples 1 through 6.

47. $\dfrac{4}{3x^2y^3} + \dfrac{5}{3x^2y^3}$

48. $\dfrac{7}{2xy^4} + \dfrac{1}{2xy^4}$

49. $\dfrac{13x - 5}{2x} - \dfrac{13x + 5}{2x}$

50. $\dfrac{17x + 4}{4x} - \dfrac{17x - 4}{4x}$

51. $\dfrac{3}{2x + 10} + \dfrac{8}{3x + 15}$

52. $\dfrac{10}{3x - 3} + \dfrac{1}{7x - 7}$

53. $\dfrac{-2}{x^2 - 3x} - \dfrac{1}{x^3 - 3x^2}$

54. $\dfrac{-3}{2a + 8} - \dfrac{8}{a^2 + 4a}$

55. $\dfrac{ab}{a^2 - b^2} + \dfrac{b}{a + b}$

56. $\dfrac{x}{25 - x^2} + \dfrac{2}{3x - 15}$

57. $\dfrac{5}{x^2 - 4} - \dfrac{3}{x^2 + 4x + 4}$

58. $\dfrac{3z}{z^2 - 9} - \dfrac{2}{3 - z}$

59. $\dfrac{3x}{2x^2 - 11x + 5} + \dfrac{7}{x^2 - 2x - 15}$

60. $\dfrac{2x}{3x^2 - 13x + 4} + \dfrac{5}{x^2 - 2x - 8}$

61. $\dfrac{2}{x + 1} - \dfrac{3x}{3x + 3} + \dfrac{1}{2x + 2}$

62. $\dfrac{5}{3x - 6} - \dfrac{x}{x - 2} + \dfrac{3 + 2x}{5x - 10}$

63. $\dfrac{3}{x + 3} + \dfrac{5}{x^2 + 6x + 9} - \dfrac{x}{x^2 - 9}$

64. $\dfrac{x + 2}{x^2 - 2x - 3} + \dfrac{x}{x - 3} - \dfrac{x}{x + 1}$

65. $\dfrac{x}{x^2 - 9} + \dfrac{3}{x^2 - 6x + 9} - \dfrac{1}{x + 3}$

66. $\dfrac{3}{x^2 - 9} - \dfrac{x}{x^2 - 6x + 9} + \dfrac{1}{x + 3}$

67. $\left(\dfrac{1}{x} + \dfrac{2}{3}\right) - \left(\dfrac{1}{x} - \dfrac{2}{3}\right)$

68. $\left(\dfrac{1}{2} + \dfrac{2}{x}\right) - \left(\dfrac{1}{2} - \dfrac{1}{x}\right)$

MIXED PRACTICE (SECTIONS 6.1, 6.2)

Perform the indicated operation. If possible, simplify your answer.

69. $\left(\dfrac{2}{3} - \dfrac{1}{x}\right) \cdot \left(\dfrac{3}{x} + \dfrac{1}{2}\right)$

70. $\left(\dfrac{2}{3} - \dfrac{1}{x}\right) \div \left(\dfrac{3}{x} + \dfrac{1}{2}\right)$

71. $\left(\dfrac{2a}{3}\right)^2 \div \left(\dfrac{a^2}{a + 1} - \dfrac{1}{a + 1}\right)$

72. $\left(\dfrac{x + 2}{2x} - \dfrac{x - 2}{2x}\right) \cdot \left(\dfrac{5x}{4}\right)^2$

73. $\left(\dfrac{2x}{3}\right)^2 \div \left(\dfrac{x}{3}\right)^2$

74. $\left(\dfrac{2x}{3}\right)^2 \cdot \left(\dfrac{3}{x}\right)^2$

75. $\left(\dfrac{x}{x + 1} - \dfrac{x}{x - 1}\right) \div \dfrac{x}{2x + 2}$

76. $\dfrac{x}{2x + 2} \div \left(\dfrac{x}{x + 1} + \dfrac{x}{x - 1}\right)$

77. $\dfrac{4}{x} \cdot \left(\dfrac{2}{x + 2} - \dfrac{2}{x - 2}\right)$

78. $\dfrac{1}{x + 1} \cdot \left(\dfrac{5}{x} + \dfrac{2}{x - 3}\right)$

REVIEW AND PREVIEW

Use the distributive property to multiply the following. See Section 1.4.

79. $12\left(\dfrac{2}{3} + \dfrac{1}{6}\right)$

80. $14\left(\dfrac{1}{7} + \dfrac{3}{14}\right)$

81. $x^2\left(\dfrac{4}{x^2} + 1\right)$

82. $5y^2\left(\dfrac{1}{y^2} - \dfrac{1}{5}\right)$

Find each root. See Section 1.3.

83. $\sqrt{100}$

84. $\sqrt{25}$

85. $\sqrt[3]{8}$

86. $\sqrt[3]{27}$

87. $\sqrt[4]{81}$

88. $\sqrt[4]{16}$

Use the Pythagorean theorem to find each unknown length of a right triangle. See Section 5.8.

△ **89.**

3 meters

4 meters

△ **90.**

7 feet

24 feet

CONCEPT EXTENSIONS

Find and correct each error. See the Concept Check in this section.

91. $\dfrac{2x - 3}{x^2 + 1} - \dfrac{x - 6}{x^2 + 1} = \dfrac{2x - 3 - x - 6}{x^2 + 1}$

$$= \dfrac{x - 9}{x^2 + 1}$$

92.
$$\frac{7}{x+7} - \frac{x+3}{x+7} = \frac{7-x-3}{(x+7)^2}$$
$$= \frac{-x+4}{(x+7)^2}$$

△ **93.** Find the perimeter and the area of the square.

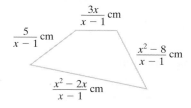

$\dfrac{x}{x+5}$ ft

△ **94.** Find the perimeter of the quadrilateral.

$\dfrac{3x}{x-1}$ cm

$\dfrac{5}{x-1}$ cm

$\dfrac{x^2-8}{x-1}$ cm

$\dfrac{x^2-2x}{x-1}$ cm

95. When is the LCD of two rational expressions equal to the product of their denominators? $\left(\textit{Hint: } \text{What is the LCD of } \dfrac{1}{x} \text{ and } \dfrac{7}{x+5}?\right)$

96. When is the LCD of two rational expressions with different denominators equal to one of the denominators? $\left(\textit{Hint: } \text{What is the LCD of } \dfrac{3x}{x+2} \text{ and } \dfrac{7x+1}{(x+2)^3}?\right)$

97. In your own words, explain how to add rational expressions with different denominators.

98. In your own words, explain how to multiply rational expressions.

99. In your own words, explain how to divide rational expressions.

100. In your own words, explain how to subtract rational expressions with different denominators.

Perform each indicated operation. (Hint: First write each expression with positive exponents.)

101. $x^{-1} + (2x)^{-1}$

102. $y^{-1} + (4y)^{-1}$

103. $4x^{-2} - 3x^{-1}$

104. $(4x)^{-2} - (3x)^{-1}$

Use a graphing calculator to support the results of each exercise.

105. Exercise 3

106. Exercise 4

6.3 SIMPLIFYING COMPLEX FRACTIONS

OBJECTIVES

1 Simplify complex fractions by simplifying the numerator and denominator and then dividing.

2 Simplify complex fractions by multiplying by a common denominator.

3 Simplify expressions with negative exponents.

OBJECTIVE 1 ▶ Simplifying complex fractions: Method 1. A rational expression whose numerator, denominator, or both contain one or more rational expressions is called a **complex rational expression** or a **complex fraction.**

Complex Fractions

$$\frac{\dfrac{1}{a}}{\dfrac{b}{2}} \qquad \frac{\dfrac{x}{2y^2}}{\dfrac{6x-2}{9y}} \qquad \frac{x+\dfrac{1}{y}}{y+1}$$

The parts of a complex fraction are

$$\left.\dfrac{x}{y+2}\right\} \leftarrow \text{Numerator of complex fraction}$$
$$\leftarrow \text{Main fraction bar}$$
$$\left.7+\dfrac{1}{y}\right\} \leftarrow \text{Denominator of complex fraction}$$

Our goal in this section is to simplify complex fractions. A complex fraction is simplified when it is in the form $\dfrac{P}{Q}$, where P and Q are polynomials that have no common factors. Two methods of simplifying complex fractions are introduced. The first method evolves from the definition of a fraction as a quotient.

Simplifying a Complex Fraction: Method I

STEP 1. Simplify the numerator and the denominator of the complex fraction so that each is a single fraction.

STEP 2. Perform the indicated division by multiplying the numerator of the complex fraction by the reciprocal of the denominator of the complex fraction.

STEP 3. Simplify if possible.

EXAMPLE 1   Simplify each complex fraction.

a. $\dfrac{\dfrac{2x}{27y^2}}{\dfrac{6x^2}{9}}$

b. $\dfrac{\dfrac{5x}{x+2}}{\dfrac{10}{x-2}}$

c. $\dfrac{\dfrac{x}{y^2}+\dfrac{1}{y}}{\dfrac{y}{x^2}+\dfrac{1}{x}}$

Solution

a. The numerator of the complex fraction is already a single fraction, and so is the denominator. Perform the indicated division by multiplying the numerator, $\dfrac{2x}{27y^2}$, by the reciprocal of the denominator, $\dfrac{6x^2}{9}$. Then simplify.

$$\dfrac{\dfrac{2x}{27y^2}}{\dfrac{6x^2}{9}} = \dfrac{2x}{27y^2} \div \dfrac{6x^2}{9}$$

$$= \dfrac{2x}{27y^2} \cdot \dfrac{9}{6x^2} \qquad \text{Multiply by the reciprocal of } \dfrac{6x^2}{9}.$$

$$= \dfrac{2x \cdot 9}{27y^2 \cdot 6x^2}$$

$$= \dfrac{1}{9xy^2}$$

> ▶ **Helpful Hint**
>
> Both the numerator and denominator are single fractions, so we perform the indicated division.

b. $\dfrac{\dfrac{5x}{x+2}}{\dfrac{10}{x-2}} = \dfrac{5x}{x+2} \div \dfrac{10}{x-2} = \dfrac{5x}{x+2} \cdot \dfrac{x-2}{10} \qquad \text{Multiply by the reciprocal of } \dfrac{10}{x-2}.$

$$= \dfrac{5x(x-2)}{2 \cdot 5(x+2)}$$

$$= \dfrac{x(x-2)}{2(x+2)} \qquad \text{Simplify.}$$

c. First simplify the numerator and the denominator of the complex fraction separately so that each is a single fraction. Then perform the indicated division.

$$\frac{\dfrac{x}{y^2} + \dfrac{1}{y}}{\dfrac{y}{x^2} + \dfrac{1}{x}} = \frac{\dfrac{x}{y^2} + \dfrac{1 \cdot y}{y \cdot y}}{\dfrac{y}{x^2} + \dfrac{1 \cdot x}{x \cdot x}}$$

Simplify the numerator. The LCD is y^2.

Simplify the denominator. The LCD is x^2.

$$= \frac{\dfrac{x + y}{y^2}}{\dfrac{y + x}{x^2}}$$

Add.

$$= \frac{x + y}{y^2} \cdot \frac{x^2}{y + x}$$

Multiply by the reciprocal of $\dfrac{y + x}{x^2}$.

$$= \frac{x^2(x + y)}{y^2(y + x)}$$

$$= \frac{x^2}{y^2}$$

Simplify.

□

PRACTICE

1 Simplify each complex fraction.

a. $\dfrac{\dfrac{5k}{36m}}{\dfrac{15k}{9}}$

b. $\dfrac{\dfrac{8x}{x - 4}}{\dfrac{3}{x + 4}}$

c. $\dfrac{\dfrac{5}{a} + \dfrac{b}{a^2}}{\dfrac{5a}{b^2} + \dfrac{1}{b}}$

Concept Check ☑

Which of the following are equivalent to $\dfrac{\dfrac{1}{x}}{\dfrac{3}{y}}$?

a. $\dfrac{1}{x} \div \dfrac{3}{y}$

b. $\dfrac{1}{x} \cdot \dfrac{y}{3}$

c. $\dfrac{1}{x} \div \dfrac{y}{3}$

OBJECTIVE 2 ▶ Simplifying complex fractions: Method 2. Next we look at another method of simplifying complex fractions. With this method we multiply the numerator and the denominator of the complex fraction by the LCD of all fractions in the complex fraction.

> **Simplifying a Complex Fraction: Method II**
>
> **STEP 1.** Multiply the numerator and the denominator of the complex fraction by the LCD of the fractions in both the numerator and the denominator.
>
> **STEP 2.** Simplify.

EXAMPLE 2 Simplify each complex fraction.

a. $\dfrac{\dfrac{5x}{x+2}}{\dfrac{10}{x-2}}$

b. $\dfrac{\dfrac{x}{y^2}+\dfrac{1}{y}}{\dfrac{y}{x^2}+\dfrac{1}{x}}$

Solution

a. The least common denominator of $\dfrac{5x}{x+2}$ and $\dfrac{10}{x-2}$ is $(x+2)(x-2)$. Multiply both the numerator, $\dfrac{5x}{x+2}$, and the denominator, $\dfrac{10}{x-2}$, by the LCD.

$$\dfrac{\dfrac{5x}{x+2}}{\dfrac{10}{x-2}}=\dfrac{\left(\dfrac{5x}{x+2}\right)\cdot(x+2)(x-2)}{\left(\dfrac{10}{x-2}\right)\cdot(x+2)(x-2)}$$ Multiply numerator and denominator by the LCD.

$$=\dfrac{5\,x\cdot(x-2)}{2\cdot5\cdot(x+2)}$$ Simplify.

$$=\dfrac{x(x-2)}{2(x+2)}$$ Simplify.

b. The least common denominator of $\dfrac{x}{y^2},\dfrac{1}{y},\dfrac{y}{x^2}$, and $\dfrac{1}{x}$ is x^2y^2.

$$\dfrac{\dfrac{x}{y^2}+\dfrac{1}{y}}{\dfrac{y}{x^2}+\dfrac{1}{x}}=\dfrac{\left(\dfrac{x}{y^2}+\dfrac{1}{y}\right)\cdot x^2y^2}{\left(\dfrac{y}{x^2}+\dfrac{1}{x}\right)\cdot x^2y^2}$$ Multiply the numerator and denominator by the LCD.

$$=\dfrac{\dfrac{x}{y^2}\cdot x^2y^2+\dfrac{1}{y}\cdot x^2y^2}{\dfrac{y}{x^2}\cdot x^2y^2+\dfrac{1}{x}\cdot x^2y^2}$$ Use the distributive property.

$$=\dfrac{x^3+x^2y}{y^3+xy^2}$$ Simplify.

$$=\dfrac{x^2(x+y)}{y^2(y+x)}$$ Factor.

$$=\dfrac{x^2}{y^2}$$ Simplify. □

PRACTICE
2 Use Method 2 to simplify:

a. $\dfrac{\dfrac{8x}{x-4}}{\dfrac{3}{x+4}}$

b. $\dfrac{\dfrac{b}{a^2}+\dfrac{1}{a}}{\dfrac{a}{b^2}+\dfrac{1}{b}}$

OBJECTIVE 3 ▶ Simplifying expressions with negative exponents. If an expression contains negative exponents, write the expression as an equivalent expression with positive exponents.

EXAMPLE 3   Simplify.

$$\frac{x^{-1} + 2xy^{-1}}{x^{-2} - x^{-2}y^{-1}}$$

Solution   This fraction does not appear to be a complex fraction. If we write it by using only positive exponents, however, we see that it is a complex fraction.

$$\frac{x^{-1} + 2xy^{-1}}{x^{-2} - x^{-2}y^{-1}} = \frac{\dfrac{1}{x} + \dfrac{2x}{y}}{\dfrac{1}{x^2} - \dfrac{1}{x^2y}}$$

The LCD of $\dfrac{1}{x}, \dfrac{2x}{y}, \dfrac{1}{x^2}$, and $\dfrac{1}{x^2y}$ is x^2y. Multiply both the numerator and denominator by x^2y.

$$= \frac{\left(\dfrac{1}{x} + \dfrac{2x}{y}\right) \cdot x^2y}{\left(\dfrac{1}{x^2} - \dfrac{1}{x^2y}\right) \cdot x^2y}$$

$$= \frac{\dfrac{1}{x} \cdot x^2y + \dfrac{2x}{y} \cdot x^2y}{\dfrac{1}{x^2} \cdot x^2y - \dfrac{1}{x^2y} \cdot x^2y} \qquad \text{Apply the distributive property.}$$

$$= \frac{xy + 2x^3}{y - 1} \quad \text{or} \quad \frac{x(y + 2x^2)}{y - 1} \qquad \text{Simplify.} \qquad \square$$

PRACTICE
3   Simplify: $\dfrac{3x^{-1} + x^{-2}y^{-1}}{y^{-2} + xy^{-1}}$.

EXAMPLE 4   Simplify: $\dfrac{(2x)^{-1} + 1}{2x^{-1} - 1}$

Solution $\dfrac{(2x)^{-1} + 1}{2x^{-1} - 1} = \dfrac{\dfrac{1}{2x} + 1}{\dfrac{2}{x} - 1}$ Write using positive exponents.

> **Helpful Hint**
>
> Don't forget that $(2x)^{-1} = \dfrac{1}{2x}$,
> but $2x^{-1} = 2 \cdot \dfrac{1}{x} = \dfrac{2}{x}$.

$$= \frac{\left(\dfrac{1}{2x} + 1\right) \cdot 2x}{\left(\dfrac{2}{x} - 1\right) \cdot 2x} \qquad \text{The LDC of } \dfrac{1}{2x} \text{ and } \dfrac{2}{x} \text{ is } 2x.$$

$$= \frac{\dfrac{1}{2x} \cdot 2x + 1 \cdot 2x}{\dfrac{2}{x} \cdot 2x - 1 \cdot 2x} \qquad \text{Use distributive property.}$$

$$= \frac{1 + 2x}{4 - 2x} \quad \text{or} \quad \frac{1 + 2x}{2(2 - x)} \qquad \text{Simplify.} \qquad \square$$

PRACTICE
4   Simplify: $\dfrac{(3x)^{-1} - 2}{5x^{-1} + 2}$.

VOCABULARY & READINESS CHECK

Complete the steps by writing the simplified complex fraction.

1. $\dfrac{\dfrac{7}{x}}{\dfrac{1}{x} + \dfrac{z}{x}} = \dfrac{x\left(\dfrac{7}{x}\right)}{x\left(\dfrac{1}{x}\right) + x\left(\dfrac{z}{x}\right)} = $ _____

2. $\dfrac{\dfrac{x}{4}}{\dfrac{x^2}{2} + \dfrac{1}{4}} = \dfrac{4\left(\dfrac{x}{4}\right)}{4\left(\dfrac{x^2}{2}\right) + 4\left(\dfrac{1}{4}\right)} = $ _____

Write each with positive exponents.

3. $x^{-2} = $ _____

4. $y^{-3} = $ _____

5. $2x^{-1} = $ _____

6. $(2x)^{-1} = $ _____

7. $(9y)^{-1} = $ _____

8. $9y^{-2} = $ _____

6.3 EXERCISE SET

Simplify each complex fraction. See Examples 1 and 2.

1. $\dfrac{\dfrac{10}{3x}}{\dfrac{5}{6x}}$

2. $\dfrac{\dfrac{15}{2x}}{\dfrac{5}{6x}}$

3. $\dfrac{1 + \dfrac{2}{5}}{2 + \dfrac{3}{5}}$

4. $\dfrac{2 + \dfrac{1}{7}}{3 - \dfrac{4}{7}}$

5. $\dfrac{\dfrac{4}{x - 1}}{\dfrac{x}{x - 1}}$

6. $\dfrac{\dfrac{x}{x + 2}}{\dfrac{2}{x + 2}}$

7. $\dfrac{1 - \dfrac{2}{x}}{x + \dfrac{4}{9x}}$

8. $\dfrac{5 - \dfrac{3}{x}}{x + \dfrac{2}{3x}}$

9. $\dfrac{\dfrac{4x^2 - y^2}{xy}}{\dfrac{2}{y} - \dfrac{1}{x}}$

10. $\dfrac{\dfrac{x^2 - 9y^2}{xy}}{\dfrac{1}{y} - \dfrac{3}{x}}$

11. $\dfrac{\dfrac{x + 1}{3}}{\dfrac{2x - 1}{6}}$

12. $\dfrac{\dfrac{x + 3}{12}}{\dfrac{4x - 5}{15}}$

13. $\dfrac{\dfrac{2}{x} + \dfrac{3}{x^2}}{\dfrac{4}{x^2} - \dfrac{9}{x}}$

14. $\dfrac{\dfrac{2}{x^2} + \dfrac{1}{x}}{\dfrac{4}{x^2} - \dfrac{1}{x}}$

15. $\dfrac{\dfrac{1}{x} + \dfrac{2}{x^2}}{x + \dfrac{8}{x^2}}$

16. $\dfrac{\dfrac{1}{y} + \dfrac{3}{y^2}}{y + \dfrac{27}{y^2}}$

17. $\dfrac{\dfrac{4}{5 - x} + \dfrac{5}{x - 5}}{\dfrac{2}{x} + \dfrac{3}{x - 5}}$

18. $\dfrac{\dfrac{3}{x - 4} - \dfrac{2}{4 - x}}{\dfrac{2}{x - 4} - \dfrac{2}{x}}$

19. $\dfrac{\dfrac{x + 2}{x} - \dfrac{2}{x - 1}}{\dfrac{x + 1}{x} + \dfrac{x + 1}{x - 1}}$

20. $\dfrac{\dfrac{5}{a + 2} - \dfrac{1}{a - 2}}{\dfrac{3}{2 + a} + \dfrac{6}{2 - a}}$

21. $\dfrac{\dfrac{2}{x} + 3}{\dfrac{4}{x^2} - 9}$

22. $\dfrac{2 + \dfrac{1}{x}}{4x - \dfrac{1}{x}}$

23. $\dfrac{1 - \dfrac{x}{y}}{\dfrac{x^2}{y^2} - 1}$

24. $\dfrac{1 - \dfrac{2}{x}}{x - \dfrac{4}{x}}$

25. $\dfrac{\dfrac{-2x}{x - y}}{\dfrac{y}{x^2}}$

26. $\dfrac{\dfrac{7y}{x^2 + xy}}{\dfrac{y^2}{x^2}}$

27. $\dfrac{\dfrac{2}{x} + \dfrac{1}{x^2}}{\dfrac{y}{x^2}}$

28. $\dfrac{\dfrac{5}{x^2} - \dfrac{2}{x}}{\dfrac{1}{x} + 2}$

29. $\dfrac{\dfrac{x}{9} - \dfrac{1}{x}}{1 + \dfrac{3}{x}}$

30. $\dfrac{\dfrac{x}{4} - \dfrac{4}{x}}{1 - \dfrac{4}{x}}$

31. $\dfrac{\dfrac{x - 1}{x^2 - 4}}{1 + \dfrac{1}{x - 2}}$

32. $\dfrac{\dfrac{x + 3}{x^2 - 9}}{1 + \dfrac{1}{x - 3}}$

33. $\dfrac{\dfrac{2}{x+5}+\dfrac{4}{x+3}}{\dfrac{3x+13}{x^2+8x+15}}$

34. $\dfrac{\dfrac{2}{x+2}+\dfrac{6}{x+7}}{\dfrac{4x+13}{x^2+9x+14}}$

Simplify. See Examples 3 and 4.

35. $\dfrac{x^{-1}}{x^{-2}+y^{-2}}$

36. $\dfrac{a^{-3}+b^{-1}}{a^{-2}}$

37. $\dfrac{2a^{-1}+3b^{-2}}{a^{-1}-b^{-1}}$

38. $\dfrac{x^{-1}+y^{-1}}{3x^{-2}+5y^{-2}}$

39. $\dfrac{1}{x-x^{-1}}$

40. $\dfrac{x^{-2}}{x+3x^{-1}}$

41. $\dfrac{a^{-1}+1}{a^{-1}-1}$

42. $\dfrac{a^{-1}-4}{4+a^{-1}}$

43. $\dfrac{3x^{-1}+(2y)^{-1}}{x^{-2}}$

44. $\dfrac{5x^{-2}-3y^{-1}}{x^{-1}+y^{-1}}$

45. $\dfrac{2a^{-1}+(2a)^{-1}}{a^{-1}+2a^{-2}}$

46. $\dfrac{a^{-1}+2a^{-2}}{2a^{-1}+(2a)^{-1}}$

47. $\dfrac{5x^{-1}+2y^{-1}}{x^{-2}y^{-2}}$

48. $\dfrac{x^{-2}y^{-2}}{5x^{-1}+2y^{-1}}$

49. $\dfrac{5x^{-1}-2y^{-1}}{25x^{-2}-4y^{-2}}$

50. $\dfrac{3x^{-1}+3y^{-1}}{4x^{-2}-9y^{-2}}$

REVIEW AND PREVIEW

Simplify. See Sections 5.1 and 5.2.

51. $\dfrac{3x^3y^2}{12x}$

52. $\dfrac{-36xb^3}{9xb^2}$

53. $\dfrac{144x^5y^5}{-16x^2y}$

54. $\dfrac{48x^3y^2}{-4xy}$

Solve the following. See Section 2.6.

55. $|x-5|=9$

56. $|2y+1|=1$

CONCEPT EXTENSIONS

Solve. See the Concept Check in the Section.

57. Which of the following are equivalent to $\dfrac{\dfrac{x+1}{9}}{\dfrac{y-2}{5}}$?

a. $\dfrac{x+1}{9}\div\dfrac{y-2}{5}$ **b.** $\dfrac{x+1}{9}\cdot\dfrac{y-2}{5}$ **c.** $\dfrac{x+1}{9}\cdot\dfrac{5}{y-2}$

58. Which of the following are equivalent to $\dfrac{\dfrac{a}{7}}{\dfrac{b}{13}}$?

a. $\dfrac{a}{7}\cdot\dfrac{b}{13}$ **b.** $\dfrac{a}{7}\div\dfrac{b}{13}$ **c.** $\dfrac{a}{7}\div\dfrac{13}{b}$ **d.** $\dfrac{a}{7}\cdot\dfrac{13}{b}$

59. When the source of a sound is traveling toward a listener, the pitch that the listener hears due to the Doppler effect is given by the complex rational compression $\dfrac{a}{1-\dfrac{s}{770}}$, where a is the

actual pitch of the sound and s is the speed of the sound source. Simplify this expression.

60. In baseball, the earned run average (ERA) statistic gives the average number of earned runs scored on a pitcher per game. It is computed with the following expression: $\dfrac{E}{\dfrac{I}{9}}$, where E is

the number of earned runs scored on a pitcher and I is the total number of innings pitched by the pitcher. Simplify this expression.

61. Which of the following are equivalent to $\dfrac{\dfrac{1}{x}}{\dfrac{3}{y}}$?

a. $\dfrac{1}{x}\div\dfrac{3}{y}$ **b.** $\dfrac{1}{x}\cdot\dfrac{y}{3}$ **c.** $\dfrac{1}{x}\div\dfrac{y}{3}$

62. In your own words, explain one method for simplifying a complex fraction.

Simplify.

63. $\dfrac{1}{1+(1+x)^{-1}}$

64. $\dfrac{(x+2)^{-1}+(x-2)^{-1}}{(x^2-4)^{-1}}$

65. $\dfrac{x}{1-\dfrac{1}{1+\dfrac{1}{x}}}$

66. $\dfrac{x}{1-\dfrac{1}{1-\dfrac{1}{x}}}$

67. $\dfrac{\dfrac{2}{y^2}-\dfrac{5}{xy}-\dfrac{3}{x^2}}{\dfrac{2}{y^2}+\dfrac{7}{xy}+\dfrac{3}{x^2}}$

68. $\dfrac{\dfrac{2}{x^2}-\dfrac{1}{xy}-\dfrac{1}{y^2}}{\dfrac{1}{x^2}-\dfrac{3}{xy}+\dfrac{2}{y^2}}$

69. $\dfrac{3(a + 1)^{-1} + 4a^{-2}}{(a^3 + a^2)^{-1}}$

70. $\dfrac{9x^{-1} - 5(x - y)^{-1}}{4(x - y)^{-1}}$

In the study of calculus, the difference quotient $\dfrac{f(a + h) - f(a)}{h}$ *is often found and simplified. Find and simplify this quotient for each function f(x) by following steps **a** through **d**.*

a. *Find* $(a + h)$.

b. *Find* $f(a)$.

c. *Use steps **a** and **b** to find* $\dfrac{f(a + h) - f(a)}{h}$

d. *Simplify the result of step **c**.*

71. $f(x) = \dfrac{1}{x}$

72. $f(x) = \dfrac{5}{x}$

73. $\dfrac{3}{x + 1}$

74. $\dfrac{2}{x^2}$

 STUDY SKILLS BUILDER

How Are You Doing?

If you haven't done so yet, take a few moments and think about how you are doing in this course. Are you working toward your goal of successfully completing this course? Is your performance on homework, quizzes, and tests satisfactory? If not, you might want to see your instructor to see if he/she has any suggestions on how you can improve your performance. Reread Section 1.1 for ideas on places to get help with your mathematics course.

Answer the following.

1. List any textbook supplements you are using to help you through this course.

2. List any campus resources you are using to help you through this course.

3. Write a short paragraph describing how you are doing in your mathematics course.

4. If improvement is needed, list ways that you can work toward improving your situation as described in Exercise 3.

6.4 DIVIDING POLYNOMIALS: LONG DIVISION AND SYNTHETIC DIVISION

OBJECTIVES

1 Divide a polynomial by a monomial.

2 Divide by a polynomial.

3 Use synthetic division to divide a polynomial by a binomial.

4 Use the remainder theorem to evaluate polynomials.

OBJECTIVE 1 ▶ Dividing a polynomial by a monomial. Recall that a rational expression is a quotient of polynomials. An equivalent form of a rational expression can be obtained by performing the indicated division. For example, the rational expression $\dfrac{10x^3 - 5x^2 + 20x}{5x}$ can be thought of as the polynomial $10x^3 - 5x^2 + 20x$ divided by the monomial $5x$. To perform this division of a polynomial by a monomial (which we do below) recall the following addition fact for fractions with a common denominator.

$$\frac{a}{c} + \frac{b}{c} = \frac{a + b}{c}$$

If a, b, and c are monomials, we might read this equation from right to left and gain insight into dividing a polynomial by a monomial.

Dividing a Polynomial by a Monomial
Divide each term in the polynomial by the monomial.

$$\frac{a + b}{c} = \frac{a}{c} + \frac{b}{c}, \quad \text{where } c \neq 0$$

EXAMPLE 1   Divide $10x^3 - 5x^2 + 20x$ by $5x$.

Solution   We divide each term of $10x^3 - 5x^2 + 20x$ by $5x$ and simplify.

$$\frac{10x^3 - 5x^2 + 20x}{5x} = \frac{10x^3}{5x} - \frac{5x^2}{5x} + \frac{20x}{5x} = 2x^2 - x + 4$$

Check: To check, see that (quotient) (divisor) = dividend, or

$$(2x^2 - x + 4)(5x) = 10x^3 - 5x^2 + 20x.$$

PRACTICE
1   Divide $18a^3 - 12a^2 + 30a$ by $6a$.

EXAMPLE 2   Divide: $\dfrac{3x^5y^2 - 15x^3y - x^2y - 6x}{x^2y}$.

Solution   We divide each term in the numerator by x^2y.

$$\frac{3x^5y^2 - 15x^3y - x^2y - 6x}{x^2y} = \frac{3x^5y^2}{x^2y} - \frac{15x^3y}{x^2y} - \frac{x^2y}{x^2y} - \frac{6x}{x^2y}$$

$$= 3x^3y - 15x - 1 - \frac{6}{xy}$$

PRACTICE
2   Divide: $\dfrac{5a^3b^4 - 8a^2b^3 + ab^2 - 8b}{ab^2}$.

OBJECTIVE 2 ▶ Dividing by a polynomial. To divide a polynomial by a polynomial other than a monomial, we use **long division.** Polynomial long division is similar to long division of real numbers. We review long division of real numbers by dividing 7 into 296.

$$
\begin{array}{r}
42 \\
7\overline{)296} \\
\end{array}
$$

Divisor: $7\overline{)296}$

$\quad\quad\underline{-28}\quad$ 4(7) = 28.

$\quad\quad\quad 16\quad$ Subtract and bring down the next digit in the dividend.

$\quad\quad\underline{-14}\quad$ 2(7) = 14.

$\quad\quad\quad\ 2\quad$ Subtract. The remainder is 2.

The quotient is $42\dfrac{2 \text{ (remainder)}}{7 \text{ (divisor)}}$.

Check: To check, notice that

$$42(7) + 2 = 296, \text{ the dividend.}$$

This same division process can be applied to polynomials, as shown next.

EXAMPLE 3   Divide $2x^2 - x - 10$ by $x + 2$.

Solution $2x^2 - x - 10$ is the dividend, and $x + 2$ is the divisor.

STEP 1. Divide $2x^2$ by x.

$$
\begin{array}{r}
2x \\
x + 2\overline{)2x^2 - x - 10} \\
\end{array}
$$

$\dfrac{2x^2}{x} = 2x$, so $2x$ is the first term of the quotient.

STEP 2. Multiply $2x(x + 2)$.

$$
\begin{array}{r}
2x \phantom{{}-x-10} \\
x + 2 \overline{) 2x^2 - x - 10} \\
2x^2 + 4x \phantom{{}-10}
\end{array}
$$

$2x(x + 2)$
Like terms are lined up vertically.

STEP 3. Subtract $(2x^2 + 4x)$ from $(2x^2 - x - 10)$ by changing the signs of $(2x^2 + 4x)$ and adding.

$$
\begin{array}{r}
2x \phantom{{}-x-10} \\
x + 2 \overline{) 2x^2 - x - 10} \\
\cancel{-}2x^2 \cancel{-} 4x \phantom{{}-10} \\
-5x \phantom{{}-10}
\end{array}
$$

STEP 4. Bring down the next term, -10, and start the process over.

$$
\begin{array}{r}
2x \phantom{{}-x-10} \\
x + 2 \overline{) 2x^2 - x - 10} \\
\cancel{-}2x^2 \cancel{-} 4x \downarrow \\
-5x - 10
\end{array}
$$

STEP 5. Divide $-5x$ by x.

$$
\begin{array}{r}
2x - 5 \\
x + 2 \overline{) 2x^2 - x - 10} \\
\cancel{-}2x^2 \cancel{-} 4x \phantom{{}-10} \\
-5x - 10
\end{array}
$$

$\dfrac{-5x}{x} = -5$, so -5 is the second term of the quotient.

STEP 6. Multiply $-5(x + 2)$.

$$
\begin{array}{r}
2x - 5 \\
x + 2 \overline{) 2x^2 - x - 10} \\
\cancel{-}2x^2 \cancel{-} 4x \phantom{{}-10} \\
-5x - 10 \\
-5x - 10
\end{array}
$$

Multiply: $-5(x + 2)$. Like terms are lined up vertically.

STEP 7. Subtract by changing signs of $-5x - 10$ and adding.

$$
\begin{array}{r}
2x - 5 \\
x + 2 \overline{) 2x^2 - x - 10} \\
\cancel{-}2x^2 \cancel{-} 4x \phantom{{}-10} \\
-5x - 10 \\
\cancel{-}5x \cancel{-} 10 \\
0
\end{array}
$$

Subtract.
Remainder

Then $\dfrac{2x^2 - x - 10}{x + 2} = 2x - 5$. There is no remainder.

Check: Check this result by multiplying $2x - 5$ by $x + 2$. Their product is $(2x - 5)(x + 2) = 2x^2 - x - 10$, the dividend. $\square$

PRACTICE

3 Divide $3x^2 + 7x - 6$ by $x + 3$.

EXAMPLE 4   Divide: $(6x^2 - 19x + 12) \div (3x - 5)$

Solution

$$
\begin{array}{r}
2x \\
3x - 5 \overline{)6x^2 - 19x + 12} \\
\underline{6x^2 - 10x} \quad \downarrow \\
-9x + 12
\end{array}
$$

Divide $\dfrac{6x^2}{3x} = 2x$.

Multiply $2x(3x - 5)$.
Subtract by adding the opposite.
Bring down the next term, $+12$.

$$
\begin{array}{r}
2x - 3 \\
3x - 5 \overline{)6x^2 - 19x + 12} \\
\underline{6x^2 - 10x} \\
-9x + 12 \\
\underline{-9x + 15} \\
-3
\end{array}
$$

Divide $\dfrac{-9x}{3x} = -3$.

Multiply $-3(3x - 5)$.
Subtract by adding the opposite.

Check: divisor · quotient + remainder

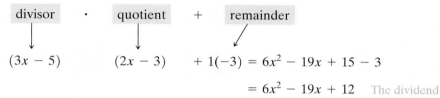

$(3x - 5)$ $(2x - 3)$ $+ 1(-3) = 6x^2 - 19x + 15 - 3$

$= 6x^2 - 19x + 12$ The dividend

The division checks, so

$$
\frac{6x^2 - 19x + 12}{3x - 5} = 2x - 3 + \frac{-3}{3x - 5}
$$

▶ **Helpful Hint**
This fraction is the remainder over the divisor.

$$
\text{or} \quad 2x - 3 - \frac{3}{3x - 5}
$$

PRACTICE
4   Divide $(6x^2 - 7x + 2)$ by $(2x - 1)$.

EXAMPLE 5   Divide: $(7x^3 + 16x^2 + 2x - 1) \div (x + 4)$.

Solution

$$
\begin{array}{r}
7x^2 - 12x + 50 \\
x + 4 \overline{)7x^3 + 16x^2 + 2x - 1} \\
\underline{7x^3 + 28x^2} \\
-12x^2 + 2x \\
\underline{-12x^2 - 48x} \\
50x - 1 \\
\underline{50x + 200} \\
-201
\end{array}
$$

Divide $\dfrac{7x^3}{x} = 7x^2$.

$7x^2(x + 4)$
Subtract. Bring down $2x$.

$\dfrac{-12x^2}{x} = -12x$, a term of the quotient.

$-12x(x + 4)$ Subtract. Bring down -1.

$\dfrac{50x}{x} = 50$, a term of the quotient.

$50(x + 4)$.   Subtract.

Thus, $\dfrac{7x^3 + 16x^2 + 2x - 1}{x + 4} = 7x^2 - 12x + 50 + \dfrac{-201}{x + 4}$ or

$$
7x^2 - 12x + 50 - \frac{201}{x + 4}.
$$

PRACTICE
5   Divide $(5x^3 + 9x^2 - 10x + 30) \div (x + 3)$.

EXAMPLE 6 Divide $3x^4 + 2x^3 - 8x + 6$ by $x^2 - 1$.

Solution Before dividing, we represent any "missing powers" by the product of 0 and the variable raised to the missing power. There is no x^2 term in the dividend, so we include $0x^2$ to represent the missing term. Also, there is no x term in the divisor, so we include $0x$ in the divisor.

$$
\begin{array}{r}
3x^2 + 2x + 3 \\
x^2 + 0x - 1 \overline{)3x^4 + 2x^3 + 0x^2 - 8x + 6} \\
\underline{3x^4 + 0x^3 - 3x^2} \\
2x^3 + 3x^2 - 8x \\
\underline{2x^3 + 0x^2 - 2x} \\
3x^2 - 6x + 6 \\
\underline{3x^2 + 0x - 3} \\
-6x + 9
\end{array}
$$

$\dfrac{3x^4}{x^2} = 3x^2$

$3x^2(x^2 + 0x - 1)$

Subtract. Bring down $-8x$.

$\dfrac{2x^3}{x^2} = 2x$, a term of the quotient.

$2x(x^2 + 0x - 1)$

Subtract. Bring down 6.

$\dfrac{3x^2}{x^2} = 3$, a term of the quotient.

$3(x^2 + 0x - 1)$

Subtract.

The division process is finished when the degree of the remainder polynomial is less than the degree of the divisor. Thus,

$$
\frac{3x^4 + 2x^3 - 8x + 6}{x^2 - 1} = 3x^2 + 2x + 3 + \frac{-6x + 9}{x^2 - 1}
$$

☐

PRACTICE
6 Divide $2x^4 + 3x^3 - 5x + 2$ by $x^2 + 1$.

EXAMPLE 7 Divide $27x^3 + 8$ by $3x + 2$.

Solution We replace the missing terms in the dividend with $0x^2$ and $0x$.

$$
\begin{array}{r}
9x^2 - 6x + 4 \\
3x + 2 \overline{)27x^3 + 0x^2 + 0x + 8} \\
\underline{27x^3 + 18x^2} \\
-18x^2 + 0x \\
\underline{-18x^2 - 12x} \\
12x + 8 \\
\underline{12x + 8}
\end{array}
$$

$9x^2(3x + 2)$

Subtract. Bring down $0x$.

$-6x(3x + 2)$

Subtract. Bring down 8.

$4(3x + 2)$

Thus, $\dfrac{27x^3 + 8}{3x + 2} = 9x^2 - 6x + 4$.

☐

PRACTICE
7 Divide $64x^3 - 125$ by $4x - 5$.

Concept Check ✓

In a division problem, the divisor is $4x^3 - 5$. The division process can be stopped when which of these possible remainder polynomials is reached?

a. $2x^4 + x^2 - 3$ **b.** $x^3 - 5^2$ **c.** $4x^2 + 25$

OBJECTIVE 3 ▶ Using synthetic division to divide a polynomial by a binomial. When a polynomial is to be divided by a binomial of the form $x - c$, a shortcut process called **synthetic division** may be used. On the left is an example of long division, and on the right, the same example showing the coefficients of the variables only.

$$
\begin{array}{r}
2x^2 + 5x + 2 \\
x-3\overline{\smash{)}2x^3 - x^2 - 13x + 1} \\
\underline{2x^3 - 6x^2} \\
5x^2 - 13x \\
\underline{5x^2 - 15x} \\
2x + 1 \\
\underline{2x - 6} \\
7
\end{array}
\qquad
\begin{array}{r}
2 \quad 5 \quad 2 \\
1-3\overline{\smash{)}2 - 1 - 13 + 1} \\
\underline{2 - 6} \\
5 - 13 \\
\underline{5 - 15} \\
2 + 1 \\
\underline{2 - 6} \\
7
\end{array}
$$

Notice that as long as we keep coefficients of powers of x in the same column, we can perform division of polynomials by performing algebraic operations on the coefficients only. This shortcut process of dividing with coefficients only in a special format is called synthetic division. To find $(2x^3 - x^2 - 13x + 1) \div (x - 3)$ by synthetic division, follow the next example.

EXAMPLE 8 Use synthetic division to divide $2x^3 - x^2 - 13x + 1$ by $x - 3$.

Solution To use synthetic division, the divisor must be in the form $x - c$. Since we are dividing by $x - 3$, c is 3. Write down 3 and the coefficients of the dividend.

$$
\begin{array}{c|cccc}
c \searrow & & & & \\
3 & 2 & -1 & -13 & 1 \\
& \downarrow & & & \\
\hline
& 2 & & &
\end{array}
$$
Next, draw a line and bring down the first coefficient of the dividend.

$$
\begin{array}{c|cccc}
3 & 2 & -1 & -13 & 1 \\
& & 6 & & \\
\hline
& 2 & & &
\end{array}
$$
Multiply $3 \cdot 2$ and write down the product, 6.

$$
\begin{array}{c|cccc}
3 & 2 & -1 & -13 & 1 \\
& & 6 & & \\
\hline
& 2 & 5 & &
\end{array}
$$
Add $-1 + 6$. Write down the sum, 5.

$$
\begin{array}{c|cccc}
3 & 2 & -1 & -13 & 1 \\
& & 6 & 15 & \\
\hline
& 2 & 5 & 2 &
\end{array}
$$
$3 \cdot 5 = 15.$
$-13 + 15 = 2.$

$$
\begin{array}{c|cccc}
3 & 2 & -1 & -13 & 1 \\
& & 6 & 15 & 6 \\
\hline
& 2 & 5 & 2 & 7
\end{array}
$$
$3 \cdot 2 = 6.$
$1 + 6 = 7.$

The quotient is found in the bottom row. The numbers 2, 5, and 2 are the coefficients of the quotient polynomial, and the number 7 is the remainder. The degree of the quotient polynomial is one less than the degree of the dividend. In our example, the degree of the dividend is 3, so the degree of the quotient polynomial is 2. As we found when we performed the long division, the quotient is

$$2x^2 + 5x + 2, \quad \text{remainder } 7$$

or

$$2x^2 + 5x + 2 + \frac{7}{x - 3}$$

☐

PRACTICE
8 Use synthetic division to divide $4x^3 - 3x^2 + 6x + 5$ by $x - 1$.

EXAMPLE 9 Use synthetic division to divide $x^4 - 2x^3 - 11x^2 + 5x + 34$ by $x + 2$.

Solution The divisor is $x + 2$, which we write in the form $x - c$ as $x - (-2)$. Thus, c is -2. The dividend coefficients are $1, -2, -11, 5$, and 34.

$$
\begin{array}{r|rrrrr}
-2 & 1 & -2 & -11 & 5 & 34 \\
   &   & -2 & 8 & 6 & -22 \\
\hline
   & 1 & -4 & -3 & 11 & 12
\end{array}
$$

The dividend is a fourth-degree polynomial, so the quotient polynomial is a third-degree polynomial. The quotient is $x^3 - 4x^2 - 3x + 11$ with a remainder of 12. Thus,

$$\frac{x^4 - 2x^3 - 11x^2 + 5x + 34}{x + 2} = x^3 - 4x^2 - 3x + 11 + \frac{12}{x + 2}$$

PRACTICE
9 Use synthetic division to divide $x^4 + 3x^3 - 5x^2 + 6x + 12$ by $x + 3$.

Concept Check ✓

Which division problems are candidates for the synthetic division process?

a. $(3x^2 + 5) \div (x + 4)$

b. $(x^3 - x^2 + 2) \div (3x^3 - 2)$

c. $(y^4 + y - 3) \div (x^2 + 1)$

d. $x^5 \div (x - 5)$

> ▶ **Helpful Hint**
> Before dividing by synthetic division, write the dividend in descending order of variable exponents. Any "missing powers" of the variable should be represented by 0 times the variable raised to the missing power.

EXAMPLE 10 If $P(x) = 2x^3 - 4x^2 + 5$,

a. Find $P(2)$ by substitution.

b. Use synthetic division to find the remainder when $P(x)$ is divided by $x - 2$.

Solution

a. $P(x) = 2x^3 - 4x^2 + 5$

$P(2) = 2(2)^3 - 4(2)^2 + 5$

$\quad\quad = 2(8) - 4(4) + 5 = 16 - 16 + 5 = 5$

Thus, $P(2) = 5$.

b. The coefficients of $P(x)$ are $2, -4, 0$, and 5. The number 0 is a coefficient of the missing power of x^1. The divisor is $x - 2$, so c is 2.

$$
\begin{array}{r|rrrr}
2 & 2 & -4 & 0 & 5 \\
  &   & 4 & 0 & 0 \\
\hline
  & 2 & 0 & 0 & 5 \;\text{remainder}
\end{array}
$$

The remainder when $P(x)$ is divided by $x - 2$ is 5.

PRACTICE
10 If $P(x) = x^3 - 5x - 2$,

a. Find $P(2)$ by substitution.

b. Use synthetic division to find the remainder when $P(x)$ is divided by $x - 2$.

OBJECTIVE 4 ▶ **Using the remainder theorem to evaluate polynomials.** Notice in the preceding example that $P(2) = 5$ and that the remainder when $P(x)$ is divided by $x - 2$ is 5. This is no accident. This illustrates the **remainder theorem.**

> **Remainder Theorem**
> If a polynomial $P(x)$ is divided by $x - c$, then the remainder is $P(c)$.

EXAMPLE 11 Use the remainder theorem and synthetic division to find $P(4)$ if

$$P(x) = 4x^6 - 25x^5 + 35x^4 + 17x^2.$$

Solution To find $P(4)$ by the remainder theorem, we divide $P(x)$ by $x - 4$. The coefficients of $P(x)$ are $4, -25, 35, 0, 17, 0,$ and 0. Also, c is 4.

$$
\begin{array}{r|rrrrrrr}
c \\
4 & 4 & -25 & 35 & 0 & 17 & 0 & 0 \\
  &   & 16 & -36 & -4 & -16 & 4 & 16 \\
\hline
  & 4 & -9 & -1 & -4 & 1 & 4 & 16 \quad \text{remainder}
\end{array}
$$

Thus, $P(4) = 16$, the remainder.

PRACTICE
11 Use the remainder theorem and synthetic division to find $P(3)$ if $P(x) = 2x^5 - 18x^4 + 90x^2 + 59x$.

6.4 EXERCISE SET

MyMathLab *Powered by CourseCompass and MathXL*

PRACTICE · WATCH · DOWNLOAD · READ · REVIEW

Divide. See Examples 1 and 2.

1. $4a^2 + 8a$ by $2a$

2. $6x^4 - 3x^3$ by $3x^2$

3. $\dfrac{12a^5b^2 + 16a^4b}{4a^4b}$

4. $\dfrac{4x^3y + 12x^2y^2 - 4xy^3}{4xy}$

5. $\dfrac{4x^2y^2 + 6xy^2 - 4y^2}{2x^2y}$

6. $\dfrac{6x^5y + 75x^4y - 24x^3y^2}{3x^4y}$

Divide. See Examples 3 through 7.

7. $(x^2 + 3x + 2) \div (x + 2)$

8. $(y^2 + 7y + 10) \div (y + 5)$

9. $(2x^2 - 6x - 8) \div (x + 1)$

10. $(3x^2 + 19x + 20) \div (x + 5)$

11. $2x^2 + 3x - 2$ by $2x + 4$

12. $6x^2 - 17x - 3$ by $3x - 9$

13. $(4x^3 + 7x^2 + 8x + 20) \div (2x + 4)$

14. $(8x^3 + 18x^2 + 16x + 24) \div (4x + 8)$

15. $(2x^2 + 6x^3 - 18x - 6) \div (3x + 1)$

16. $(4x - 15x^2 + 10x^3 - 6) \div (2x - 3)$

17. $(3x^5 - x^3 + 4x^2 - 12x - 8) \div (x^2 - 2)$

18. $(2x^5 - 6x^4 + x^3 - 4x + 3) \div (x^2 - 3)$

19. $\left(2x^4 + \dfrac{1}{2}x^3 + x^2 + x \right) \div (x - 2)$

20. $\left(x^4 - \dfrac{2}{3}x^3 + x \right) \div (x - 3)$

Use synthetic division to divide. See Examples 8 and 9.

21. $\dfrac{x^2 + 3x - 40}{x - 5}$

22. $\dfrac{x^2 - 14x + 24}{x - 2}$

23. $\dfrac{x^2 + 5x - 6}{x + 6}$

24. $\dfrac{x^2 + 12x + 32}{x + 4}$

25. $\dfrac{x^3 - 7x^2 - 13x + 5}{x - 2}$

26. $\dfrac{x^3 + 6x^2 + 4x - 7}{x + 5}$

27. $\dfrac{4x^2 - 9}{x - 2}$

28. $\dfrac{3x^2 - 4}{x - 1}$

MIXED PRACTICE

Divide. See Examples 1–9.

29. $\dfrac{4x^7y^4 + 8xy^2 + 4xy^3}{4xy^3}$

30. $\dfrac{15x^3y - 5x^2y + 10xy^2}{5x^2y}$

31. $(10x^3 - 5x^2 - 12x + 1) \div (2x - 1)$

32. $(20x^3 - 8x^2 + 5x - 5) \div (5x - 2)$

33. $(2x^3 - 6x^2 - 4) \div (x - 4)$

34. $(3x^3 + 4x - 10) \div (x + 2)$

35. $\dfrac{2x^4 - 13x^3 + 16x^2 - 9x + 20}{x - 5}$

36. $\dfrac{3x^4 + 5x^3 - x^2 + x - 2}{x + 2}$

37. $\dfrac{7x^2 - 4x + 12 + 3x^3}{x + 1}$

38. $\dfrac{4x^3 + x^4 - x^2 - 16x - 4}{x - 2}$

39. $\dfrac{3x^3 + 2x^2 - 4x + 1}{x - \dfrac{1}{3}}$

40. $\dfrac{9y^3 + 9y^2 - y + 2}{y + \dfrac{2}{3}}$

41. $\dfrac{x^3 - 1}{x - 1}$

42. $\dfrac{y^3 - 8}{y - 2}$

43. $(25xy^2 + 75xyz + 125x^2yz) \div (-5x^2y)$

44. $(x^6y^6 - x^3y^3z + 7x^3y) \div (-7yz^2)$

45. $(9x^5 + 6x^4 - 6x^2 - 4x) \div (3x + 2)$

46. $(5x^4 - 5x^2 + 10x^3 - 10x) \div (5x + 10)$

For the given polynomial P(x) and the given c, use the remainder theorem to find P(c). See Examples 10 and 11.

47. $P(x) = x^3 + 3x^2 - 7x + 4; 1$

48. $P(x) = x^3 + 5x^2 - 4x - 6; 2$

49. $P(x) = 3x^3 - 7x^2 - 2x + 5; -3$

50. $P(x) = 4x^3 + 5x^2 - 6x - 4; -2$

51. $P(x) = 4x^4 + x^2 - 2; -1$

52. $P(x) = x^4 - 3x^2 - 2x + 5; -2$

53. $P(x) = 2x^4 - 3x^2 - 2; \dfrac{1}{3}$

54. $P(x) = 4x^4 - 2x^3 + x^2 - x - 4; \dfrac{1}{2}$

55. $P(x) = x^5 + x^4 - x^3 + 3; \dfrac{1}{2}$

56. $P(x) = x^5 - 2x^3 + 4x^2 - 5x + 6; \dfrac{2}{3}$

REVIEW AND PREVIEW

Solve each equation for x. See Sections 2.1 and 5.8.

57. $7x + 2 = x - 3$

58. $4 - 2x = 17 - 5x$

59. $x^2 = 4x - 4$

60. $5x^2 + 10x = 15$

61. $\dfrac{x}{3} - 5 = 13$

62. $\dfrac{2x}{9} + 1 = \dfrac{7}{9}$

Factor the following. See Sections 5.5 and 5.7.

63. $x^3 - 1$

64. $8y^3 + 1$

65. $125z^3 + 8$

66. $a^3 - 27$

67. $xy + 2x + 3y + 6$

68. $x^2 - x + xy - y$

69. $x^3 - 9x$

70. $2x^3 - 32x$

CONCEPT EXTENSIONS

Which division problems are candidates for the synthetic division process? See the Concept Checks in this section.

71. $(5x^2 - 3x + 2) \div (x + 2)$

72. $(x^4 - 6) \div (x^3 + 3x - 1)$

73. $(x^7 - 2) \div (x^5 + 1)$

74. $(3x^2 + 7x - 1) \div \left(x - \dfrac{1}{3}\right)$

75. In a long division exercise, if the divisor is $9x^3 - 2x$, then the division process can be stopped when the degree of the remainder is

   a. 1   **b.** 3   **c.** 9   **d.** 2

76. In a division exercise, if the divisor is $x - 3$, then the division process can be stopped when the degree of the remainder is

   a. 1   **b.** 0   **c.** 2   **d.** 3

△ **77.** A board of length $(3x^4 + 6x^2 - 18)$ meters is to be cut into three pieces of the same length. Find the length of each piece.

△ **78.** The perimeter of a regular hexagon is given to be $(12x^5 - 48x^3 + 3)$ miles. Find the length of each side.

△ **79.** If the area of the rectangle is $(15x^2 - 29x - 14)$ square inches, and its length is $(5x + 2)$ inches, find its width.

$(5x + 2)$ in.

80. If the area of a parallelogram is $(2x^2 - 17x + 35)$ square centimeters and its base is $(2x - 7)$ centimeters, find its height.

$(2x - 7)$ cm

81. If the area of a parallelogram is $(x^4 - 23x^2 + 9x - 5)$ square centimeters and its base is $(x + 5)$ centimeters, find its height.

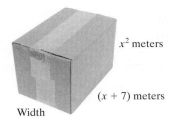

Height

$(x + 5)$ centimeters

82. If the volume of a box is $(x^4 + 6x^3 - 7x^2)$ cubic meters, its height is x^2 meters, and its length is $(x + 7)$ meters, find its width.

x^2 meters

$(x + 7)$ meters

Width

Divide.

83. $\left(x^4 + \dfrac{2}{3}x^3 + x\right) \div (x - 1)$

84. $\left(2x^3 + \dfrac{9}{2}x^2 - 4x - 10\right) \div (x + 2)$

85. $\left(3x^4 - x - x^3 + \dfrac{1}{2}\right) \div (2x - 1)$

86. $\left(2x^4 + \dfrac{1}{2}x^3 - \dfrac{1}{4}x^2 + x\right) \div (2x + 1)$

87. $(5x^4 - 2x^2 + 10x^3 - 4x) \div (5x + 10)$

88. $(9x^5 + 6x^4 - 6x^2 - 4x) \div (3x + 2)$

For each given f(x) and g(x), find $\dfrac{f(x)}{g(x)}$. Also find any x-values that are not in the domain of $\dfrac{f(x)}{g(x)}$. (Note: Since g(x) is in the denominator, g(x) cannot be 0).

89. $f(x) = 25x^2 - 5x + 30; g(x) = 5x$

90. $f(x) = 12x^4 - 9x^3 + 3x - 1; g(x) = 3x$

91. $f(x) = 7x^4 - 3x^2 + 2; g(x) = x - 2$

92. $f(x) = 2x^3 - 4x^2 + 1; g(x) = x + 3$

93. Try performing the following division without changing the order of the terms. Describe why this makes the process more complicated. Then perform the division again after putting the terms in the dividend in descending order of exponents.

$$\frac{4x^2 - 12x - 12 + 3x^3}{x - 2}$$

94. Explain how to check polynomial long division.

95. Explain an advantage of using the remainder theorem instead of direct substitution.

96. Explain an advantage of using synthetic division instead of long division.

We say that 2 is a factor of 8 because 2 divides 8 evenly, or with a remainder of 0. In the same manner, the polynomial $x - 2$ is a factor of the polynomial $x^3 - 14x^2 + 24x$ because the remainder is 0 when $x^3 - 14x^2 + 24x$ is divided by $x - 2$. Use this information for Exercises 97 through 99.

97. Use synthetic division to show that $x + 3$ is a factor of $x^3 + 3x^2 + 4x + 12$.

98. Use synthetic division to show that $x - 2$ is a factor of $x^3 - 2x^2 - 3x + 6$.

99. From the remainder theorem, the polynomial $x - c$ is a factor of a polynomial function $P(x)$ if $P(c)$ is what value?

100. If a polynomial is divided by $x - 5$, the quotient is $2x^2 + 5x - 6$ and the remainder is 3. Find the original polynomial.

101. If a polynomial is divided by $x + 3$, the quotient is $x^2 - x + 10$ and the remainder is -2. Find the original polynomial.

102. eBay is the leading online auction house. eBay's annual net profit can be modeled by the polynomial function $P(x) = -7x^3 + 94x^2 - 76x + 59$, where $P(x)$ is net profit in millions of dollars and x is the year after 2000. eBay's annual revenue can be modeled by the function $R(x) = 939x - 194$, where $R(x)$ is revenue of millions of dollars and x is years since 2000. (*Source:* eBay, Inc.)

a. Given that

$$\text{Net profit margin} = \frac{\text{net profit}}{\text{revenue}},$$

write a function, $m(x)$, that models eBay's net profit margin.

b. Use part **a** to predict eBay's profit margin in 2010. Round to the nearest hundredth.

6.5 SOLVING EQUATIONS CONTAINING RATIONAL EXPRESSIONS

OBJECTIVE

1 Solve equations containing rational expressions.

▶ **Helpful Hint**

The method described here is for equations only. It may *not* be used for performing operations on expressions.

OBJECTIVE 1 ▶ Solving equations containing rational expressions. In this section, we solve equations containing rational expressions. Before beginning this section, make sure that you understand the difference between an *equation* and an *expression*. An **equation** contains an equal sign and an **expression** does not.

Equation	*Expression*
$\dfrac{x}{2} + \dfrac{x}{6} = \dfrac{2}{3}$	$\dfrac{x}{2} + \dfrac{x}{6}$

Solving Equations Containing Rational Expressions

To solve *equations* containing rational expressions, first clear the equation of fractions by multiplying both sides of the equation by the LCD of all rational expressions. Then solve as usual.

Concept Check ☑

True or false? Clearing fractions is valid when solving an equation and when simplifying rational expressions. Explain.

EXAMPLE 1 Solve: $\dfrac{4x}{5} + \dfrac{3}{2} = \dfrac{3x}{10}$.

Solution The LCD of $\dfrac{4x}{5}, \dfrac{3}{2}$, and $\dfrac{3x}{10}$ is 10. We multiply both sides of the equation by 10.

$$\frac{4x}{5} + \frac{3}{2} = \frac{3x}{10}$$

$$10\left(\frac{4x}{5} + \frac{3}{2}\right) = 10\left(\frac{3x}{10}\right) \quad \text{Multiply both sides by the LCD.}$$

$$10 \cdot \frac{4x}{5} + 10 \cdot \frac{3}{2} = 10 \cdot \frac{3x}{10} \quad \text{Use the distributive property.}$$

$$8x + 15 = 3x \quad \text{Simplify.}$$

$$15 = -5x \quad \text{Subtract } 8x \text{ from both sides.}$$

$$-3 = x \quad \text{Solve.}$$

Verify this solution by replacing x with -3 in the original equation.

Check:

$$\frac{4x}{5} + \frac{3}{2} = \frac{3x}{10}$$

$$\frac{4(-3)}{5} + \frac{3}{2} \stackrel{?}{=} \frac{3(-3)}{10}$$

$$\frac{-12}{5} + \frac{3}{2} \stackrel{?}{=} \frac{-9}{10}$$

$$-\frac{24}{10} + \frac{15}{10} \stackrel{?}{=} -\frac{9}{10}$$

$$-\frac{9}{10} = -\frac{9}{10} \quad \text{True}$$

The solution is -3 or the solution set is $\{-3\}$.

PRACTICE
1 Solve: $\dfrac{5x}{4} - \dfrac{3}{2} = \dfrac{7x}{8}$.

Answer to Concept Check:
false; answers may vary

The important difference of the equations in this section is that the denominator of a rational expression may contain a variable. Recall that a rational expression is undefined for values of the variable that make the denominator 0. If a proposed solution makes the denominator 0, then it must be rejected as a solution of the original equation. Such proposed solutions are called **extraneous solutions.**

EXAMPLE 2 Solve: $\dfrac{3}{x} - \dfrac{x + 21}{3x} = \dfrac{5}{3}$.

Solution The LCD of the denominators $x, 3x,$ and 3 is $3x$. We multiply both sides by $3x$.

$$\frac{3}{x} - \frac{x + 21}{3x} = \frac{5}{3}$$

$$3x\left(\frac{3}{x} - \frac{x + 21}{3x}\right) = 3x\left(\frac{5}{3}\right) \quad \text{Multiply both sides by the LCD.}$$

$$3x \cdot \frac{3}{x} - 3x \cdot \frac{x + 21}{3x} = 3x \cdot \frac{5}{3} \quad \text{Use the distributive property.}$$

$$9 - (x + 21) = 5x \quad \text{Simplify.}$$

$$9 - x - 21 = 5x$$

$$-12 = 6x$$

$$-2 = x \quad \text{Solve.}$$

The proposed solution is -2.

Check: Check the proposed solution in the original equation.

$$\frac{3}{x} - \frac{x + 21}{3x} = \frac{5}{3}$$

$$\frac{3}{-2} - \frac{-2 + 21}{3(-2)} \stackrel{?}{=} \frac{5}{3}$$

$$-\frac{9}{6} + \frac{19}{6} \stackrel{?}{=} \frac{5}{3}$$

$$\frac{10}{6} \stackrel{?}{=} \frac{5}{3} \quad \text{True}$$

The solution is -2 or the solution set is $\{-2\}$. □

PRACTICE
2 Solve: $\dfrac{6}{x} - \dfrac{x + 9}{5x} = \dfrac{2}{5}$.

The following steps may be used to solve equations containing rational expressions.

Solving an Equation Containing Rational Expressions

STEP 1. Multiply both sides of the equation by the LCD of all rational expressions in the equation.

STEP 2. Simplify both sides.

STEP 3. Determine whether the equation is linear, quadratic, or higher degree and solve accordingly.

STEP 4. Check the solution in the original equation.

EXAMPLE 3 Solve: $\dfrac{x+6}{x-2} = \dfrac{2(x+2)}{x-2}$.

Solution First we multiply both sides of the equation by the LCD, $x - 2$. (Remember, we can only do this if $x \neq 2$ so that we are not multiplying by 0.)

$$\frac{x+6}{x-2} = \frac{2(x+2)}{x-2}$$

$$(x-2) \cdot \frac{x+6}{x-2} = (x-2) \cdot \frac{2(x+2)}{x-2} \qquad \text{Multiply both sides by } x - 2.$$

$$x + 6 = 2(x+2) \qquad \text{Simplify.}$$

$$x + 6 = 2x + 4 \qquad \text{Use the distributive property.}$$

$$2 = x \qquad \text{Solve.}$$

From above, we assumed that $x \neq 2$, so this equation has no solution. This will also show as we attempt to check this proposed solution.

Check: The proposed solution is 2. Notice that 2 makes a denominator 0 in the original equation. This can also be seen in a check. Check the proposed solution 2 in the original equation.

$$\frac{x+6}{x-2} = \frac{2(x+2)}{x-2}$$

$$\frac{2+6}{2-2} = \frac{2(2+2)}{2-2}$$

$$\frac{8}{0} = \frac{2(4)}{0}$$

The denominators are 0, so 2 is not a solution of the original equation. The solution is $\{\ \}$ or $\varnothing$.

PRACTICE
3 Solve: $\dfrac{x-5}{x+3} = \dfrac{2(x-1)}{x+3}$.

EXAMPLE 4 Solve: $\dfrac{2x}{2x-1} + \dfrac{1}{x} = \dfrac{1}{2x-1}$.

Solution The LCD is $x(2x-1)$. Multiply both sides by $x(2x-1)$. By the distributive property, this is the same as multiplying each term by $x(2x-1)$.

$$x(2x-1) \cdot \frac{2x}{2x-1} + x(2x-1) \cdot \frac{1}{x} = x(2x-1) \cdot \frac{1}{2x-1}$$

$$x(2x) + (2x-1) = x \qquad \text{Simplify.}$$

$$2x^2 + 2x - 1 - x = 0$$

$$2x^2 + x - 1 = 0$$

$$(x+1)(2x-1) = 0$$

$$x + 1 = 0 \quad \text{or} \quad 2x - 1 = 0$$

$$x = -1 \qquad \qquad x = \frac{1}{2}$$

The number $\dfrac{1}{2}$ makes the denominator $2x - 1$ equal 0, so it is not a solution. The solution is -1.

PRACTICE
4 Solve: $\dfrac{5x}{5x-1} + \dfrac{1}{x} = \dfrac{1}{5x-1}$.

EXAMPLE 5 Solve: $\dfrac{2x}{x-3} + \dfrac{6-2x}{x^2-9} = \dfrac{x}{x+3}$.

Solution We factor the second denominator to find that the LCD is $(x+3)(x-3)$. We multiply both sides of the equation by $(x+3)(x-3)$. By the distributive property, this is the same as multiplying each term by $(x+3)(x-3)$.

$$\frac{2x}{x-3} + \frac{6-2x}{x^2-9} = \frac{x}{x+3}$$

$$(x+3)(x-3)\cdot\frac{2x}{x-3} + (x+3)(x-3)\cdot\frac{6-2x}{(x+3)(x-3)}$$

$$= (x+3)(x-3)\left(\frac{x}{x+3}\right)$$

$$2x(x+3) + (6-2x) = x(x-3) \quad \text{Simplify.}$$
$$2x^2 + 6x + 6 - 2x = x^2 - 3x \quad \text{Use the distributive property.}$$

Next we solve this quadratic equation by the factoring method. To do so, we first write the equation so that one side is 0.

$$x^2 + 7x + 6 = 0$$
$$(x+6)(x+1) = 0 \quad \text{Factor.}$$
$$x = -6 \text{ or } x = -1 \quad \text{Set each factor equal to 0.}$$

Neither -6 nor -1 makes any denominator 0 so they are both solutions. The solutions are -6 and -1. ☐

PRACTICE
5 Solve: $\dfrac{2}{x-2} - \dfrac{5+2x}{x^2-4} = \dfrac{x}{x+2}$.

EXAMPLE 6 Solve: $\dfrac{z}{2z^2+3z-2} - \dfrac{1}{2z} = \dfrac{3}{z^2+2z}$.

Solution Factor the denominators to find that the LCD is $2z(z+2)(2z-1)$. Multiply both sides by the LCD. Remember, by using the distributive property, this is the same as multiplying each term by $2z(z+2)(2z-1)$.

$$\frac{z}{2z^2+3z-2} - \frac{1}{2z} = \frac{3}{z^2+2z}$$

$$\frac{z}{(2z-1)(z+2)} - \frac{1}{2z} = \frac{3}{z(z+2)}$$

$$2z(z+2)(2z-1)\cdot\frac{z}{(2z-1)(z+2)} - 2z(z+2)(2z-1)\cdot\frac{1}{2z}$$

$$= 2z(z+2)(2z-1)\cdot\frac{3}{z(z+2)} \quad \begin{array}{l}\text{Apply the distributive}\\\text{property.}\end{array}$$

$$2z(z) - (z+2)(2z-1) = 3\cdot2(2z-1) \quad \text{Simplify.}$$
$$2z^2 - (2z^2+3z-2) = 12z - 6$$
$$2z^2 - 2z^2 - 3z + 2 = 12z - 6$$
$$-3z + 2 = 12z - 6$$
$$-15z = -8$$
$$z = \frac{8}{15} \quad \text{Solve.}$$

The proposed solution $\dfrac{8}{15}$ does not make any denominator 0; the solution is $\dfrac{8}{15}$. ☐

PRACTICE
6 Solve: $\dfrac{z}{2z^2-z-6} - \dfrac{1}{3z} = \dfrac{2}{z^2-2z}$.

A graph can be helpful in visualizing solutions of equations. For example, to visualize the solution of the equation $\dfrac{3}{x} - \dfrac{x+21}{3x} = \dfrac{5}{3}$ in Example 2, the graph of the related rational function $f(x) = \dfrac{3}{x} - \dfrac{x+21}{3x}$ is shown. A solution of the equation is an x-value that corresponds to a y-value of $\dfrac{5}{3}$.

Notice that an x-value of -2 corresponds to a y-value of $\dfrac{5}{3}$. The solution of the equation is indeed -2 as shown in Example 2.

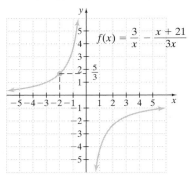

VOCABULARY & READINESS CHECK

Choose the least common denominator (LCD) for the rational expressions in each equation. Do not solve.

1. $\dfrac{x}{7} - \dfrac{x}{2} = \dfrac{1}{2}$; LCD = _____

   a. 7   **b.** 2   **c.** 14   **d.** 28

2. $\dfrac{9}{x+1} + \dfrac{5}{(x+1)^2} = \dfrac{x}{x+1}$; LCD = _____

   a. $x+1$ **b.** $(x+1)^2$ **c.** $(x+1)^3$

3. $\dfrac{7}{x-4} = \dfrac{x}{x^2-16} + \dfrac{1}{x+4}$; LCD = _____

   a. $(x+4)(x-4)$ **b.** $x-4$ **c.** $x+4$ **d.** $(x^2-16)(x-4)(x+4)$

4. $3 = \dfrac{1}{x-5} - \dfrac{2}{x^2-5x}$; LCD = _____

   a. $x-5$ **b.** $3(x-5)$ **c.** $3x(x-5)$ **d.** $x(x-5)$

6.5 EXERCISE SET

Solve each equation. See Examples 1 and 2.

1. $\dfrac{x}{2} - \dfrac{x}{3} = 12$

2. $x = \dfrac{x}{2} - 4$

3. $\dfrac{x}{3} = \dfrac{1}{6} + \dfrac{x}{4}$

4. $\dfrac{x}{2} = \dfrac{21}{10} - \dfrac{x}{5}$

5. $\dfrac{2}{x} + \dfrac{1}{2} = \dfrac{5}{x}$

6. $\dfrac{5}{3x} + 1 = \dfrac{7}{6}$

7. $\dfrac{x^2+1}{x} = \dfrac{5}{x}$

8. $\dfrac{x^2-14}{2x} = -\dfrac{5}{2x}$

Solve each equation. See Examples 3 through 6.

9. $\dfrac{x+5}{x+3} = \dfrac{2}{x+3}$

10. $\dfrac{x-7}{x-1} = \dfrac{11}{x-1}$

11. $\dfrac{5}{x-2} - \dfrac{2}{x+4} = -\dfrac{4}{x^2+2x-8}$

12. $\dfrac{1}{x-1} + \dfrac{1}{x+1} = \dfrac{2}{x^2-1}$

13. $\dfrac{1}{x-1} = \dfrac{2}{x+1}$

14. $\dfrac{6}{x+3} = \dfrac{4}{x-3}$

15. $\dfrac{x^2-23}{2x^2-5x-3} + \dfrac{2}{x-3} = \dfrac{-1}{2x+1}$

16. $\dfrac{4x^2-24x}{3x^2-x-2} + \dfrac{3}{3x+2} = \dfrac{-4}{x-1}$

17. $\dfrac{1}{x-4} - \dfrac{3x}{x^2-16} = \dfrac{2}{x+4}$

18. $\dfrac{3}{2x+3} - \dfrac{1}{2x-3} = \dfrac{4}{4x^2-9}$

19. $\dfrac{1}{x-4} = \dfrac{8}{x^2-16}$

20. $\dfrac{2}{x^2-4} = \dfrac{1}{2x-4}$

21. $\dfrac{1}{x-2} - \dfrac{2}{x^2-2x} = 1$

22. $\dfrac{12}{3x^2+12x} = 1 - \dfrac{1}{x+4}$

MIXED PRACTICE

Solve each equation. See Examples 1 through 6.

23. $\dfrac{5}{x} = \dfrac{20}{12}$

24. $\dfrac{2}{x} = \dfrac{10}{5}$

25. $1 - \dfrac{4}{a} = 5$

26. $7 + \dfrac{6}{a} = 5$

27. $\dfrac{x^2+5}{x} - 1 = \dfrac{5(x+1)}{x}$

28. $\dfrac{x^2+6}{x} + 5 = \dfrac{2(x+3)}{x}$

29. $\dfrac{1}{2x} - \dfrac{1}{x+1} = \dfrac{1}{3x^2+3x}$

30. $\dfrac{2}{x-5} + \dfrac{1}{2x} = \dfrac{5}{3x^2-15x}$

31. $\dfrac{1}{x} - \dfrac{x}{25} = 0$

32. $\dfrac{x}{4} + \dfrac{5}{x} = 3$

33. $5 - \dfrac{2}{2y-5} = \dfrac{3}{2y-5}$

34. $1 - \dfrac{5}{y+7} = \dfrac{4}{y+7}$

35. $\dfrac{x-1}{x+2} = \dfrac{2}{3}$

36. $\dfrac{6x+7}{2x+9} = \dfrac{5}{3}$

37. $\dfrac{x+3}{x+2} = \dfrac{1}{x+2}$

38. $\dfrac{2x+1}{4-x} = \dfrac{9}{4-x}$

39. $\dfrac{1}{a-3} + \dfrac{2}{a+3} = \dfrac{1}{a^2-9}$

40. $\dfrac{12}{9-a^2} + \dfrac{3}{3+a} = \dfrac{2}{3-a}$

41. $\dfrac{64}{x^2-16} + 1 = \dfrac{2x}{x-4}$

42. $2 + \dfrac{3}{x} = \dfrac{2x}{x+3}$

43. $\dfrac{-15}{4y+1} + 4 = y$

44. $\dfrac{36}{x^2-9} + 1 = \dfrac{2x}{x+3}$

45. $\dfrac{28}{x^2-9} + \dfrac{2x}{x-3} + \dfrac{6}{x+3} = 0$

46. $\dfrac{x^2-20}{x^2-7x+12} = \dfrac{3}{x-3} + \dfrac{5}{x-4}$

47. $\dfrac{x+2}{x^2+7x+10} = \dfrac{1}{3x+6} - \dfrac{1}{x+5}$

48. $\dfrac{3}{2x-5} + \dfrac{2}{2x+3} = 0$

REVIEW AND PREVIEW

Write each sentence as an equation and solve. See Section 2.2.

49. Four more than 3 times a number is 19.

50. The sum of two consecutive integers is 147.

51. The length of a rectangle is 5 inches more than the width. Its perimeter is 50 inches. Find the length and width.

52. The sum of a number and its reciprocal is $\dfrac{5}{2}$.

The following graph is from statistics gathered for the National Health and Nutrition Examination Survey. Use this histogram to answer Exercises 53 through 57. (Source: Economic Research Service: USDA). See Section 2.2.

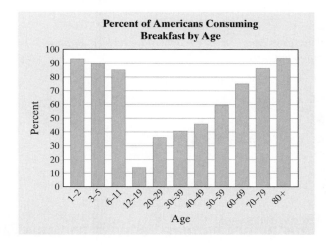

Percent of Americans Consuming Breakfast by Age

53. What percent of Americans ages 20–29 eat breakfast regularly?

54. What percent of Americans over age 80 eat breakfast regularly?

55. What age category shows the smallest percentage of Americans who eat breakfast regularly?

56. What percent of Americans ages 40–49 eat breakfast regularly?

57. According to the New York City Department of Education, there were about 284,000 high schools students at the end of 2006. Approximately how many of these students would you expect to eat breakfast regularly? Round to the nearest ten thousand.

CONCEPT EXTENSIONS

58. In your own words, explain the differences between equations and expressions.

59. In your own words, explain why it is necessary to check solutions to equations containing rational expressions.

60. The average cost of producing x game disks for a computer is given by the function $f(x) = 3.3 + \dfrac{5400}{x}$. Find the number of game disks that must be produced for the average cost to be $5.10.

61. The average cost of producing x electric pencil sharpeners is given by the function $f(x) = 20 + \dfrac{4000}{x}$. Find the number of electric pencil sharpeners that must be produced for the average cost to be \$25.

Solve each equation. Begin by writing each equation with positive exponents only.

62. $x^{-2} - 19x^{-1} + 48 = 0$

63. $x^{-2} - 5x^{-1} - 36 = 0$

64. $p^{-2} + 4p^{-1} - 5 = 0$

65. $6p^{-2} - 5p^{-1} + 1 = 0$

Solve each equation. Round solutions to two decimal places.

66. $\dfrac{1.4}{x - 2.6} = \dfrac{-3.5}{x + 7.1}$

67. $\dfrac{-8.5}{x + 1.9} = \dfrac{5.7}{x - 3.6}$

68. $\dfrac{10.6}{y} - 14.7 = \dfrac{9.92}{3.2} + 7.6$

69. $\dfrac{12.2}{x} + 17.3 = \dfrac{9.6}{x} - 14.7$

Solve each equation by substitution.

For example, to solve Exercise 70, first let $u = x - 1$. After substituting, we have $u^2 + 3u + 2 = 0$. Solve for u and then substitute back to solve for x.

70. $(x - 1)^2 + 3(x - 1) + 2 = 0$

71. $(4 - x)^2 - 5(4 - x) + 6 = 0$

72. $\left(\dfrac{3}{x - 1}\right)^2 + 2\left(\dfrac{3}{x - 1}\right) + 1 = 0$

73. $\left(\dfrac{5}{2 + x}\right)^2 + \left(\dfrac{5}{2 + x}\right) - 20 = 0$

Use a graphing calculator to verify the solution of each given exercise.

74. Exercise 23

75. Exercise 24

76. Exercise 35

77. Exercise 36

THE BIGGER PICTURE   SOLVING EQUATIONS AND INEQUALITIES

Continue the outline from Sections 2.4, 2.5, 2.7, and 5.8. Write how to recognize and how to solve equations with rational expressions in your own words. For example:

Solving Equations and Inequalities

I. Equations

   A. Linear equations (Sec. 2.1)

   B. Absolute value equations (Sec. 2.6)

   C. Quadratic equations (Sec. 5.8)

   D. Equations with rational expressions: Equation contains rational expressions.

$$\frac{7}{x - 1} + \frac{3}{x + 1} = \frac{x + 3}{x^2 - 1} \qquad \text{Equation with rational expressions.}$$

$$(x - 1)(x + 1) \cdot \frac{7}{x - 1} + (x - 1)(x + 1) \cdot \frac{3}{x + 1} = (x - 1)(x + 1) \cdot \frac{x + 3}{(x - 1)(x + 1)} \qquad \text{Multiply by the LCD.}$$

$$7(x + 1) + 3(x - 1) = x + 3 \qquad \text{Simplify.}$$

$$7x + 7 + 3x - 3 = x + 3$$

$$9x = -1$$

$$x = -\frac{1}{9} \qquad \text{Solve.}$$

II. Inequalities

    A. Linear inequalities (Sec. 2.4)

    B. Compound inequalities (Sec. 2.5)

    C. Absolute value inequalities (Sec. 2.7)

Solve. Write solutions to inequalities using interval notation.

1. $|-7x + 1| < 15$

2. $|-7x + 1| = 15$

3. $x^2 - 121 = 0$

4. $\dfrac{8}{x + 2} - \dfrac{3}{x - 1} = \dfrac{x + 6}{x^2 + x - 2}$

5. $9x + 6 = 4x - 2$

6. $3x \le 6 \text{ or } -x \ge 5$

7. $3x \le 6 \text{ and } -x \ge 5$

8. $-9 \le -3x + 21 < 0$

9. $\left|\dfrac{2x - 1}{5}\right| > 7$

10. $15x^3 - 16x^2 = 7x$

INTEGRATED REVIEW   EXPRESSIONS AND EQUATIONS CONTAINING RATIONAL EXPRESSIONS

Sections 6.1–6.5

It is very important that you understand the difference between an expression and an equation containing rational expressions. An equation contains an equal sign; an expression does not.

Expression to be Simplified

$$\frac{x}{2} + \frac{x}{6}$$

Write both rational expressions with the LCD, 6, as the denominator.

$$\frac{x}{2} + \frac{x}{6} = \frac{x \cdot 3}{2 \cdot 3} + \frac{x}{6}$$

$$= \frac{3x}{6} + \frac{x}{6}$$

$$= \frac{4x}{6} = \frac{2x}{3}$$

Equation to be Solved

$$\frac{x}{2} + \frac{x}{6} = \frac{2}{3}$$

Multiply both sides by the LCD, 6.

$$6\left(\frac{1}{2} + \frac{x}{6}\right) = 6\left(\frac{2}{3}\right)$$

$$3 + x = 4$$

$$x = 1$$

Check to see that the solution set is 1.

> ❯ **Helpful Hint**
>
> Remember: Equations can be cleared of fractions; expressions cannot.

Perform each indicated operation and simplify, or solve the equation for the variable.

1. $\dfrac{x}{2} = \dfrac{1}{8} + \dfrac{x}{4}$

2. $\dfrac{x}{4} = \dfrac{3}{2} + \dfrac{x}{10}$

3. $\dfrac{1}{8} + \dfrac{x}{4}$

4. $\dfrac{3}{2} + \dfrac{x}{10}$

5. $\dfrac{4}{x + 2} - \dfrac{2}{x - 1}$

6. $\dfrac{5}{x - 2} - \dfrac{10}{x + 4}$

7. $\dfrac{4}{x + 2} = \dfrac{2}{x - 1}$

8. $\dfrac{5}{x - 2} = \dfrac{10}{x + 4}$

9. $\dfrac{2}{x^2 - 4} = \dfrac{1}{x + 2} - \dfrac{3}{x - 2}$

10. $\dfrac{3}{x^2 - 25} = \dfrac{1}{x + 5} + \dfrac{2}{x - 5}$

11. $\dfrac{5}{x^2 - 3x} + \dfrac{4}{2x - 6}$

12. $\dfrac{5}{x^2 - 3x} \div \dfrac{4}{2x - 6}$

13. $\dfrac{x - 1}{x + 1} + \dfrac{x + 7}{x - 1} = \dfrac{4}{x^2 - 1}$

14. $\left(1 - \dfrac{y}{x}\right) \div \left(1 - \dfrac{x}{y}\right)$

15. $\dfrac{a^2 - 9}{a - 6} \cdot \dfrac{a^2 - 5a - 6}{a^2 - a - 6}$

16. $\dfrac{2}{a-6} + \dfrac{3a}{a^2-5a-6} - \dfrac{a}{5a+5}$

17. $\dfrac{2x+3}{3x-2} = \dfrac{4x+1}{6x+1}$

18. $\dfrac{5x-3}{2x} = \dfrac{10x+3}{4x+1}$

19. $\dfrac{a}{9a^2-1} + \dfrac{2}{6a-2}$

20. $\dfrac{3}{4a-8} - \dfrac{a+2}{a^2-2a}$

21. $-\dfrac{3}{x^2} - \dfrac{1}{x} + 2 = 0$

22. $\dfrac{x}{2x+6} + \dfrac{5}{x^2-9}$

23. $\dfrac{x-8}{x^2-x-2} + \dfrac{2}{x-2}$

24. $\dfrac{x-8}{x^2-x-2} + \dfrac{2}{x-2} = \dfrac{3}{x+1}$

25. $\dfrac{3}{a} - 5 = \dfrac{7}{a} - 1$

26. $\dfrac{7}{3z-9} + \dfrac{5}{z}$

Use $\dfrac{x}{5} - \dfrac{x}{4} = \dfrac{1}{10}$ *and* $\dfrac{x}{5} - \dfrac{x}{4} + \dfrac{1}{10}$ *for Exercises 27 and 28.*

27. a. Which one above is an expression?
  b. Describe the first step to simplify this expression.
  c. Simplify the expression.

28. a. Which one above is an equation?
  b. Describe the first step to solve this equation.
  c. Solve the equation.

For each exercise, choose the correct statement. [*] *Each figure represents a real number and no denominators are 0.*

29. a. $\dfrac{\triangle + \square}{\triangle} = \square$ **b.** $\dfrac{\triangle + \square}{\triangle} = 1 + \dfrac{\square}{\triangle}$ **c.** $\dfrac{\triangle + \square}{\triangle} = \dfrac{\square}{\triangle}$ **d.** $\dfrac{\triangle + \square}{\triangle} = 1 + \square$ **e.** $\dfrac{\triangle + \square}{\triangle - \square} = -1$

30. a. $\dfrac{\triangle}{\square} + \dfrac{\square}{\triangle} = \dfrac{\triangle + \square}{\square + \triangle} = 1$ **b.** $\dfrac{\triangle}{\square} + \dfrac{\square}{\triangle} = \dfrac{\triangle + \square}{\triangle\square}$ **c.** $\dfrac{\triangle}{\square} + \dfrac{\square}{\triangle} = \triangle\triangle + \square\square$

  d. $\dfrac{\triangle}{\square} + \dfrac{\square}{\triangle} = \dfrac{\triangle\triangle + \square\square}{\square\triangle}$ **e.** $\dfrac{\triangle}{\square} + \dfrac{\square}{\triangle} = \dfrac{\triangle\square}{\square\triangle} = 1$

31. a. $\dfrac{\triangle}{\square} \cdot \dfrac{\bigcirc}{\square} = \dfrac{\triangle\bigcirc}{\square}$ **b.** $\dfrac{\triangle}{\square} \cdot \dfrac{\bigcirc}{\square} = \triangle\bigcirc$ **c.** $\dfrac{\triangle}{\square} \cdot \dfrac{\bigcirc}{\square} = \dfrac{\triangle + \bigcirc}{\square + \square}$ **d.** $\dfrac{\triangle}{\square} \cdot \dfrac{\bigcirc}{\square} = \dfrac{\triangle\bigcirc}{\square\square}$

32. a. $\dfrac{\triangle}{\square} \div \dfrac{\bigcirc}{\triangle} = \dfrac{\triangle\triangle}{\square\bigcirc}$ **b.** $\dfrac{\triangle}{\square} \div \dfrac{\bigcirc}{\triangle} = \dfrac{\bigcirc\square}{\triangle\triangle}$ **c.** $\dfrac{\triangle}{\square} \div \dfrac{\bigcirc}{\triangle} = \dfrac{\bigcirc}{\square}$ **d.** $\dfrac{\triangle}{\square} \div \dfrac{\bigcirc}{\triangle} = \dfrac{\triangle + \triangle}{\square + \bigcirc}$

33. a. $\dfrac{\frac{\triangle + \square}{\bigcirc}}{\frac{\triangle}{\bigcirc}} = \square$ **b.** $\dfrac{\frac{\triangle + \square}{\bigcirc}}{\frac{\triangle}{\bigcirc}} = \dfrac{\triangle\triangle + \triangle\square}{\bigcirc\bigcirc}$ **c.** $\dfrac{\frac{\triangle + \square}{\bigcirc}}{\frac{\triangle}{\bigcirc}} = 1 + \square$ **d.** $\dfrac{\frac{\triangle + \square}{\bigcirc}}{\frac{\triangle}{\bigcirc}} = \dfrac{\triangle + \square}{\triangle}$

[*] My thanks to Kelly Champagne for permission to use her Exercises for 29 through 33.

6.6 RATIONAL EQUATIONS AND PROBLEM SOLVING

OBJECTIVES

1 Solve an equation containing rational expressions for a specified variable.

2 Solve problems by writing equations containing rational expressions.

OBJECTIVE 1 ▶ Solving equations with rational expressions for a specified variable. In Section 2.3 we solved equations for a specified variable. In this section, we continue practicing this skill by solving equations containing rational expressions for a specified variable. The steps given in Section 2.3 for solving equations for a specified variable are repeated here.

Solving Equations for a Specified Variable

STEP 1. Clear the equation of fractions or rational expressions by multiplying each side of the equation by the least common denominator (LCD) of all denominators in the equation.

STEP 2. Use the distributive property to remove grouping symbols such as parentheses.

STEP 3. Combine like terms on each side of the equation.

STEP 4. Use the addition property of equality to rewrite the equation as an equivalent equation with terms containing the specified variable on one side and all other terms on the other side.

STEP 5. Use the distributive property and the multiplication property of equality to get the specified variable alone.

EXAMPLE 1   Solve: $\dfrac{1}{x} + \dfrac{1}{y} = \dfrac{1}{z}$ for x.

Solution   To clear this equation of fractions, we multiply both sides of the equation by xyz, the LCD of $\dfrac{1}{x}, \dfrac{1}{y},$ and $\dfrac{1}{z}$.

$$\frac{1}{x} + \frac{1}{y} = \frac{1}{z}$$

$$xyz\left(\frac{1}{x} + \frac{1}{y}\right) = xyz\left(\frac{1}{z}\right) \quad \text{Multiply both sides by } xyz.$$

$$xyz\left(\frac{1}{x}\right) + xyz\left(\frac{1}{y}\right) = xyz\left(\frac{1}{z}\right) \quad \text{Use the distributive property.}$$

$$yz + xz = xy \quad \text{Simplify.}$$

Notice the two terms that contain the specified variable x.

Next, we subtract xz from both sides so that all terms containing the specified variable x are on one side of the equation and all other terms are on the other side.

$$yz = xy - xz$$

Now we use the distributive property to factor x from $xy - xz$ and then the multiplication property of equality to solve for x.

$$yz = x(y - z)$$

$$\frac{yz}{y - z} = x \quad \text{or} \quad x = \frac{yz}{y - z} \quad \text{Divide both sides by } y - z.$$

□

PRACTICE
1   Solve: $\dfrac{1}{a} - \dfrac{1}{b} = \dfrac{1}{c}$ for a.

OBJECTIVE 2 ▶ **Solving problems modeled by equations with rational expressions.**
Problem solving sometimes involves modeling a described situation with an equation
containing rational expressions. In Examples 2 through 5, we practice solving such
problems and use the problem-solving steps first introduced in Section 2.2.

> **EXAMPLE 2** **Finding an Unknown Number**
>
> If a certain number is subtracted from the numerator and added to the denominator of
> $\frac{9}{19}$, the new fraction is equivalent to $\frac{1}{3}$. Find the number.

Solution

1. **UNDERSTAND** the problem. Read and reread the problem and try guessing the
   solution. For example, if the unknown number is 3, we have

$$\frac{9 - 3}{19 + 3} = \frac{1}{3}$$

To see if this is a true statement, we simplify the fraction on the left side.

$$\frac{6}{22} = \frac{1}{3} \quad \text{or} \quad \frac{3}{11} = \frac{1}{3} \quad \text{False}$$

Since this is not a true statement, 3 is not the correct number. Remember that the
purpose of this step is not to guess the correct solution but to gain an understanding
of the problem posed.

   We will let n = the number to be subtracted from the numerator and added to
the denominator.

2. **TRANSLATE** the problem.

In words:	when the number is subtracted from the numerator and added to the denominator of the fraction $\frac{9}{19}$	this is equivalent to	$\frac{1}{3}$
	↓	↓	↓
Translate:	$\frac{9 - n}{19 + n}$	=	$\frac{1}{3}$

3. **SOLVE** the equation for n.

$$\frac{9 - n}{19 + n} = \frac{1}{3}$$

To solve for n, we begin by multiplying both sides by the LCD of $3(19 + n)$.

$$3(19 + n) \cdot \frac{9 - n}{19 + n} = 3(19 + n) \cdot \frac{1}{3} \quad \text{Multiply both sides by the LCD.}$$
$$3(9 - n) = 19 + n \quad \text{Simplify.}$$
$$27 - 3n = 19 + n$$
$$8 = 4n$$
$$2 = n \quad \text{Solve.}$$

4. **INTERPRET** the results.

Check: If we subtract 2 from the numerator and add 2 to the denominator of $\frac{9}{19}$, we
have $\frac{9 - 2}{19 + 2} = \frac{7}{21} = \frac{1}{3}$, and the problem checks.

State: The unknown number is 2. □

PRACTICE

2 Find a number that when added to the numerator and subtracted from the
denominator of $\frac{3}{11}$ results in a fraction equivalent to $\frac{5}{2}$.

A **ratio** is the quotient of two number or two quantities. Since rational expressions are quotients of quantities, rational expressions are ratios, also. A **proportion** is a mathematical statement that two ratios are equal.

EXAMPLE 3   Calculating Homes Heat by Electricity

In the United States, 8 out of every 25 homes are heated by electricity. At this rate, how many homes in a community of 36,000 homes would you predict are heated by electricity? (*Source: 2005 American Housing Survey for the United States*)

Solution

1. **UNDERSTAND. Read and reread the problem.** Try to estimate a reasonable solution. For example, since 8 is less than $\frac{1}{3}$ of 25, we might reason that the solution would be less than $\frac{1}{3}$ of 36,000 or 12,000.

   Let's let x = number of homes in the community heated by electricity.

2. **TRANSLATE.**

   homes heated by electricity $\rightarrow$ $\dfrac{8}{25} = \dfrac{x}{36,000}$ $\leftarrow$ homes heated by electricity

   total homes $\rightarrow$ $\qquad\qquad\quad$ $\leftarrow$ total homes

3. **SOLVE.** To solve this proportion we can multiply both sides by the LCD, 36,000, or we can set cross products equal. We will set cross products equal.

$$\frac{8}{25} = \frac{x}{36,000}$$

$$25x = 8 \cdot 36,000$$

$$x = \frac{288,000}{25}$$

$$x = 11,520$$

4. **INTERPRET.**

Check: To check, replace x with 11,520 in the proportion and see that a true statement results. Notice that our answer is reasonable since it is less than 12,000 as we stated above.

State: We predict that 11,520 homes are heated by electricity.   □

PRACTICE

3   In the United States, 1 out of 12 homes is heated by fuel oil. At this rate, how many homes in a community of 36,000 homes are heated by fuel oil? (*Source: 2005 American Housing Survey for the United States*)

The following work example leads to an equation containing rational expressions.

EXAMPLE 4   Calculating Work Hours

Melissa Scarlatti can clean the house in 4 hours, whereas her husband, Zack, can do the same job in 5 hours. They have agreed to clean together so that they can finish in time to watch a movie on TV that starts in 2 hours. How long will it take them to clean the house together? Can they finish before the movie starts?

Solution

1. **UNDERSTAND. Read and reread the problem.** The key idea here is the relationship between the *time* (in hours) it takes to complete the job and the *part of the job* completed in 1 unit of time (1 hour). For example, if the *time* it takes Melissa to complete the job is 4 hours, the part of the job she can complete in 1 hour is $\frac{1}{4}$.

   Similarly, Zack can complete $\frac{1}{5}$ of the job in 1 hour.

We will let $t = $ *the time* in hours it takes Melissa and Zack to clean the house together. Then $\frac{1}{t}$ represents the *part of the job* they complete in 1 hour. We summarize the given information in a chart.

	Hours to Complete the Job	Part of Job Completed in 1 Hour
MELISSA ALONE	4	$\frac{1}{4}$
ZACK ALONE	5	$\frac{1}{5}$
TOGETHER	t	$\frac{1}{t}$

2. TRANSLATE.

	part of job Melissa can complete in 1 hour	added to	part of job Zack can complete in 1 hour	is equal to	part of job they can complete together in 1 hour
In words:	↓	↓	↓	↓	↓
Translate:	$\frac{1}{4}$	$+$	$\frac{1}{5}$	$=$	$\frac{1}{t}$

3. SOLVE.

$$\frac{1}{4} + \frac{1}{5} = \frac{1}{t}$$

$$20t\left(\frac{1}{4} + \frac{1}{5}\right) = 20t\left(\frac{1}{t}\right) \qquad \text{Multiply both sides by the LCD, } 20t.$$

$$5t + 4t = 20$$

$$9t = 20$$

$$t = \frac{20}{9} \quad \text{or} \quad 2\frac{2}{9} \qquad \text{Solve.}$$

4. INTERPRET.

Check: The proposed solution is $2\frac{2}{9}$. That is, Melissa and Zack would take $2\frac{2}{9}$ hours to clean the house together. This proposed solution is reasonable since $2\frac{2}{9}$ hours is more than half of Melissa's time and less than half of Zack's time. Check this solution in the originally stated problem.

State: Melissa and Zack can clean the house together in $2\frac{2}{9}$ hours. They cannot complete the job before the movie starts. □

PRACTICE

4 Elissa Juarez can clean the animal cages at the animal shelter where she volunteers in 3 hours. Bill Stiles can do the same job in 2 hours. How long would it take them to clean the cages if they work together?

EXAMPLE 5 **Finding the Speed of a Current**

Steve Deitmer takes $1\frac{1}{2}$ times as long to go 72 miles upstream in his boat as he does to return. If the boat cruises at 30 mph in still water, what is the speed of the current?

Solution

1. UNDERSTAND. Read and reread the problem. Guess a solution. Suppose that the current is 4 mph. The speed of the boat upstream is slowed down by the current: $30 - 4$, or 26 mph, and the speed of the boat downstream is speeded up by the current: 30 + 4, or 34 mph. Next let's find out how long it takes to travel 72 miles upstream and 72 miles downstream. To do so, we use the formula $d = rt$, or $\dfrac{d}{r} = t$.

Upstream   **Downstream**

$$\frac{d}{r} = t \qquad\qquad\qquad \frac{d}{r} = t$$

$$\frac{72}{26} = t \qquad\qquad\qquad \frac{72}{34} = t$$

$$2\frac{10}{13} = t \qquad\qquad\qquad 2\frac{2}{17} = t$$

Since the time upstream $\left(2\dfrac{10}{13} \text{ hours}\right)$ is not $1\dfrac{1}{2}$ times the time downstream $\left(2\dfrac{2}{17} \text{ hours}\right)$, our guess is not correct. We do, however, have a better understanding of the problem.

We will let

$$x = \text{the speed of the current}$$
$$30 + x = \text{the speed of the boat downstream}$$
$$30 - x = \text{the speed of the boat upstream}$$

This information is summarized in the following chart, where we use the formula $\dfrac{d}{r} = t$.

	Distance	*Rate*	*Time* $\left(\dfrac{d}{r}\right)$
UPSTREAM	72	$30 - x$	$\dfrac{72}{30 - x}$
DOWNSTREAM	72	$30 + x$	$\dfrac{72}{30 + x}$

2. **TRANSLATE.** Since the time spent traveling upstream is $1\dfrac{1}{2}$ times the time spent traveling downstream, we have

In words:
time upstream   is $1\dfrac{1}{2}$ times   times downstream

Translate:
$$\frac{72}{30 - x} \qquad = \qquad \frac{3}{2} \qquad \cdot \qquad \frac{72}{30 + x}$$

3. **SOLVE.** $\dfrac{72}{30 - x} = \dfrac{3}{2} \cdot \dfrac{72}{30 + x}$

First we multiply both sides by the LCD, $2(30 + x)(30 - x)$.

$$2(30 + x)(30 - x) \cdot \frac{72}{30 - x} = 2(30 + x)(30 - x)\left(\frac{3}{2} \cdot \frac{72}{30 + x}\right)$$

$$72 \cdot 2(30 + x) = 3 \cdot 72 \cdot (30 - x) \quad \text{Simplify.}$$

$$2(30 + x) = 3(30 - x) \qquad\quad \text{Divide both sides by 72.}$$

$$60 + 2x = 90 - 3x \qquad\qquad \text{Use the distributive property.}$$

$$5x = 30$$

$$x = 6 \qquad\qquad\qquad\qquad \text{Solve.}$$

4. **INTERPRET.**

Check: Check the proposed solution of 6 mph in the originally stated problem.

State: The current's speed is 6 mph.

PRACTICE

5 An airplane flying from Los Angeles to Boston at a speed of 450 mph had a tailwind assisting its flight. At the same time, there was another flight doing the same speed, going from Boston to Los Angeles. This second flight encountered a headwind. It took the pilot heading west $1\frac{1}{4}$ times as long to travel from Boston to Los Angeles as it took the pilot flying east from Los Angeles to Boston. What was the speed of the wind?

6.6 | EXERCISE SET

MyMathLab Powered by CourseCompass™ and MathXL®

 PRACTICE WATCH DOWNLOAD READ REVIEW

Solve each equation for the specified variable. See Example 1.

1. $F = \frac{9}{5}C + 32$ for C (Meteorology)

△ **2.** $V = \frac{1}{3}\pi r^2 h$ for h (Volume)

3. $Q = \frac{A - I}{L}$ for I (Finance)

4. $P = 1 - \frac{C}{S}$ for S (Finance)

5. $\frac{1}{R} = \frac{1}{R_1} + \frac{1}{R_2}$ for R (Electronics)

6. $\frac{1}{R} = \frac{1}{R_1} + \frac{1}{R_2}$ for R_1 (Electronics)

7. $S = \frac{n(a + L)}{2}$ for n (Sequences)

8. $S = \frac{n(a + L)}{2}$ for a (Sequences)

△ **9.** $A = \frac{h(a + b)}{2}$ for b (Geometry)

△ **10.** $A = \frac{h(a + b)}{2}$ for h (Geometry)

11. $\frac{P_1 V_1}{T_1} = \frac{P_2 V_2}{T_2}$ for T_2 (Chemistry)

12. $H = \frac{kA(T_1 - T_2)}{L}$ for T_2 (Physics)

13. $f = \frac{f_1 f_2}{f_1 + f_2}$ for f_2 (Optics)

14. $I = \frac{E}{R + r}$ for r (Electronics)

15. $\lambda = \frac{2L}{n}$ for L (Physics)

16. $S = \frac{a_1 - a_n r}{1 - r}$ for a_1 (Sequences)

17. $\frac{\theta}{\omega} = \frac{2L}{c}$ for c

18. $F = \frac{-GMm}{r^2}$ for M (Physics)

Solve. See Example 2.

19. The sum of a number and 5 times its reciprocal is 6. Find the number(s).

20. The quotient of a number and 9 times its reciprocal is 1. Find the number(s).

21. If a number is added to the numerator of $\frac{12}{41}$ and twice the number is added to the denominator of $\frac{12}{41}$, the resulting fraction is equivalent to $\frac{1}{3}$. Find the number.

22. If a number is subtracted from the numerator of $\frac{13}{8}$ and added to the denominator of $\frac{13}{8}$, the resulting fraction is equivalent to $\frac{2}{5}$. Find the number.

Solve. See Example 3.

23. An Arabian camel can drink 15 gallons of water in 10 minutes. At this rate, how much water can the camel drink in 3 minutes? (*Source:* Grolier, Inc.)

24. An Arabian camel can travel 20 miles in 8 hours, carrying a 300-pound load on its back. At this rate, how far can the camel travel in 10 hours? (*Source:* Grolier, Inc.)

25. In 2005, 5.5 out of every 50 Coast Guard personnel were women. If there are 40,639 total Coast Guard personnel on active duty, estimate the number of women. Round to the nearest whole. (*Source: The World Almanac,* 2007)

26. In 2005, 42.8 out of every 50 Navy personnel were men. If there are 353,496 total Navy personnel on active duty, estimate the number of men. Round to the nearest whole. (*Source: The World Almanac,* 2007)

Solve. See Example 4.

27. An experienced roofer can roof a house in 26 hours. A beginning roofer needs 39 hours to complete the same job. Find how long it takes for the two to do the job together.

28. Alan Cantrell can word process a research paper in 6 hours. With Steve Isaac's help, the paper can be processed in 4 hours. Find how long it takes Steve to word process the paper alone.

29. Three postal workers can sort a stack of mail in 20 minutes, 30 minutes, and 60 minutes, respectively. Find how long it takes them to sort the mail if all three work together.

30. A new printing press can print newspapers twice as fast as the old one can. The old one can print the afternoon edition in 4 hours. Find how long it takes to print the afternoon edition if both printers are operating.

Solve. See Example 5.

31. Mattie Evans drove 150 miles in the same amount of time that it took a turbopropeller plane to travel 600 miles. The speed of the plane was 150 mph faster than the speed of the car. Find the speed of the plane.

32. An F-100 plane and a Toyota truck leave the same town at sunrise and head for a town 450 miles away. The speed of the plane is three times the speed of the truck, and the plane arrives 6 hours ahead of the truck. Find the speed of the truck.

33. The speed of Lazy River's current is 5 mph. If a boat travels 20 miles downstream in the same time that it takes to travel 10 miles upstream, find the speed of the boat in still water.

34. The speed of a boat in still water is 24 mph. If the boat travels 54 miles upstream in the same time that it takes to travel 90 miles downstream, find the speed of the current.

MIXED PRACTICE

Solve.

35. The sum of the reciprocals of two consecutive integers is $-\dfrac{15}{56}$. Find the two integers.

36. The sum of the reciprocals of two consecutive odd integers is $\dfrac{20}{99}$. Find the two integers.

37. One hose can fill a goldfish pond in 45 minutes, and two hoses can fill the same pond in 20 minutes. Find how long it takes the second hose alone to fill the pond.

38. If Sarah Clark can do a job in 5 hours and Dick Belli and Sarah working together can do the same job in 2 hours, find how long it takes Dick to do the job alone.

39. Two trains going in opposite directions leave at the same time. One train travels 15 mph faster than the other. In 6 hours the trains are 630 miles apart. Find the speed of each.

40. The speed of a bicyclist is 10 mph faster than the speed of a walker. If the bicyclist travels 26 miles in the same amount of time that the walker travels 6 miles, find the speed of the bicyclist.

41. A giant tortoise can travel 0.17 miles in 1 hour. At this rate, how long would it take the tortoise to travel 1 mile? Round to the nearest tenth of an hour. (*Source: The World Almanac*)

42. A black mamba snake can travel 88 feet in 3 seconds. At this rate, how long does it take to travel 300 feet (the length of a football field)? Round to the nearest tenth of a second. (*Source: The World Almanac*)

43. A local dairy has three machines to fill half-gallon milk cartons. The machines can fill the daily quota in 5 hours, 6 hours, and 7.5 hours, respectively. Find how long it takes to fill the daily quota if all three machines are running.

44. The inlet pipe of an oil tank can fill the tank in 1 hour, 30 minutes. The outlet pipe can empty the tank in 1 hour. Find how long it takes to empty a full tank if both pipes are open.

45. A plane flies 465 miles with the wind and 345 miles against the wind in the same length of time. If the speed of the wind is 20 mph, find the speed of the plane in still air.

46. Two rockets are launched. The first travels at 9000 mph. Fifteen minutes later the second is launched at 10,000 mph. Find the distance at which both rockets are an equal distance from Earth.

47. Two joggers, one averaging 8 mph and one averaging 6 mph, start from a designated initial point. The slower jogger arrives at the end of the run a half-hour after the other jogger. Find the distance of the run.

48. A semi truck travels 300 miles through the flatland in the same amount of time that it travels 180 miles through the Great Smoky Mountains. The rate of the truck is 20 miles per hour slower in the mountains than in the flatland. Find both the flatland rate and mountain rate.

49. The denominator of a fraction is 1 more than the numerator. If both the numerator and the denominator are decreased by 3, the resulting fraction is equivalent to $\dfrac{4}{5}$. Find the fraction.

50. The numerator of a fraction is 4 less than the denominator. If both the numerator and the denominator are increased by 2, the resulting fraction is equivalent to $\dfrac{2}{3}$. Find the fraction.

51. In 2 minutes, a conveyor belt can move 300 pounds of recyclable aluminum from the delivery truck to a storage area. A smaller belt can move the same quantity of cans the same distance in 6 minutes. If both belts are used, find how long it takes to move the cans to the storage area.

52. Gary Marcus and Tony Alva work at Lombardo's Pipe and Concrete. Mr. Lombardo is preparing an estimate for a customer. He knows that Gary can lay a slab of concrete in 6 hours. Tony can lay the same size slab in 4 hours. If both work on the job and the cost of labor is $45.00 per hour, determine what the labor estimate should be.

53. Smith Engineering is in the process of reviewing the salaries of their surveyors. During this review, the company found that an experienced surveyor can survey a roadbed in 4 hours. An apprentice surveyor needs 5 hours to survey the same stretch of road. If the two work together, find how long it takes them to complete the job.

54. Mr. Dodson can paint his house by himself in four days. His son will need an additional day to complete the job if he works by himself. If they work together, find how long it takes to paint the house.

55. Cyclist Lance Armstrong of the United States won the Tours de France a record seven times. This inspired an amateur cyclist to train for a local road race. He rode the first 20-mile portion of his workout at a constant rate. For the 16-mile cool-down portion of his workout, he reduced his speed by 2 miles per hour. Each portion of the workout took equal time. Find the cyclist's rate during the first portion and his rate during the cool-down portion.

56. The world record for the largest white bass caught is held by Ronald Sprouse of Virginia. The bass weighed 6 pounds 13 ounces. If Ronald rows to his favorite fishing spot 9 miles downstream in the same amount of time that he rows 3 miles upstream and if the current is 6 mph, find how long it takes him to cover the 12 miles.

57. An experienced bricklayer can construct a small wall in 3 hours. An apprentice can complete the job in 6 hours. Find how long it takes if they work together.

58. Scanner A can scan a document in 3 hours. Scanner B takes 5 hours to do the same job. If both scanners are used, how long will it take for the document to be scanned?

59. A marketing manager travels 1080 miles in a corporate jet and then an additional 240 miles by car. If the car ride takes 1 hour longer, and if the rate of the jet is 6 times the rate of the car, find the time the manager travels by jet and find the time she travels by car.

60. In a recent year, 13 out of 20 top grossing movies were rated PG-13. At this rate, how many movies in a year with 599 new releases would you predict to be rated PG-13? Round to the nearest whole movie. (*Source:* Motion Picture Association)

61. In a recent year, 5 out of 7 movies cost between $50 and $99 million to make. At this rate, how many movies in a year with 599 new releases would you predict to cost between $50 and $99 million to make? Round to the nearest whole movie. (*Source:* Motion Picture Association)

REVIEW AND PREVIEW

Solve each equation for x. See Section 2.1.

62. $\dfrac{x}{5} = \dfrac{x+2}{3}$

63. $\dfrac{x}{4} = \dfrac{x+3}{6}$

64. $\dfrac{x-3}{2} = \dfrac{x-5}{6}$

65. $\dfrac{x-6}{4} = \dfrac{x-2}{5}$

CONCEPT EXTENSIONS

Calculating body-mass index (BMI) is a way to gauge whether a person should lose weight. Doctors recommend that body-mass index values fall between 19 and 25. The formula for body-mass index B is $B = \dfrac{705w}{h^2}$, where w is weight in pounds and h is height in inches. Use this formula to answer Exercises 66 and 67.

66. A patient is 5 ft 8 in. tall. What should his or her weight be to have a body-mass index of 25? Round to the nearest whole pound.

67. A doctor recorded a body-mass index of 47 on a patient's chart. Later, a nurse notices that the doctor recorded the patient's weight as 240 pounds but neglected to record the patient's height. Explain how the nurse can use the information from the chart to find the patient's height. Then find the height.

In physics, when the source of a sound is traveling toward an observer, the relationship between the actual pitch a of the sound and the pitch h that the observer hears due to the Doppler effect is described by the formula $h = \dfrac{a}{1 - \dfrac{s}{770}}$, where s is the speed of the sound source in miles per hour. Use this formula to answer Exercise 68.

68. An emergency vehicle has a single-tone siren with the pitch of the musical note E. As it approaches an observer standing by the road, the vehicle is traveling 50 mph. Is the pitch that the observer hears due to the Doppler effect lower or higher than the actual pitch? To which musical note is the pitch that the observer hears closest?

Pitch of an Octave of Musical Notes in Hertz (Hz)	
Note	*Pitch*
Middle C	261.63
D	293.66
E	329.63
F	349.23
G	392.00
A	440.00
B	493.88

Note: Greater numbers indicate higher pitches (acoustically).
(*Source:* American Standards Association)

In electronics, the relationship among the resistances R_1 and R_2 of two resistors wired in a parallel circuit and their combined resistance R is described by the formula $\dfrac{1}{R} = \dfrac{1}{R_1} + \dfrac{1}{R_2}$. Use this formula to solve Exercises 69 through 71.

69. If the combined resistance is 2 ohms and one of the two resistances is 3 ohms, find the other resistance.

70. Find the combined resistance of two resistors of 12 ohms each when they are wired in a parallel circuit.

71. The relationship among resistance of two resistors wired in a parallel circuit and their combined resistance may be extended to three resistors of resistances R_1, R_2, and R_3. Write an equation you believe may describe the relationship, and use it to find the combined resistance if R_1 is 5, R_2 is 6, and R_3 is 2.

▶ **Helpful Hint**

Are you preparing for your test? Don't forget to take the Chapter 6 Test on page 375. Then check your answers at the back of the text and use the Chapter Test Prep Video CD to see the fully worked-out solutions to any of the exercises you want to review.

CHAPTER 6 HIGHLIGHTS

DEFINITIONS AND CONCEPTS	EXAMPLES

SECTION 6.1 RATIONAL FUNCTIONS AND MULTIPLYING AND DIVIDING RATIONAL EXPRESSIONS

A rational expression is the quotient $\dfrac{P}{Q}$ of two polynomials P and Q, as long as Q is not 0.

$$\frac{2x - 6}{7}, \quad \frac{t^2 - 3t + 5}{t - 1}$$

To Simplify a Rational Expression

Step 1. Completely factor the numerator and the denominator.

Step 2. Apply the fundamental principle of rational expressions.

Simplify.

$$\frac{2x^2 + 9x - 5}{x^2 - 25} = \frac{(2x - 1)(x + 5)}{(x - 5)(x + 5)}$$
$$= \frac{2x - 1}{x - 5}$$

To Multiply Rational Expressions

Step 1. Completely factor numerators and denominators.

Step 2. Multiply the numerators and multiply the denominators.

Step 3. Apply the fundamental principle of rational expressions.

Multiply $\dfrac{x^3 + 8}{12x - 18} \cdot \dfrac{14x^2 - 21x}{x^2 + 2x}$.

$$= \frac{(x + 2)(x^2 - 2x + 4)}{6(2x - 3)} \cdot \frac{7x(2x - 3)}{x(x + 2)}$$
$$= \frac{7(x^2 - 2x + 4)}{6}$$

To Divide Rational Expressions

Multiply the first rational expression by the reciprocal of the second rational expression.

Divide $\dfrac{x^2 + 6x + 9}{5xy - 5y} \div \dfrac{x + 3}{10y}$.

$$= \frac{(x + 3)(x + 3)}{5y(x - 1)} \cdot \frac{2 \cdot 5y}{x + 3}$$
$$= \frac{2(x + 3)}{x - 1}$$

A rational function is a function described by a rational expression.

$$f(x) = \frac{2x - 6}{7}, \quad h(t) = \frac{t^2 - 3t + 5}{t - 1}$$

SECTION 6.2 ADDING AND SUBTRACTING RATIONAL EXPRESSIONS

To Add or Subtract Rational Expressions

Step 1. Find the LCD.

Step 2. Write each rational expression as an equivalent rational expression whose denominator is the LCD.

Step 3. Add or subtract numerators and write the result over the common denominator.

Step 4. Simplify the resulting rational expression.

Subtract $\dfrac{3}{x + 2} - \dfrac{x + 1}{x - 3}$.

$$= \frac{3 \cdot (x - 3)}{(x + 2) \cdot (x - 3)} - \frac{(x + 1) \cdot (x + 2)}{(x - 3) \cdot (x + 2)}$$
$$= \frac{3(x - 3) - (x + 1)(x + 2)}{(x + 2)(x - 3)}$$
$$= \frac{3x - 9 - (x^2 + 3x + 2)}{(x + 2)(x - 3)}$$
$$= \frac{3x - 9 - x^2 - 3x - 2}{(x + 2)(x - 3)}$$
$$= \frac{-x^2 - 11}{(x + 2)(x - 3)}$$

DEFINITIONS AND CONCEPTS	EXAMPLES

Method 1: Simplify the numerator and the denominator so that each is a single fraction. Then perform the indicated division and simplify if possible.

Simplify $\dfrac{\dfrac{x+2}{x}}{x-\dfrac{4}{x}}$.

Method 1: $\dfrac{\dfrac{x+2}{x}}{\dfrac{x\cdot x}{1\cdot x}-\dfrac{4}{x}}=\dfrac{\dfrac{x+2}{x}}{\dfrac{x^2-4}{x}}$

$=\dfrac{x+2}{x}\cdot\dfrac{x}{(x+2)(x-2)}=\dfrac{1}{x-2}$

Method 2: Multiply the numerator and the denominator of the complex fraction by the LCD of the fractions in both the numerator and the denominator. Then simplify if possible.

Method 2: $\dfrac{\left(\dfrac{x+2}{x}\right)\cdot x}{\left(x-\dfrac{4}{x}\right)\cdot x}=\dfrac{x+2}{x\cdot x-\dfrac{4}{x}\cdot x}$

$=\dfrac{x+2}{x^2-4}=\dfrac{x+2}{(x+2)(x-2)}=\dfrac{1}{x-2}$

To divide a polynomial by a monomial: Divide each term in the polynomial by the monomial.

Divide $\dfrac{12a^5b^3-6a^2b^2+ab}{6a^2b^2}$

$=\dfrac{12a^5b^3}{6a^2b^2}-\dfrac{6a^2b^2}{6a^2b^2}+\dfrac{ab}{6a^2b^2}$

$=2a^3b-1+\dfrac{1}{6ab}$

To divide a polynomial by a polynomial, other than a monomial:

Use long division.

Divide $2x^3-x^2-8x-1$ by $x-2$.

$$
\begin{array}{r}
2x^2+3x-2 \\
x-2{\overline{\smash{\big)}\,2x^3-\ x^2-8x-1}} \\
\underline{2x^3-4x^2} \\
3x^2-8x \\
\underline{3x^2-6x} \\
-2x-1 \\
\underline{-2x+4} \\
-5
\end{array}
$$

The quotient is $2x^2+3x-2-\dfrac{5}{x-2}$.

A shortcut method called **synthetic division** may be used to divide a polynomial by a binomial of the form $x-c$.

Use synthetic division to divide $2x^3-x^2-8x-1$ by $x-2$.

$$
\begin{array}{r|rrrr}
2 & 2 & -1 & -8 & -1 \\
& \downarrow & 4 & 6 & -4 \\
\hline
& 2 & 3 & -2 & -5
\end{array}
$$

The quotient is $2x^2+3x-2-\dfrac{5}{x-2}$.

DEFINITIONS AND CONCEPTS	EXAMPLES

SECTION 6.5   SOLVING EQUATIONS CONTAINING RATIONAL EXPRESSIONS

To solve an equation containing rational expressions: Multiply both sides of the equation by the LCD of all rational expressions. Then apply the distributive property and simplify. Solve the resulting equation and then check each proposed solution to see whether it makes the denominator 0. If so, it is an **extraneous solution.**

Solve $x - \dfrac{3}{x} = \dfrac{1}{2}$.

$$2x\left(x - \dfrac{3}{x}\right) = 2x\left(\dfrac{1}{2}\right) \quad \text{The LCD is } 2x.$$

$$2x \cdot x - 2x\left(\dfrac{3}{x}\right) = 2x\left(\dfrac{1}{2}\right) \quad \text{Distribute.}$$

$$2x^2 - 6 = x$$

$$2x^2 - x - 6 = 0 \quad \text{Subtract } x.$$

$$(2x + 3)(x - 2) = 0 \quad \text{Factor.}$$

$$x = -\dfrac{3}{2} \quad \text{or} \quad x = 2 \quad \text{Solve.}$$

Both $-\dfrac{3}{2}$ and 2 check. The solutions are 2 and $-\dfrac{3}{2}$.

SECTION 6.6   RATIONAL EQUATIONS AND PROBLEM SOLVING

Solving an Equation for a Specified Variable

Treat the specified variable as the only variable of the equation and solve as usual.

Problem-Solving Steps to Follow

Solve for x.

$$A = \dfrac{2x + 3y}{5}$$

$$5A = 2x + 3y \quad \text{Multiply both sides by 5.}$$

$$5A - 3y = 2x \quad \text{Subtract } 3y \text{ from both sides.}$$

$$\dfrac{5A - 3y}{2} = x \quad \text{Divide both sides by 2.}$$

Jeanee and David Dillon volunteer every year to clean a strip of Lake Ponchartrain Beach. Jeanee can clean all the trash in this area of beach in 6 hours; David takes 5 hours. Find how long it will take them to clean the area of beach together.

1. UNDERSTAND.

1. Read and reread the problem.

Let x = time in hours that it takes Jeanee and David to clean the beach together.

	Hours to Complete	*Part Completed in 1 Hour*
Jeanee Alone	6	$\dfrac{1}{6}$
David Alone	5	$\dfrac{1}{5}$
Together	x	$\dfrac{1}{x}$

(continued)

DEFINITIONS AND CONCEPTS	EXAMPLES

SECTION 6.6   RATIONAL EQUATIONS AND PROBLEM SOLVING (continued)

2. TRANSLATE.

2. In words:

part Jeanee can complete in 1 hour	+	part David can complete in 1 hour	=	part they can complete together in 1 hour
↓		↓		↓

Translate:

$$\frac{1}{6} + \frac{1}{5} = \frac{1}{x}$$

3. SOLVE.

3. $\frac{1}{6} + \frac{1}{5} = \frac{1}{x}$ Multiply both sides by $30x$.

$$5x + 6x = 30$$
$$11x = 30$$
$$x = \frac{30}{11} \quad \text{or} \quad 2\frac{8}{11}$$

4. INTERPRET.

4. *Check* and then *state*. Together, they can clean the beach in $2\frac{8}{11}$ hours.

CHAPTER 6 REVIEW

(6.1) *Find the domain for each rational function.*

1. $f(x) = \dfrac{3 - 5x}{7}$

2. $g(x) = \dfrac{2x + 4}{11}$

3. $F(x) = \dfrac{-3x^2}{x - 5}$

4. $h(x) = \dfrac{4x}{3x - 12}$

5. $f(x) = \dfrac{x^3 + 2}{x^2 + 8x}$

6. $G(x) = \dfrac{20}{3x^2 - 48}$

Write each rational expression in lowest terms.

7. $\dfrac{x - 12}{12 - x}$

8. $\dfrac{5x - 15}{25x - 75}$

9. $\dfrac{2x}{2x^2 - 2x}$

10. $\dfrac{x + 7}{x^2 - 49}$

11. $\dfrac{2x^2 + 4x - 30}{x^2 + x - 20}$

12. The average cost (per bookcase) of manufacturing x bookcases is given by the rational function.

$$C(x) = \frac{35x + 4200}{x}$$

a. Find the average cost per bookcase of manufacturing 50 bookcases.

b. Find the average cost per bookcase of manufacturing 100 bookcases.

c. As the number of bookcases increases, does the average cost per bookcase increase or decrease? (See parts (a) and (b).)

Perform each indicated operation. Write your answers in lowest terms.

13. $\dfrac{4 - x}{5} \cdot \dfrac{15}{2x - 8}$

14. $\dfrac{x^2 - 6x + 9}{2x^2 - 18} \cdot \dfrac{4x + 12}{5x - 15}$

15. $\dfrac{a - 4b}{a^2 + ab} \cdot \dfrac{b^2 - a^2}{8b - 2a}$

16. $\dfrac{x^2 - x - 12}{2x^2 - 32} \cdot \dfrac{x^2 + 8x + 16}{3x^2 + 21x + 36}$

17. $\dfrac{4x + 8y}{3} \div \dfrac{5x + 10y}{9}$

18. $\dfrac{x^2 - 25}{3} \div \dfrac{x^2 - 10x + 25}{x^2 - x - 20}$

19. $\dfrac{a - 4b}{a^2 + ab} \div \dfrac{20b - 5a}{b^2 - a^2}$

20. $\dfrac{3x + 3}{x - 1} \div \dfrac{x^2 - 6x - 7}{x^2 - 1}$

21. $\dfrac{2x - x^2}{x^3 - 8} \div \dfrac{x^2}{x^2 + 2x + 4}$

22. $\dfrac{5x - 15}{3 - x} \cdot \dfrac{x + 2}{10x + 20} \cdot \dfrac{x^2 - 9}{x^2 - x - 6}$

(6.2) *Find the LCD of the rational expressions in each list.*

23. $\dfrac{5}{4x^2y^5}, \dfrac{3}{10x^2y^4}, \dfrac{x}{6y^4}$

24. $\dfrac{5}{2x}, \dfrac{7}{x - 2}$

25. $\dfrac{3}{5x}, \dfrac{2}{x - 5}$

26. $\dfrac{1}{5x^3}, \dfrac{4}{x^2 + 3x - 28}, \dfrac{11}{10x^2 - 30x}$

Perform each indicated operation. Write your answers in lowest terms.

27. $\dfrac{4}{x - 4} + \dfrac{x}{x - 4}$

28. $\dfrac{4}{3x^2} + \dfrac{2}{3x^2}$

29. $\dfrac{1}{x - 2} - \dfrac{1}{4 - 2x}$

30. $\dfrac{1}{10 - x} + \dfrac{x - 1}{x - 10}$

31. $\dfrac{x}{9 - x^2} - \dfrac{2}{5x - 15}$

32. $2x + 1 - \dfrac{1}{x - 3}$

33. $\dfrac{2}{a^2 - 2a + 1} + \dfrac{3}{a^2 - 1}$

34. $\dfrac{x}{9x^2 + 12x + 16} - \dfrac{3x + 4}{27x^3 - 64}$

Perform each indicated operation. Write your answers in lowest terms.

35. $\dfrac{2}{x - 1} - \dfrac{3x}{3x - 3} + \dfrac{1}{2x - 2}$

△ **36.** Find the perimeter of the heptagon (a polygon with seven sides).

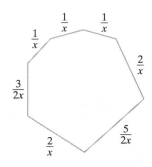

(6.3) *Simplify each complex fraction.*

37. $\dfrac{1 - \dfrac{3x}{4}}{2 + \dfrac{x}{4}}$

38. $\dfrac{\dfrac{x^2}{15}}{\dfrac{x + 1}{5x}}$

39. $\dfrac{2 - \dfrac{3}{2x}}{x - \dfrac{2}{5x}}$

40. $\dfrac{1 + \dfrac{x}{y}}{\dfrac{x^2}{y^2} - 1}$

41. $\dfrac{\dfrac{5}{x} + \dfrac{1}{xy}}{\dfrac{3}{x^2}}$

42. $\dfrac{\dfrac{x}{3} - \dfrac{3}{x}}{1 + \dfrac{3}{x}}$

43. $\dfrac{\dfrac{1}{x - 1} + 1}{\dfrac{1}{x + 1} - 1}$

44. $\dfrac{\dfrac{x - 3}{x + 3} + \dfrac{x + 3}{x - 3}}{\dfrac{x - 3}{x + 3} - \dfrac{x + 3}{x - 3}}$

If $f(x) = \dfrac{3}{x}, x \neq 0$, find each of the following

45. $f(a + h)$

46. $f(a)$

47. Use Exercises 45 and 46 to find $\dfrac{f(a + h) - f(a)}{h}$.

48. Simplify the results of Exercise 47.

(6.4)

49. $(4xy + 2x^2 - 9) \div 4xy$

50. Divide $12xb^2 + 16xb^4$ by $4xb^3$.

51. $(3x^4 - 25x^2 - 20) \div (x - 3)$

52. $(-x^2 + 2x^4 + 5x - 12) \div (x + 2)$

53. $(2x^3 + 3x^2 - 2x + 2) \div (2x + 3)$

54. $(3x^4 + 5x^3 + 7x^2 + 3x - 2) \div (x^2 + x + 2)$

Use synthetic division to find each quotient.

55. $(3x^3 + 12x - 4) \div (x - 2)$

56. $(x^5 - 1) \div (x + 1)$

57. $(x^3 - 81) \div (x - 3)$

58. $(3x^4 - 2x^2 + 10) \div (x + 2)$

If $P(x) = 3x^5 - 9x + 7$, use the remainder theorem to find the following.

59. $P(4)$

60. $P(-5)$

△ **61.** $P\left(-\dfrac{1}{2}\right)$

62. If the area of the rectangle is $(x^4 - x^3 - 6x^2 - 6x + 18)$ square miles and its width is $(x - 3)$ miles, find the length.

$$\boxed{\begin{array}{c} x^4 - x^3 - 6x^2 - 6x + 18 \\ \text{square miles} \end{array}} \quad \begin{array}{c} x - 3 \\ \text{miles} \end{array}$$

(6.5) *Solve each equation.*

63. $\dfrac{3}{x} + \dfrac{1}{3} = \dfrac{5}{x}$

64. $\dfrac{2x + 3}{5x - 9} = \dfrac{3}{2}$

65. $\dfrac{1}{x - 2} - \dfrac{3x}{x^2 - 4} = \dfrac{2}{x + 2}$

66. $\dfrac{7}{x} - \dfrac{x}{7} = 0$

Solve each equation or perform each indicated operation. Simplify.

67. $\dfrac{5}{x^2 - 7x} + \dfrac{4}{2x - 14}$

68. $3 - \dfrac{5}{x} - \dfrac{2}{x^2} = 0$

69. $\dfrac{4}{3 - x} - \dfrac{7}{2x - 6} + \dfrac{5}{x}$

(6.6) *Solve each equation for the specified variable.*

△ **70.** $A = \dfrac{h(a + b)}{2}$ for a

71. $\dfrac{1}{R} = \dfrac{1}{R_1} + \dfrac{1}{R_2}$ for R_2

72. $I = \dfrac{E}{R + r}$ for R

73. $A = P + Prt$ for r

74. $H = \dfrac{kA(T_1 - T_2)}{L}$ for A

Solve.

75. The sum of a number and twice its reciprocal is 3. Find the number(s).

76. If a number is added to the numerator of $\dfrac{3}{7}$, and twice that number is added to the denominator of $\dfrac{3}{7}$, the result is equivalent to $\dfrac{10}{21}$. Find the number.

77. Three boys can paint a fence in 4 hours, 5 hours, and 6 hours, respectively. Find how long it will take all three boys to paint the fence.

78. If Sue Katz can type a certain number of mailing labels in 6 hours and Tom Neilson and Sue working together can type the same number of mailing labels in 4 hours, find how long it takes Tom alone to type the mailing labels.

79. The speed of a Ranger boat in still water is 32 mph. If the boat travels 72 miles upstream in the same time that it takes to travel 120 miles downstream, find the current of the stream.

80. The speed of a jogger is 3 mph faster than the speed of a walker. If the jogger travels 14 miles in the same amount of time that the walker travels 8 miles, find the speed of the walker.

MIXED REVIEW

For expressions, perform the indicated operation and/or simplify. For equations, solve the equation for the unknown variable.

83. $\dfrac{22x + 8}{11x + 4}$

84. $\dfrac{xy - 3x + 2y - 6}{x^2 + 4x + 4}$

85. $\dfrac{2}{5x} \div \dfrac{4 - 18x}{6 - 27x}$

86. $\dfrac{7x + 28}{2x + 4} \div \dfrac{x^2 + 2x - 8}{x^2 - 2x - 8}$

87. $\dfrac{5a^2 - 20}{a^3 + 2a^2 + a + 2} \div \dfrac{7a}{a^3 + a}$

88. $\dfrac{4a + 8}{5a^2 - 20} \cdot \dfrac{3a^2 - 6a}{a + 3} \div \dfrac{2a^2}{5a + 15}$

89. $\dfrac{7}{2x} + \dfrac{5}{6x}$

90. $\dfrac{x - 2}{x + 1} - \dfrac{x - 3}{x - 1}$

91. $\dfrac{2x + 1}{x^2 + x - 6} + \dfrac{2 - x}{x^2 + x - 6}$

92. $\dfrac{2}{x^2 - 16} - \dfrac{3x}{x^2 + 8x + 16} + \dfrac{3}{x + 4}$

93. $\dfrac{\dfrac{1}{x} - \dfrac{2}{3x}}{\dfrac{5}{2x} - \dfrac{1}{3}}$

94. $\dfrac{2}{1 - \dfrac{2}{x}}$

95. $\dfrac{\dfrac{x^2 + 5x - 6}{4x + 3}}{\dfrac{(x + 6)^2}{8x + 6}}$

96. $\dfrac{\dfrac{3}{x - 1} - \dfrac{2}{1 - x}}{\dfrac{2}{x - 1} - \dfrac{2}{x}}$

97. $4 + \dfrac{8}{x} = 8$

98. $\dfrac{x - 2}{x^2 - 7x + 10} = \dfrac{1}{5x - 10} - \dfrac{1}{x - 5}$

99. The denominator of a fraction is 2 more than the numerator. If the numerator is decreased by 3 and the denominator is increased by 5, the resulting fraction is equivalent to $\dfrac{2}{3}$. Find the fraction.

100. The sum of the reciprocals of two consecutive even integers is $-\dfrac{9}{40}$. Find the two integers.

101. The inlet pipe of a water tank can fill the tank in 2 hours and 30 minutes. The outlet pipe can empty the tank in 2 hours. Find how long it takes to empty a full tank if both pipes are open.

102. Timmy Garnica drove 210 miles in the same amount of time that it took a DC-10 jet to travel 1715 miles. The speed of the jet was 430 mph faster than the speed of the car. Find the speed of the jet.

103. Two Amtrak trains traveling on parallel tracks leave Tucson at the same time. In 6 hours the faster train is 382 miles from Tucson and the trains are 112 miles apart. Find how fast each train is traveling.

106. Divide $(x^3 - x^2 + 3x^4 - 2)$ by $(x - 4)$.

CHAPTER 6 TEST TEST PREP VIDEO

Remember to use the Chapter Test Prep Video CD to see the fully worked-out solutions to any of the exercises you want to review.

Find the domain of each rational function.

1. $f(x) = \dfrac{5x^2}{1 - x}$

2. $g(x) = \dfrac{9x^2 - 9}{x^2 + 4x + 3}$

Write each rational expression in lowest terms.

3. $\dfrac{7x - 21}{24 - 8x}$

4. $\dfrac{x^2 - 4x}{x^2 + 5x - 36}$

5. $\dfrac{x^3 - 8}{x - 2}$

Perform the indicated operation. If possible, simplify your answer.

6. $\dfrac{2x^3 + 16}{6x^2 + 12x} \cdot \dfrac{5}{x^2 - 2x + 4}$

7. $\dfrac{5}{4x^3} + \dfrac{7}{4x^3}$

8. $\dfrac{3x^2 - 12}{x^2 + 2x - 8} \div \dfrac{6x + 18}{x + 4}$

9. $\dfrac{4x - 12}{2x - 9} \div \dfrac{3 - x}{4x^2 - 81} \cdot \dfrac{x + 3}{5x + 15}$

10. $\dfrac{3 + 2x}{10 - x} + \dfrac{13 + x}{x - 10}$

11. $\dfrac{2x^2 + 7}{2x^4 - 18x^2} - \dfrac{6x + 7}{2x^4 - 18x^2}$

12. $\dfrac{3}{x^2 - x - 6} + \dfrac{2}{x^2 - 5x + 6}$

13. $\dfrac{5}{x - 7} - \dfrac{2x}{3x - 21} + \dfrac{x}{2x - 14}$

14. $\dfrac{3x}{5} \cdot \left(\dfrac{5}{x} - \dfrac{5}{2x} \right)$

Simplify each complex fraction.

15. $\dfrac{\dfrac{5}{x} - \dfrac{7}{3x}}{\dfrac{9}{8x} - \dfrac{1}{x}}$

16. $\dfrac{\dfrac{x^2 - 5x + 6}{x + 3}}{\dfrac{x^2 - 4x + 4}{x^2 - 9}}$

Divide.

17. $(4x^2y + 9x + 3xz) \div 3xz$

18. $(4x^3 - 5x) \div (2x + 1)$

19. Use synthetic division to divide $(4x^4 - 3x^3 - x - 1)$ by $(x + 3)$.

20. If $P(x) = 4x^4 + 7x^2 - 2x - 5$, use the remainder theorem to find $P(-2)$.

Solve each equation for x.

21. $\dfrac{x}{x-4} = 3 - \dfrac{4}{x-4}$

22. $\dfrac{3}{x+2} - \dfrac{1}{5x} = \dfrac{2}{5x^2+10x}$

23. $\dfrac{x^2+8}{x} - 1 = \dfrac{2(x+4)}{x}$

24. Solve for x: $\dfrac{x+b}{a} = \dfrac{4x-7a}{b}$

25. The product of one more than a number and twice the reciprocal of the number is $\dfrac{12}{5}$. Find the number.

26. If Jan can weed the garden in 2 hours and her husband can weed it in 1 hour and 30 minutes, find how long it takes them to weed the garden together.

CHAPTER 6 CUMULATIVE REVIEW

1. Translate each phrase to an algebraic expression. Use the variable x to represent each unknown number.

  a. Eight times a number

  b. Three more than eight times a number

  c. The quotient of a number and -7

  d. One and six-tenths subtracted from twice a number

  e. Six less than a number

  f. Twice the sum of four and a number

2. Translate each phrase to an algebraic expression. Use the variable x to represent each unknown number.

  a. One third subtracted from a number

  b. Six less than five times a number

  c. Three more than eight times a number

  d. The quotient of seven and the difference of two and a number.

3. Solve for y: $\dfrac{y}{3} - \dfrac{y}{4} = \dfrac{1}{6}$

4. Solve $\dfrac{x}{7} + \dfrac{x}{5} = \dfrac{12}{5}$

5. In the United States, the annual consumption of cigarettes is declining. The consumption c in billions of cigarettes per year since the year 1990 can be approximated by the formula $c = -9.2t + 527.33$ where t is the number of years after 1990. Use this formula to predict the years that the consumption of cigarettes will be less than 200 billion per year.

6. Olivia has scores of 78, 65, 82, and 79 on her algebra tests. Use an inequality to find the minimum score she can make or her final exam to pass the course with a 78 average or higher, given that the final exam counts as two tests.

7. Solve: $\left|\dfrac{3x+1}{2}\right| = -2$

8. Solve: $\left|\dfrac{2x-1}{3}\right| + 6 = 3$

9. Solve for x: $\left|\dfrac{2(x+1)}{3}\right| \le 0$

10. Solve for x: $\left|\dfrac{3(x-1)}{4}\right| \ge 2$

11. Graph the equation $y = -2x + 3$.

12. Graph the equation $y = -x + 3$.

13. Which of the following relations are also functions?

  a. $\{(-2,5), (2,7), (-3,5), (9,9)\}$

  b.

  c.

Input	Correspondence	Output
People in a certain city	Each person's age	The set of nonegative integers

14. If $f(x) = -x^2 + 3x - 2$, find

    a. f(0)   **b.** $f(-3)$ **c.** $f\left(\dfrac{1}{3}\right)$

15. Graph $3x + 4y = -12$ by plotting intercept points.

16. Graph $3x - y = 6$ by plotting x- and y-intercepts.

17. Find an equation of the line with slope -3 containing the point $(1, -5)$. Write the equation in slope–intercept form $y = mx + b$.

18. Find an equation of the line with slope $\dfrac{1}{2}$ containing the point $(-1, 3)$. Use function notation to write the equation.

19. Graph the intersection of $x \geq 1$ and $y \geq 2x - 1$.

21. Use the elimination method to solve the system.
$$\begin{cases} 3x - 2y = 10 \\ 4x - 3y = 15 \end{cases}$$

22. Use the substitution method to solve the system.
$$\begin{cases} -2x + 3y = 6 \\ 3x - y = 5 \end{cases}$$

23. Solve the system. $\begin{cases} 2x - 4y + 8z = 2 \\ -x - 3y + z = 11 \\ x - 2y + 4z = 0 \end{cases}$

24. Solve the system. $\begin{cases} 2x - 2y + 4z = 6 \\ -4x - y + z = -8 \\ 3x - y + z = 6 \end{cases}$

25. The measure of the largest angle of a triangle is 80° more than the measure of the smallest angle, and the measure of the remaining angle is 10° more than the measure of the smallest angle. Find the measure of each angle.

26. Kernersville office supply sold three reams of paper and two boxes of manila folders for $21.90. Also, five reams of paper and one box of manila folders cost $24.25. Find the price of a ream of paper and a box of manila folders.

27. Use matrices to solve the system. $\begin{cases} x + 2y + z = 2 \\ -2x - y + 2z = 5 \\ x + 3y - 2z = -8 \end{cases}$

28. Use matrices to solve the system. $\begin{cases} x + y + z = 9 \\ 2x - 2y + 3z = 2 \\ -3x + y - z = 1 \end{cases}$

29. Evaluate the following.

    a. 7^0 **b.** -7^0

    c. $(2x + 5)^0$ **d.** $2x^0$

30. Simplify the following. Write answers with positive exponents.

    a. $2^{-2} + 3^{-1}$ **b.** $-6a^0$ **c.** $\dfrac{x^{-5}}{x^{-2}}$

31. Simplify each. Assume that a and b are integers and that x and y are not 0.

    a. $x^{-b}(2x^b)^2$ **b.** $\dfrac{(y^{3a})^2}{y^{a-6}}$

32. Simplify each. Assume that a and b are integers and that x and y are not 0.

    a. $3x^{4a}(4x^{-a})^2$ **b.** $\dfrac{(y^{4b})^3}{y^{2b-3}}$

33. Find the degree of each term.

    a. $3x^2$ **b.** -2^3x^5 **c.** y

    d. $12x^2yz^3$ **e.** 5.27

34. Subtract $(2x - 7)$ from $2x^2 + 8x - 3$

35. Multiply $[3 + (2a + b)]^2$

36. Multiply $[4 + (3x - y)]^2$

37. Factor $ab - 6a + 2b - 12$

38. Factor $xy + 2x - 5y - 10$

39. Factor $2n^2 - 38n + 80$

40. Factor $6x^2 - x - 35$

41. Factor $x^2 + 4x + 4 - y^2$

42. Factor $4x^2 - 4x + 1 - 9y^2$

43. Solve $(x + 2)(x - 6) = 0$

44. Solve $2x(3x + 1)(x - 3) = 0$

45. Simplify

    a. $\dfrac{2x^2}{10x^3 - 2x^2}$

    b. $\dfrac{9x^2 + 13x + 4}{8x^2 + x - 7}$

46. For the graph of $f(x)$, answer the following:

    a. Find the domain and range.

    b. List the x- and y-intercepts.

    c. Find the coordinates of the point with the greatest y-value.

    d. Find the coordinates of the point with the least y-value.

    e. List the x-values whose y-values are equal to 0.

    f. List the x-values whose y-values are less than 0.

    g. Find the solutions of $f(x) = 0$.

47. Subtract $\dfrac{5k}{k^2 - 4} - \dfrac{2}{k^2 + k - 2}$.

48. Subtract $\dfrac{5a}{a^2 - 4} - \dfrac{3}{2 - a}$.

49. Solve: $\dfrac{3}{x} - \dfrac{x + 21}{3x} = \dfrac{5}{3}$.

50. Solve: $\dfrac{3x - 4}{2x} = -\dfrac{8}{x}$.

7 Rational Exponents, Radicals, and Complex Numbers

In this chapter, radical notation is reviewed, and then rational exponents are introduced. As the name implies, rational exponents are exponents that are rational numbers. We present an interpretation of rational exponents that is consistent with the meaning and rules already established for integer exponents, and we present two forms of notation for roots: radical and exponent. We conclude this chapter with complex numbers, a natural extension of the real number system.

What is a zorb? Simply put, a zorb is a large inflated ball within a ball, and zorbing is a recreational activity which may involve rolling down a hill while strapped in a zorb. Zorbing started in New Zealand (as well as bungee jumping) and was invented by Andrew Akers and Dwane van der Sluis. The first site was set up in New Zealand's North Island. This downhill course has a length of about 490 feet, and you can reach speeds of up to 20 mph.

An example of a course is shown in the diagram below, and you can see the mathematics involved. In Section 7.3, Exercise 115, page 402, you will calculate the outer radius of a zorb, which would certainly be closely associated with the cost of production.

7 meters

9 feet

7.1 RADICALS AND RADICAL FUNCTIONS

OBJECTIVES

1 Find square roots.

2 Approximate roots.

3 Find cube roots.

4 Find nth roots.

5 Find $\sqrt[n]{a^n}$ where a is a real number.

6 Graph square and cube root functions.

OBJECTIVE 1 ▶ Finding square roots. Recall from Section 1.3 that to find a **square root** of a number a, we find a number that was squared to get a.

Thus, because

$$5^2 = 25 \quad \text{and} \quad (-5)^2 = 25, \text{then}$$

both 5 and -5 are square roots of 25.

Recall that we denote the **nonnegative,** or **principal, square root** with the **radical sign.**

$$\sqrt{25} = 5$$

We denote the **negative square root** with the **negative radical sign.**

$$-\sqrt{25} = -5$$

An expression containing a radical sign is called a **radical expression.** An expression within, or "under," a radical sign is called a **radicand.**

radical expression : $\overset{\nearrow \text{radical sign}}{\underset{\nwarrow \text{radicand}}{\sqrt{a}}}$

Principal and Negative Square Roots

If a is a nonnegative number, then

$\sqrt{a}$ is the **principal,** or **nonnegative square root** of a

$-\sqrt{a}$ is the **negative square root** of a

 EXAMPLE 1   Simplify. Assume that all variables represent positive numbers.

a. $\sqrt{36}$ 　　**b.** $\sqrt{0}$ 　　**c.** $\sqrt{\dfrac{4}{49}}$ 　　**d.** $\sqrt{0.25}$

e. $\sqrt{x^6}$ 　　**f.** $\sqrt{9x^{12}}$ 　　**g.** $-\sqrt{81}$ 　　**h.** $\sqrt{-81}$

Solution

a. $\sqrt{36} = 6$ because $6^2 = 36$ and 6 is not negative.

b. $\sqrt{0} = 0$ because $0^2 = 0$ and 0 is not negative.

c. $\sqrt{\dfrac{4}{49}} = \dfrac{2}{7}$ because $\left(\dfrac{2}{7}\right)^2 = \dfrac{4}{49}$ and $\dfrac{2}{7}$ is not negative.

d. $\sqrt{0.25} = 0.5$ because $(0.5)^2 = 0.25$.

e. $\sqrt{x^6} = x^3$ because $(x^3)^2 = x^6$.

f. $\sqrt{9x^{12}} = 3x^6$ because $(3x^6)^2 = 9x^{12}$.

g. $-\sqrt{81} = -9$. The negative in front of the radical indicates the negative square root of 81.

h. $\sqrt{-81}$ is not a real number. ☐

PRACTICE

1   Simplify. Assume that all variables represent positive numbers.

a. $\sqrt{49}$ 　　**b.** $\sqrt{\dfrac{0}{1}}$ 　　**c.** $\sqrt{\dfrac{16}{81}}$ 　　**d.** $\sqrt{0.64}$

e. $\sqrt{z^8}$ 　　**f.** $\sqrt{16b^4}$ 　　**g.** $-\sqrt{36}$ 　　**h.** $\sqrt{-36}$

Recall from Section 1.3 our discussion of the square root of a negative number. For example, can we simplify $\sqrt{-4}$? That is, can we find a real number whose square is -4? No, there is no real number whose square is -4, and we say that $\sqrt{-4}$ is not a real number. In general:

The square root of a negative number is not a real number.

> ▶ **Helpful Hint**
> - Remember: $\sqrt{0} = 0$
> - Don't forget, the square root of a negative number, such as $\sqrt{-9}$, is not a real number. In Section 7.7, we will see what kind of a number $\sqrt{-9}$ is.

OBJECTIVE 2 ▶ Approximating roots. Recall that numbers such as 1, 4, 9, and 25 are called **perfect squares,** since $1 = 1^2, 4 = 2^2, 9 = 3^2$, and $25 = 5^2$. Square roots of perfect square radicands simplify to rational numbers. What happens when we try to simplify a root such as $\sqrt{3}$? Since there is no rational number whose square is 3, then $\sqrt{3}$ is not a rational number. It is called an **irrational number,** and we can find a decimal **approximation** of it. To find decimal approximations, use a calculator. For example, an approximation for $\sqrt{3}$ is

$$\sqrt{3} \approx 1.732$$
↑
approximation symbol

To see if the approximation is reasonable, notice that since

$$1 < 3 < 4, \text{ then}$$
$$\sqrt{1} < \sqrt{3} < \sqrt{4}, \text{ or}$$
$$1 < \sqrt{3} < 2.$$

We found $\sqrt{3} \approx 1.732$, a number between 1 and 2, so our result is reasonable.

EXAMPLE 2 Use a calculator to approximate $\sqrt{20}$. Round the approximation to 3 decimal places and check to see that your approximation is reasonable.

$$\sqrt{20} \approx 4.472$$

Solution Is this reasonable? Since $16 < 20 < 25$, then $\sqrt{16} < \sqrt{20} < \sqrt{25}$, or $4 < \sqrt{20} < 5$. The approximation is between 4 and 5 and thus is reasonable. □

PRACTICE
2 Use a calculator to approximate $\sqrt{45}$. Round the approximation to three decimal places and check to see that your approximation is reasonable.

OBJECTIVE 3 ▶ Finding cube roots. Finding roots can be extended to other roots such as cube roots. For example, since $2^3 = 8$, we call 2 the **cube root** of 8. In symbols, we write

$$\sqrt[3]{8} = 2$$

> **Cube Root**
> The **cube root** of a real number a is written as $\sqrt[3]{a}$, and
> $$\sqrt[3]{a} = b \text{ only if } b^3 = a$$

From this definition, we have

$$\sqrt[3]{64} = 4 \text{ since } 4^3 = 64$$
$$\sqrt[3]{-27} = -3 \text{ since } (-3)^3 = -27$$
$$\sqrt[3]{x^3} = x \text{ since } x^3 = x^3$$

Notice that, unlike with square roots, *it is possible to have a negative radicand when finding a cube root.* This is so because the *cube* of a negative number is a negative number. Therefore, the *cube root* of a negative number is a negative number.

EXAMPLE 3   Find the cube roots.

a. $\sqrt[3]{1}$ **b.** $\sqrt[3]{-64}$ **c.** $\sqrt[3]{\dfrac{8}{125}}$ **d.** $\sqrt[3]{x^6}$ **e.** $\sqrt[3]{-27x^9}$

Solution

a. $\sqrt[3]{1} = 1$ because $1^3 = 1$.

b. $\sqrt[3]{-64} = -4$ because $(-4)^3 = -64$.

c. $\sqrt[3]{\dfrac{8}{125}} = \dfrac{2}{5}$ because $\left(\dfrac{2}{5}\right)^3 = \dfrac{8}{125}$.

d. $\sqrt[3]{x^6} = x^2$ because $(x^2)^3 = x^6$.

e. $\sqrt[3]{-27x^9} = -3x^3$ because $(-3x^3)^3 = -27x^9$.

PRACTICE

3   Find the cube roots.

a. $\sqrt[3]{-1}$ **b.** $\sqrt[3]{27}$ **c.** $\sqrt[3]{\dfrac{27}{64}}$ **d.** $\sqrt[3]{x^{12}}$ **e.** $\sqrt[3]{-8x^3}$

OBJECTIVE 4 ▶ Finding *n*th roots. Just as we can raise a real number to powers other than 2 or 3, we can find roots other than square roots and cube roots. In fact, we can find the ***n*th root** of a number, where *n* is any natural number. In symbols, the *n*th root of *a* is written as $\sqrt[n]{a}$, where *n* is called the **index.** The index 2 is usually omitted for square roots.

> ▶ **Helpful Hint**
>
> If the index is even, such as $\sqrt{}$, $\sqrt[4]{}$, $\sqrt[6]{}$, and so on, the radicand must be non-negative for the root to be a real number. For example,
>
> $$\sqrt[4]{16} = 2, \text{ but } \sqrt[4]{-16} \text{ is not a real number.}$$
> $$\sqrt[6]{64} = 2, \text{ but } \sqrt[6]{-64} \text{ is not a real number.}$$
>
> If the index is odd, such as $\sqrt[3]{}$, $\sqrt[5]{}$, and so on, the radicand may be any real number. For example,
>
> $$\sqrt[3]{64} = 4 \quad \text{and} \quad \sqrt[3]{-64} = -4$$
> $$\sqrt[5]{32} = 2 \quad \text{and} \quad \sqrt[5]{-32} = -2$$

Concept Check ☑

Which one is not a real number?

a. $\sqrt[3]{-15}$ **b.** $\sqrt[4]{-15}$ **c.** $\sqrt[5]{-15}$ **d.** $\sqrt{(-15)^2}$

EXAMPLE 4   Simplify the following expressions.

a. $\sqrt[4]{81}$ **b.** $\sqrt[5]{-243}$ **c.** $-\sqrt{25}$ **d.** $\sqrt[4]{-81}$ **e.** $\sqrt[3]{64x^3}$

Solution

a. $\sqrt[4]{81} = 3$ because $3^4 = 81$ and 3 is positive.

b. $\sqrt[5]{-243} = -3$ because $(-3)^5 = -243$.

c. $-\sqrt{25} = -5$ because -5 is the opposite of $\sqrt{25}$.

Answer to Concept Check: b

d. $\sqrt[4]{-81}$ is not a real number. There is no real number that, when raised to the fourth power, is -81.

e. $\sqrt[3]{64x^3} = 4x$ because $(4x)^3 = 64x^3$. ☐

PRACTICE
4 Simplify the following expressions.

a. $\sqrt[4]{10000}$ **b.** $\sqrt[5]{-1}$ **c.** $-\sqrt{81}$ **d.** $\sqrt[4]{-625}$ **e.** $\sqrt[3]{27x^9}$

OBJECTIVE 5 ▶ Finding $\sqrt[n]{a^n}$ where a is a real number. Recall that the notation $\sqrt{a^2}$ indicates the positive square root of a^2 only. For example,

$$\sqrt{(-5)^2} = \sqrt{25} = 5$$

When variables are present in the radicand and it is unclear whether the variable represents a positive number or a negative number, absolute value bars are sometimes needed to ensure that the result is a positive number. For example,

$$\sqrt{x^2} = |x|$$

This ensures that the result is positive. This same situation may occur when the index is any *even* positive integer. When the index is any *odd* positive integer, absolute value bars are not necessary.

Finding $\sqrt[n]{a^n}$

If n is an *even* positive integer, then $\sqrt[n]{a^n} = |a|$.

If n is an *odd* positive integer, then $\sqrt[n]{a^n} = a$.

EXAMPLE 5 Simplify.

a. $\sqrt{(-3)^2}$ **b.** $\sqrt{x^2}$ **c.** $\sqrt[4]{(x-2)^4}$ **d.** $\sqrt[3]{(-5)^3}$

e. $\sqrt[5]{(2x-7)^5}$ **f.** $\sqrt{25x^2}$ **g.** $\sqrt{x^2+2x+1}$

Solution

a. $\sqrt{(-3)^2} = |-3| = 3$ When the index is even, the absolute value bars ensure us that our result is not negative.

b. $\sqrt{x^2} = |x|$

c. $\sqrt[4]{(x-2)^4} = |x-2|$

d. $\sqrt[3]{(-5)^3} = -5$

e. $\sqrt[5]{(2x-7)^5} = 2x - 7$ Absolute value bars are not needed when the index is odd.

f. $\sqrt{25x^2} = 5|x|$

g. $\sqrt{x^2+2x+1} = \sqrt{(x+1)^2} = |x+1|$ ☐

PRACTICE
5 Simplify.

a. $\sqrt{(-4)^2}$ **b.** $\sqrt{x^{14}}$ **c.** $\sqrt[4]{(x+7)^4}$ **d.** $\sqrt[3]{(-7)^3}$

e. $\sqrt[5]{(3x-5)^5}$ **f.** $\sqrt{49x^2}$ **g.** $\sqrt{x^2+4x+4}$

OBJECTIVE 6 ▶ Graphing square and cube root functions. Recall that an equation in x and y describes a function if each x-value is paired with exactly one y-value. With this in mind, does the equation

$$y = \sqrt{x}$$

describe a function? First, notice that replacement values for x must be nonnegative real numbers, since $\sqrt{x}$ is not a real number if $x < 0$. The notation $\sqrt{x}$ denotes the principal square root of x, so for every nonnegative number x, there is exactly one number, $\sqrt{x}$. Therefore, $y = \sqrt{x}$ describes a function, and we may write it as

$$f(x) = \sqrt{x}$$

In general, radical functions are functions of the form

$$f(x) = \sqrt[n]{x}.$$

Recall that the domain of a function in x is the set of all possible replacement values of x. This means that if n is even, the domain is the set of all nonnegative numbers, or $\{x \mid x \geq 0\}$. If n is odd, the domain is the set of all real numbers. Keep this in mind as we find function values.

EXAMPLE 6 If $f(x) = \sqrt{x - 4}$ and $g(x) = \sqrt[3]{x + 2}$, find each function value.

a. $f(8)$ **b.** $f(6)$ **c.** $g(-1)$ **d.** $g(1)$

Solution

a. $f(8) = \sqrt{8 - 4} = \sqrt{4} = 2$ **b.** $f(6) = \sqrt{6 - 4} = \sqrt{2}$

c. $g(-1) = \sqrt[3]{-1 + 2} = \sqrt[3]{1} = 1$ **d.** $g(1) = \sqrt[3]{1 + 2} = \sqrt[3]{3}$

PRACTICE

6 If $f(x) = \sqrt{x + 5}$ and $g(x) = \sqrt[3]{x - 3}$, find each function value.

a. $f(11)$ **b.** $f(-1)$ **c.** $g(11)$ **d.** $g(-5)$

> ▶ **Helpful Hint**
>
> Notice that for the function $f(x) = \sqrt{x - 4}$, the domain includes all real numbers that make the radicand ≥ 0. To see what numbers these are, solve $x - 4 \geq 0$ and find that $x \geq 4$. The domain is $\{x \mid x \geq 4\}$.
>
> The domain of the cube root function $g(x) = \sqrt[3]{x + 2}$ is the set of real numbers.

EXAMPLE 7 Graph the square root function $f(x) = \sqrt{x}$.

Solution To graph, we identify the domain, evaluate the function for several values of x, plot the resulting points, and connect the points with a smooth curve. Since $\sqrt{x}$ represents the nonnegative square root of x, the domain of this function is the set of all nonnegative numbers, $\{x \mid x \geq 0\}$, or $[0, \infty)$. We have approximated $\sqrt{3}$ below to help us locate the point corresponding to $(3, \sqrt{3})$.

x	$f(x) = \sqrt{x}$
0	0
1	1
3	$\sqrt{3} \approx 1.7$
4	2
9	3

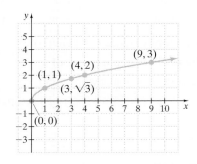

Notice that the graph of this function passes the vertical line test, as expected.

PRACTICE

7 Graph the square root function $h(x) = \sqrt{x + 2}$.

The equation $f(x) = \sqrt[3]{x}$ also describes a function. Here x may be any real number, so the domain of this function is the set of all real numbers, or $(-\infty, \infty)$. A few function values are given next.

$$f(0) = \sqrt[3]{0} = 0$$
$$f(1) = \sqrt[3]{1} = 1$$
$$f(-1) = \sqrt[3]{-1} = -1$$
$$\left.\begin{array}{l} f(6) = \sqrt[3]{6} \\ f(-6) = \sqrt[3]{-6} \end{array}\right\}$$ Here, there is no rational number whose cube is 6. Thus, the radicals do not simplify to rational numbers.
$$f(8) = \sqrt[3]{8} = 2$$
$$f(-8) = \sqrt[3]{-8} = -2$$

EXAMPLE 8   Graph the function $f(x) = \sqrt[3]{x}$.

Solution   To graph, we identify the domain, plot points, and connect the points with a smooth curve. The domain of this function is the set of all real numbers. The table comes from the function values obtained earlier. We have approximated $\sqrt[3]{6}$ and $\sqrt[3]{-6}$ for graphing purposes.

x	$f(x) = \sqrt[3]{x}$
0	0
1	1
−1	−1
6	$\sqrt[3]{6} \approx 1.8$
−6	$\sqrt[3]{-6} \approx -1.8$
8	2
−8	−2

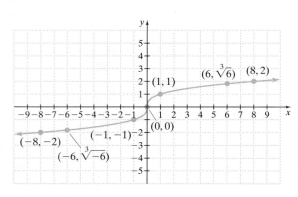

The graph of this function passes the vertical line test, as expected.

PRACTICE
8   Graph the function $f(x) = \sqrt[3]{x} - 4$.

VOCABULARY & READINESS CHECK

Use the choices below to fill in each blank. Not all choices will be used.

is	cubes	$-\sqrt{a}$	radical sign	index
is not	squares	$\sqrt{-a}$	radicand	

1. In the expression $\sqrt[n]{a}$, the n is called the _____, the $\sqrt{}$ is called the _____, and a is called the _____.
2. If $\sqrt{a}$ is the positive square root of a, $a \neq 0$, then _____ is the negative square root of a.
3. The square root of a negative number _____ a real number.
4. Numbers such as 1, 4, 9, and 25 are called perfect _____ where numbers such as 1, 8, 27, and 125 are called perfect _____.

Fill in the blank.

5. The domain of the function $f(x) = \sqrt{x}$ is _____.
6. The domain of the function $f(x) = \sqrt[3]{x}$ is _____.
7. If $f(16) = 4$, the corresponding ordered pair is _____.
8. If $g(-8) = -2$, the corresponding ordered pair is _____.

Choose the correct letter or letters. No pencil is needed, just think your way through these.

9. Which radical is not a real number?

a. $\sqrt{3}$ **b.** $-\sqrt{11}$ **c.** $\sqrt[3]{-10}$ **d.** $\sqrt{-10}$

10. Which radical(s) simplify to 3?

a. $\sqrt{9}$ **b.** $\sqrt{-9}$ **c.** $\sqrt[3]{27}$ **d.** $\sqrt[3]{-27}$

11. Which radical(s) simplify to -3?

a. $\sqrt{9}$ **b.** $\sqrt{-9}$ **c.** $\sqrt[3]{27}$ **d.** $\sqrt[3]{-27}$

12. Which radical does not simplify to a whole number?

a. $\sqrt{64}$ **b.** $\sqrt[3]{64}$ **c.** $\sqrt{8}$ **d.** $\sqrt[3]{8}$

7.1 EXERCISE SET

MyMathLab · PRACTICE · WATCH · DOWNLOAD · READ · REVIEW

Simplify. Assume that variables represent positive real numbers. See Example 1.

1. $\sqrt{100}$ **2.** $\sqrt{400}$

3. $\sqrt{\dfrac{1}{4}}$ **4.** $\sqrt{\dfrac{9}{25}}$

5. $\sqrt{0.0001}$ **6.** $\sqrt{0.04}$

7. $-\sqrt{36}$ **8.** $-\sqrt{9}$

9. $\sqrt{x^{10}}$ **10.** $\sqrt{x^{16}}$

11. $\sqrt{16y^6}$ **12.** $\sqrt{64y^{20}}$

Use a calculator to approximate each square root to 3 decimal places. Check to see that each approximation is reasonable. See Example 2.

13. $\sqrt{7}$ **14.** $\sqrt{11}$

15. $\sqrt{38}$ **16.** $\sqrt{56}$

17. $\sqrt{200}$ **18.** $\sqrt{300}$

Find each cube root. See Example 3.

19. $\sqrt[3]{64}$ **20.** $\sqrt[3]{27}$

21. $\sqrt[3]{\dfrac{1}{8}}$ **22.** $\sqrt[3]{\dfrac{27}{64}}$

23. $\sqrt[3]{-1}$ **24.** $\sqrt[3]{-125}$

25. $\sqrt[3]{x^{12}}$ **26.** $\sqrt[3]{x^{15}}$

27. $\sqrt[3]{-27x^9}$ **28.** $\sqrt[3]{-64x^6}$

Find each root. Assume that all variables represent nonnegative real numbers. See Example 4.

29. $-\sqrt[4]{16}$ **30.** $\sqrt[5]{-243}$

31. $\sqrt[4]{-16}$ **32.** $\sqrt{-16}$

33. $\sqrt[5]{-32}$ **34.** $\sqrt[5]{-1}$

35. $\sqrt[5]{x^{20}}$ **36.** $\sqrt[4]{x^{20}}$

37. $\sqrt[6]{64x^{12}}$ **38.** $\sqrt[5]{-32x^{15}}$

39. $\sqrt{81x^4}$ **40.** $\sqrt[4]{81x^4}$

41. $\sqrt[4]{256x^8}$ **42.** $\sqrt{256x^8}$

Simplify. Assume that the variables represent any real number. See Example 5.

43. $\sqrt{(-8)^2}$ **44.** $\sqrt{(-7)^2}$

45. $\sqrt[3]{(-8)^3}$ **46.** $\sqrt[5]{(-7)^5}$

47. $\sqrt{4x^2}$ **48.** $\sqrt[4]{16x^4}$

49. $\sqrt[3]{x^3}$ **50.** $\sqrt[5]{x^5}$

51. $\sqrt{(x-5)^2}$ **52.** $\sqrt{(y-6)^2}$

53. $\sqrt{x^2+4x+4}$

   (*Hint:* Factor the polynomial first.)

54. $\sqrt{x^2-8x+16}$

   (*Hint:* Factor the polynomial first.)

MIXED PRACTICE

Simplify each radical. Assume that all variables represent positive real numbers.

55. $-\sqrt{121}$ **56.** $-\sqrt[3]{125}$

57. $\sqrt[3]{8x^3}$ **58.** $\sqrt{16x^8}$

59. $\sqrt{y^{12}}$ **60.** $\sqrt[3]{y^{12}}$

61. $\sqrt{25a^2b^{20}}$ **62.** $\sqrt{9x^4y^6}$

63. $\sqrt[3]{-27x^{12}y^9}$ **64.** $\sqrt[3]{-8a^{21}b^6}$

65. $\sqrt[4]{a^{16}b^4}$ **66.** $\sqrt[4]{x^8y^{12}}$

67. $\sqrt[5]{-32x^{10}y^5}$ **68.** $\sqrt[5]{-243z^{15}}$

69. $\sqrt{\dfrac{25}{49}}$ **70.** $\sqrt{\dfrac{4}{81}}$

71. $\sqrt{\dfrac{x^2}{4y^2}}$ **72.** $\sqrt{\dfrac{y^{10}}{9x^6}}$

73. $-\sqrt[3]{\dfrac{z^{21}}{27x^3}}$ **74.** $-\sqrt[3]{\dfrac{64a^3}{b^9}}$

75. $\sqrt[4]{\dfrac{x^4}{16}}$ **76.** $\sqrt[4]{\dfrac{y^4}{81x^4}}$

If $f(x) = \sqrt{2x+3}$ and $g(x) = \sqrt[3]{x-8}$, find the following function values. See Example 6.

77. $f(0)$ **78.** $g(0)$

79. $g(7)$ **80.** $f(-1)$

81. $g(-19)$ **82.** $f(3)$

83. $f(2)$ **84.** $g(1)$

Identify the domain and then graph each function. See Example 7.

85. $f(x) = \sqrt{x} + 2$

86. $f(x) = \sqrt{x} - 2$

87. $f(x) = \sqrt{x - 3}$; use the following table.

x	$f(x)$
3	
4	
7	
12	

88. $f(x) = \sqrt{x + 1}$; use the following table.

x	$f(x)$
-1	
0	
3	
8	

Identify the domain and then graph each function. See Example 8.

89. $f(x) = \sqrt[3]{x} + 1$

90. $f(x) = \sqrt[3]{x} - 2$

91. $g(x) = \sqrt[3]{x - 1}$; use the following table.

x	$g(x)$
1	
2	
0	
9	
-7	

92. $g(x) = \sqrt[3]{x + 1}$; use the following table.

x	$g(x)$
-1	
0	
-2	
7	
-9	

REVIEW AND PREVIEW

Simplify each exponential expression. See Sections 5.1 and 5.2.

93. $(-2x^3y^2)^5$ **94.** $(4y^6z^7)^3$

95. $(-3x^2y^3z^5)(20x^5y^7)$ **96.** $(-14a^5bc^2)(2abc^4)$

97. $\dfrac{7x^{-1}y}{14(x^5y^2)^{-2}}$ **98.** $\dfrac{(2a^{-1}b^2)^3}{(8a^2b)^{-2}}$

CONCEPT EXTENSIONS

Which of the following are not real numbers? See the Concept Check in this section.

99. $\sqrt{-17}$ **100.** $\sqrt[3]{-17}$

101. $\sqrt[10]{-17}$ **102.** $\sqrt[15]{-17}$

103. Explain why $\sqrt{-64}$ is not a real number.

104. Explain why $\sqrt[3]{-64}$ is a real number.

For Exercises 105 through 108, do not use a calculator.

105. $\sqrt{160}$ is closest to

     a. 10   **b.** 13   **c.** 20   **d.** 40

106. $\sqrt{1000}$ is closest to

     a. 10   **b.** 30   **c.** 100   **d.** 500

107. The perimeter of the triangle is closest to

     a. 12   **b.** 18

     c. 66   **d.** 132

108. The length of the bent wire is closest to

     a. 5   **b.** $\sqrt{28}$

     c. 7   **d.** 14

The Mosteller formula for calculating adult body surface area is $B = \sqrt{\dfrac{hw}{3131}}$, *where B is an individual's body surface area in square meters, h is the individual's height in inches, and w is the individual's weight in pounds. Use this information to answer Exercises 109 and 110. Round answers to 2 decimal places.*

109. Find the body surface area of an individual who is 66 inches tall and who weighs 135 pounds.

110. Find the body surface area of an individual who is 74 inches tall and who weighs 225 pounds.

111. Suppose that a friend tells you that $\sqrt{13} \approx 5.7$. Without a calculator, how can you convince your friend that he or she must have made an error?

112. Escape velocity is the minimum speed that an object must reach to escape a planet's pull of gravity. Escape velocity v is given by the equation $v = \sqrt{\dfrac{2Gm}{r}}$, where m is the mass of the planet, r is its radius, and G is the universal gravitational constant, which has a value of $G = 6.67 \times 10^{-11}$ m^3/kg·sec^2. The mass of Earth is 5.97×10^{24} kg and its radius is 6.37×10^6 m. Use this information to find the escape velocity for Earth. Round to the nearest whole number. (*Source:* National Space Science Data Center)

Use a graphing calculator to verify the domain of each function and its graph.

113. Exercise 85   **114.** Exercise 86

115. Exercise 89   **116.** Exercise 90

📖 STUDY SKILLS BUILDER

How Are Your Homework Assignments Going?

Remember that it is important to keep up with homework. Why? Many concepts in mathematics build on each other. Often, your understanding of a day's lecture depends on an understanding of the previous day's material.

　　To complete a homework assignment, remember these four things:

- Attempt all of it.
- Check it.
- Correct it.
- If needed, ask questions about it.

Take a moment and review your completed homework assignments. Answer the exercises below based on this review.

1. Approximate the fraction of your homework you have attempted.

2. Approximate the fraction of your homework you have checked (if possible).

3. If you are able to check your homework, have you corrected it when errors have been found?

4. What do you do, if you do not understand a concept while working on homework?

7.2 RATIONAL EXPONENTS

OBJECTIVES

1. Understand the meaning of $a^{1/n}$.

2. Understand the meaning of $a^{m/n}$.

3. Understand the meaning of $a^{-m/n}$.

4. Use rules for exponents to simplify expressions that contain rational exponents.

5. Use rational exponents to simplify radical expressions.

OBJECTIVE 1 ▶ Understanding the meaning of $a^{1/n}$**.** So far in this text, we have not defined expressions with rational exponents such as $3^{1/2}$, $x^{2/3}$, and $-9^{-1/4}$. We will define these expressions so that the rules for exponents will apply to these rational exponents as well.

　　Suppose that $x = 5^{1/3}$. Then

$$x^3 = (5^{1/3})^3 = 5^{1/3 \cdot 3} = 5^1 \text{ or } 5$$

$$\underset{\text{using rules}}{\underbrace{\qquad}}$$
$$\text{for exponents}$$

Since $x^3 = 5$, then x is the number whose cube is 5, or $x = \sqrt[3]{5}$. Notice that we also know that $x = 5^{1/3}$. This means

$$5^{1/3} = \sqrt[3]{5}$$

Definition of $a^{1/n}$

If n is a positive integer greater than 1 and $\sqrt[n]{a}$ is a real number, then

$$a^{1/n} = \sqrt[n]{a}$$

Notice that the denominator of the rational exponent corresponds to the index of the radical.

EXAMPLE 1　Use radical notation to write the following. Simplify if possible.

a. $4^{1/2}$　　**b.** $64^{1/3}$　　**c.** $x^{1/4}$　　**d.** $0^{1/6}$　　**e.** $-9^{1/2}$　　**f.** $(81x^8)^{1/4}$　　**g.** $(5y)^{1/3}$

Solution

a. $4^{1/2} = \sqrt{4} = 2$　　　　　　　**b.** $64^{1/3} = \sqrt[3]{64} = 4$

c. $x^{1/4} = \sqrt[4]{x}$　　　　　　　　　**d.** $0^{1/6} = \sqrt[6]{0} = 0$

e. $-9^{1/2} = -\sqrt{9} = -3$　　　　**f.** $(81x^8)^{1/4} = \sqrt[4]{81x^8} = 3x^2$

g. $(5y)^{1/3} = \sqrt[3]{5y}$

1 Use radical notation to write the following. Simplify if possible.

a. $36^{1/2}$ **b.** $1000^{1/3}$ **c.** $x^{1/5}$ **d.** $1^{1/4}$ **e.** $-64^{1/2}$
f. $(125x^9)^{1/3}$ **g.** $(3x)^{1/4}$

OBJECTIVE 2 ▶ **Understanding the meaning of** $a^{m/n}$. As we expand our use of exponents to include $\dfrac{m}{n}$, we define their meaning so that rules for exponents still hold true. For example, by properties of exponents,

$$8^{2/3} = (8^{1/3})^2 = \left(\sqrt[3]{8}\right)^2 \quad \text{or}$$
$$8^{2/3} = (8^2)^{1/3} = \sqrt[3]{8^2}$$

> **Definition of $a^{m/n}$**
> If m and n are positive integers greater than 1 with $\dfrac{m}{n}$ in lowest terms, then
> $$a^{m/n} = \sqrt[n]{a^m} = \left(\sqrt[n]{a}\right)^m$$
> as long as $\sqrt[n]{a}$ is a real number.

Notice that the denominator n of the rational exponent corresponds to the index of the radical. The numerator m of the rational exponent indicates that the base is to be raised to the mth power. This means

$$8^{2/3} = \sqrt[3]{8^2} = \sqrt[3]{64} = 4 \quad \text{or}$$
$$8^{2/3} = \left(\sqrt[3]{8}\right)^2 = 2^2 = 4$$

From simplifying $8^{2/3}$, can you see that it doesn't matter whether you raise to a power first and then take the nth root or you take the nth root first and then raise to a power?

> ▶ **Helpful Hint**
> Most of the time, $\left(\sqrt[n]{a}\right)^m$ will be easier to calculate than $\sqrt[n]{a^m}$.

EXAMPLE 2 Use radical notation to write the following. Then simplify if possible.
a. $4^{3/2}$ **b.** $-16^{3/4}$ **c.** $(-27)^{2/3}$
d. $\left(\dfrac{1}{9}\right)^{3/2}$ **e.** $(4x-1)^{3/5}$

Solution

a. $4^{3/2} = \left(\sqrt{4}\right)^3 = 2^3 = 8$ **b.** $-16^{3/4} = -\left(\sqrt[4]{16}\right)^3 = -(2)^3 = -8$

c. $(-27)^{2/3} = \left(\sqrt[3]{-27}\right)^2 = (-3)^2 = 9$ **d.** $\left(\dfrac{1}{9}\right)^{3/2} = \left(\sqrt{\dfrac{1}{9}}\right)^3 = \left(\dfrac{1}{3}\right)^3 = \dfrac{1}{27}$

e. $(4x-1)^{3/5} = \sqrt[5]{(4x-1)^3}$

2 Use radical notation to write the following. Simplify if possible.

a. $16^{3/2}$ **b.** $-1^{3/5}$ **c.** $-(81)^{3/4}$
d. $\left(\dfrac{1}{25}\right)^{3/2}$ **e.** $(3x+2)^{5/9}$

▶ **Helpful Hint**

The *denominator* of a rational exponent is the index of the corresponding radical. For example, $x^{1/5} = \sqrt[5]{x}$ and $z^{2/3} = \sqrt[3]{z^2}$, or $z^{2/3} = \left(\sqrt[3]{z}\right)^2$.

OBJECTIVE 3 ▶ **Understanding the meaning of** $a^{-m/n}$. The rational exponents we have given meaning to exclude negative rational numbers. To complete the set of definitions, we define $a^{-m/n}$.

Definition of $a^{-m/n}$

$$a^{-m/n} = \frac{1}{a^{m/n}}$$

as long as $a^{m/n}$ is a nonzero real number.

EXAMPLE 3   Write each expression with a positive exponent, and then simplify.

a. $16^{-3/4}$ **b.** $(-27)^{-2/3}$

Solution

a. $16^{-3/4} = \dfrac{1}{16^{3/4}} = \dfrac{1}{\left(\sqrt[4]{16}\right)^3} = \dfrac{1}{2^3} = \dfrac{1}{8}$

b. $(-27)^{-2/3} = \dfrac{1}{(-27)^{2/3}} = \dfrac{1}{\left(\sqrt[3]{-27}\right)^2} = \dfrac{1}{(-3)^2} = \dfrac{1}{9}$

PRACTICE
3   Write each expression with a positive exponent; then simplify.

a. $9^{-3/2}$ **b.** $(-64)^{-2/3}$

▶ **Helpful Hint**

If an expression contains a negative rational exponent, such as $9^{-3/2}$, you may want to first write the expression with a positive exponent and then interpret the rational exponent. Notice that the sign of the base is not affected by the sign of its exponent. For example,

$$9^{-3/2} = \frac{1}{9^{3/2}} = \frac{1}{\left(\sqrt{9}\right)^3} = \frac{1}{27}$$

Also,

$$(-27)^{-1/3} = \frac{1}{(-27)^{1/3}} = -\frac{1}{3}$$

Concept Check ☑
Which one is correct?

a. $-8^{2/3} = \dfrac{1}{4}$ **b.** $8^{-2/3} = -\dfrac{1}{4}$ **c.** $8^{-2/3} = -4$ **d.** $-8^{-2/3} = -\dfrac{1}{4}$

OBJECTIVE 4 ▶ **Using rules for exponents to simplify expressions.** It can be shown that the properties of integer exponents hold for rational exponents. By using these properties and definitions, we can now simplify expressions that contain rational exponents.

These rules are repeated here for review.

Note: For the remainder of this chapter, we will assume that variables represent positive real numbers. Since this is so, we need not insert absolute value bars when we simplify even roots.

Summary of Exponent Rules

If m and n are rational numbers, and a, b, and c are numbers for which the expressions below exist, then

Product rule for exponents: $\qquad\qquad\quad a^m \cdot a^n = a^{m+n}$

Power rule for exponents: $\qquad\qquad\quad (a^m)^n = a^{m \cdot n}$

Power rules for products and quotients: $\quad (ab)^n = a^n b^n \qquad\qquad$ and

$$\left(\frac{a}{c}\right)^n = \frac{a^n}{c^n}, c \neq 0$$

Quotient rule for exponents: $\qquad\qquad \dfrac{a^m}{a^n} = a^{m-n}, a \neq 0$

Zero exponent: $\qquad\qquad\qquad\qquad\quad a^0 = 1, a \neq 0$

Negative exponent: $\qquad\qquad\qquad\quad a^{-n} = \dfrac{1}{a^n}, a \neq 0$

EXAMPLE 4 Use properties of exponents to simplify. Write results with only positive exponents.

a. $b^{1/3} \cdot b^{5/3}$ $\qquad$ **b.** $x^{1/2} x^{1/3}$ $\qquad$ **c.** $\dfrac{7^{1/3}}{7^{4/3}}$

d. $y^{-4/7} \cdot y^{6/7}$ $\qquad$ **e.** $\dfrac{(2x^{2/5} y^{-1/3})^5}{x^2 y}$

Solution

a. $b^{1/3} \cdot b^{5/3} = b^{(1/3+5/3)} = b^{6/3} = b^2$

b. $x^{1/2} x^{1/3} = x^{(1/2+1/3)} = x^{3/6+2/6} = x^{5/6}$ $\quad$ Use the product rule.

c. $\dfrac{7^{1/3}}{7^{4/3}} = 7^{1/3-4/3} = 7^{-3/3} = 7^{-1} = \dfrac{1}{7}$ $\quad$ Use the quotient rule.

d. $y^{-4/7} \cdot y^{6/7} = y^{-4/7+6/7} = y^{2/7}$ $\quad$ Use the product rule.

e. We begin by using the power rule $(ab)^m = a^m b^m$ to simplify the numerator.

$$\frac{(2x^{2/5} y^{-1/3})^5}{x^2 y} = \frac{2^5 (x^{2/5})^5 (y^{-1/3})^5}{x^2 y} = \frac{32 x^2 y^{-5/3}}{x^2 y} \qquad \text{Use the power rule and simplify}$$

$$= 32 x^{2-2} y^{-5/3-3/3} \qquad\qquad \text{Apply the quotient rule.}$$

$$= 32 x^0 y^{-8/3}$$

$$= \frac{32}{y^{8/3}}$$

PRACTICE

4 Use properties of exponents to simplify.

a. $y^{2/3} \cdot y^{8/3}$ $\qquad$ **b.** $x^{3/5} \cdot x^{1/4}$ $\qquad$ **c.** $\dfrac{9^{2/7}}{9^{9/7}}$

d. $b^{4/9} \cdot b^{-2/9}$ $\qquad$ **e.** $\dfrac{\left(3x^{1/4} y^{-2/3}\right)^4}{x^4 y}$

EXAMPLE 5 Multiply.

a. $z^{2/3}(z^{1/3} - z^5)$ $\qquad\qquad\qquad$ **b.** $(x^{1/3} - 5)(x^{1/3} + 2)$

Solution

a. $z^{2/3}(z^{1/3} - z^5) = z^{2/3}z^{1/3} - z^{2/3}z^5$ Apply the distributive property.

$\qquad = z^{(2/3+1/3)} - z^{(2/3+5)}$ Use the product rule.

$\qquad = z^{3/3} - z^{(2/3+15/3)}$

$\qquad = z - z^{17/3}$

b. $(x^{1/3} - 5)(x^{1/3} + 2) = x^{2/3} + 2x^{1/3} - 5x^{1/3} - 10$ Think of $(x^{1/3} - 5)$ and $(x^{1/3} + 2)$

$\qquad = x^{2/3} - 3x^{1/3} - 10$ as 2 binomials, and FOIL.

PRACTICE
5   Multiply.

a. $x^{3/5}(x^{1/3} - x^2)$ 　　　　　　**b.** $(x^{1/2} + 6)(x^{1/2} - 2)$

EXAMPLE 6   Factor $x^{-1/2}$ from the expression $3x^{-1/2} - 7x^{5/2}$. Assume that all variables represent positive numbers.

Solution

$$3x^{-1/2} - 7x^{5/2} = (x^{-1/2})(3) - (x^{-1/2})(7x^{6/2})$$
$$= x^{-1/2}(3 - 7x^3)$$

To check, multiply $x^{-1/2}(3 - 7x^3)$ to see that the product is $3x^{-1/2} - 7x^{5/2}$.

PRACTICE
6   Factor $x^{-1/5}$ from the expression $2x^{-1/5} - 7x^{4/5}$.

OBJECTIVE 5 ▶ Using rational exponents to simplify radical expressions. Some radical expressions are easier to simplify when we first write them with rational exponents. We can simplify some radical expressions by first writing the expression with rational exponents. Use properties of exponents to simplify, and then convert back to radical notation.

EXAMPLE 7   Use rational exponents to simplify. Assume that variables represent positive numbers.

a. $\sqrt[8]{x^4}$ 　　**b.** $\sqrt[6]{25}$ 　　**c.** $\sqrt[4]{r^2s^6}$

Solution

a. $\sqrt[8]{x^4} = x^{4/8} = x^{1/2} = \sqrt{x}$

b. $\sqrt[6]{25} = 25^{1/6} = (5^2)^{1/6} = 5^{2/6} = 5^{1/3} = \sqrt[3]{5}$

c. $\sqrt[4]{r^2s^6} = (r^2s^6)^{1/4} = r^{2/4}s^{6/4} = r^{1/2}s^{3/2} = (rs^3)^{1/2} = \sqrt{rs^3}$

PRACTICE
7   Use rational exponents to simplify. Assume that the variables represent positive numbers.

a. $\sqrt[9]{x^3}$ 　　　　**b.** $\sqrt[4]{36}$ 　　　　**c.** $\sqrt[8]{a^4b^2}$

EXAMPLE 8   Use rational exponents to write as a single radical.

a. $\sqrt{x} \cdot \sqrt[4]{x}$ 　　**b.** $\dfrac{\sqrt{x}}{\sqrt[3]{x}}$ 　　**c.** $\sqrt[3]{3} \cdot \sqrt{2}$

Solution

a. $\sqrt{x} \cdot \sqrt[4]{x} = x^{1/2} \cdot x^{1/4} = x^{1/2+1/4}$

$\qquad\qquad = x^{3/4} = \sqrt[4]{x^3}$

b. $\dfrac{\sqrt{x}}{\sqrt[3]{x}} = \dfrac{x^{1/2}}{x^{1/3}} = x^{1/2-1/3} = x^{3/6-2/6}$

$\qquad\qquad = x^{1/6} = \sqrt[6]{x}$

c. $\sqrt[3]{3} \cdot \sqrt{2} = 3^{1/3} \cdot 2^{1/2}$ Write with rational exponents.

$\qquad\qquad = 3^{2/6} \cdot 2^{3/6}$ Write the exponents so that they have the same denominator.

$\qquad\qquad = (3^2 \cdot 2^3)^{1/6}$ Use $a^n b^n = (ab)^n$

$\qquad\qquad = \sqrt[6]{3^2 \cdot 2^3}$ Write with radical notation.

$\qquad\qquad = \sqrt[6]{72}$ Multiply $3^2 \cdot 2^3$.   □

PRACTICE
8   Use rational expressions to write each of the following as a single radical.

a. $\sqrt[3]{x} \cdot \sqrt[4]{x}$ **b.** $\dfrac{\sqrt[3]{y}}{\sqrt[5]{y}}$ **c.** $\sqrt[3]{5} \cdot \sqrt{3}$

VOCABULARY & READINESS CHECK

Answer each true or false.

1. $9^{-1/2}$ is a positive number. _____

2. $9^{-1/2}$ is a whole number. _____

3. $\dfrac{1}{a^{-m/n}} = a^{m/n}$ (where $a^{m/n}$ is a nonzero real number). _____

Fill in the blank with the correct choice.

4. To simplify $x^{2/3} \cdot x^{1/5}$, _____ the exponents.
   a. add   **b.** subtract   **c.** multiply   **d.** divide

5. To simplify $(x^{2/3})^{1/5}$, _____ the exponents.
   a. add   **b.** subtract   **c.** multiply   **d.** divide

6. To simplify $\dfrac{x^{2/3}}{x^{1/5}}$, _____ the exponents.
   a. add   **b.** subtract   **c.** multiply   **d.** divide

Choose the correct letter for each exercise. Letters will be used more than once. No pencil is needed. Just think about the meaning of each expression.

A = 2, B = −2, C = not a real number

7. $4^{1/2}$ ____   **8.** $-4^{1/2}$ ____   **9.** $(-4)^{1/2}$ ____   **10.** $8^{1/3}$ ____   **11.** $-8^{1/3}$ ____   **12.** $(-8)^{1/3}$ ____

7.2 EXERCISE SET
PRACTICE   WATCH   DOWNLOAD   READ   REVIEW

Use radical notation to write each expression. Simplify if possible.
See Example 1.

1. $49^{1/2}$

2. $64^{1/3}$

3. $27^{1/3}$

4. $8^{1/3}$

5. $\left(\dfrac{1}{16}\right)^{1/4}$

6. $\left(\dfrac{1}{64}\right)^{1/2}$

7. $169^{1/2}$

8. $81^{1/4}$

9. $2m^{1/3}$

10. $(2m)^{1/3}$

11. $(9x^4)^{1/2}$ **12.** $(16x^8)^{1/2}$

13. $(-27)^{1/3}$ **14.** $-64^{1/2}$

15. $-16^{1/4}$ **16.** $(-32)^{1/5}$

Use radical notation to write each expression. Simplify if possible. See Example 2.

17. $16^{3/4}$ **18.** $4^{5/2}$

19. $(-64)^{2/3}$ **20.** $(-8)^{4/3}$

21. $(-16)^{3/4}$ **22.** $(-9)^{3/2}$

23. $(2x)^{3/5}$ **24.** $2x^{3/5}$

25. $(7x+2)^{2/3}$ **26.** $(x-4)^{3/4}$

27. $\left(\dfrac{16}{9}\right)^{3/2}$ **28.** $\left(\dfrac{49}{25}\right)^{3/2}$

Write with positive exponents. Simplify if possible. See Example 3.

29. $8^{-4/3}$ **30.** $64^{-2/3}$

31. $(-64)^{-2/3}$ **32.** $(-8)^{-4/3}$

33. $(-4)^{-3/2}$ **34.** $(-16)^{-5/4}$

35. $x^{-1/4}$ **36.** $y^{-1/6}$

37. $\dfrac{1}{a^{-2/3}}$ **38.** $\dfrac{1}{n^{-8/9}}$

39. $\dfrac{5}{7x^{-3/4}}$ **40.** $\dfrac{2}{3y^{-5/7}}$

Use the properties of exponents to simplify each expression. Write with positive exponents. See Example 4.

41. $a^{2/3}a^{5/3}$ **42.** $b^{9/5}b^{8/5}$

43. $x^{-2/5} \cdot x^{7/5}$ **44.** $y^{4/3} \cdot y^{-1/3}$

45. $3^{1/4} \cdot 3^{3/8}$ **46.** $5^{1/2} \cdot 5^{1/6}$

47. $\dfrac{y^{1/3}}{y^{1/6}}$ **48.** $\dfrac{x^{3/4}}{x^{1/8}}$

49. $(4u^2)^{3/2}$ **50.** $(32^{1/5}x^{2/3})^3$

51. $\dfrac{b^{1/2}b^{3/4}}{-b^{1/4}}$ **52.** $\dfrac{a^{1/4}a^{-1/2}}{a^{2/3}}$

53. $\dfrac{(x^3)^{1/2}}{x^{7/2}}$ **54.** $\dfrac{y^{11/3}}{(y^5)^{1/3}}$

55. $\dfrac{(3x^{1/4})^3}{x^{1/12}}$ **56.** $\dfrac{(2x^{1/5})^4}{x^{3/10}}$

57. $\dfrac{(y^3z)^{1/6}}{y^{-1/2}z^{1/3}}$ **58.** $\dfrac{(m^2n)^{1/4}}{m^{-1/2}n^{5/8}}$

59. $\dfrac{(x^3y^2)^{1/4}}{(x^{-5}y^{-1})^{-1/2}}$ **60.** $\dfrac{(a^{-2}b^3)^{1/8}}{(a^{-3}b)^{-1/4}}$

Multiply. See Example 5.

61. $y^{1/2}(y^{1/2} - y^{2/3})$

62. $x^{1/2}(x^{1/2} + x^{3/2})$

63. $x^{2/3}(x-2)$

64. $3x^{1/2}(x+y)$

65. $(2x^{1/3} + 3)(2x^{1/3} - 3)$

66. $(y^{1/2} + 5)(y^{1/2} + 5)$

Factor the common factor from the given expression. See Example 6.

67. $x^{8/3}$; $x^{8/3} + x^{10/3}$

68. $x^{3/2}$; $x^{5/2} - x^{3/2}$

69. $x^{1/5}$; $x^{2/5} - 3x^{1/5}$

70. $x^{2/7}$; $x^{3/7} - 2x^{2/7}$

71. $x^{-1/3}$; $5x^{-1/3} + x^{2/3}$

72. $x^{-3/4}$; $x^{-3/4} + 3x^{1/4}$

Use rational exponents to simplify each radical. Assume that all variables represent positive numbers. See Example 7.

73. $\sqrt[6]{x^3}$ **74.** $\sqrt[9]{a^3}$

75. $\sqrt[6]{4}$ **76.** $\sqrt[4]{36}$

77. $\sqrt[4]{16x^2}$ **78.** $\sqrt[8]{4y^2}$

79. $\sqrt[8]{x^4y^4}$ **80.** $\sqrt[9]{y^6z^3}$

81. $\sqrt[12]{a^8b^4}$ **82.** $\sqrt[10]{a^5b^5}$

83. $\sqrt[4]{(x+3)^2}$ **84.** $\sqrt[8]{(y+1)^4}$

Use rational expressions to write as a single radical expression. See Example 8.

85. $\sqrt[3]{y} \cdot \sqrt[5]{y^2}$ **86.** $\sqrt[3]{y^2} \cdot \sqrt[6]{y}$

87. $\dfrac{\sqrt[3]{b^2}}{\sqrt[4]{b}}$ **88.** $\dfrac{\sqrt[4]{a}}{\sqrt[5]{a}}$

89. $\sqrt[3]{x} \cdot \sqrt[4]{x} \cdot \sqrt[8]{x^3}$ **90.** $\sqrt[6]{y} \cdot \sqrt[3]{y} \cdot \sqrt[5]{y^2}$

91. $\dfrac{\sqrt[3]{a^2}}{\sqrt[6]{a}}$ **92.** $\dfrac{\sqrt[5]{b^2}}{\sqrt[10]{b^3}}$

93. $\sqrt{3} \cdot \sqrt[3]{4}$ **94.** $\sqrt[3]{5} \cdot \sqrt{2}$

95. $\sqrt[5]{7} \cdot \sqrt[3]{y}$ **96.** $\sqrt[4]{5} \cdot \sqrt[3]{x}$

97. $\sqrt{5r} \cdot \sqrt[3]{s}$ **98.** $\sqrt[3]{b} \cdot \sqrt[5]{4a}$

REVIEW AND PREVIEW

Write each integer as a product of two integers such that one of the factors is a perfect square. For example, write 18 as $9 \cdot 2$, because 9 is a perfect square.

99. 75   **100.** 20

101. 48   **102.** 45

Write each integer as a product of two integers such that one of the factors is a perfect cube. For example, write 24 as $8 \cdot 3$, because 8 is a perfect cube.

103. 16   **104.** 56

105. 54   **106.** 80

CONCEPT EXTENSIONS

Basal metabolic rate (BMR) is the number of calories per day a person needs to maintain life. A person's basal metabolic rate $B(w)$ in calories per day can be estimated with the function $B(w) = 70w^{3/4}$, where w is the person's weight in kilograms. Use this information to answer Exercises 107 and 108.

107. Estimate the BMR for a person who weighs 60 kilograms. Round to the nearest calorie. (*Note:* 60 kilograms is approximately 132 pounds.)

108. Estimate the BMR for a person who weighs 90 kilograms. Round to the nearest calorie. (*Note:* 90 kilograms is approximately 198 pounds.)

The number of cellular telephone subscriptions in the United States from 1996 through 2006 can be modeled by the function $f(x) = 33.3x^{4/5}$, where y is the number of cellular telephone subscriptions in millions, x years after 1996. (Source: Based on data from the Cellular Telecommunications & Internet Association, 1994–2000) Use this information to answer Exercises 109 and 110.

109. Use this model to estimate the number of cellular telephone subscriptions in the United States in 2006. Round to the nearest tenth of a million.

110. Predict the number of cellular telephone subscriptions in the United States in 2010. Round to the nearest tenth of a million.

Fill in each box with the correct expression.

111. $\square \cdot a^{2/3} = a^{3/3}$, or a

112. $\square \cdot x^{1/8} = x^{4/8}$, or $x^{1/2}$

113. $\dfrac{\square}{x^{-2/5}} = x^{3/5}$

114. $\dfrac{\square}{y^{-3/4}} = y^{4/4}$, or y

Use a calculator to write a four-decimal-place approximation of each number.

115. $8^{1/4}$ **116.** $20^{1/5}$

117. $18^{3/5}$ **118.** $76^{5/7}$

119. In physics, the speed of a wave traveling over a stretched string with tension t and density u is given by the expression $\dfrac{\sqrt{t}}{\sqrt{u}}$. Write this expression with rational exponents.

120. In electronics, the angular frequency of oscillations in a certain type of circuit is given by the expression $(LC)^{-1/2}$. Use radical notation to write this expression.

7.3 | SIMPLIFYING RADICAL EXPRESSIONS

OBJECTIVES

1. Use the product rule for radicals.
2. Use the quotient rule for radicals.
3. Simplify radicals.
4. Use the distance and midpoint formula.

OBJECTIVE 1 ▶ Using the product rule. It is possible to simplify some radicals that do not evaluate to rational numbers. To do so, we use a product rule and a quotient rule for radicals. To discover the product rule, notice the following pattern.

$$\sqrt{9} \cdot \sqrt{4} = 3 \cdot 2 = 6$$
$$\sqrt{9 \cdot 4} = \sqrt{36} = 6$$

Since both expressions simplify to 6, it is true that

$$\sqrt{9} \cdot \sqrt{4} = \sqrt{9 \cdot 4}$$

This pattern suggests the following product rule for radicals.

Product Rule for Radicals

If $\sqrt[n]{a}$ and $\sqrt[n]{b}$ are real numbers, then

$$\sqrt[n]{a} \cdot \sqrt[n]{b} = \sqrt[n]{ab}$$

Notice that the product rule is the relationship $a^{1/n} \cdot b^{1/n} = (ab)^{1/n}$ stated in radical notation.

EXAMPLE 1   Multiply.

a. $\sqrt{3} \cdot \sqrt{5}$ **b.** $\sqrt{21} \cdot \sqrt{x}$ **c.** $\sqrt[3]{4} \cdot \sqrt[3]{2}$

d. $\sqrt[4]{5y^2} \cdot \sqrt[4]{2x^3}$ **e.** $\sqrt{\dfrac{2}{a}} \cdot \sqrt{\dfrac{b}{3}}$

Solution

a. $\sqrt{3} \cdot \sqrt{5} = \sqrt{3 \cdot 5} = \sqrt{15}$

b. $\sqrt{21} \cdot \sqrt{x} = \sqrt{21x}$

c. $\sqrt[3]{4} \cdot \sqrt[3]{2} = \sqrt[3]{4 \cdot 2} = \sqrt[3]{8} = 2$

d. $\sqrt[4]{5y^2} \cdot \sqrt[4]{2x^3} = \sqrt[4]{5y^2 \cdot 2x^3} = \sqrt[4]{10y^2x^3}$

e. $\sqrt{\dfrac{2}{a}} \cdot \sqrt{\dfrac{b}{3}} = \sqrt{\dfrac{2}{a} \cdot \dfrac{b}{3}} = \sqrt{\dfrac{2b}{3a}}$

PRACTICE
1   Multiply.

a. $\sqrt{5} \cdot \sqrt{7}$ **b.** $\sqrt{13} \cdot \sqrt{z}$ **c.** $\sqrt[4]{125} \cdot \sqrt[4]{5}$

d. $\sqrt[3]{5y} \cdot \sqrt[3]{3x^2}$ **e.** $\sqrt{\dfrac{5}{m}} \cdot \sqrt{\dfrac{t}{2}}$

OBJECTIVE 2 ▶ Using the quotient rule. To discover a quotient rule for radicals, notice the following pattern.

$$\sqrt{\dfrac{4}{9}} = \dfrac{2}{3}$$

$$\dfrac{\sqrt{4}}{\sqrt{9}} = \dfrac{2}{3}$$

Since both expressions simplify to $\dfrac{2}{3}$, it is true that

$$\sqrt{\dfrac{4}{9}} = \dfrac{\sqrt{4}}{\sqrt{9}}$$

This pattern suggests the following quotient rule for radicals.

> **Quotient Rule for Radicals**
> If $\sqrt[n]{a}$ and $\sqrt[n]{b}$ are real numbers and $\sqrt[n]{b}$ is not zero, then
> $$\sqrt[n]{\dfrac{a}{b}} = \dfrac{\sqrt[n]{a}}{\sqrt[n]{b}}$$

Notice that the quotient rule is the relationship $\left(\dfrac{a}{b}\right)^{1/n} = \dfrac{a^{1/n}}{b^{1/n}}$ stated in radical notation. We can use the quotient rule to simplify radical expressions by reading the rule from left to right, or to divide radicals by reading the rule from right to left.

For example,

$$\sqrt{\frac{x}{16}} = \frac{\sqrt{x}}{\sqrt{16}} = \frac{\sqrt{x}}{4} \qquad \text{Using } \sqrt[n]{\frac{a}{b}} = \frac{\sqrt[n]{a}}{\sqrt[n]{b}}$$

$$\frac{\sqrt{75}}{\sqrt{3}} = \sqrt{\frac{75}{3}} = \sqrt{25} = 5 \qquad \text{Using } \frac{\sqrt[n]{a}}{\sqrt[n]{b}} = \sqrt[n]{\frac{a}{b}}$$

Note: *Recall that from Section 7.2 on, we assume that variables represent positive real numbers. Since this is so, we need not insert absolute value bars when we simplify even roots.*

EXAMPLE 2   Use the quotient rule to simplify.

a. $\sqrt{\dfrac{25}{49}}$ **b.** $\sqrt{\dfrac{x}{9}}$ **c.** $\sqrt[3]{\dfrac{8}{27}}$ **d.** $\sqrt[4]{\dfrac{3}{16y^4}}$

Solution

a. $\sqrt{\dfrac{25}{49}} = \dfrac{\sqrt{25}}{\sqrt{49}} = \dfrac{5}{7}$ **b.** $\sqrt{\dfrac{x}{9}} = \dfrac{\sqrt{x}}{\sqrt{9}} = \dfrac{\sqrt{x}}{3}$

c. $\sqrt[3]{\dfrac{8}{27}} = \dfrac{\sqrt[3]{8}}{\sqrt[3]{27}} = \dfrac{2}{3}$ **d.** $\sqrt[4]{\dfrac{3}{16y^4}} = \dfrac{\sqrt[4]{3}}{\sqrt[4]{16y^4}} = \dfrac{\sqrt[4]{3}}{2y}$

PRACTICE
2   Use the quotient rule to simplify.

a. $\sqrt{\dfrac{36}{49}}$ **b.** $\sqrt{\dfrac{z}{16}}$ **c.** $\sqrt[3]{\dfrac{125}{8}}$ **d.** $\sqrt[4]{\dfrac{5}{81x^8}}$

OBJECTIVE 3 ▶ Simplifying radicals. Both the product and quotient rules can be used to simplify a radical. If the product rule is read from right to left, we have that

$$\sqrt[n]{ab} = \sqrt[n]{a} \cdot \sqrt[n]{b}.$$

This is used to simplify the following radicals.

EXAMPLE 3   Simplify the following.

a. $\sqrt{50}$ **b.** $\sqrt[3]{24}$ **c.** $\sqrt{26}$ **d.** $\sqrt[4]{32}$

Solution

a. Factor 50 such that one factor is the largest perfect square that divides 50. The largest perfect square factor of 50 is 25, so we write 50 as $25 \cdot 2$ and use the product rule for radicals to simplify.

$$\sqrt{50} = \sqrt{25 \cdot 2} = \sqrt{25} \cdot \sqrt{2} = 5\sqrt{2}$$

The largest perfect square factor of 50

> **▶ Helpful Hint**
> Don't forget that, for example, $5\sqrt{2}$ means $5 \cdot \sqrt{2}$.

b. $\sqrt[3]{24} = \sqrt[3]{8 \cdot 3} = \sqrt[3]{8} \cdot \sqrt[3]{3} = 2\sqrt[3]{3}$

The largest perfect cube factor of 24

c. $\sqrt{26}$ The largest perfect square factor of 26 is 1, so $\sqrt{26}$ cannot be simplified further.

d. $\sqrt[4]{32} = \sqrt[4]{16 \cdot 2} = \sqrt[4]{16} \cdot \sqrt[4]{2} = 2\sqrt[4]{2}$

The largest fourth power factor of 32

PRACTICE
3   Simplify the following.

a. $\sqrt{98}$ **b.** $\sqrt[3]{54}$ **c.** $\sqrt{35}$ **d.** $\sqrt[4]{243}$

After simplifying a radical such as a square root, always check the radicand to see that it contains no other perfect square factors. It may, if the largest perfect square factor of the radicand was not originally recognized. For example,

$$\sqrt{200} = \sqrt{4 \cdot 50} = \sqrt{4} \cdot \sqrt{50} = 2\sqrt{50}$$

Notice that the radicand 50 still contains the perfect square factor 25. This is because 4 is not the largest perfect square factor of 200. We continue as follows.

$$2\sqrt{50} = 2\sqrt{25 \cdot 2} = 2 \cdot \sqrt{25} \cdot \sqrt{2} = 2 \cdot 5 \cdot \sqrt{2} = 10\sqrt{2}$$

The radical is now simplified since 2 contains no perfect square factors (other than 1).

▶ **Helpful Hint**

To help you recognize largest perfect power factors of a radicand, it will help if you are familiar with some perfect powers. A few are listed below.

Perfect Squares	1,	4,	9,	16,	25,	36,	49,	64,	81,	100,	121,	144
	1^2	2^2	3^2	4^2	5^2	6^2	7^2	8^2	9^2	10^2	11^2	12^2

Perfect Cubes	1,	8,	27,	64,	125
	1^3	2^3	3^3	4^3	5^3

Perfect Fourth Powers	1,	16,	81,	256
	1^4	2^4	3^4	4^4

In general, we say that a radicand of the form $\sqrt[n]{a}$ is simplified when the radicand a contains no factors that are perfect nth powers (other than 1 or -1).

EXAMPLE 4   Use the product rule to simplify.

a. $\sqrt{25x^3}$ **b.** $\sqrt[3]{54x^6y^8}$ **c.** $\sqrt[4]{81z^{11}}$

Solution

a. $\sqrt{25x^3} = \sqrt{25x^2 \cdot x}$ Find the largest perfect square factor.

$\qquad\quad = \sqrt{25x^2} \cdot \sqrt{x}$ Apply the product rule.

$\qquad\quad = 5x\sqrt{x}$ Simplify.

b. $\sqrt[3]{54x^6y^8} = \sqrt[3]{27 \cdot 2 \cdot x^6 \cdot y^6 \cdot y^2}$ Factor the radicand and identify perfect cube factors.

$\qquad\quad = \sqrt[3]{27x^6y^6 \cdot 2y^2}$

$\qquad\quad = \sqrt[3]{27x^6y^6} \cdot \sqrt[3]{2y^2}$ Apply the product rule.

$\qquad\quad = 3x^2y^2\sqrt[3]{2y^2}$ Simplify.

c. $\sqrt[4]{81z^{11}} = \sqrt[4]{81 \cdot z^8 \cdot z^3}$ Factor the radicand and identify perfect fourth power factors.

$\qquad\quad = \sqrt[4]{81z^8} \cdot \sqrt[4]{z^3}$ Apply the product rule.

$\qquad\quad = 3z^2\sqrt[4]{z^3}$ Simplify.   □

PRACTICE
4   Use the product rule to simplify.

a. $\sqrt{36z^7}$ **b.** $\sqrt[3]{32p^4q^7}$ **c.** $\sqrt[4]{16x^{15}}$

EXAMPLE 5   Use the quotient rule to divide, and simplify if possible.

a. $\dfrac{\sqrt{20}}{\sqrt{5}}$ **b.** $\dfrac{\sqrt{50x}}{2\sqrt{2}}$ **c.** $\dfrac{7\sqrt[3]{48x^4y^8}}{\sqrt[3]{6y^2}}$ **d.** $\dfrac{2\sqrt[4]{32a^8b^6}}{\sqrt[4]{a^{-1}b^2}}$

Solution

a. $\dfrac{\sqrt{20}}{\sqrt{5}} = \sqrt{\dfrac{20}{5}}$ Apply the quotient rule.

   $= \sqrt{4}$ Simplify.
   $= 2$ Simplify.

b. $\dfrac{\sqrt{50x}}{2\sqrt{2}} = \dfrac{1}{2} \cdot \sqrt{\dfrac{50x}{2}}$ Apply the quotient rule.

   $= \dfrac{1}{2} \cdot \sqrt{25x}$ Simplify.

   $= \dfrac{1}{2} \cdot \sqrt{25} \cdot \sqrt{x}$ Factor 25x.

   $= \dfrac{1}{2} \cdot 5 \cdot \sqrt{x}$ Simplify.

   $= \dfrac{5}{2}\sqrt{x}$

c. $\dfrac{7\sqrt[3]{48x^4y^8}}{\sqrt[3]{6y^2}} = 7 \cdot \sqrt[3]{\dfrac{48x^4y^8}{6y^2}}$ Apply the quotient rule.

   $= 7 \cdot \sqrt[3]{8x^4y^6}$ Simplify.

   $= 7\sqrt[3]{8x^3y^6 \cdot x}$ Factor.

   $= 7 \cdot \sqrt[3]{8x^3y^6} \cdot \sqrt[3]{x}$ Apply the product rule.

   $= 7 \cdot 2xy^2 \cdot \sqrt[3]{x}$ Simplify.

   $= 14xy^2\sqrt[3]{x}$

d. $\dfrac{2\sqrt[4]{32a^8b^6}}{\sqrt[4]{a^{-1}b^2}} = 2\sqrt[4]{\dfrac{32a^8b^6}{a^{-1}b^2}} = 2\sqrt[4]{32a^9b^4} = 2\sqrt[4]{16 \cdot a^8 \cdot b^4 \cdot 2 \cdot a}$

   $= 2\sqrt[4]{16a^8b^4} \cdot \sqrt[4]{2a} = 2 \cdot 2a^2b \cdot \sqrt[4]{2a} = 4a^2b\sqrt[4]{2a}$

PRACTICE
5   Use the quotient rule to divide and simplify.

a. $\dfrac{\sqrt{80}}{\sqrt{5}}$ **b.** $\dfrac{\sqrt{98z}}{3\sqrt{2}}$ **c.** $\dfrac{5\sqrt[3]{40x^5y^7}}{\sqrt[3]{5y}}$ **d.** $\dfrac{3\sqrt[5]{64x^9y^8}}{\sqrt[5]{x^{-1}y^2}}$

Concept Check ☑
Find and correct the error:

$$\frac{\sqrt[3]{27}}{\sqrt{9}} \;\; \cancel{=} \;\; \sqrt[3]{\frac{27}{9}} = \sqrt[3]{3}$$

Answer to Concept Check:
$\dfrac{\sqrt[3]{27}}{\sqrt{9}} = \dfrac{3}{3} = 1$

OBJECTIVE 4 ▶ Using the distance and midpoint formulas. Now that we know how to simplify radicals, we can derive and use the distance formula. The midpoint formula is often confused with the distance formula, so to clarify both, we will also review the midpoint formula.

The Cartesian coordinate system helps us visualize a distance between points. To find the distance between two points, we use the distance formula, which is derived from the Pythagorean theorem.

To find the distance d between two points (x_1, y_1) and (x_2, y_2) as shown to the left, notice that the length of leg a is $x_2 - x_1$ and that the length of leg b is $y_2 - y_1$.

Thus, the Pythagorean theorem tells us that

$$d^2 = a^2 + b^2$$

or

$$d^2 = (x_2 - x_1)^2 + (y_2 - y_1)^2$$

or

$$d = \sqrt{(x_2 - x_1)^2 + (y_2 - y_1)^2}$$

This formula gives us the distance between any two points on the real plane.

> **Distance Formula**
>
> The distance d between two points (x_1, y_1) and (x_2, y_2) is given by
> $$d = \sqrt{(x_2 - x_1)^2 + (y_2 - y_1)^2}$$

EXAMPLE 6 Find the distance between $(2, -5)$ and $(1, -4)$. Give an exact distance and a three-decimal-place approximation.

Solution To use the distance formula, it makes no difference which point we call (x_1, y_1) and which point we call (x_2, y_2). We will let $(x_1, y_1) = (2, -5)$ and $(x_2, y_2) = (1, -4)$.

$$
\begin{aligned}
d &= \sqrt{(x_2 - x_1)^2 + (y_2 - y_1)^2} \\
  &= \sqrt{(1 - 2)^2 + [-4 - (-5)]^2} \\
  &= \sqrt{(-1)^2 + (1)^2} \\
  &= \sqrt{1 + 1} \\
  &= \sqrt{2} \approx 1.414
\end{aligned}
$$

The distance between the two points is exactly $\sqrt{2}$ units, or approximately 1.414 units.

PRACTICE

6 Find the distance between $P(-3, 7)$ and $Q(-2, 3)$. Give an exact distance and a three-decimal-place approximation.

The **midpoint** of a line segment is the **point** located exactly halfway between the two endpoints of the line segment. On the graph to the left, the point M is the midpoint of line segment PQ. Thus, the distance between M and P equals the distance between M and Q.

Note: We usually need no knowledge of roots to calculate the midpoint of a line segment. We review midpoint here only because it is often confused with the distance between two points.

The x-coordinate of M is at half the distance between the x-coordinates of P and Q, and the y-coordinate of M is at half the distance between the y-coordinates of P and Q. That is, the x-coordinate of M is the average of the x-coordinates of P and Q; the y-coordinate of M is the average of the y-coordinates of P and Q.

> **Midpoint Formula**
>
> The midpoint of the line segment whose endpoints are (x_1, y_1) and (x_2, y_2) is the point with coordinates
>
> $$\left(\frac{x_1 + x_2}{2}, \frac{y_1 + y_2}{2} \right)$$

EXAMPLE 7 Find the midpoint of the line segment that joins points $P(-3, 3)$ and $Q(1, 0)$.

Solution Use the midpoint formula. It makes no difference which point we call (x_1, y_1) or which point we call (x_2, y_2). Let $(x_1, y_1) = (-3, 3)$ and $(x_2, y_2) = (1, 0)$.

$$\text{midpoint} = \left(\frac{x_1 + x_2}{2}, \frac{y_1 + y_2}{2} \right)$$

$$= \left(\frac{-3 + 1}{2}, \frac{3 + 0}{2} \right)$$

$$= \left(\frac{-2}{2}, \frac{3}{2} \right)$$

$$= \left(-1, \frac{3}{2} \right)$$

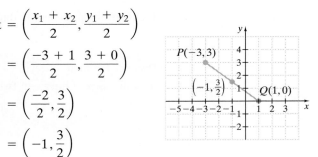

The midpoint of the segment is $\left(-1, \dfrac{3}{2} \right)$.

PRACTICE
7 Find the midpoint of the line segment that joins points $P(5, -2)$ and $Q(8, -6)$.

> ▶ **Helpful Hint**
>
> The distance between two points is a distance. The midpoint of a line segment is the point halfway between the endpoints of the segment.
>
> distance—measured in units
>
> midpoint—it is a point

VOCABULARY & READINESS CHECK

Use the choices below to fill in each blank. Some choices may be used more than once.

distance   midpoint   point

1. The _____ of a line segment is a _____ exactly halfway between the two endpoints of the line segment.

2. The _____ formula is $d = \sqrt{(x_2 - x_1)^2 + (y_2 - y_1)^2}$.

3. The _____ formula is $\left(\dfrac{x_1 + x_2}{2}, \dfrac{y_1 + y_2}{2} \right)$.

Answer true or false. Assume all radicals represent nonzero real numbers.

4. $\sqrt[n]{a} \cdot \sqrt[n]{b} = \sqrt[n]{ab}$ _____

5. $\sqrt[3]{7} \cdot \sqrt[3]{11} = \sqrt[3]{18}$ _____

6. $\sqrt[3]{7} \cdot \sqrt{11} = \sqrt{77}$ _____

7. $\sqrt{x^7 y^8} = \sqrt{x^7} \cdot \sqrt{y^8}$ _____

8. $\dfrac{\sqrt[n]{a}}{\sqrt[n]{b}} = \sqrt[n]{\dfrac{a}{b}}$ _____

9. $\dfrac{\sqrt[3]{12}}{\sqrt[3]{4}} = \sqrt[3]{8}$ _____

10. $\dfrac{\sqrt[n]{x^7}}{\sqrt[n]{x}} = \sqrt[n]{x^6}$ _____

7.3 | EXERCISE SET

MyMathLab *Powered by CourseCompass™ and MathXL®*

PRACTICE   WATCH   DOWNLOAD   READ   REVIEW

Use the product rule to multiply. See Example 1.

1. $\sqrt{7} \cdot \sqrt{2}$

2. $\sqrt{11} \cdot \sqrt{10}$

3. $\sqrt[4]{8} \cdot \sqrt[4]{2}$

4. $\sqrt[4]{27} \cdot \sqrt[4]{3}$

5. $\sqrt[3]{4} \cdot \sqrt[3]{9}$

6. $\sqrt[3]{10} \cdot \sqrt[3]{5}$

7. $\sqrt{2} \cdot \sqrt{3x}$

8. $\sqrt{3y} \cdot \sqrt{5x}$

9. $\sqrt{\dfrac{7}{x}} \cdot \sqrt{\dfrac{2}{y}}$

10. $\sqrt{\dfrac{6}{m}} \cdot \sqrt{\dfrac{n}{5}}$

11. $\sqrt[4]{4x^3} \cdot \sqrt[4]{5}$

12. $\sqrt[4]{ab^2} \cdot \sqrt[4]{27ab}$

Use the quotient rule to simplify. See Examples 2 and 3.

13. $\sqrt{\dfrac{6}{49}}$

14. $\sqrt{\dfrac{8}{81}}$

15. $\sqrt{\dfrac{2}{49}}$

16. $\sqrt{\dfrac{5}{121}}$

17. $\sqrt[4]{\dfrac{x^3}{16}}$

18. $\sqrt[4]{\dfrac{y}{81x^4}}$

19. $\sqrt[3]{\dfrac{4}{27}}$

20. $\sqrt[3]{\dfrac{3}{64}}$

21. $\sqrt[4]{\dfrac{8}{x^8}}$

22. $\sqrt[4]{\dfrac{a^3}{81}}$

23. $\sqrt[3]{\dfrac{2x}{81y^{12}}}$

24. $\sqrt[3]{\dfrac{3}{8x^6}}$

25. $\sqrt{\dfrac{x^2 y}{100}}$

26. $\sqrt{\dfrac{y^2 z}{36}}$

27. $\sqrt{\dfrac{5x^2}{4y^2}}$

28. $\sqrt{\dfrac{y^{10}}{9x^6}}$

29. $-\sqrt[3]{\dfrac{z^7}{27x^3}}$

30. $-\sqrt[3]{\dfrac{64a}{b^9}}$

Simplify. See Examples 3 and 4.

31. $\sqrt{32}$

32. $\sqrt{27}$

33. $\sqrt[3]{192}$

34. $\sqrt[3]{108}$

35. $5\sqrt{75}$

36. $3\sqrt{8}$

37. $\sqrt{24}$

38. $\sqrt{20}$

39. $\sqrt{100x^5}$

40. $\sqrt{64y^9}$

41. $\sqrt[3]{16y^7}$

42. $\sqrt[3]{64y^9}$

43. $\sqrt[4]{a^8 b^7}$

44. $\sqrt[5]{32z^{12}}$

45. $\sqrt{y^5}$

46. $\sqrt[3]{y^5}$

47. $\sqrt{25a^2 b^3}$

48. $\sqrt{9x^5 y^7}$

49. $\sqrt[5]{-32x^{10}y}$

50. $\sqrt[5]{-243z^9}$

51. $\sqrt[3]{50x^{14}}$

52. $\sqrt[3]{40y^{10}}$

53. $-\sqrt{32a^8 b^7}$

54. $-\sqrt{20ab^6}$

55. $\sqrt{9x^7 y^9}$

56. $\sqrt{12r^9 s^{12}}$

57. $\sqrt[3]{125r^9 s^{12}}$

58. $\sqrt[3]{8a^6 b^9}$

Use the quotient rule to divide. Then simplify if possible. See Example 5.

59. $\dfrac{\sqrt{14}}{\sqrt{7}}$

60. $\dfrac{\sqrt{45}}{\sqrt{9}}$

61. $\dfrac{\sqrt[3]{24}}{\sqrt[3]{3}}$

62. $\dfrac{\sqrt[3]{10}}{\sqrt[3]{2}}$

63. $\dfrac{5\sqrt[4]{48}}{\sqrt[4]{3}}$

64. $\dfrac{7\sqrt[4]{162}}{\sqrt[4]{2}}$

65. $\dfrac{\sqrt{x^5 y^3}}{\sqrt{xy}}$

66. $\dfrac{\sqrt{a^7 b^6}}{\sqrt{a^3 b^2}}$

67. $\dfrac{8\sqrt[3]{54m^7}}{\sqrt[3]{2m}}$

68. $\dfrac{\sqrt[3]{128x^3}}{-3\sqrt[3]{2x}}$

69. $\dfrac{3\sqrt{100x^2}}{2\sqrt{2x^{-1}}}$

70. $\dfrac{\sqrt{270y^2}}{5\sqrt{3y^{-4}}}$

71. $\dfrac{\sqrt[4]{96a^{10}b^3}}{\sqrt[4]{3a^2 b^3}}$

72. $\dfrac{\sqrt[5]{64x^{10}y^3}}{\sqrt[5]{2x^3 y^{-7}}}$

Find the distance between each pair of points. Give an exact distance and a three-decimal-place approximation. See Example 6.

73. $(5, 1)$ and $(8, 5)$

74. $(2, 3)$ and $(14, 8)$

75. $(-3, 2)$ and $(1, -3)$

76. $(3, -2)$ and $(-4, 1)$

77. $(-9, 4)$ and $(-8, 1)$

78. $(-5, -2)$ and $(-6, -6)$

79. $\left(0, -\sqrt{2}\right)$ and $\left(\sqrt{3}, 0\right)$

80. $\left(-\sqrt{5}, 0\right)$ and $\left(0, \sqrt{7}\right)$

81. $(1.7, -3.6)$ and $(-8.6, 5.7)$

82. $(9.6, 2.5)$ and $(-1.9, -3.7)$

Find the midpoint of the line segment whose endpoints are given. See Example 7.

83. $(6, -8), (2, 4)$

84. $(3, 9), (7, 11)$

85. $(-2, -1), (-8, 6)$

86. $(-3, -4), (6, -8)$

87. $(7, 3), (-1, -3)$

88. $(-2, 5), (-1, 6)$

89. $\left(\frac{1}{2}, \frac{3}{8}\right), \left(-\frac{3}{2}, \frac{5}{8}\right)$

90. $\left(-\frac{2}{5}, \frac{7}{15}\right), \left(-\frac{2}{5}, -\frac{4}{15}\right)$

91. $\left(\sqrt{2}, 3\sqrt{5}\right), \left(\sqrt{2}, -2\sqrt{5}\right)$

92. $\left(\sqrt{8}, -\sqrt{12}\right), \left(3\sqrt{2}, 7\sqrt{3}\right)$

93. $(4.6, -3.5), (7.8, -9.8)$

94. $(-4.6, 2.1), (-6.7, 1.9)$

REVIEW AND PREVIEW

Perform each indicated operation. See Sections 1.4 and 5.4.

95. $6x + 8x$

96. $(6x)(8x)$

97. $(2x + 3)(x - 5)$

98. $(2x + 3) + (x - 5)$

99. $9y^2 - 8y^2$

100. $(9y^2)(-8y^2)$

101. $-3(x + 5)$

102. $-3 + x + 5$

103. $(x - 4)^2$

104. $(2x + 1)^2$

CONCEPT EXTENSIONS

Find and correct the error. See a Concept Check in this section.

105. $\dfrac{\sqrt[3]{64}}{\sqrt{64}} = \sqrt[3]{\dfrac{64}{64}} = \sqrt[3]{1} = 1$

106. $\dfrac{\sqrt[4]{16}}{\sqrt{4}} = \sqrt[4]{\dfrac{16}{4}} = \sqrt[4]{4}$

Simplify. See a Concept Check in this section. Assume variables represent positive numbers.

107. $\sqrt[5]{x^{35}}$

108. $\sqrt[6]{y^{48}}$

109. $\sqrt[4]{a^{12}b^4c^{20}}$

110. $\sqrt[3]{a^9b^{21}c^3}$

111. $\sqrt[3]{z^{32}}$

112. $\sqrt[5]{x^{49}}$

113. $\sqrt{q^{17}r^{40}s^7}$

114. $\sqrt[4]{p^{11}q^4r^{45}}$

115. The formula for the radius r of a sphere with surface area A is given by $r = \sqrt{\dfrac{A}{4\pi}}$. Calculate the radius of a standard zorb whose outside surface area is 32.17 sq m. Round to the nearest tenth. (See the chapter opener, page 378. *Source:* Zorb, Ltd.)

116. The formula for the surface area A of a cone with height h and radius r is given by
$$A = \pi r \sqrt{r^2 + h^2}$$

   a. Find the surface area of a cone whose height is 3 centimeters and whose radius is 4 centimeters.

   b. Approximate to two decimal places the surface area of a cone whose height is 7.2 feet and whose radius is 6.8 feet.

117. The owner of Knightime Video has determined that the demand equation for renting older releases is given by the equation $F(x) = 0.6\sqrt{49 - x^2}$, where x is the price in dollars per two-day rental and $F(x)$ is the number of times the video is demanded per week.

   a. Approximate to one decimal place the demand per week of an older release if the rental price is $3 per two-day rental.

   b. Approximate to one decimal place the demand per week of an older release if the rental price is $5 per two-day rental.

   c. Explain how the owner of the video store can use this equation to predict the number of copies of each tape that should be in stock.

118. Before Mount Vesuvius, a volcano in Italy, erupted violently in 79 A.D., its height was 4190 feet. Vesuvius was roughly cone-shaped, and its base had a radius of approximately 25,200 feet. Use the formula for the surface area of a cone, given in Exercise 116, to approximate the surface area this volcano had before it erupted. (*Source:* Global Volcanism Network)

4190 ft

25,200 ft

7.4 ADDING, SUBTRACTING, AND MULTIPLYING RADICAL EXPRESSIONS

OBJECTIVE 1 ▶ Adding or subtracting radical expressions. We have learned that sums or differences of like terms can be simplified. To simplify these sums or differences, we use the distributive property. For example,

$$2x + 3x = (2 + 3)x = 5x \quad \text{and} \quad 7x^2y - 4x^2y = (7 - 4)x^2y = 3x^2y$$

The distributive property can also be used to add **like radicals.**

> **Like Radicals**
>
> Radicals with the same index and the same radicand are like radicals.

For example, $2\sqrt{7} + 3\sqrt{7} = (2 + 3)\sqrt{7} = 5\sqrt{7}$. Also,

Like radicals

$$5\sqrt{3x} - 7\sqrt{3x} = (5 - 7)\sqrt{3x} = -2\sqrt{3x}$$

The expression $2\sqrt{7} + 2\sqrt[3]{7}$ cannot be simplified further since $2\sqrt{7}$ and $2\sqrt[3]{7}$ are not like radicals.

Unlike radicals

EXAMPLE 1 Add or subtract as indicated. Assume all variables represent positive real numbers.

a. $4\sqrt{11} + 8\sqrt{11}$ **b.** $5\sqrt[3]{3x} - 7\sqrt[3]{3x}$ **c.** $2\sqrt{7} + 2\sqrt[3]{7}$

Solution

a. $4\sqrt{11} + 8\sqrt{11} = (4 + 8)\sqrt{11} = 12\sqrt{11}$

b. $5\sqrt[3]{3x} - 7\sqrt[3]{3x} = (5 - 7)\sqrt[3]{3x} = -2\sqrt[3]{3x}$

c. $2\sqrt{7} + 2\sqrt[3]{7}$

This expression cannot be simplified since $2\sqrt{7}$ and $2\sqrt[3]{7}$ do not contain like radicals.

□

PRACTICE

1 Add or subtract as indicated.

a. $3\sqrt{17} + 5\sqrt{17}$ **b.** $7\sqrt[3]{5z} - 12\sqrt[3]{5z}$ **c.** $3\sqrt{2} + 5\sqrt[3]{2}$

When adding or subtracting radicals, always check first to see whether any radicals can be simplified.

Concept Check ☑

True or false?

$$\sqrt{a} + \sqrt{b} = \sqrt{a + b}$$

Explain.

Answer to Concept Check:
false; answers may vary

EXAMPLE 2   Add or subtract. Assume that variables represent positive real numbers.

a. $\sqrt{20} + 2\sqrt{45}$ **b.** $\sqrt[3]{54} - 5\sqrt[3]{16} + \sqrt[3]{2}$ **c.** $\sqrt{27x} - 2\sqrt{9x} + \sqrt{72x}$
d. $\sqrt[3]{98} + \sqrt{98}$ **e.** $\sqrt[3]{48y^4} + \sqrt[3]{6y^4}$

Solution   First, simplify each radical. Then add or subtract any like radicals.

a.
$$\begin{aligned}
\sqrt{20} + 2\sqrt{45} &= \sqrt{4\cdot 5} + 2\sqrt{9\cdot 5} && \text{Factor 20 and 45.}\\
&= \sqrt{4}\cdot\sqrt{5} + 2\cdot\sqrt{9}\cdot\sqrt{5} && \text{Use the product rule.}\\
&= 2\cdot\sqrt{5} + 2\cdot 3\cdot\sqrt{5} && \text{Simplify } \sqrt{4} \text{ and } \sqrt{9}.\\
&= 2\sqrt{5} + 6\sqrt{5} && \text{Add like radicals.}\\
&= 8\sqrt{5}
\end{aligned}$$

b.
$$\begin{aligned}
\sqrt[3]{54} - 5\sqrt[3]{16} + \sqrt[3]{2}\\
= \sqrt[3]{27}\cdot\sqrt[3]{2} - 5\cdot\sqrt[3]{8}\cdot\sqrt[3]{2} + \sqrt[3]{2} && \text{Factor and use the product rule.}\\
= 3\cdot\sqrt[3]{2} - 5\cdot 2\cdot\sqrt[3]{2} + \sqrt[3]{2} && \text{Simplify } \sqrt[3]{27} \text{ and } \sqrt[3]{8}.\\
= 3\sqrt[3]{2} - 10\sqrt[3]{2} + \sqrt[3]{2} && \text{Write } 5\cdot 2 \text{ as 10.}\\
= -6\sqrt[3]{2} && \text{Combine like radicals.}
\end{aligned}$$

c.
$$\begin{aligned}
\sqrt{27x} - 2\sqrt{9x} + \sqrt{72x}\\
= \sqrt{9}\cdot\sqrt{3x} - 2\cdot\sqrt{9}\cdot\sqrt{x} + \sqrt{36}\cdot\sqrt{2x} && \text{Factor and use the product rule.}\\
= 3\cdot\sqrt{3x} - 2\cdot 3\cdot\sqrt{x} + 6\cdot\sqrt{2x} && \text{Simplify } \sqrt{9} \text{ and } \sqrt{36}.\\
= 3\sqrt{3x} - 6\sqrt{x} + 6\sqrt{2x} && \text{Write } 2\cdot 3 \text{ as 6.}
\end{aligned}$$

> ▶ **Helpful Hint**
> None of these terms contain like radicals. We can simplify no further.

d.
$$\begin{aligned}
\sqrt[3]{98} + \sqrt{98} &= \sqrt[3]{98} + \sqrt{49}\cdot\sqrt{2} && \text{Factor and use the product rule.}\\
&= \sqrt[3]{98} + 7\sqrt{2} && \text{No further simplification is possible.}
\end{aligned}$$

e.
$$\begin{aligned}
\sqrt[3]{48y^4} + \sqrt[3]{6y^4} &= \sqrt[3]{8y^3}\cdot\sqrt[3]{6y} + \sqrt[3]{y^3}\cdot\sqrt[3]{6y} && \text{Factor and use the product rule.}\\
&= 2y\sqrt[3]{6y} + y\sqrt[3]{6y} && \text{Simplify } \sqrt[3]{8y^3} \text{ and } \sqrt[3]{y^3}.\\
&= 3y\sqrt[3]{6y} && \text{Combine like radicals.} \qquad \square
\end{aligned}$$

PRACTICE
2   Add or subtract.

a. $\sqrt{24} + 3\sqrt{54}$ **b.** $\sqrt[3]{24} - 4\sqrt[3]{81} + \sqrt[3]{3}$ **c.** $\sqrt{75x} - 3\sqrt{27x} + \sqrt{12x}$
d. $\sqrt{40} + \sqrt[3]{40}$ **e.** $\sqrt[3]{81x^4} + \sqrt[3]{3x^4}$

Let's continue to assume that variables represent positive real numbers.

EXAMPLE 3   Add or subtract as indicated.

a. $\dfrac{\sqrt{45}}{4} - \dfrac{\sqrt{5}}{3}$ **b.** $\sqrt[3]{\dfrac{7x}{8}} + 2\sqrt[3]{7x}$

Solution

a.
$$\begin{aligned}
\frac{\sqrt{45}}{4} - \frac{\sqrt{5}}{3} &= \frac{3\sqrt{5}}{4} - \frac{\sqrt{5}}{3} && \text{To subtract, notice that the LCD is 12.}\\
&= \frac{3\sqrt{5}\cdot 3}{4\cdot 3} - \frac{\sqrt{5}\cdot 4}{3\cdot 4} && \text{Write each expression as an equivalent expression with a denominator of 12.}\\
&= \frac{9\sqrt{5}}{12} - \frac{4\sqrt{5}}{12} && \text{Multiply factors in the numerator and the denominator.}\\
&= \frac{5\sqrt{5}}{12} && \text{Subtract.}
\end{aligned}$$

b. $\sqrt[3]{\dfrac{7x}{8}} + 2\sqrt[3]{7x} = \dfrac{\sqrt[3]{7x}}{\sqrt[3]{8}} + 2\sqrt[3]{7x}$ Apply the quotient rule for radicals.

$\qquad = \dfrac{\sqrt[3]{7x}}{2} + 2\sqrt[3]{7x}$ Simplify.

$\qquad = \dfrac{\sqrt[3]{7x}}{2} + \dfrac{2\sqrt[3]{7x}\cdot 2}{2}$ Write each expression as an equivalent expression with a denominator of 2.

$\qquad = \dfrac{\sqrt[3]{7x}}{2} + \dfrac{4\sqrt[3]{7x}}{2}$

$\qquad = \dfrac{5\sqrt[3]{7x}}{2}$ Add. □

PRACTICE
3   Add or subtract as indicated.

a. $\dfrac{\sqrt{28}}{3} - \dfrac{\sqrt{7}}{4}$

b. $\sqrt[3]{\dfrac{6y}{64}} + 3\sqrt[3]{6y}$

OBJECTIVE 2 ▶ Multiplying radical expressions. We can multiply radical expressions by using many of the same properties used to multiply polynomial expressions. For instance, to multiply $\sqrt{2}(\sqrt{6} - 3\sqrt{2})$, we use the distributive property and multiply $\sqrt{2}$ by each term inside the parentheses.

$\sqrt{2}(\sqrt{6} - 3\sqrt{2}) = \sqrt{2}(\sqrt{6}) - \sqrt{2}(3\sqrt{2})$ Use the distributive property.

$\qquad = \sqrt{2\cdot 6} - 3\sqrt{2\cdot 2}$

$\qquad = \sqrt{2\cdot 2\cdot 3} - 3\cdot 2$ Use the product rule for radicals.

$\qquad = 2\sqrt{3} - 6$

EXAMPLE 4   Multiply.

a. $\sqrt{3}(5 + \sqrt{30})$ **b.** $(\sqrt{5} - \sqrt{6})(\sqrt{7} + 1)$ **c.** $(7\sqrt{x} + 5)(3\sqrt{x} - \sqrt{5})$

d. $(4\sqrt{3} - 1)^2$ **e.** $(\sqrt{2x} - 5)(\sqrt{2x} + 5)$ **f.** $(\sqrt{x - 3} + 5)^2$

Solution

a. $\sqrt{3}(5 + \sqrt{30}) = \sqrt{3}(5) + \sqrt{3}(\sqrt{30})$

$\qquad = 5\sqrt{3} + \sqrt{3\cdot 30}$

$\qquad = 5\sqrt{3} + \sqrt{3\cdot 3\cdot 10}$

$\qquad = 5\sqrt{3} + 3\sqrt{10}$

b. To multiply, we can use the FOIL method.

$$(\sqrt{5} - \sqrt{6})(\sqrt{7} + 1) = \overset{\text{First}}{\sqrt{5}\cdot\sqrt{7}} + \overset{\text{Outer}}{\sqrt{5}\cdot 1} - \overset{\text{Inner}}{\sqrt{6}\cdot\sqrt{7}} - \overset{\text{Last}}{\sqrt{6}\cdot 1}$$

$\qquad = \sqrt{35} + \sqrt{5} - \sqrt{42} - \sqrt{6}$

c. $(7\sqrt{x} + 5)(3\sqrt{x} - \sqrt{5}) = 7\sqrt{x}(3\sqrt{x}) - 7\sqrt{x}(\sqrt{5}) + 5(3\sqrt{x}) - 5(\sqrt{5})$

$\qquad = 21x - 7\sqrt{5x} + 15\sqrt{x} - 5\sqrt{5}$

d. $(4\sqrt{3} - 1)^2 = (4\sqrt{3} - 1)(4\sqrt{3} - 1)$

$\qquad = 4\sqrt{3}(4\sqrt{3}) - 4\sqrt{3}(1) - 1(4\sqrt{3}) - 1(-1)$

$\qquad = 16\cdot 3 - 4\sqrt{3} - 4\sqrt{3} + 1$

$\qquad = 48 - 8\sqrt{3} + 1$

$\qquad = 49 - 8\sqrt{3}$

e. $\left(\sqrt{2x} - 5\right)\left(\sqrt{2x} + 5\right) = \sqrt{2x} \cdot \sqrt{2x} + 5\sqrt{2x} - 5\sqrt{2x} - 5 \cdot 5$

$$= 2x - 25$$

f. $\underbrace{\left(\sqrt{x-3} + 5\right)^2}_{} = \underbrace{\left(\sqrt{x-3}\right)^2}_{} + \underbrace{2 \cdot \sqrt{x-3}}_{} \cdot 5 + 5^2$

$$\underset{a}{\uparrow} \quad \underset{b}{\uparrow} \qquad \underset{a^2}{\uparrow} \quad \underset{+\,2\,\cdot}{\uparrow\uparrow} \quad \underset{a}{\uparrow} \quad \underset{\cdot\, b}{\uparrow} + \underset{b^2}{\uparrow}$$

$$= x - 3 + 10\sqrt{x-3} + 25 \qquad \text{Simplify.}$$

$$= x + 22 + 10\sqrt{x-3} \qquad \text{Combine like terms.} \qquad \square$$

PRACTICE
4 Multiply.

a. $\sqrt{5}\left(2 + \sqrt{15}\right)$ **b.** $\left(\sqrt{2} - \sqrt{5}\right)\left(\sqrt{6} + 2\right)$

c. $\left(3\sqrt{z} - 4\right)\left(2\sqrt{z} + 3\right)$ **d.** $\left(\sqrt{6} - 3\right)^2$

e. $\left(\sqrt{5x} + 3\right)\left(\sqrt{5x} - 3\right)$ **f.** $\left(\sqrt{x+2} + 3\right)^2$

VOCABULARY & READINESS CHECK

Complete the table with "Like" or "Unlike."

	Terms	Like or Unlike Radical Terms?
1.	$\sqrt{7}, \sqrt[3]{7}$	
2.	$\sqrt[3]{x^2 y}, \sqrt[3]{y x^2}$	
3.	$\sqrt[3]{abc}, \sqrt[3]{cba}$	
4.	$2x\sqrt{5}, 2x\sqrt{10}$	

Simplify. Assume that all variables represent positive real numbers.

5. $2\sqrt{3} + 4\sqrt{3} =$ _____

6. $5\sqrt{7} + 3\sqrt{7} =$ _____

7. $8\sqrt{x} - \sqrt{x} =$ _____

8. $3\sqrt{y} - \sqrt{y} =$ _____

9. $7\sqrt[3]{x} + \sqrt[3]{x} =$ _____

10. $8\sqrt[3]{z} + \sqrt[3]{z} =$ _____

Add or subtract if possible.

11. $\sqrt{11} + \sqrt[3]{11} =$ _____

12. $9\sqrt{13} - \sqrt[4]{13} =$ _____

13. $8\sqrt[3]{2x} + 3\sqrt[3]{2x} - \sqrt[3]{2x} =$ _____

14. $8\sqrt[3]{2x} + 3\sqrt[3]{2x^2} - \sqrt[3]{2x} =$ _____

7.4 EXERCISE SET

 MyMathLab Powered by CourseCompass™ and MathXL®   PRACTICE   WATCH   DOWNLOAD   READ   REVIEW

Add or subtract. See Examples 1 through 3.

1. $\sqrt{8} - \sqrt{32}$

2. $\sqrt{27} - \sqrt{75}$

3. $2\sqrt{2x^3} + 4x\sqrt{8x}$

4. $3\sqrt{45x^3} + x\sqrt{5x}$

5. $2\sqrt{50} - 3\sqrt{125} + \sqrt{98}$

6. $4\sqrt{32} - \sqrt{18} + 2\sqrt{128}$

7. $\sqrt[3]{16x} - \sqrt[3]{54x}$

8. $2\sqrt[3]{3a^4} - 3a\sqrt[3]{81a}$

9. $\sqrt{9b^3} - \sqrt{25b^3} + \sqrt{49b^3}$

10. $\sqrt{4x^7} + 9x^2\sqrt{x^3} - 5x\sqrt{x^5}$

11. $\dfrac{5\sqrt{2}}{3} + \dfrac{2\sqrt{2}}{5}$

12. $\dfrac{\sqrt{3}}{2} + \dfrac{4\sqrt{3}}{3}$

13. $\sqrt[3]{\dfrac{11}{8}} - \dfrac{\sqrt[3]{11}}{6}$

14. $\dfrac{2\sqrt[3]{4}}{7} - \dfrac{\sqrt[3]{4}}{14}$

15. $\dfrac{\sqrt{20x}}{9} + \sqrt{\dfrac{5x}{9}}$

16. $\dfrac{3x\sqrt{7}}{5} + \sqrt{\dfrac{7x^2}{100}}$

17. $7\sqrt{9} - 7 + \sqrt{3}$

18. $\sqrt{16} - 5\sqrt{10} + 7$

19. $2 + 3\sqrt{y^2} - 6\sqrt{y^2} + 5$

20. $3\sqrt{7} - \sqrt[3]{x} + 4\sqrt{7} - 3\sqrt[3]{x}$

21. $3\sqrt{108} - 2\sqrt{18} - 3\sqrt{48}$

22. $-\sqrt{75} + \sqrt{12} - 3\sqrt{3}$

23. $-5\sqrt[3]{625} + \sqrt[3]{40}$

24. $-2\sqrt[3]{108} - \sqrt[3]{32}$

25. $\sqrt{9b^3} - \sqrt{25b^3} + \sqrt{16b^3}$

26. $\sqrt{4x^7y^5} + 9x^2\sqrt{x^3y^5} - 5xy\sqrt{x^5y^3}$

27. $5y\sqrt{8y} + 2\sqrt{50y^3}$

28. $3\sqrt{8x^2y^3} - 2x\sqrt{32y^3}$

29. $\sqrt[3]{54xy^3} - 5\sqrt[3]{2xy^3} + y\sqrt[3]{128x}$

30. $2\sqrt[3]{24x^3y^4} + 4x\sqrt[3]{81y^4}$

31. $6\sqrt[3]{11} + 8\sqrt{11} - 12\sqrt{11}$

32. $3\sqrt[3]{5} + 4\sqrt{5}$

33. $-2\sqrt[4]{x^7} + 3\sqrt[4]{16x^7}$

34. $6\sqrt[3]{24x^3} - 2\sqrt[3]{81x^3} - x\sqrt[3]{3}$

35. $\dfrac{4\sqrt{3}}{3} - \dfrac{\sqrt{12}}{3}$

36. $\dfrac{\sqrt{45}}{10} + \dfrac{7\sqrt{5}}{10}$

37. $\dfrac{\sqrt[3]{8x^4}}{7} + \dfrac{3x\sqrt[3]{x}}{7}$

38. $\dfrac{\sqrt[4]{48}}{5x} - \dfrac{2\sqrt[4]{3}}{10x}$

39. $\sqrt{\dfrac{28}{x^2}} + \sqrt{\dfrac{7}{4x^2}}$

40. $\dfrac{\sqrt{99}}{5x} - \sqrt{\dfrac{44}{x^2}}$

41. $\sqrt[3]{\dfrac{16}{27}} - \dfrac{\sqrt[3]{54}}{6}$

42. $\dfrac{\sqrt[3]{3}}{10} + \sqrt[3]{\dfrac{24}{125}}$

43. $-\dfrac{\sqrt[3]{2x^4}}{9} + \sqrt[3]{\dfrac{250x^4}{27}}$

44. $\dfrac{\sqrt[3]{y^5}}{8} + \dfrac{5y\sqrt[3]{y^2}}{4}$

△ **45.** Find the perimeter of the trapezoid.

$2\sqrt{12}$ in.

$3\sqrt{3}$ in.　$\sqrt{12}$ in.

$2\sqrt{27}$ in.

△ **46.** Find the perimeter of the triangle.

$\sqrt{8}$ m　$\sqrt{32}$ m

$\sqrt{45}$ m

Multiply, and then simplify if possible. See Example 4.

47. $\sqrt{7}\left(\sqrt{5} + \sqrt{3}\right)$

48. $\sqrt{5}\left(\sqrt{15} - \sqrt{35}\right)$

49. $\left(\sqrt{5} - \sqrt{2}\right)^2$

50. $\left(3x - \sqrt{2}\right)\left(3x - \sqrt{2}\right)$

51. $\sqrt{3x}\left(\sqrt{3} - \sqrt{x}\right)$

52. $\sqrt{5y}\left(\sqrt{y} + \sqrt{5}\right)$

53. $\left(2\sqrt{x} - 5\right)\left(3\sqrt{x} + 1\right)$

54. $\left(8\sqrt{y} + z\right)\left(4\sqrt{y} - 1\right)$

55. $\left(\sqrt[3]{a} - 4\right)\left(\sqrt[3]{a} + 5\right)$

56. $\left(\sqrt[3]{a} + 2\right)\left(\sqrt[3]{a} + 7\right)$

57. $6\left(\sqrt{2} - 2\right)$

58. $\sqrt{5}\left(6 - \sqrt{5}\right)$

59. $\sqrt{2}\left(\sqrt{2} + x\sqrt{6}\right)$

60. $\sqrt{3}\left(\sqrt{3} - 2\sqrt{5x}\right)$

61. $\left(2\sqrt{7} + 3\sqrt{5}\right)\left(\sqrt{7} - 2\sqrt{5}\right)$

62. $\left(\sqrt{6} - 4\sqrt{2}\right)\left(3\sqrt{6} + \sqrt{2}\right)$

63. $\left(\sqrt{x} - y\right)\left(\sqrt{x} + y\right)$

64. $\left(\sqrt{3x} + 2\right)\left(\sqrt{3x} - 2\right)$

65. $\left(\sqrt{3} + x\right)^2$

66. $\left(\sqrt{y} - 3x\right)^2$

67. $\left(\sqrt{5x} - 2\sqrt{3x}\right)\left(\sqrt{5x} - 3\sqrt{3x}\right)$

68. $\left(5\sqrt{7x} - \sqrt{2x}\right)\left(4\sqrt{7x} + 6\sqrt{2x}\right)$

69. $\left(\sqrt[3]{4} + 2\right)\left(\sqrt[3]{2} - 1\right)$

70. $\left(\sqrt[3]{3} + \sqrt[3]{2}\right)\left(\sqrt[3]{9} - \sqrt[3]{4}\right)$

71. $\left(\sqrt[3]{x} + 1\right)\left(\sqrt[3]{x^2} - \sqrt[3]{x} + 1\right)$

72. $\left(\sqrt[3]{3x} + 2\right)\left(\sqrt[3]{9x^2} - 2\sqrt[3]{3x} + 4\right)$

73. $\left(\sqrt{x - 1} + 5\right)^2$

74. $\left(\sqrt{3x + 1} + 2\right)^2$

75. $\left(\sqrt{2x + 5} - 1\right)^2$

76. $\left(\sqrt{x - 6} - 7\right)^2$

REVIEW AND PREVIEW

Factor each numerator and denominator. Then simplify if possible. See Section 6.1.

77. $\dfrac{2x - 14}{2}$

78. $\dfrac{8x - 24y}{4}$

79. $\dfrac{7x - 7y}{x^2 - y^2}$

80. $\dfrac{x^3 - 8}{4x - 8}$

81. $\dfrac{6a^2b - 9ab}{3ab}$

82. $\dfrac{14r - 28r^2s^2}{7rs}$

83. $\dfrac{-4 + 2\sqrt{3}}{6}$

84. $\dfrac{-5 + 10\sqrt{7}}{5}$

87. a. Add: $\sqrt{3} + \sqrt{3}$.
   b. Multiply: $\sqrt{3} \cdot \sqrt{3}$.
   c. Describe the differences in parts **a** and **b**.

88. Multiply: $\left(\sqrt{2} + \sqrt{3} - 1\right)^2$.

89. Explain how simplifying $2x + 3x$ is similar to simplifying $2\sqrt{x} + 3\sqrt{x}$.

90. Explain how multiplying $(x - 2)(x + 3)$ is similar to multiplying $\left(\sqrt{x} - \sqrt{2}\right)\left(\sqrt{x} + 3\right)$.

CONCEPT EXTENSIONS

△ **85.** Find the perimeter and area of the rectangle.

$\sqrt{125}$ ft

$3\sqrt{20}$ ft

△ **86.** Find the area and perimeter of the trapezoid. (*Hint:* The area of a trapezoid is the product of half the height $6\sqrt{3}$ meters and the sum of the bases $2\sqrt{63}$ and $7\sqrt{7}$ meters.)

$2\sqrt{63}$ m

$2\sqrt{27}$ m $\qquad$ $6\sqrt{3}$ m

$7\sqrt{7}$ m

📖 STUDY SKILLS BUILDER

Have You Decided to Successfully Complete This Course?

Hopefully by now, one of your current goals is to successfully complete this course.

If it is not a goal of yours, ask yourself why? One common reason is fear of failure. Amazingly enough, fear of failure alone can be strong enough to keep many of us from doing our best in any endeavor. Another common reason is that you simply haven't taken the time to make successfully completing this course one of your goals.

Anytime you are registered for a course, successfully completing this course should probably be a goal. How do you do this? Start by writing this goal in your mathematics notebook. Then list steps you will take to ensure success. A great first step is to read or reread Section 1.1 and make a commitment to try the suggestions in this section.

Good luck, and don't forget that a positive attitude will make a big difference.

Let's see how you are doing.

1. Have you made the decision to make "successfully completing this course" a goal of yours? If not, please list

reasons that this has not happened. Study your list and talk to your instructor about this.

2. If your answer to Exercise 1 is yes, take a moment and list, in your notebook, further specific goals that will help you achieve this major goal of successfully completing this course. (For example, my goal this semester is not to miss any of my mathematics classes.)

3. Rate your commitment to this course with a number between 1 and 5. Use the diagram below to help.

High Commitment		Average Commitment		Not Committed at All
5	4	3	2	1

4. If you have rated your personal commitment level (from the exercise above) as a 1, 2, or 3, list the reasons why this is so. Then determine whether it is possible to increase your commitment level to a 4 or 5.

7.5 RATIONALIZING DENOMINATORS AND NUMERATORS OF RADICAL EXPRESSIONS

OBJECTIVES

1 Rationalize denominators.

2 Rationalize denominators having two terms.

3 Rationalize numerators.

OBJECTIVE 1 ▶ Rationalizing denominators of radical expressions. Often in mathematics, it is helpful to write a radical expression such as $\frac{\sqrt{3}}{\sqrt{2}}$ either without a radical in the denominator or without a radical in the numerator. The process of writing this expression as an equivalent expression but without a radical in the denominator is called **rationalizing the denominator.** To rationalize the denominator of $\frac{\sqrt{3}}{\sqrt{2}}$, we use the fundamental principle of fractions and multiply the numerator and the denominator by $\sqrt{2}$. Recall that this is the same as multiplying by $\frac{\sqrt{2}}{\sqrt{2}}$, which simplifies to 1.

$$\frac{\sqrt{3}}{\sqrt{2}} = \frac{\sqrt{3}\cdot\sqrt{2}}{\sqrt{2}\cdot\sqrt{2}} = \frac{\sqrt{6}}{\sqrt{4}} = \frac{\sqrt{6}}{2}$$

In this section, we continue to assume that variables represent positive real numbers.

EXAMPLE 1   Rationalize the denominator of each expression.

a. $\dfrac{2}{\sqrt{5}}$ **b.** $\dfrac{2\sqrt{16}}{\sqrt{9x}}$ **c.** $\sqrt[3]{\dfrac{1}{2}}$

Solution

a. To rationalize the denominator, we multiply the numerator and denominator by a factor that makes the radicand in the denominator a perfect square.

$$\frac{2}{\sqrt{5}} = \frac{2\cdot\sqrt{5}}{\sqrt{5}\cdot\sqrt{5}} = \frac{2\sqrt{5}}{5} \quad \text{The denominator is now rationalized.}$$

b. First, we simplify the radicals and then rationalize the denominator.

$$\frac{2\sqrt{16}}{\sqrt{9x}} = \frac{2(4)}{3\sqrt{x}} = \frac{8}{3\sqrt{x}}$$

To rationalize the denominator, multiply the numerator and denominator by $\sqrt{x}$. Then

$$\frac{8}{3\sqrt{x}} = \frac{8\cdot\sqrt{x}}{3\sqrt{x}\cdot\sqrt{x}} = \frac{8\sqrt{x}}{3x}$$

c. $\sqrt[3]{\dfrac{1}{2}} = \dfrac{\sqrt[3]{1}}{\sqrt[3]{2}} = \dfrac{1}{\sqrt[3]{2}}$. Now we rationalize the denominator. Since $\sqrt[3]{2}$ is a cube root, we want to multiply by a value that will make the radicand 2 a perfect cube. If we multiply $\sqrt[3]{2}$ by $\sqrt[3]{2^2}$, we get $\sqrt[3]{2^3} = \sqrt[3]{8} = 2$.

$$\frac{1\cdot\sqrt[3]{2^2}}{\sqrt[3]{2}\cdot\sqrt[3]{2^2}} = \frac{\sqrt[3]{4}}{\sqrt[3]{2^3}} = \frac{\sqrt[3]{4}}{2} \quad \text{Multiply the numerator and denominator by } \sqrt[3]{2^2} \text{ and then simplify.}$$

PRACTICE

1   Rationalize the denominator of each expression.

a. $\dfrac{5}{\sqrt{3}}$ **b.** $\dfrac{3\sqrt{25}}{\sqrt{4x}}$ **c.** $\sqrt[3]{\dfrac{2}{9}}$

Concept Check ☑

Determine by which number both the numerator and denominator can be multiplied to rationalize the denominator of the radical expression.

a. $\dfrac{1}{\sqrt[3]{7}}$ **b.** $\dfrac{1}{\sqrt[4]{8}}$

EXAMPLE 2 Rationalize the denominator of $\sqrt{\dfrac{7x}{3y}}$.

Solution

$$\sqrt{\dfrac{7x}{3y}} = \dfrac{\sqrt{7x}}{\sqrt{3y}} \qquad \text{Use the quotient rule. No radical may be simplified further.}$$

$$= \dfrac{\sqrt{7x}\cdot\sqrt{3y}}{\sqrt{3y}\cdot\sqrt{3y}} \qquad \text{Multiply numerator and denominator by } \sqrt{3y} \text{ so that the radicand in the denominator is a perfect square.}$$

$$= \dfrac{\sqrt{21xy}}{3y} \qquad \text{Use the product rule in the numerator and denominator. Remember that } \sqrt{3y}\cdot\sqrt{3y} = 3y. \qquad \square$$

PRACTICE
2 Rationalize the denominator of $\sqrt{\dfrac{3z}{5y}}$.

EXAMPLE 3 Rationalize the denominator of $\dfrac{\sqrt[4]{x}}{\sqrt[4]{81y^5}}$.

Solution First, simplify each radical if possible.

$$\dfrac{\sqrt[4]{x}}{\sqrt[4]{81y^5}} = \dfrac{\sqrt[4]{x}}{\sqrt[4]{81y^4}\cdot\sqrt[4]{y}} \qquad \text{Use the product rule in the denominator.}$$

$$= \dfrac{\sqrt[4]{x}}{3y\sqrt[4]{y}} \qquad \text{Write } \sqrt[4]{81y^4} \text{ as } 3y.$$

$$= \dfrac{\sqrt[4]{x}\cdot\sqrt[4]{y^3}}{3y\sqrt[4]{y}\cdot\sqrt[4]{y^3}} \qquad \text{Multiply numerator and denominator by } \sqrt[4]{y^3} \text{ so that the radicand in the denominator is a perfect fourth power.}$$

$$= \dfrac{\sqrt[4]{xy^3}}{3y\sqrt[4]{y^4}} \qquad \text{Use the product rule in the numerator and denominator.}$$

$$= \dfrac{\sqrt[4]{xy^3}}{3y^2} \qquad \text{In the denominator, } \sqrt[4]{y^4} = y \text{ and } 3y\cdot y = 3y^2. \qquad \square$$

PRACTICE
3 Rationalize the denominator of $\dfrac{\sqrt[3]{z^2}}{\sqrt[3]{27x^4}}$.

OBJECTIVE 2 ▶ Rationalizing denominators having two terms. Remember the product of the sum and difference of two terms?

$$(a + b)(a - b) = a^2 - b^2$$

These two expressions are called **conjugates** of each other.

Answer to Concept Check:

a. $\sqrt[3]{7^2}$ or $\sqrt[3]{49}$ **b.** $\sqrt[4]{2}$

To rationalize a numerator or denominator that is a sum or difference of two terms, we use conjugates. To see how and why this works, let's rationalize the denominator of the expression $\dfrac{5}{\sqrt{3} - 2}$. To do so, we multiply both the numerator and the denominator by $\sqrt{3} + 2$, the **conjugate** of the denominator $\sqrt{3} - 2$, and see what happens.

$$\frac{5}{\sqrt{3} - 2} = \frac{5(\sqrt{3} + 2)}{(\sqrt{3} - 2)(\sqrt{3} + 2)}$$

$$= \frac{5(\sqrt{3} + 2)}{(\sqrt{3})^2 - 2^2} \qquad \text{Multiply the sum and difference}$$
$$\text{of two terms: } (a + b)(a - b) = a^2 - b^2.$$

$$= \frac{5(\sqrt{3} + 2)}{3 - 4}$$

$$= \frac{5(\sqrt{3} + 2)}{-1}$$

$$= -5(\sqrt{3} + 2) \quad \text{or} \quad -5\sqrt{3} - 10$$

Notice in the denominator that the product of $(\sqrt{3} - 2)$ and its conjugate, $(\sqrt{3} + 2)$, is -1. In general, the product of an expression and its conjugate will contain no radical terms. This is why, when rationalizing a denominator or a numerator containing two terms, we multiply by its conjugate. Examples of conjugates are

$$\sqrt{a} - \sqrt{b} \quad \text{and} \quad \sqrt{a} + \sqrt{b}$$
$$x + \sqrt{y} \quad \text{and} \quad x - \sqrt{y}$$

EXAMPLE 4   Rationalize each denominator.

a. $\dfrac{2}{3\sqrt{2} + 4}$ **b.** $\dfrac{\sqrt{6} + 2}{\sqrt{5} - \sqrt{3}}$ **c.** $\dfrac{2\sqrt{m}}{3\sqrt{x} + \sqrt{m}}$

Solution

a. Multiply the numerator and denominator by the conjugate of the denominator, $3\sqrt{2} + 4$.

$$\frac{2}{3\sqrt{2} + 4} = \frac{2(3\sqrt{2} - 4)}{(3\sqrt{2} + 4)(3\sqrt{2} - 4)}$$

$$= \frac{2(3\sqrt{2} - 4)}{(3\sqrt{2})^2 - 4^2}$$

$$= \frac{2(3\sqrt{2} - 4)}{18 - 16}$$

$$= \frac{2(3\sqrt{2} - 4)}{2}, \quad \text{or} \quad 3\sqrt{2} - 4$$

It is often useful to leave a numerator in factored form to help determine whether the expression can be simplified.

b. Multiply the numerator and denominator by the conjugate of $\sqrt{5} - \sqrt{3}$.

$$\frac{\sqrt{6} + 2}{\sqrt{5} - \sqrt{3}} = \frac{(\sqrt{6} + 2)(\sqrt{5} + \sqrt{3})}{(\sqrt{5} - \sqrt{3})(\sqrt{5} + \sqrt{3})}$$

$$= \frac{\sqrt{6}\sqrt{5} + \sqrt{6}\sqrt{3} + 2\sqrt{5} + 2\sqrt{3}}{(\sqrt{5})^2 - (\sqrt{3})^2}$$

$$= \frac{\sqrt{30} + \sqrt{18} + 2\sqrt{5} + 2\sqrt{3}}{5 - 3}$$

$$= \frac{\sqrt{30} + 3\sqrt{2} + 2\sqrt{5} + 2\sqrt{3}}{2}$$

c. Multiply by the conjugate of $3\sqrt{x} + \sqrt{m}$ to eliminate the radicals from the denominator.

$$\frac{2\sqrt{m}}{3\sqrt{x} + \sqrt{m}} = \frac{2\sqrt{m}(3\sqrt{x} - \sqrt{m})}{(3\sqrt{x} + \sqrt{m})(3\sqrt{x} - \sqrt{m})} = \frac{6\sqrt{mx} - 2m}{(3\sqrt{x})^2 - (\sqrt{m})^2}$$

$$= \frac{6\sqrt{mx} - 2m}{9x - m}$$

PRACTICE
4   Rationalize the denominator.

a. $\dfrac{5}{3\sqrt{5} + 2}$ **b.** $\dfrac{\sqrt{2} + 5}{\sqrt{3} - \sqrt{5}}$ **c.** $\dfrac{3\sqrt{x}}{2\sqrt{x} + \sqrt{y}}$

OBJECTIVE 3 ▶ Rationalizing numerators. As mentioned earlier, it is also often helpful to write an expression such as $\dfrac{\sqrt{3}}{\sqrt{2}}$ as an equivalent expression without a radical in the numerator. This process is called **rationalizing the numerator.** To rationalize the numerator of $\dfrac{\sqrt{3}}{\sqrt{2}}$, we multiply the numerator and the denominator by $\sqrt{3}$.

$$\frac{\sqrt{3}}{\sqrt{2}} = \frac{\sqrt{3} \cdot \sqrt{3}}{\sqrt{2} \cdot \sqrt{3}} = \frac{\sqrt{9}}{\sqrt{6}} = \frac{3}{\sqrt{6}}$$

EXAMPLE 5   Rationalize the numerator of $\dfrac{\sqrt{7}}{\sqrt{45}}$.

Solution   First we simplify $\sqrt{45}$.

$$\frac{\sqrt{7}}{\sqrt{45}} = \frac{\sqrt{7}}{\sqrt{9 \cdot 5}} = \frac{\sqrt{7}}{3\sqrt{5}}$$

Next we rationalize the numerator by multiplying the numerator and the denominator by $\sqrt{7}$.

$$\frac{\sqrt{7}}{3\sqrt{5}} = \frac{\sqrt{7} \cdot \sqrt{7}}{3\sqrt{5} \cdot \sqrt{7}} = \frac{7}{3\sqrt{5 \cdot 7}} = \frac{7}{3\sqrt{35}}$$

PRACTICE
5   Rationalize the numerator of $\dfrac{\sqrt{32}}{\sqrt{80}}$.

EXAMPLE 6 Rationalize the numerator of $\dfrac{\sqrt[3]{2x^2}}{\sqrt[3]{5y}}$.

Solution The numerator and the denominator of this expression are already simplified. To rationalize the numerator, $\sqrt[3]{2x^2}$, we multiply the numerator and denominator by a factor that will make the radicand a perfect cube. If we multiply $\sqrt[3]{2x^2}$ by $\sqrt[3]{4x}$, we get $\sqrt[3]{8x^3} = 2x$.

$$\frac{\sqrt[3]{2x^2}}{\sqrt[3]{5y}} = \frac{\sqrt[3]{2x^2} \cdot \sqrt[3]{4x}}{\sqrt[3]{5y} \cdot \sqrt[3]{4x}} = \frac{\sqrt[3]{8x^3}}{\sqrt[3]{20xy}} = \frac{2x}{\sqrt[3]{20xy}} \qquad \square$$

PRACTICE
6 Rationalize the numerator of $\dfrac{\sqrt[3]{5b}}{\sqrt[3]{2a}}$.

EXAMPLE 7 Rationalize the numerator of $\dfrac{\sqrt{x} + 2}{5}$.

Solution We multiply the numerator and the denominator by the conjugate of the numerator, $\sqrt{x} + 2$.

$$\frac{\sqrt{x} + 2}{5} = \frac{(\sqrt{x} + 2)(\sqrt{x} - 2)}{5(\sqrt{x} - 2)} \qquad \text{Multiply by } \sqrt{x} - 2, \text{ the conjugate of } \sqrt{x} + 2.$$

$$= \frac{(\sqrt{x})^2 - 2^2}{5(\sqrt{x} - 2)} \qquad (a + b)(a - b) = a^2 - b^2$$

$$= \frac{x - 4}{5(\sqrt{x} - 2)} \qquad \square$$

PRACTICE
7 Rationalize the numerator of $\dfrac{\sqrt{x} - 3}{4}$.

VOCABULARY & READINESS CHECK

Use the choices below to fill in each blank. Not all choices will be used.

rationalizing the numerator   conjugate $\dfrac{\sqrt{3}}{\sqrt{3}}$

rationalizing the denominator $\dfrac{5}{5}$

1. The _____ of $a + b$ is $a - b$.

2. The process of writing an equivalent expression, but without a radical in the denominator is called _____.

3. The process of writing an equivalent expression, but without a radical in the numerator is called _____.

4. To rationalize the denominator of $\dfrac{5}{\sqrt{3}}$, we multiply by _____.

Find the conjugate of each expression.

5. $\sqrt{2} + x$ **6.** $\sqrt{3} + y$ **7.** $5 - \sqrt{a}$ **8.** $6 - \sqrt{b}$

9. $-7\sqrt{5} + 8\sqrt{x}$ **10.** $-9\sqrt{2} - 6\sqrt{y}$

7.5 EXERCISE SET

PRACTICE WATCH DOWNLOAD READ REVIEW

Rationalize each denominator. See Examples 1 through 3.

1. $\dfrac{\sqrt{2}}{\sqrt{7}}$

2. $\dfrac{\sqrt{3}}{\sqrt{2}}$

3. $\sqrt{\dfrac{1}{5}}$

4. $\sqrt{\dfrac{1}{2}}$

5. $\sqrt{\dfrac{4}{x}}$

6. $\sqrt{\dfrac{25}{y}}$

7. $\dfrac{4}{\sqrt[3]{3}}$

8. $\dfrac{6}{\sqrt[3]{9}}$

9. $\dfrac{3}{\sqrt{8x}}$

10. $\dfrac{5}{\sqrt{27a}}$

11. $\dfrac{3}{\sqrt[3]{4x^2}}$

12. $\dfrac{5}{\sqrt[3]{3y}}$

13. $\dfrac{9}{\sqrt{3a}}$

14. $\dfrac{x}{\sqrt{5}}$

15. $\dfrac{3}{\sqrt[3]{2}}$

16. $\dfrac{5}{\sqrt[3]{9}}$

17. $\dfrac{2\sqrt{3}}{\sqrt{7}}$

18. $\dfrac{-5\sqrt{2}}{\sqrt{11}}$

19. $\sqrt{\dfrac{2x}{5y}}$

20. $\sqrt{\dfrac{13a}{2b}}$

21. $\sqrt[3]{\dfrac{3}{5}}$

22. $\sqrt[3]{\dfrac{7}{10}}$

23. $\sqrt{\dfrac{3x}{50}}$

24. $\sqrt{\dfrac{11y}{45}}$

25. $\dfrac{1}{\sqrt{12z}}$

26. $\dfrac{1}{\sqrt{32x}}$

27. $\dfrac{\sqrt[3]{2y^2}}{\sqrt[3]{9x^2}}$

28. $\dfrac{\sqrt[3]{3x}}{\sqrt[3]{4y^4}}$

29. $\sqrt[4]{\dfrac{81}{8}}$

30. $\sqrt[4]{\dfrac{1}{9}}$

31. $\sqrt[4]{\dfrac{16}{9x^7}}$

32. $\sqrt[5]{\dfrac{32}{m^6 n^{13}}}$

33. $\dfrac{5a}{\sqrt[5]{8a^9 b^{11}}}$

34. $\dfrac{9y}{\sqrt[4]{4y^9}}$

Rationalize each denominator. See Example 4.

35. $\dfrac{6}{2-\sqrt{7}}$

36. $\dfrac{3}{\sqrt{7}-4}$

37. $\dfrac{-7}{\sqrt{x}-3}$

38. $\dfrac{-8}{\sqrt{y}+4}$

39. $\dfrac{\sqrt{2}-\sqrt{3}}{\sqrt{2}+\sqrt{3}}$

40. $\dfrac{\sqrt{3}+\sqrt{4}}{\sqrt{2}-\sqrt{3}}$

41. $\dfrac{\sqrt{a}+1}{2\sqrt{a}-\sqrt{b}}$

42. $\dfrac{2\sqrt{a}-3}{2\sqrt{a}+\sqrt{b}}$

43. $\dfrac{8}{1+\sqrt{10}}$

44. $\dfrac{-3}{\sqrt{6}-2}$

45. $\dfrac{\sqrt{x}}{\sqrt{x}+\sqrt{y}}$

46. $\dfrac{2\sqrt{a}}{2\sqrt{x}-\sqrt{y}}$

47. $\dfrac{2\sqrt{3}+\sqrt{6}}{4\sqrt{3}-\sqrt{6}}$

48. $\dfrac{4\sqrt{5}+\sqrt{2}}{2\sqrt{5}-\sqrt{2}}$

Rationalize each numerator. See Examples 5 and 6.

49. $\sqrt{\dfrac{5}{3}}$

50. $\sqrt{\dfrac{3}{2}}$

51. $\sqrt{\dfrac{18}{5}}$

52. $\sqrt{\dfrac{12}{7}}$

53. $\dfrac{\sqrt{4x}}{7}$

54. $\dfrac{\sqrt{3x^5}}{6}$

55. $\dfrac{\sqrt[3]{5y^2}}{\sqrt[3]{4x}}$

56. $\dfrac{\sqrt[3]{4x}}{\sqrt[3]{z^4}}$

57. $\sqrt{\dfrac{2}{5}}$

58. $\sqrt{\dfrac{3}{7}}$

59. $\dfrac{\sqrt{2x}}{11}$

60. $\dfrac{\sqrt{y}}{7}$

61. $\sqrt[3]{\dfrac{7}{8}}$

62. $\sqrt[3]{\dfrac{25}{2}}$

63. $\dfrac{\sqrt[3]{3x^5}}{10}$

64. $\sqrt[3]{\dfrac{9y}{7}}$

65. $\sqrt{\dfrac{18x^4 y^6}{3z}}$

66. $\sqrt{\dfrac{8x^5 y}{2z}}$

67. When rationalizing the denominator of $\dfrac{\sqrt{5}}{\sqrt{7}}$, explain why both the numerator and the denominator must be multiplied by $\sqrt{7}$.

68. When rationalizing the numerator of $\dfrac{\sqrt{5}}{\sqrt{7}}$, explain why both the numerator and the denominator must be multiplied by $\sqrt{5}$.

Rationalize each numerator. See Example 7.

69. $\dfrac{2-\sqrt{11}}{6}$

70. $\dfrac{\sqrt{15}+1}{2}$

71. $\dfrac{2-\sqrt{7}}{-5}$

72. $\dfrac{\sqrt{5}+2}{\sqrt{2}}$

73. $\dfrac{\sqrt{x}+3}{\sqrt{x}}$

74. $\dfrac{5+\sqrt{2}}{\sqrt{2x}}$

75. $\dfrac{\sqrt{2}-1}{\sqrt{2}+1}$

76. $\dfrac{\sqrt{8}-\sqrt{3}}{\sqrt{2}+\sqrt{3}}$

77. $\dfrac{\sqrt{x}+1}{\sqrt{x}-1}$

78. $\dfrac{\sqrt{x}+\sqrt{y}}{\sqrt{x}-\sqrt{y}}$

REVIEW AND PREVIEW

Solve each equation. See Sections 2.1 and 5.8.

79. $2x - 7 = 3(x - 4)$ **80.** $9x - 4 = 7(x - 2)$

81. $(x - 6)(2x + 1) = 0$ **82.** $(y + 2)(5y + 4) = 0$

83. $x^2 - 8x = -12$ **84.** $x^3 = x$

CONCEPTS EXTENSIONS

Determine the smallest number both the numerator and denominator should be multiplied by to rationalize the denominator of the radical expression. See the Concept Check in this section.

85. $\dfrac{9}{\sqrt[3]{5}}$ **86.** $\dfrac{5}{\sqrt{27}}$

△ **87.** The formula of the radius r of a sphere with surface area A is

$$r = \sqrt{\dfrac{A}{4\pi}}$$

Rationalize the denominator of the radical expression in this formula.

△ **88.** The formula for the radius r of a cone with height 7 centimeters and volume V is

$$r = \sqrt{\dfrac{3V}{7\pi}}$$

Rationalize the numerator of the radical expression in this formula.

7 cm

r

89. Explain why rationalizing the denominator does not change the value of the original expression.

90. Explain why rationalizing the numerator does not change the value of the original expression.

INTEGRATED REVIEW   RADICALS AND RATIONAL EXPONENTS

Sections 7.1–7.5

Find each root. Throughout this review, assume that all variables represent positive real numbers.

1. $\sqrt{81}$ **2.** $\sqrt[3]{-8}$ **3.** $\sqrt[4]{\dfrac{1}{16}}$ **4.** $\sqrt{x^6}$

5. $\sqrt[3]{y^9}$ **6.** $\sqrt{4y^{10}}$ **7.** $\sqrt[5]{-32y^5}$ **8.** $\sqrt[4]{81b^{12}}$

Use radical notation to rewrite each expression. Simplify if possible.

9. $36^{1/2}$ **10.** $(3y)^{1/4}$ **11.** $64^{-2/3}$ **12.** $(x + 1)^{3/5}$

Use the properties of exponents to simplify each expression. Write with positive exponents.

13. $y^{-1/6} \cdot y^{7/6}$ **14.** $\dfrac{(2x^{1/3})^4}{x^{5/6}}$ **15.** $\dfrac{x^{1/4}x^{3/4}}{x^{-1/4}}$ **16.** $4^{1/3} \cdot 4^{2/5}$

Use rational exponents to simplify each radical.

17. $\sqrt[3]{8x^6}$ **18.** $\sqrt[12]{a^9b^6}$

Use rational exponents to write each as a single radical expression.

19. $\sqrt[4]{x} \cdot \sqrt{x}$ **20.** $\sqrt{5} \cdot \sqrt[3]{2}$

Simplify.

21. $\sqrt{40}$ **22.** $\sqrt[4]{16x^7y^{10}}$ **23.** $\sqrt[3]{54x^4}$ **24.** $\sqrt[5]{-64b^{10}}$

Multiply or divide. Then simplify if possible.

25. $\sqrt{5} \cdot \sqrt{x}$

26. $\sqrt[3]{8x} \cdot \sqrt[3]{8x^2}$

27. $\dfrac{\sqrt{98y^6}}{\sqrt{2y}}$

28. $\dfrac{\sqrt[4]{48a^9b^3}}{\sqrt[4]{ab^3}}$

Perform each indicated operation.

29. $\sqrt{20} - \sqrt{75} + 5\sqrt{7}$

30. $\sqrt[3]{54y^4} - y\sqrt[3]{16y}$

31. $\sqrt{3}\left(\sqrt{5} - \sqrt{2}\right)$

32. $\left(\sqrt{7} + \sqrt{3}\right)^2$

33. $\left(2x - \sqrt{5}\right)\left(2x + \sqrt{5}\right)$

34. $\left(\sqrt{x+1} - 1\right)^2$

Rationalize each denominator.

35. $\sqrt{\dfrac{7}{3}}$

36. $\dfrac{5}{\sqrt[3]{2x^2}}$

37. $\dfrac{\sqrt{3} - \sqrt{7}}{2\sqrt{3} + \sqrt{7}}$

Rationalize each numerator.

38. $\sqrt{\dfrac{7}{3}}$

39. $\sqrt[3]{\dfrac{9y}{11}}$

40. $\dfrac{\sqrt{x} - 2}{\sqrt{x}}$

7.6 RADICAL EQUATIONS AND PROBLEM SOLVING

OBJECTIVE 1 ▶ Solving equations that contain radical expressions. In this section, we present techniques to solve equations containing radical expressions such as

$$\sqrt{2x - 3} = 9$$

We use the power rule to help us solve these radical equations.

> **Power Rule**
>
> If both sides of an equation are raised to the same power, **all** solutions of the original equation are **among** the solutions of the new equation.

This property *does not* say that raising both sides of an equation to a power yields an equivalent equation. A solution of the new equation *may or may not* be a solution of the original equation. For example, $(-2)^2 = 2^2$, but $-2 \neq 2$. Thus, *each solution of the new equation must be checked* to make sure it is a solution of the original equation. Recall that a proposed solution that is not a solution of the original equation is called an **extraneous solution.**

EXAMPLE 1 Solve: $\sqrt{2x - 3} = 9$.

Solution We use the power rule to square both sides of the equation to eliminate the radical.

$$\sqrt{2x - 3} = 9$$
$$\left(\sqrt{2x - 3}\right)^2 = 9^2$$
$$2x - 3 = 81$$
$$2x = 84$$
$$x = 42$$

Now we, check the solution in the original equation.

Check:

$$\sqrt{2x - 3} = 9$$

$$\sqrt{2(42) - 3} \overset{?}{=} 9 \quad \text{Let } x = 42.$$

$$\sqrt{84 - 3} \overset{?}{=} 9$$

$$\sqrt{81} \overset{?}{=} 9$$

$$9 = 9 \quad \text{True}$$

The solution checks, so we conclude that the solution is 42 or the solution set is $\{42\}$. ☐

PRACTICE
1   Solve: $\sqrt{3x - 5} = 7$.

To solve a radical equation, first isolate a radical on one side of the equation.

EXAMPLE 2   Solve: $\sqrt{-10x - 1} + 3x = 0$.

Solution   First, isolate the radical on one side of the equation. To do this, we subtract $3x$ from both sides.

$$\sqrt{-10x - 1} + 3x = 0$$

$$\sqrt{-10x - 1} + 3x - 3x = 0 - 3x$$

$$\sqrt{-10x - 1} = -3x$$

Next we use the power rule to eliminate the radical.

$$\left(\sqrt{-10x - 1}\right)^2 = (-3x)^2$$

$$-10x - 1 = 9x^2$$

Since this is a quadratic equation, we can set the equation equal to 0 and try to solve by factoring.

$$9x^2 + 10x + 1 = 0$$

$$(9x + 1)(x + 1) = 0 \quad \text{Factor.}$$

$$9x + 1 = 0 \quad \text{or} \quad x + 1 = 0 \quad \text{Set each factor equal to 0.}$$

$$x = -\frac{1}{9} \quad \text{or} \quad x = -1$$

Check: Let $x = -\frac{1}{9}$.

$$\sqrt{-10x - 1} + 3x = 0$$

$$\sqrt{-10\left(-\frac{1}{9}\right) - 1} + 3\left(-\frac{1}{9}\right) \overset{?}{=} 0$$

$$\sqrt{\frac{10}{9} - \frac{9}{9}} - \frac{3}{9} \overset{?}{=} 0$$

$$\sqrt{\frac{1}{9}} - \frac{1}{3} \overset{?}{=} 0$$

$$\frac{1}{3} - \frac{1}{3} = 0 \quad \text{True}$$

Let $x = -1$.

$$\sqrt{-10x - 1} + 3x = 0$$

$$\sqrt{-10(-1) - 1} + 3(-1) \overset{?}{=} 0$$

$$\sqrt{10 - 1} - 3 \overset{?}{=} 0$$

$$\sqrt{9} - 3 \overset{?}{=} 0$$

$$3 - 3 = 0 \quad \text{True}$$

Both solutions check. The solutions are $-\frac{1}{9}$ and -1 or the solution set is $\left\{-\frac{1}{9}, -1\right\}$.

☐

PRACTICE
2   Solve: $\sqrt{3 - 2x} - 4x = 0$.

The following steps may be used to solve a radical equation.

> **Solving a Radical Equation**
>
> **STEP 1.** Isolate one radical on one side of the equation.
>
> **STEP 2.** Raise each side of the equation to a power equal to the index of the radical and simplify.
>
> **STEP 3.** If the equation still contains a radical term, repeat Steps 1 and 2. If not, solve the equation.
>
> **STEP 4.** Check all proposed solutions in the original equation.

EXAMPLE 3 Solve: $\sqrt[3]{x + 1} + 5 = 3$.

Solution First we isolate the radical by subtracting 5 from both sides of the equation.

$$\sqrt[3]{x + 1} + 5 = 3$$
$$\sqrt[3]{x + 1} = -2$$

Next we raise both sides of the equation to the third power to eliminate the radical.

$$\left(\sqrt[3]{x + 1}\right)^3 = (-2)^3$$
$$x + 1 = -8$$
$$x = -9$$

The solution checks in the original equation, so the solution is -9. □

PRACTICE
3 Solve: $\sqrt[3]{x - 2} + 1 = 3$.

EXAMPLE 4 Solve: $\sqrt{4 - x} = x - 2$.

Solution

$$\sqrt{4 - x} = x - 2$$
$$\left(\sqrt{4 - x}\right)^2 = (x - 2)^2$$
$$4 - x = x^2 - 4x + 4$$
$$x^2 - 3x = 0 \qquad \text{Write the quadratic equation in standard form.}$$
$$x(x - 3) = 0 \qquad \text{Factor.}$$
$$x = 0 \quad \text{or} \quad x - 3 = 0 \qquad \text{Set each factor equal to 0.}$$
$$x = 3$$

Check:

$$\sqrt{4 - x} = x - 2 \qquad\qquad \sqrt{4 - x} = x - 2$$
$$\sqrt{4 - 0} \stackrel{?}{=} 0 - 2 \quad \text{Let } x = 0. \qquad \sqrt{4 - 3} \stackrel{?}{=} 3 - 2 \quad \text{Let } x = 3.$$
$$2 = -2 \qquad \text{False} \qquad\qquad 1 = 1 \qquad \text{True}$$

The proposed solution 3 checks, but 0 does not. Since 0 is an extraneous solution, the only solution is 3. □

PRACTICE
4 Solve: $\sqrt{16 + x} = x - 4$.

> ▶ **Helpful Hint**
> In Example 4, notice that $(x - 2)^2 = x^2 - 4x + 4$. Make sure binomials are squared correctly.

Concept Check ☑

How can you immediately tell that the equation $\sqrt{2y + 3} = -4$ has no real solution?

EXAMPLE 5   Solve: $\sqrt{2x + 5} + \sqrt{2x} = 3$.

Solution   We get one radical alone by subtracting $\sqrt{2x}$ from both sides.

$$\sqrt{2x + 5} + \sqrt{2x} = 3$$
$$\sqrt{2x + 5} = 3 - \sqrt{2x}$$

Now we use the power rule to begin eliminating the radicals. First we square both sides.

$$\left(\sqrt{2x + 5}\right)^2 = \left(3 - \sqrt{2x}\right)^2$$

$$2x + 5 = 9 - 6\sqrt{2x} + 2x \quad \text{Multiply } \left(3 - \sqrt{2x}\right)\left(3 - \sqrt{2x}\right).$$

There is still a radical in the equation, so we get a radical alone again. Then we square both sides.

$$2x + 5 = 9 - 6\sqrt{2x} + 2x \quad \text{Get the radical alone.}$$
$$6\sqrt{2x} = 4$$
$$36(2x) = 16 \qquad\qquad \text{Square both sides of the equation to eliminate the radical.}$$
$$72x = 16 \qquad\qquad \text{Multiply.}$$
$$x = \frac{16}{72} \qquad\qquad \text{Solve.}$$
$$x = \frac{2}{9} \qquad\qquad \text{Simplify.}$$

The proposed solution, $\frac{2}{9}$, checks in the original equation. The solution is $\frac{2}{9}$.   ☐

PRACTICE
5   Solve: $\sqrt{8x + 1} + \sqrt{3x} = 2$.

▶ **Helpful Hint**
Make sure expressions are squared correctly. In Example 5, we squared $\left(3 - \sqrt{2x}\right)$ as

$$\left(3 - \sqrt{2x}\right)^2 = \left(3 - \sqrt{2x}\right)\left(3 - \sqrt{2x}\right)$$
$$= 3 \cdot 3 - 3\sqrt{2x} - 3\sqrt{2x} + \sqrt{2x} \cdot \sqrt{2x}$$
$$= 9 - 6\sqrt{2x} + 2x$$

Concept Check ☑

What is wrong with the following solution?

$$\sqrt{2x + 5} + \sqrt{4 - x} = 8$$
$$\left(\sqrt{2x + 5} + \sqrt{4 - x}\right)^2 = 8^2$$
$$(2x + 5) + (4 - x) = 64$$
$$x + 9 = 64$$
$$x = 55$$

Answers to Concept Check:
answers may vary

$\left(\sqrt{2x + 5} + \sqrt{4 - x}\right)^2$ is not
$(2x + 5) + (4 - x)$.

OBJECTIVE 2 ▶ **Using the pythagorean theorem.** Recall that the Pythagorean theorem states that in a right triangle, the length of the hypotenuse squared equals the sum of the lengths of each of the legs squared.

Pythagorean Theorem

If a and b are the lengths of the legs of a right triangle and c is the length of the hypotenuse, then $a^2 + b^2 = c^2$.

△ **EXAMPLE 6** Find the length of the unknown leg of the right triangle.

Solution In the formula $a^2 + b^2 = c^2$, c is the hypotenuse. Here, $c = 10$, the length of the hypotenuse, and $a = 4$. We solve for b. Then $a^2 + b^2 = c^2$ becomes

$$4^2 + b^2 = 10^2$$
$$16 + b^2 = 100$$
$$b^2 = 84 \quad \text{Subtract 16 from both sides.}$$
$$b = \pm\sqrt{84} = \pm\sqrt{4 \cdot 21} = \pm 2\sqrt{21}$$

Since b is a length and thus is positive, we will use the positive value only. The unknown leg of the triangle is $2\sqrt{21}$ meters long. ☐

PRACTICE
6 Find the length of the unknown leg of the right triangle.

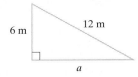

△ **EXAMPLE 7** **Calculating Placement of a Wire**

A 50-foot supporting wire is to be attached to a 75-foot antenna. Because of surrounding buildings, sidewalks, and roadways, the wire must be anchored exactly 20 feet from the base of the antenna.

a. How high from the base of the antenna is the wire attached?

b. Local regulations require that a supporting wire be attached at a height no less than $\frac{3}{5}$ of the total height of the antenna. From part **a**, have local regulations been met?

Solution

1. **UNDERSTAND.** Read and reread the problem. From the diagram we notice that a right triangle is formed with hypotenuse 50 feet and one leg 20 feet. Let x be the height from the base of the antenna to the attached wire.

2. **TRANSLATE.** Use the Pythagorean theorem.

$$a^2 + b^2 = c^2$$
$$20^2 + x^2 = 50^2 \quad a = 20, c = 50$$

3. **SOLVE.**

$$20^2 + x^2 = 50^2$$
$$400 + x^2 = 2500$$
$$x^2 = 2100 \qquad \text{Subtract 400 from both sides.}$$
$$x = \pm\sqrt{2100}$$
$$= \pm 10\sqrt{21}$$

4. **INTERPRET.** *Check* the work and *state* the solution.

Check: We will use only the positive value, $x = 10\sqrt{21}$ because x represents length. The wire is attached exactly $10\sqrt{21}$ feet from the base of the pole, or approximately 45.8 feet.

State: The supporting wire must be attached at a height no less than $\frac{3}{5}$ of the total height of the antenna. This height is $\frac{3}{5}$(75 feet), or 45 feet. Since we know from part **a** that the wire is to be attached at a height of approximately 45.8 feet, local regulations have been met. □

PRACTICE

7 Keith Robinson bought two Siamese fighting fish, but when he got home he found he only had one rectangular tank that was 12 in. long, 7 in. wide, and 5 in. deep. Since the fish must be kept separated, he needed to insert a plastic divider in the diagonal of the tank. He already has a piece that is 5 in. in one dimension, but how long must it be to fit corner to corner in the tank?

Graphing Calculator Explorations

We can use a graphing calculator to solve radical equations. For example, to use a graphing calculator to approximate the solutions of the equation solved in Example 4, we graph the following.

$$Y_1 = \sqrt{4 - x} \quad \text{and} \quad Y_2 = x - 2$$

The x-value of the point of intersection is the solution. Use the Intersect feature or the Zoom and Trace features of your graphing calculator to see that the solution is 3.

Use a graphing calculator to solve each radical equation. Round all solutions to the nearest hundredth.

1. $\sqrt{x + 7} = x$

2. $\sqrt{3x + 5} = 2x$

3. $\sqrt{2x + 1} = \sqrt{2x + 2}$

4. $\sqrt{10x - 1} = \sqrt{-10x + 10} - 1$

5. $1.2x = \sqrt{3.1x + 5}$

6. $\sqrt{1.9x^2 - 2.2} = -0.8x + 3$

VOCABULARY & READINESS CHECK

Use the choices below to fill in each blank. Not all choices will be used.

hypotenuse	right	$x^2 + 25$	$16 - 8\sqrt{7x} + 7x$
extraneous solution	legs	$x^2 - 10x + 25$	$16 + 7x$

1. A proposed solution that is not a solution of the original equation is called an _____.

2. The Pythagorean Theorem states that $a^2 + b^2 = c^2$ where a and b are the lengths of the _____ of a _____ triangle and c is the length of the _____.

3. The square of $x - 5$, or $(x - 5)^2 = $ _____.

4. The square of $4 - \sqrt{7x}$, or $(4 - \sqrt{7x})^2 = $ _____.

7.6 EXERCISE SET

MyMathLab | PRACTICE | WATCH | DOWNLOAD | READ | REVIEW

Solve. See Examples 1 and 2.

1. $\sqrt{2x} = 4$

2. $\sqrt{3x} = 3$

3. $\sqrt{x - 3} = 2$

4. $\sqrt{x + 1} = 5$

5. $\sqrt{2x} = -4$

6. $\sqrt{5x} = -5$

7. $\sqrt{4x - 3} - 5 = 0$

8. $\sqrt{x - 3} - 1 = 0$

9. $\sqrt{2x - 3} - 2 = 1$

10. $\sqrt{3x + 3} - 4 = 8$

Solve. See Example 3.

11. $\sqrt[3]{6x} = -3$

12. $\sqrt[3]{4x} = -2$

13. $\sqrt[3]{x - 2} - 3 = 0$

14. $\sqrt[3]{2x - 6} - 4 = 0$

Solve. See Examples 4 and 5.

15. $\sqrt{13 - x} = x - 1$

16. $\sqrt{2x - 3} = 3 - x$

17. $x - \sqrt{4 - 3x} = -8$

18. $2x + \sqrt{x + 1} = 8$

19. $\sqrt{y + 5} = 2 - \sqrt{y - 4}$

20. $\sqrt{x + 3} + \sqrt{x - 5} = 3$

21. $\sqrt{x - 3} + \sqrt{x + 2} = 5$

22. $\sqrt{2x - 4} - \sqrt{3x + 4} = -2$

MIXED PRACTICE

Solve. See Examples 1 through 5.

23. $\sqrt{3x - 2} = 5$

24. $\sqrt{5x - 4} = 9$

25. $-\sqrt{2x} + 4 = -6$

26. $-\sqrt{3x + 9} = -12$

27. $\sqrt{3x + 1} + 2 = 0$

28. $\sqrt{3x + 1} - 2 = 0$

29. $\sqrt[4]{4x + 1} - 2 = 0$

30. $\sqrt[4]{2x - 9} - 3 = 0$

31. $\sqrt{4x - 3} = 7$

32. $\sqrt{3x + 9} = 6$

33. $\sqrt[3]{6x - 3} - 3 = 0$

34. $\sqrt[3]{3x + 4} = 7$

35. $\sqrt[3]{2x - 3} - 2 = -5$

36. $\sqrt[3]{x - 4} - 5 = -7$

37. $\sqrt{x + 4} = \sqrt{2x - 5}$

38. $\sqrt{3y + 6} = \sqrt{7y - 6}$

39. $x - \sqrt{1 - x} = -5$

40. $x - \sqrt{x - 2} = 4$

41. $\sqrt[3]{-6x - 1} = \sqrt[3]{-2x - 5}$

42. $\sqrt[3]{-4x - 3} = \sqrt[3]{-x - 15}$

43. $\sqrt{5x - 1} - \sqrt{x + 2} = 3$

44. $\sqrt{2x - 1} - 4 = -\sqrt{x - 4}$

45. $\sqrt{2x - 1} = \sqrt{1 - 2x}$

46. $\sqrt{7x - 4} = \sqrt{4 - 7x}$

47. $\sqrt{3x + 4} - 1 = \sqrt{2x + 1}$

48. $\sqrt{x - 2} + 3 = \sqrt{4x + 1}$

49. $\sqrt{y + 3} - \sqrt{y - 3} = 1$

50. $\sqrt{x + 1} - \sqrt{x - 1} = 2$

Find the length of the unknown side of each triangle. See Example 6.

51.

6 ft

3 ft

52.

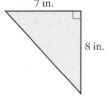

7 in.

8 in.

53.

3 m

7 m

54.

4 cm

7 cm

Find the length of the unknown side of each triangle. Give the exact length and a one-decimal-place approximation. See Example 6.

55.

9 m

$11\sqrt{5}$ m

56.

$5\sqrt{3}$ cm

10 cm

57.

7 mm   7.2 mm

58.

2.7 in.

2.3 in.

Solve. See Example 7. Give exact answers and two-decimal-place approximations where appropriate.

59. A wire is needed to support a vertical pole 15 feet high. The cable will be anchored to a stake 8 feet from the base of the pole. How much cable is needed?

15 ft

8 ft

60. The tallest structure in the United States is a TV tower in Blanchard, North Dakota. Its height is 2063 feet. A 2382-foot length of wire is to be used as a guy wire attached to the top of the tower. Approximate to the nearest foot how far from the base of the tower the guy wire must be anchored. (*Source:* U.S. Geological Survey)

2382 ft   2063 ft

?

61. A spotlight is mounted on the eaves of a house 12 feet above the ground. A flower bed runs between the house and the sidewalk, so the closest the ladder can be placed to the house is 5 feet. How long a ladder is needed so that an electrician can reach the place where the light is mounted?

12 ft

5 ft

62. A wire is to be attached to support a telephone pole. Because of surrounding buildings, sidewalks, and roadways, the wire must be anchored exactly 15 feet from the base of the pole. Telephone company workers have only 30 feet of cable, and 2 feet of that must be used to attach the cable to the pole and

to the stake on the ground. How high from the base of the pole can the wire be attached?

15 ft

63. The radius of the Moon is 1080 miles. Use the formula for the radius r of a sphere given its surface area A,

$$r = \sqrt{\frac{A}{4\pi}}$$

to find the surface area of the Moon. Round to the nearest square mile. (*Source:* National Space Science Data Center)

64. Police departments find it very useful to be able to approximate the speed of a car when they are given the distance that the car skidded before it came to a stop. If the road surface is wet concrete, the function $S(x) = \sqrt{10.5x}$ is used, where $S(x)$ is the speed of the car in miles per hour and x is the distance skidded in feet. Find how fast a car was moving if it skidded 280 feet on wet concrete.

65. The formula $v = \sqrt{2gh}$ gives the velocity v, in feet per second, of an object when it falls h feet accelerated by gravity g, in feet per second squared. If g is approximately 32 feet per second squared, find how far an object has fallen if its velocity is 80 feet per second.

66. Two tractors are pulling a tree stump from a field. If two forces A and B pull at right angles (90°) to each other, the size of the resulting force R is given by the formula $R = \sqrt{A^2 + B^2}$. If tractor A is exerting 600 pounds of force and the resulting force is 850 pounds, find how much force tractor B is exerting.

600 lb   ?

In psychology, it has been suggested that the number S of nonsense syllables that a person can repeat consecutively depends on his or her IQ score I according to the equation $S = 2\sqrt{I} - 9$.

67. Use this relationship to estimate the IQ of a person who can repeat 11 nonsense syllables consecutively.

68. Use this relationship to estimate the IQ of a person who can repeat 15 nonsense syllables consecutively.

*The **period** of a pendulum is the time it takes for the pendulum to make one full back-and-forth swing. The period of a pendulum depends on the length of the pendulum. The formula for the period P, in seconds, is $P = 2\pi\sqrt{\dfrac{l}{32}}$, where l is the length of the pendulum in feet. Use this formula for Exercises 69 through 74.*

69. Find the period of a pendulum whose length is 2 feet. Give an exact answer and a two-decimal-place approximation.

70. Klockit sells a 43-inch lyre pendulum. Find the period of this pendulum. Round your answer to 2 decimal places. (*Hint:* First convert inches to feet.)

71. Find the length of a pendulum whose period is 4 seconds. Round your answer to 2 decimal places.

72. Find the length of a pendulum whose period is 3 seconds. Round your answer to 2 decimal places.

73. Study the relationship between period and pendulum length in Exercises 69 through 72 and make a conjecture about this relationship.

74. Galileo experimented with pendulums. He supposedly made conjectures about pendulums of equal length with different bob weights. Try this experiment. Make two pendulums 3 feet long. Attach a heavy weight (lead) to one and a light weight (a cork) to the other. Pull both pendulums back the same angle measure and release. Make a conjecture from your observations. (There is more about pendulums in the Chapter 7 Group Activity.)

If the three lengths of the sides of a triangle are known, Heron's formula can be used to find its area. If a, b, and c are the three lengths of the sides, Heron's formula for area is

$$A = \sqrt{s(s - a)(s - b)(s - c)}$$

where s is half the perimeter of the triangle, or $s = \dfrac{1}{2}(a + b + c)$. Use this formula to find the area of each triangle. Give an exact answer and then a two-decimal place approximation.

75.

76.

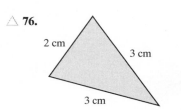

77. Describe when Heron's formula might be useful.

78. In your own words, explain why you think s in Heron's formula is called the *semiperimeter*.

The maximum distance D(h) in kilometers that a person can see from a height h kilometers above the ground is given by the function $D(h) = 111.7\sqrt{h}$. Use this function for Exercises 79 and 80. Round your answers to two decimal places.

79. Find the height that would allow a person to see 80 kilometers.

80. Find the height that would allow a person to see 40 kilometers.

REVIEW AND PREVIEW

Use the vertical line test to determine whether each graph represents the graph of a function. See Section 3.2.

81.

82.

83.

84.

85.   **86.**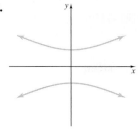

Simplify. See Section 6.3.

87. $\dfrac{\dfrac{x}{6}}{\dfrac{2x}{3} + \dfrac{1}{2}}$

88. $\dfrac{\dfrac{1}{y} + \dfrac{4}{5}}{\dfrac{-3}{20}}$

89. $\dfrac{\dfrac{z}{5} + \dfrac{1}{10}}{\dfrac{z}{20} - \dfrac{z}{5}}$

90. $\dfrac{\dfrac{1}{y} + \dfrac{1}{x}}{\dfrac{1}{y} - \dfrac{1}{x}}$

CONCEPT EXTENSIONS

91. Find the error in the following solution and correct. See the Concept Check in this section.

$$\sqrt{5x - 1} + 4 = 7$$
$$(\sqrt{5x - 1} + 4)^2 = 7^2$$
$$5x - 1 + 16 = 49$$
$$5x = 34$$
$$x = \frac{34}{5}$$

92. Explain why proposed solutions of radical equations must be checked.

93. Solve: $\sqrt{\sqrt{x + 3} + \sqrt{x}} = \sqrt{3}$

94. The cost $C(x)$ in dollars per day to operate a small delivery service is given by $C(x) = 80\sqrt[3]{x} + 500$, where x is the number of deliveries per day. In July, the manager decides that it is necessary to keep delivery costs below \$1620.00. Find the greatest number of deliveries this company can make per day and still keep overhead below \$1620.00.

95. Consider the equations $\sqrt{2x} = 4$ and $\sqrt[3]{2x} = 4$.

  a. Explain the difference in solving these equations.

  b. Explain the similarity in solving these equations.

Example

For Exercises 96 through 99, see the example below.
Solve $(t^2 - 3t) - 2\sqrt{t^2 - 3t} = 0$.

Solution

Substitution can be used to make this problem somewhat simpler. Since $t^2 - 3t$ occurs more than once, let $x = t^2 - 3t$.

$$(t^2 - 3t) - 2\sqrt{t^2 - 3t} = 0$$
$$x - 2\sqrt{x} = 0$$
$$x = 2\sqrt{x}$$
$$x^2 = (2\sqrt{x})^2$$
$$x^2 = 4x$$
$$x^2 - 4x = 0$$
$$x(x - 4) = 0$$
$$x = 0 \quad \text{or} \quad x - 4 = 0$$
$$x = 4$$

Now we "undo" the substitution.
$x = 0$ Replace x with $t^2 - 3t$.

$$t^2 - 3t = 0$$
$$t(t - 3) = 0$$
$$t = 0 \quad \text{or} \quad t - 3 = 0$$
$$t = 3$$

$x = 4$ Replace x with $t^2 - 3t$.

$$t^2 - 3t = 4$$
$$t^2 - 3t - 4 = 0$$
$$(t - 4)(t + 1) = 0$$
$$t - 4 = 0 \quad \text{or} \quad t + 1 = 0$$
$$t = 4 \qquad\qquad t = -1$$

In this problem, we have four possible solutions: 0, 3, 4, and -1. All four solutions check in the original equation, so the solutions are $-1, 0, 3, 4$.

Solve. See the preceding example.

96. $3\sqrt{x^2 - 8x} = x^2 - 8x$

97. $\sqrt{(x^2 - x) + 7} = 2(x^2 - x) - 1$

98. $7 - (x^2 - 3x) = \sqrt{(x^2 - 3x) + 5}$

99. $x^2 + 6x = 4\sqrt{x^2 + 6x}$

THE BIGGER PICTURE   SOLVING EQUATIONS AND INEQUALITIES

Continue your outline from Sections 2.4, 2.5, 2.7, 5.8, and 6.5. Write how to recognize and how to solve equations with radicals in your own words. For example:

Solving Equations and Inequalities

I. Equations
   A. Linear equations (Sec. 2.1)
   B. Absolute value equations (Sec. 2.6)
   C. Quadratic and higher degree equations (Sec. 5.8)
   D. Equations with rational expressions (Sec. 6.5)
   E. Equations with radicals: Equation contains at least one root of a variable expression.

$$\sqrt{5x + 10} - 2 = x \qquad \text{Radical equation}$$
$$\sqrt{5x + 10} = x + 2 \qquad \text{Isolate the radical.}$$
$$(\sqrt{5x + 10})^2 = (x + 2)^2 \qquad \text{Square both sides.}$$
$$5x + 10 = x^2 + 4x + 4 \qquad \text{Simplify.}$$
$$0 = x^2 - x - 6 \qquad \text{Write in standard form.}$$
$$0 = (x - 3)(x + 2) \qquad \text{Factor.}$$
$$x - 3 = 0 \quad \text{or} \quad x + 2 = 0 \qquad \text{Set each factor equal to 0.}$$
$$x = 3 \quad \text{or} \quad x = -2 \qquad \text{Solve.}$$

Both solutions check.

II. Inequalities
   A. Linear inequalities (Sec. 2.4)
   B. Compound inequalities (Sec. 2.5)
   C. Absolute value inequalities (Sec. 2.7)

Solve. Write inequality solutions in interval notation.

1. $\dfrac{x}{4} + \dfrac{x + 18}{20} = \dfrac{x - 5}{5}$

2. $|3x - 5| = 10$

3. $2x^2 - x = 45$

4. $-6 \le -5x - 1 \le 10$

5. $4(x - 1) + 3x > 1 + 2(x - 6)$

6. $\sqrt{x} + 14 = x - 6$

7. $x \ge 10 \quad \text{or} \quad -x < 5$

8. $\sqrt{3x - 1} + 4 = 1$

9. $|x - 2| > 15$

10. $5x - 4[x - 2(3x + 1)] = 25$

7.7 COMPLEX NUMBERS

OBJECTIVES

1 Write square roots of negative numbers in the form bi.

2 Add or subtract complex numbers.

3 Multiply complex numbers.

4 Divide complex numbers.

5 Raise i to powers.

OBJECTIVE 1 ▶ Writing numbers in the form bi. Our work with radical expressions has excluded expressions such as $\sqrt{-16}$ because $\sqrt{-16}$ is not a real number; there is no real number whose square is -16. In this section, we discuss a number system that includes roots of negative numbers. This number system is the **complex number system,** and it includes the set of real numbers as a subset. The complex number system allows us to solve equations such as $x^2 + 1 = 0$ that have no real number solutions. The set of complex numbers includes the **imaginary unit.**

Imaginary Unit
The imaginary unit, written i, is the number whose square is -1. That is,

$$i^2 = -1 \quad \text{and} \quad i = \sqrt{-1}$$

To write the square root of a negative number in terms of i, use the property that if a is a positive number, then

$$\sqrt{-a} = \sqrt{-1} \cdot \sqrt{a}$$
$$= i \cdot \sqrt{a}$$

Using i, we can write $\sqrt{-16}$ as

$$\sqrt{-16} = \sqrt{-1 \cdot 16} = \sqrt{-1} \cdot \sqrt{16} = i \cdot 4, \text{ or } 4i$$

EXAMPLE 1   Write with i notation.

a. $\sqrt{-36}$ b. $\sqrt{-5}$ c. $-\sqrt{-20}$

Solution

> ▶ **Helpful Hint**
> Since $\sqrt{5}i$ can easily be confused with $\sqrt{5i}$, we write $\sqrt{5}i$ as $i\sqrt{5}$.

a. $\sqrt{-36} = \sqrt{-1 \cdot 36} = \sqrt{-1} \cdot \sqrt{36} = i \cdot 6$, or $6i$

b. $\sqrt{-5} = \sqrt{-1(5)} = \sqrt{-1} \cdot \sqrt{5} = i\sqrt{5}$.

c. $-\sqrt{-20} = -\sqrt{-1 \cdot 20} = -\sqrt{-1} \cdot \sqrt{4 \cdot 5} = -i \cdot 2\sqrt{5} = -2i\sqrt{5}$

PRACTICE
1   Write with i notation.

a. $\sqrt{-4}$ b. $\sqrt{-7}$ c. $-\sqrt{-18}$

The product rule for radicals does not necessarily hold true for imaginary numbers. *To multiply square roots of negative numbers, first we write each number in terms of the imaginary unit i.* For example, to multiply $\sqrt{-4}$ and $\sqrt{-9}$, we first write each number in the form bi.

$$\sqrt{-4}\sqrt{-9} = 2i(3i) = 6i^2 = 6(-1) = -6 \quad \text{Correct}$$

We will also use this method to simplify quotients of square roots of negative numbers. Why? The product rule does not work for this example. In other words,

$$\sqrt{-4} \cdot \sqrt{-9} = \sqrt{(-4)(-9)} = \sqrt{36} = 6 \quad \text{Incorrect}$$

EXAMPLE 2   Multiply or divide as indicated.

a. $\sqrt{-3} \cdot \sqrt{-5}$ b. $\sqrt{-36} \cdot \sqrt{-1}$ c. $\sqrt{8} \cdot \sqrt{-2}$ d. $\dfrac{\sqrt{-125}}{\sqrt{5}}$

Solution

a. $\sqrt{-3} \cdot \sqrt{-5} = i\sqrt{3}(i\sqrt{5}) = i^2\sqrt{15} = -1\sqrt{15} = -\sqrt{15}$

b. $\sqrt{-36} \cdot \sqrt{-1} = 6i(i) = 6i^2 = 6(-1) = -6$

c. $\sqrt{8} \cdot \sqrt{-2} = 2\sqrt{2}(i\sqrt{2}) = 2i(\sqrt{2}\sqrt{2}) = 2i(2) = 4i$

d. $\dfrac{\sqrt{-125}}{\sqrt{5}} = \dfrac{i\sqrt{125}}{\sqrt{5}} = i\sqrt{25} = 5i$

PRACTICE
2   Multiply or divide as indicated.

a. $\sqrt{-5} \cdot \sqrt{-6}$ b. $\sqrt{-9} \cdot \sqrt{-1}$ c. $\sqrt{125} \cdot \sqrt{-5}$ d. $\dfrac{\sqrt{-27}}{\sqrt{3}}$

Now that we have practiced working with the imaginary unit, we define complex numbers.

> **Complex Numbers**
> A **complex number** is a number that can be written in the form $a + bi$, where a and b are real numbers.

Notice that the set of real numbers is a subset of the complex numbers since any real number can be written in the form of a complex number. For example,

$$16 = 16 + 0i$$

In general, a complex number $a + bi$ is a real number if $b = 0$. Also, a complex number is called a **pure imaginary number** if $a = 0$ and $b \neq 0$. For example,

$$3i = 0 + 3i \quad \text{and} \quad i\sqrt{7} = 0 + i\sqrt{7}$$

are pure imaginary numbers.

The following diagram shows the relationship between complex numbers and their subsets.

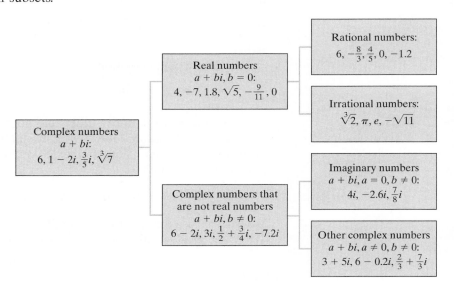

Concept Check ☑

True or false? Every complex number is also a real number.

OBJECTIVE 2 ▶ **Adding or subtracting complex numbers.** Two complex numbers $a + bi$ and $c + di$ are equal if and only if $a = c$ and $b = d$. Complex numbers can be added or subtracted by adding or subtracting their real parts and then adding or subtracting their imaginary parts.

Sum or Difference of Complex Numbers

If $a + bi$ and $c + di$ are complex numbers, then their sum is

$$(a + bi) + (c + di) = (a + c) + (b + d)i$$

Their difference is

$$(a + bi) - (c + di) = a + bi - c - di = (a - c) + (b - d)i$$

EXAMPLE 3   Add or subtract the complex numbers. Write the sum or difference in the form $a + bi$.

a. $(2 + 3i) + (-3 + 2i)$ **b.** $5i - (1 - i)$ **c.** $(-3 - 7i) - (-6)$

Solution

a. $(2 + 3i) + (-3 + 2i) = (2 - 3) + (3 + 2)i = -1 + 5i$

b. $5i - (1 - i) = 5i - 1 + i$

$$= -1 + (5 + 1)i$$

$$= -1 + 6i$$

c. $(-3 - 7i) - (-6) = -3 - 7i + 6$
$$= (-3 + 6) - 7i$$
$$= 3 - 7i$$

$\square$

PRACTICE

3   Add or subtract the complex numbers. Write the sum or difference in the form $a + bi$.

a. $(3 - 5i) + (-4 + i)$ **b.** $4i - (3 - i)$ **c.** $(-5 - 2i) - (-8)$

OBJECTIVE 3 ▶ **Multiplying complex numbers.** To multiply two complex numbers of the form $a + bi$, we multiply as though they are binomials. Then we use the relationship $i^2 = -1$ to simplify.

EXAMPLE 4   Multiply the complex numbers. Write the product in the form $a + bi$.

a. $-7i \cdot 3i$ **b.** $3i(2 - i)$ **c.** $(2 - 5i)(4 + i)$
d. $(2 - i)^2$ **e.** $(7 + 3i)(7 - 3i)$

Solution

a. $-7i \cdot 3i = -21i^2$
$$= -21(-1) \qquad \text{Replace } i^2 \text{ with } -1.$$
$$= 21$$

b. $3i(2 - i) = 3i \cdot 2 - 3i \cdot i$ Use the distributive property.
$$= 6i - 3i^2 \qquad \text{Multiply.}$$
$$= 6i - 3(-1) \qquad \text{Replace } i^2 \text{ with } -1.$$
$$= 6i + 3$$
$$= 3 + 6i$$

Use the FOIL order below. (First, Outer, Inner, Last)

c. $(2 - 5i)(4 + i) = 2(4) + 2(i) - 5i(4) - 5i(i)$
$$\qquad\qquad\qquad \text{F} \quad \text{O} \quad \text{I} \quad \text{L}$$
$$= 8 + 2i - 20i - 5i^2$$
$$= 8 - 18i - 5(-1) \qquad i^2 = -1$$
$$= 8 - 18i + 5$$
$$= 13 - 18i$$

d. $(2 - i)^2 = (2 - i)(2 - i)$
$$= 2(2) - 2(i) - 2(i) + i^2$$
$$= 4 - 4i + (-1) \qquad i^2 = -1$$
$$= 3 - 4i$$

e. $(7 + 3i)(7 - 3i) = 7(7) - 7(3i) + 3i(7) - 3i(3i)$
$$= 49 - 21i + 21i - 9i^2$$
$$= 49 - 9(-1) \qquad i^2 = -1$$
$$= 49 + 9$$
$$= 58$$

$\square$

PRACTICE

4   Multiply the complex numbers. Write the product in the form $a + bi$.

a. $-4i \cdot 5i$ **b.** $5i(2 + i)$ **c.** $(2 + 3i)(6 - i)$
d. $(3 - i)^2$ **e.** $(9 + 2i)(9 - 2i)$

Notice that if you add, subtract, or multiply two complex numbers, just like real numbers, the result is a complex number.

OBJECTIVE 4 ▶ Dividing complex numbers. From Example 4e, notice that the product of $7 + 3i$ and $7 - 3i$ is a real number. These two complex numbers are called **complex conjugates** of one another. In general, we have the following definition.

> **Complex Conjugates**
> The complex numbers $(a + bi)$ and $(a - bi)$ are called **complex conjugates** of each other, and $(a + bi)(a - bi) = a^2 + b^2$.

To see that the product of a complex number $a + bi$ and its conjugate $a - bi$ is the real number $a^2 + b^2$, we multiply.

$$(a + bi)(a - bi) = a^2 - abi + abi - b^2i^2$$
$$= a^2 - b^2(-1)$$
$$= a^2 + b^2$$

We use complex conjugates to divide by a complex number.

EXAMPLE 5   Divide. Write in the form $a + bi$.

a. $\dfrac{2 + i}{1 - i}$ **b.** $\dfrac{7}{3i}$

Solution

a. Multiply the numerator and denominator by the complex conjugate of $1 - i$ to eliminate the imaginary number in the denominator.

$$\frac{2 + i}{1 - i} = \frac{(2 + i)(1 + i)}{(1 - i)(1 + i)}$$
$$= \frac{2(1) + 2(i) + 1(i) + i^2}{1^2 - i^2}$$
$$= \frac{2 + 3i - 1}{1 + 1} \qquad \text{Here, } i^2 = -1.$$
$$= \frac{1 + 3i}{2} \quad \text{or} \quad \frac{1}{2} + \frac{3}{2}i$$

b. Multiply the numerator and denominator by the conjugate of $3i$. Note that $3i = 0 + 3i$, so its conjugate is $0 - 3i$ or $-3i$.

$$\frac{7}{3i} = \frac{7(-3i)}{(3i)(-3i)} = \frac{-21i}{-9i^2} = \frac{-21i}{-9(-1)} = \frac{-21i}{9} = \frac{-7i}{3} \quad \text{or} \quad 0 - \frac{7}{3}i \qquad \square$$

PRACTICE
5   Divide. Write in the form $a + bi$.

a. $\dfrac{4 - i}{3 + i}$ **b.** $\dfrac{5}{2i}$

> **▶ Helpful Hint**
> Recall that division can be checked by multiplication.
> To check that $\dfrac{2 + i}{1 - i} = \dfrac{1}{2} + \dfrac{3}{2}i$, in Example 5a, multiply $\left(\dfrac{1}{2} + \dfrac{3}{2}i\right)(1 - i)$ to verify that the product is $2 + i$.

OBJECTIVE 5 ▶ Finding powers of *i*. We can use the fact that $i^2 = -1$ to find higher powers of *i*. To find i^3, we rewrite it as the product of i^2 and *i*.

$$i^3 = i^2 \cdot i = (-1)i = -i$$
$$i^4 = i^2 \cdot i^2 = (-1) \cdot (-1) = 1$$

We continue this process and use the fact that $i^4 = 1$ and $i^2 = -1$ to simplify i^5 and i^6.

$$i^5 = i^4 \cdot i = 1 \cdot i = i$$
$$i^6 = i^4 \cdot i^2 = 1 \cdot (-1) = -1$$

If we continue finding powers of *i*, we generate the following pattern. Notice that the values i, -1, $-i$, and 1 repeat as *i* is raised to higher and higher powers.

$$
\begin{array}{lll}
i^1 = i & i^5 = i & i^9 = i \\
i^2 = -1 & i^6 = -1 & i^{10} = -1 \\
i^3 = -i & i^7 = -i & i^{11} = -i \\
i^4 = 1 & i^8 = 1 & i^{12} = 1
\end{array}
$$

This pattern allows us to find other powers of *i*. To do so, we will use the fact that $i^4 = 1$ and rewrite a power of *i* in terms of i^4. For example,

$$i^{22} = i^{20} \cdot i^2 = (i^4)^5 \cdot i^2 = 1^5 \cdot (-1) = 1 \cdot (-1) = -1.$$

EXAMPLE 6   Find the following powers of *i*.

a. i^7 **b.** i^{20} **c.** i^{46} **d.** i^{-12}

Solution

a. $i^7 = i^4 \cdot i^3 = 1(-i) = -i$

b. $i^{20} = (i^4)^5 = 1^5 = 1$

c. $i^{46} = i^{44} \cdot i^2 = (i^4)^{11} \cdot i^2 = 1^{11}(-1) = -1$

d. $i^{-12} = \dfrac{1}{i^{12}} = \dfrac{1}{(i^4)^3} = \dfrac{1}{(1)^3} = \dfrac{1}{1} = 1$

PRACTICE
6   Find the following powers of *i*.

a. i^9 **b.** i^{16} **c.** i^{34} **d.** i^{-24}

VOCABULARY & READINESS CHECK

Use the choices below to fill in each blank. Not all choices will be used.

-1	$\sqrt{-1}$	real	imaginary unit
1	$\sqrt{1}$	complex	pure imaginary

1. A _____ number is one that can be written in the form $a + bi$ where a and b are real numbers.

2. In the complex number system, *i* denotes the _____.

3. $i^2 =$ _____

4. $i =$ _____

5. A complex number, $a + bi$, is a _____ number if $b = 0$.

6. A complex number, $a + bi$, is a _____ number if $a = 0$ and $b \neq 0$.

Simplify. See Example 1.

7. $\sqrt{-81}$ **8.** $\sqrt{-49}$ **9.** $\sqrt{-7}$ **10.** $\sqrt{-3}$

11. $-\sqrt{16}$ **12.** $-\sqrt{4}$ **13.** $\sqrt{-64}$ **14.** $\sqrt{-100}$

7.7 | EXERCISE SET

MathXL PRACTICE   WATCH   DOWNLOAD   READ   REVIEW

Write in terms of i. See Example 1.

1. $\sqrt{-24}$ **2.** $\sqrt{-32}$

3. $-\sqrt{-36}$ **4.** $-\sqrt{-121}$

5. $8\sqrt{-63}$ **6.** $4\sqrt{-20}$

7. $-\sqrt{54}$ **8.** $\sqrt{-63}$

Multiply or divide. See Example 2.

9. $\sqrt{-2} \cdot \sqrt{-7}$ **10.** $\sqrt{-11} \cdot \sqrt{-3}$

11. $\sqrt{-5} \cdot \sqrt{-10}$ **12.** $\sqrt{-2} \cdot \sqrt{-6}$

13. $\sqrt{16} \cdot \sqrt{-1}$ **14.** $\sqrt{3} \cdot \sqrt{-27}$

15. $\dfrac{\sqrt{-9}}{\sqrt{3}}$ **16.** $\dfrac{\sqrt{49}}{\sqrt{-10}}$

17. $\dfrac{\sqrt{-80}}{\sqrt{-10}}$ **18.** $\dfrac{\sqrt{-40}}{\sqrt{-8}}$

Add or subtract. Write the sum or difference in the form a + bi. See Example 3.

19. $(4 - 7i) + (2 + 3i)$ **20.** $(2 - 4i) - (2 - i)$

21. $(6 + 5i) - (8 - i)$ **22.** $(8 - 3i) + (-8 + 3i)$

23. $6 - (8 + 4i)$ **24.** $(9 - 4i) - 9$

Multiply. Write the product in the form a + bi. See Example 4.

25. $-10i \cdot -4i$ **26.** $-2i \cdot -11i$

27. $6i(2 - 3i)$ **28.** $5i(4 - 7i)$

29. $\left(\sqrt{3} + 2i\right)\left(\sqrt{3} - 2i\right)$ **30.** $\left(\sqrt{5} - 5i\right)\left(\sqrt{5} + 5i\right)$

31. $(4 - 2i)^2$ **32.** $(6 - 3i)^2$

Write each quotient in the form a + bi. See Example 5.

33. $\dfrac{4}{i}$ **34.** $\dfrac{5}{6i}$

35. $\dfrac{7}{4 + 3i}$ **36.** $\dfrac{9}{1 - 2i}$

37. $\dfrac{3 + 5i}{1 + i}$ **38.** $\dfrac{6 + 2i}{4 - 3i}$

39. $\dfrac{5 - i}{3 - 2i}$ **40.** $\dfrac{6 - i}{2 + i}$

MIXED PRACTICE

Perform each indicated operation. Write the result in the form a + bi.

41. $(7i)(-9i)$ **42.** $(-6i)(-4i)$

43. $(6 - 3i) - (4 - 2i)$ **44.** $(-2 - 4i) - (6 - 8i)$

45. $-3i(-1 + 9i)$ **46.** $-5i(-2 + i)$

47. $\dfrac{4 - 5i}{2i}$ **48.** $\dfrac{6 + 8i}{3i}$

49. $(4 + i)(5 + 2i)$ **50.** $(3 + i)(2 + 4i)$

51. $(6 - 2i)(3 + i)$ **52.** $(2 - 4i)(2 - i)$

53. $(8 - 3i) + (2 + 3i)$ **54.** $(7 + 4i) + (4 - 4i)$

55. $(1 - i)(1 + i)$ **56.** $(6 + 2i)(6 - 2i)$

57. $\dfrac{16 + 15i}{-3i}$ **58.** $\dfrac{2 - 3i}{-7i}$

59. $(9 + 8i)^2$ **60.** $(4 - 7i)^2$

61. $\dfrac{2}{3 + i}$ **62.** $\dfrac{5}{3 - 2i}$

63. $(5 - 6i) - 4i$ **64.** $(6 - 2i) + 7i$

65. $\dfrac{2 - 3i}{2 + i}$ **66.** $\dfrac{6 + 5i}{6 - 5i}$

67. $(2 + 4i) + (6 - 5i)$ **68.** $(5 - 3i) + (7 - 8i)$

69. $(\sqrt{3} + 2i)(\sqrt{3} - 2i)$ **70.** $(\sqrt{5} - 5i)(\sqrt{5} + 5i)$

71. $(4 - 2i)^2$ **72.** $(6 - 3i)^2$

Find each power of i. See Example 6.

73. i^8 **74.** i^{10}

75. i^{21} **76.** i^{15}

77. i^{11} **78.** i^{40}

79. i^{-6} **80.** i^{-9}

81. $(2i)^6$ **82.** $(5i)^4$

83. $(-3i)^5$ **84.** $(-2i)^7$

REVIEW AND PREVIEW

Recall that the sum of the measures of the angles of a triangle is 180°. Find the unknown angle in each triangle.

85.

86.

Use synthetic division to divide the following. See Section 6.4.

87. $(x^3 - 6x^2 + 3x - 4) \div (x - 1)$

88. $(5x^4 - 3x^2 + 2) \div (x + 2)$

Thirty people were recently polled about their average monthly balance in their checking accounts. The results of this poll are shown in the following histogram. Use this graph to answer Exercises 89 through 94. See Section 1.2.

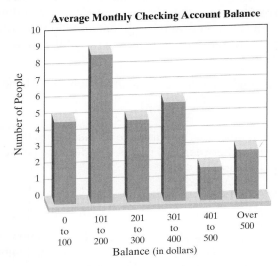

Average Monthly Checking Account Balance

89. How many people polled reported an average checking balance of $201 to $300?

90. How many people polled reported an average checking balance of $0 to $100?

91. How many people polled reported an average checking balance of $200 or less?

92. How many people polled reported an average checking balance of $301 or more?

93. What percent of people polled reported an average checking balance of $201 to $300?

94. What percent of people polled reported an average checking balance of $0 to $100?

CONCEPT EXTENSIONS

Write in the form a + bi.

95. $i^3 - i^4$

96. $i^8 - i^7$

97. $i^6 + i^8$

98. $i^4 + i^{12}$

99. $2 + \sqrt{-9}$

100. $5 - \sqrt{-16}$

101. $\dfrac{6 + \sqrt{-18}}{3}$

102. $\dfrac{4 - \sqrt{-8}}{2}$

103. $\dfrac{5 - \sqrt{-75}}{10}$

104. Describe how to find the conjugate of a complex number.

105. Explain why the product of a complex number and its complex conjugate is a real number.

Simplify.

106. $\left(8 - \sqrt{-3}\right) - \left(2 + \sqrt{-12}\right)$

107. $\left(8 - \sqrt{-4}\right) - \left(2 + \sqrt{-16}\right)$

108. Determine whether $2i$ is a solution of $x^2 + 4 = 0$.

109. Determine whether $-1 + i$ is a solution of $x^2 + 2x = -2$.

CHAPTER 7 GROUP ACTIVITY

Heron of Alexandria

Heron (also Hero) was a Greek mathematician and engineer. He lived and worked in Alexandria, Egypt, around 75 A.D. During his prolific work life, Heron developed a rotary steam engine called an aeolipile, a surveying tool called a dioptra, as well as a wind organ and a fire engine. As an engineer, he must have had the need to approximate square roots because he described an iterative method for doing so in his work *Metrica*. Heron's method for approximating a square root can be summarized as follows:

Suppose that x is not a perfect square and a^2 is the nearest perfect square to x. For a rough estimate of the value of $\sqrt{x}$, find the value of $y_1 = \dfrac{1}{2}\left(a + \dfrac{x}{a}\right)$. This estimate can be improved by calculating a second estimate using the first estimate y_1 in place of a: $y_2 = \dfrac{1}{2}\left(y_1 + \dfrac{x}{y_1}\right)$.

Repeating this process several times will give more and more accurate estimates of $\sqrt{x}$.

Critical Thinking

1. a. Which perfect square is closest to 80?

  b. Use Heron's method for approximating square roots to calculate the first estimate of the square root of 80. Give an exact decimal answer.

  c. Use the first estimate of the square root of 80 to find a more refined second estimate. Round this second estimate to 6 decimal places.

  d. Use a calculator to find the actual value of the square root of 80. List all digits shown on your calculator's display.

  e. Compare the actual value from part (d) to the values of the first and second estimates. What do you notice?

  f. How many iterations of this process are necessary to get an estimate that differs no more than one digit from the actual value recorded in part (d)?

2. Repeat Question 1 for finding an estimate of the square root of 30.

3. Repeat Question 1 for finding an estimate of the square root of 4572.

4. Why would this iterative method have been important to people of Heron's era? Would you say that this method is as important today? Why or why not?

STUDY SKILLS BUILDER

Are You Prepared for a Test on Chapter 7?

Below I have listed some common trouble areas for students in Chapter 7. After studying for your test, but before taking your test, read these.

- Remember how to convert an expression with rational expressions to one with radicals and one with radicals to one with rational expressions.

$$7^{2/3} = \sqrt[3]{7^2} \text{ or } (\sqrt[3]{7})^2$$
$$\sqrt[5]{4^3} = 4^{3/5}$$

- Remember the difference between $\sqrt{x} + \sqrt{x}$ and $\sqrt{x} \cdot \sqrt{x}, x > 0$.

$$\sqrt{x} + \sqrt{x} = 2\sqrt{x}$$
$$\sqrt{x} \cdot \sqrt{x} = x$$

- Don't forget the difference between rationalizing the denominator of $\sqrt{\dfrac{2}{x}}$ and rationalizing the denominator

of $\dfrac{\sqrt{2}}{\sqrt{x} + 1}, x > 0$.

$$\sqrt{\frac{2}{x}} = \frac{\sqrt{2}}{\sqrt{x}} = \frac{\sqrt{2} \cdot \sqrt{x}}{\sqrt{x} \cdot \sqrt{x}} = \frac{\sqrt{2x}}{x}$$
$$\frac{\sqrt{2}}{\sqrt{x} + 1} = \frac{\sqrt{2}(\sqrt{x} - 1)}{(\sqrt{x} + 1)(\sqrt{x} - 1)} = \frac{\sqrt{2}(\sqrt{x} - 1)}{x - 1}$$

- Remember that the midpoint of a segment is a *point*. The x-coordinate is the average of the x-coordinates of the endpoints of the segment and the y-coordinate is the average of the y-coordinates of the endpoints of the segment.

The midpoint of the segment joining $(-1, 5)$ and $(3, 4)$ is $\left(\dfrac{-1 + 3}{2}, \dfrac{5 + 4}{2}\right)$ or $\left(1, \dfrac{9}{2}\right)$.

- Remember that the distance formula gives the *distance* between two points. The distance between $(-1, 5)$ and $(3, 4)$ is

$$\sqrt{(3 - (-1))^2 + (4 - 5)^2} = \sqrt{4^2 + (-1)^2}$$
$$= \sqrt{16 + 1} = \sqrt{17} \text{ units}$$

Remember: This is simply a checklist of common trouble areas. For a review of Chapter 7, see the Highlights and Chapter Review at the end of this chapter.

CHAPTER 7 VOCABULARY CHECK

Fill in each blank with one of the words or phrases listed below.

index	rationalizing	conjugate	principal square root	cube root	midpoint
complex number	like radicals	radicand	imaginary unit	distance	

1. The _____ of $\sqrt{3} + 2$ is $\sqrt{3} - 2$.

2. The _____ of a nonnegative number a is written as $\sqrt{a}$.

3. The process of writing a radical expression as an equivalent expression but without a radical in the denominator is called _____ the denominator.

4. The _____ written i, is the number whose square is -1.

5. The _____ of a number is written as $\sqrt[3]{a}$.

6. In the notation $\sqrt[n]{a}$, n is called the _____ and a is called the _____.

7. Radicals with the same index and the same radicand are called _____.

8. A _____ is a number that can be written in the form $a + bi$, where a and b are real numbers.

9. The _____ formula is $d = \sqrt{(x_2 - x_1)^2 + (y_2 - y_1)^2}$.

10. The _____ formula is $\left(\dfrac{x_1 + x_2}{2}, \dfrac{y_1 + y_2}{2}\right)$.

▶ **Helpful Hint**

Are you preparing for your test? Don't forget to take the Chapter 7 Test on page 441. Then check your answers at the back of the text and use the Chapter Test Prep Video CD to see the fully worked-out solutions to any of the exercises you want to review.

CHAPTER 7 HIGHLIGHTS

DEFINITIONS AND CONCEPTS	EXAMPLES

SECTION 7.1   RADICALS AND RADICAL FUNCTIONS

The **positive,** or **principal, square root** of a nonnegative number a is written as $\sqrt{a}$.

$$\sqrt{a} = b \text{ only if } b^2 = a \text{ and } b \geq 0$$

The **negative square root of** a is written as $-\sqrt{a}$.

The **cube root** of a real number a is written as $\sqrt[3]{a}$.

$$\sqrt[3]{a} = b \text{ only if } b^3 = a$$

If n is an even positive integer, then $\sqrt[n]{a^n} = |a|$.

If n is an odd positive integer, then $\sqrt[n]{a^n} = a$.

A **radical function** in x is a function defined by an expression containing a root of x.

$$\sqrt{36} = 6 \qquad \sqrt{\frac{9}{100}} = \frac{3}{10}$$

$$-\sqrt{36} = -6 \qquad \sqrt{0.04} = 0.2$$

$$\sqrt[3]{27} = 3 \qquad \sqrt[3]{-\frac{1}{8}} = -\frac{1}{2}$$

$$\sqrt[3]{y^6} = y^2 \qquad \sqrt[3]{64x^9} = 4x^3$$

$$\sqrt{(-3)^2} = |-3| = 3$$

$$\sqrt[3]{(-7)^3} = -7$$

If $f(x) = \sqrt{x} + 2$,

$$f(1) = \sqrt{(1)} + 2 = 1 + 2 = 3$$

$$f(3) = \sqrt{(3)} + 2 \approx 3.73$$

SECTION 7.2   RATIONAL EXPONENTS

$a^{1/n} = \sqrt[n]{a}$ if $\sqrt[n]{a}$ is a real number.

If m and n are positive integers greater than 1 with $\dfrac{m}{n}$ in lowest terms and $\sqrt[n]{a}$ is a real number, then

$$a^{m/n} = (a^{1/n})^m = \left(\sqrt[n]{a}\right)^m$$

$a^{-m/n} = \dfrac{1}{a^{m/n}}$ as long as $a^{m/n}$ is a nonzero number.

Exponent rules are true for rational exponents.

$$81^{1/2} = \sqrt{81} = 9$$

$$(-8x^3)^{1/3} = \sqrt[3]{-8x^3} = -2x$$

$$4^{5/2} = \left(\sqrt{4}\right)^5 = 2^5 = 32$$

$$27^{2/3} = \left(\sqrt[3]{27}\right)^2 = 3^2 = 9$$

$$16^{-3/4} = \frac{1}{16^{3/4}} = \frac{1}{\left(\sqrt[4]{16}\right)^3} = \frac{1}{2^3} = \frac{1}{8}$$

$$x^{2/3} \cdot x^{-5/6} = x^{2/3 - 5/6} = x^{-1/6} = \frac{1}{x^{1/6}}$$

$$(8^1)^{1/2} = 8^2 = 64$$

$$\frac{a^{4/5}}{a^{-2/5}} = a^{4/5 - (-2/5)} = a^{6/5}$$

(continued)

DEFINITIONS AND CONCEPTS	**EXAMPLES**

SECTION 7.3 SIMPLIFYING RADICAL EXPRESSIONS

Product and Quotient Rules

If $\sqrt[n]{a}$ and $\sqrt[n]{b}$ are real numbers,

$$\sqrt[n]{a} \cdot \sqrt[n]{b} = \sqrt[n]{a \cdot b}$$

$$\frac{\sqrt[n]{a}}{\sqrt[n]{b}} = \sqrt[n]{\frac{a}{b}}, \text{ provided } \sqrt[n]{b} \neq 0$$

A radical of the form $\sqrt[n]{a}$ is **simplified** when a contains no factors that are perfect nth powers.

Multiply or divide as indicated:

$$\sqrt{11} \cdot \sqrt{3} = \sqrt{33}$$

$$\frac{\sqrt[3]{40x}}{\sqrt[3]{5x}} = \sqrt[3]{8} = 2$$

$$\sqrt{40} = \sqrt{4 \cdot 10} = 2\sqrt{10}$$

$$\sqrt{36x^5} = \sqrt{36x^4 \cdot x} = 6x^2\sqrt{x}$$

$$\sqrt[3]{24x^7y^3} = \sqrt[3]{8x^6y^3 \cdot 3x} = 2x^2y\sqrt[3]{3x}$$

$$\sqrt{36x^4 \cdot x} = 6x^2\sqrt{x}$$

Distance Formula

The distance d between two points (x_1, y_1) and (x_2, y_2) is given by

$$d = \sqrt{(x_2 - x_1)^2 + (y_2 - y_1)^2}$$

Find the distance between points $(-1, 6)$ and $(-2, -4)$. Let $(x_1, y_1) = (-1, 6)$ and $(x_2, y_2) = (-2, -4)$.

$$d = \sqrt{(x_2 - x_1)^2 + (y_2 - y_1)^2}$$

$$= \sqrt{(-2 - (-1))^2 + (-4 - 6)^2}$$

$$= \sqrt{1 + 100} = \sqrt{101}$$

Midpoint Formula

The midpoint of the line segment whose endpoints are (x_1, y_1) and (x_2, y_2) is the point with coordinates

$$\left(\frac{x_1 + x_2}{2}, \frac{y_1 + y_2}{2} \right)$$

Find the midpoint of the line segment whose endpoints are $(-1, 6)$ and $(-2, -4)$.

$$\left(\frac{-1 + (-2)}{2}, \frac{6 + (-4)}{2} \right)$$

The midpoint is $\left(-\frac{3}{2}, 1 \right)$.

SECTION 7.4 ADDING, SUBTRACTING, AND MULTIPLYING RADICAL EXPRESSIONS

Radicals with the same index and the same radicand are **like radicals.**

The distributive property can be used to add like radicals.

$$5\sqrt{6} + 2\sqrt{6} = (5 + 2)\sqrt{6} = 7\sqrt{6}$$

$$= \sqrt[3]{3x} - 10\sqrt[3]{3x} + 3\sqrt[3]{10x}$$

$$= (-1 - 10)\sqrt[3]{3x} + 3\sqrt[3]{10x}$$

$$= -11\sqrt[3]{3x} + 3\sqrt[3]{10x}$$

Radical expressions are multiplied by using many of the same properties used to multiply polynomials.

Multiply:

$$(\sqrt{5} - \sqrt{2x})(\sqrt{2} + \sqrt{2x})$$

$$= \sqrt{10} + \sqrt{10x} - \sqrt{4x} - 2x$$

$$= \sqrt{10} + \sqrt{10x} - 2\sqrt{x} - 2x$$

$$(2\sqrt{3} - \sqrt{8x})(2\sqrt{3} + \sqrt{8x})$$

$$= 4(3) - 8x = 12 - 8x$$

DEFINITIONS AND CONCEPTS	EXAMPLES

SECTION 7.5   RATIONALIZING DENOMINATORS AND NUMERATORS OF RADICAL EXPRESSIONS

The **conjugate** of $a + b$ is $a - b$.

The conjugate of $\sqrt{7} + \sqrt{3}$ is $\sqrt{7} - \sqrt{3}$.

The process of writing the denominator of a radical expression without a radical is called **rationalizing the denominator.**

Rationalize each denominator.

$$\frac{\sqrt{5}}{\sqrt{3}} = \frac{\sqrt{5}\cdot\sqrt{3}}{\sqrt{3}\cdot\sqrt{3}} = \frac{\sqrt{15}}{3}$$

$$\frac{6}{\sqrt{7}+\sqrt{3}} = \frac{6(\sqrt{7}-\sqrt{3})}{(\sqrt{7}+\sqrt{3})(\sqrt{7}-\sqrt{3})}$$

$$= \frac{6(\sqrt{7}-\sqrt{3})}{7-3}$$

$$= \frac{6(\sqrt{7}-\sqrt{3})}{4} = \frac{3(\sqrt{7}-\sqrt{3})}{2}$$

The process of writing the numerator of a radical expression without a radical is called **rationalizing the numerator.**

Rationalize each numerator:

$$\frac{\sqrt[3]{9}}{\sqrt[3]{5}} = \frac{\sqrt[3]{9}\cdot\sqrt[3]{3}}{\sqrt[3]{5}\cdot\sqrt[3]{3}} = \frac{\sqrt[3]{27}}{\sqrt[3]{15}} = \frac{3}{\sqrt[3]{15}}$$

$$\frac{\sqrt{9}+\sqrt{3x}}{12} = \frac{(\sqrt{9}+\sqrt{3x})(\sqrt{9}-\sqrt{3x})}{12(\sqrt{9}-\sqrt{3x})}$$

$$= \frac{9-3x}{12(\sqrt{9}-\sqrt{3x})}$$

$$= \frac{3(3-x)}{3\cdot4(3-\sqrt{3x})} = \frac{3-x}{4(3-\sqrt{3x})}$$

SECTION 7.6   RADICAL EQUATIONS AND PROBLEM SOLVING

To Solve a Radical Equation

Step 1. Write the equation so that one radical is by itself on one side of the equation.

Step 2. Raise each side of the equation to a power equal to the index of the radical and simplify.

Step 3. If the equation still contains a radical, repeat Steps 1 and 2. If not, solve the equation.

Step 4. Check all proposed solutions in the original equation.

Solve: $x = \sqrt{4x+9} + 3$.

1. $x - 3 = \sqrt{4x+9}$

2. $\quad(x-3)^2 = (\sqrt{4x+9})^2$
$x^2 - 6x + 9 = 4x + 9$

3. $x^2 - 10x = 0$
$x(x - 10) = 0$
$\quad\quad x = 0 \quad\text{or}\quad x = 10$

4. The proposed solution 10 checks, but 0 does not. The solution is 10.

(continued)

DEFINITIONS AND CONCEPTS	**EXAMPLES**

SECTION 7.7 COMPLEX NUMBERS

$i^2 = -1$ and $i = \sqrt{-1}$

A **complex number** is a number that can be written in the form $a + bi$, where a and b are real numbers.

Simplify: $\sqrt{-9}$.

$$\sqrt{-9} = \sqrt{-1 \cdot 9} = \sqrt{-1} \cdot \sqrt{9} = i \cdot 3 \text{ or } 3i$$

Complex Numbers	**Written in Form $a + bi$**
12	$12 + 0i$
$-5i$	$0 + (-5)i$
$-2 - 3i$	$-2 + (-3)i$

Multiply,

$$\sqrt{-3} \cdot \sqrt{-7} = i\sqrt{3} \cdot i\sqrt{7}$$
$$= i^2\sqrt{21}$$
$$= -\sqrt{21}$$

To add or subtract complex numbers, add or subtract their real parts and then add or subtract their imaginary parts.

To multiply complex numbers, multiply as though they are binomials.

Perform each indicated operation.

$$(-3 + 2i) - (7 - 4i) = -3 + 2i - 7 + 4i$$
$$= -10 + 6i$$
$$(-7 - 2i)(6 + i) = -42 - 7i - 12i - 2i^2$$
$$= -42 - 19i - 2(-1)$$
$$= -42 - 19i + 2$$
$$= -40 - 19i$$

The complex numbers $(a + bi)$ and $(a - bi)$ are called **complex conjugates.**

The complex conjugate of

$$(3 + 6i) \text{ is } (3 - 6i).$$

Their product is a real number:

$$(3 - 6i)(3 + 6i) = 9 - 36i^2$$
$$= 9 - 36(-1) = 9 + 36 = 45$$

To divide complex numbers, multiply the numerator and the denominator by the conjugate of the denominator.

Divide.

$$\frac{4}{2 - i} = \frac{4(2 + i)}{(2 - i)(2 + i)}$$
$$= \frac{4(2 + i)}{4 - i^2}$$
$$= \frac{4(2 + i)}{5}$$
$$= \frac{8 + 4i}{5} = \frac{8}{5} + \frac{4}{5}i$$

CHAPTER 7 REVIEW

(7.1) *Find the root. Assume that all variables represent positive numbers.*

1. $\sqrt{81}$

2. $\sqrt[4]{81}$

3. $\sqrt[3]{-8}$

4. $\sqrt[4]{-16}$

5. $-\sqrt{\dfrac{1}{49}}$

6. $\sqrt{x^{64}}$

7. $-\sqrt{36}$

8. $\sqrt[3]{64}$

9. $\sqrt[3]{-a^6 b^9}$

10. $\sqrt{16a^4 b^{12}}$

11. $\sqrt[5]{32a^5 b^{10}}$

12. $\sqrt[5]{-32x^{15}y^{20}}$

13. $\sqrt{\dfrac{x^{12}}{36y^2}}$

14. $\sqrt[3]{\dfrac{27y^3}{z^{12}}}$

Simplify. Use absolute value bars when necessary.

15. $\sqrt{(-x)^2}$

16. $\sqrt[4]{(x^2 - 4)^4}$

17. $\sqrt[3]{(-27)^3}$

18. $\sqrt[5]{(-5)^5}$

19. $-\sqrt[5]{x^5}$

20. $\sqrt[4]{16(2y + z)^{12}}$

21. $\sqrt{25(x-y)^{10}}$ **22.** $\sqrt[5]{-y^5}$

23. $\sqrt[9]{-x^9}$

Identify the domain and then graph each function.

24. $f(x) = \sqrt{x} + 3$

25. $g(x) = \sqrt[3]{x} - 3$; use the accompanying table.

x	-5	2	3	4	11
$g(x)$					

(7.2) Evaluate the following.

26. $\left(\dfrac{1}{81}\right)^{1/4}$ **27.** $\left(-\dfrac{1}{27}\right)^{1/3}$

28. $(-27)^{-1/3}$ **29.** $(-64)^{-1/3}$

30. $-9^{3/2}$ **31.** $64^{-1/3}$

32. $(-25)^{5/2}$ **33.** $\left(\dfrac{25}{49}\right)^{-3/2}$

34. $\left(\dfrac{8}{27}\right)^{-2/3}$ **35.** $\left(-\dfrac{1}{36}\right)^{-1/4}$

Write with rational exponents.

36. $\sqrt[3]{x^2}$ **37.** $\sqrt[5]{5x^2y^3}$

Write with radical notation.

38. $y^{4/5}$ **39.** $5(xy^2z^5)^{1/3}$

40. $(x+2y)^{-1/2}$

Simplify each expression. Assume that all variables represent positive numbers. Write with only positive exponents.

41. $a^{1/3}a^{4/3}a^{1/2}$ **42.** $\dfrac{b^{1/3}}{b^{4/3}}$

43. $(a^{1/2}a^{-2})^3$ **44.** $(x^{-3}y^6)^{1/3}$

45. $\left(\dfrac{b^{3/4}}{a^{-1/2}}\right)^8$ **46.** $\dfrac{x^{1/4}x^{-1/2}}{x^{2/3}}$

47. $\left(\dfrac{49c^{5/3}}{a^{-1/4}b^{5/6}}\right)^{-1}$ **48.** $a^{-1/4}(a^{5/4} - a^{9/4})$

Use a calculator and write a three-decimal-place approximation.

49. $\sqrt{20}$ **50.** $\sqrt[3]{-39}$

51. $\sqrt[4]{726}$ **52.** $56^{1/3}$

53. $-78^{3/4}$ **54.** $105^{-2/3}$

Use rational exponents to write each radical with the same index. Then multiply.

55. $\sqrt[3]{2} \cdot \sqrt{7}$ **56.** $\sqrt[3]{3} \cdot \sqrt[4]{x}$

(7.3) Perform the indicated operations and then simplify if possible. For the remainder of this review, assume that variables represent positive numbers only.

57. $\sqrt{3} \cdot \sqrt{8}$ **58.** $\sqrt[3]{7y} \cdot \sqrt[3]{x^2z}$

59. $\dfrac{\sqrt{44x^3}}{\sqrt{11x}}$ **60.** $\dfrac{\sqrt[4]{a^6b^{13}}}{\sqrt[4]{a^2b}}$

Simplify.

61. $\sqrt{60}$ **62.** $-\sqrt{75}$

63. $\sqrt[3]{162}$ **64.** $\sqrt[3]{-32}$

65. $\sqrt{36x^7}$ **66.** $\sqrt[3]{24a^5b^7}$

67. $\sqrt{\dfrac{p^{17}}{121}}$ **68.** $\sqrt[3]{\dfrac{y^5}{27x^6}}$

69. $\sqrt[4]{\dfrac{xy^6}{81}}$ **70.** $\sqrt{\dfrac{2x^3}{49y^4}}$

△ **71.** The formula for the radius r of a circle of area A is

$$r = \sqrt{\dfrac{A}{\pi}}$$

  a. Find the exact radius of a circle whose area is 25 square meters.

  b. Approximate to two decimal places the radius of a circle whose area is 104 square inches.

Find the distance between each pair of points. Give an exact value and a three-decimal-place approximation.

72. $(-6, 3)$ and $(8, 4)$

73. $(-4, -6)$ and $(-1, 5)$

74. $(-1, 5)$ and $(2, -3)$

75. $(-\sqrt{2}, 0)$ and $(0, -4\sqrt{6})$

76. $(-\sqrt{5}, -\sqrt{11})$ and $(-\sqrt{5}, -3\sqrt{11})$

77. $(7.4, -8.6)$ and $(-1.2, 5.6)$

Find the midpoint of each line segment whose endpoints are given.

78. $(2, 6); (-12, 4)$ **79.** $(-6, -5); (-9, 7)$

80. $(4, -6); (-15, 2)$ **81.** $\left(0, -\dfrac{3}{8}\right); \left(\dfrac{1}{10}, 0\right)$

82. $\left(\dfrac{3}{4}, -\dfrac{1}{7}\right); \left(-\dfrac{1}{4}, -\dfrac{3}{7}\right)$

83. $(\sqrt{3}, -2\sqrt{6})$ and $(\sqrt{3}, -4\sqrt{6})$

(7.4) Perform the indicated operation.

84. $2\sqrt{50} - 3\sqrt{125} + \sqrt{98}$

85. $x\sqrt{75xy} - \sqrt{27x^3y}$

86. $\sqrt[3]{128} + \sqrt[3]{250}$

87. $3\sqrt[4]{32a^5} - a\sqrt[4]{162a}$

88. $\dfrac{5}{\sqrt{4}} + \dfrac{\sqrt{3}}{3}$

89. $\sqrt{\dfrac{8}{x^2}} - \sqrt{\dfrac{50}{16x^2}}$

90. $2\sqrt{32x^2y^3} - xy\sqrt{98y}$

91. $2a\sqrt[4]{32b^5} - 3b\sqrt[4]{162a^4b} + \sqrt[4]{2a^4b^5}$

Multiply and then simplify if possible.

92. $\sqrt{3}(\sqrt{27} - \sqrt{3})$

93. $(\sqrt{x} - 3)^2$

94. $(\sqrt{5} - 5)(2\sqrt{5} + 2)$

95. $(2\sqrt{x} - 3\sqrt{y})(2\sqrt{x} + 3\sqrt{y})$

96. $(\sqrt{a} + 3)(\sqrt{a} - 3)$

97. $(\sqrt[3]{a} + 2)^2$

98. $(\sqrt[3]{5x} + 9)(\sqrt[3]{5x} - 9)$

99. $(\sqrt[3]{a} + 4)(\sqrt[3]{a^2} - 4\sqrt[3]{a} + 16)$

(7.5) *Rationalize each denominator.*

100. $\dfrac{3}{\sqrt{7}}$

101. $\sqrt{\dfrac{x}{12}}$

102. $\dfrac{5}{\sqrt[3]{4}}$

103. $\sqrt{\dfrac{24x^5}{3y^2}}$

104. $\sqrt[3]{\dfrac{15x^6y^7}{z^2}}$

105. $\dfrac{5}{2 - \sqrt{7}}$

106. $\dfrac{3}{\sqrt{y} - 2}$

107. $\dfrac{\sqrt{2} - \sqrt{3}}{\sqrt{2} + \sqrt{3}}$

Rationalize each numerator.

108. $\dfrac{\sqrt{11}}{3}$

109. $\sqrt{\dfrac{18}{y}}$

110. $\dfrac{\sqrt[3]{9}}{7}$

111. $\sqrt{\dfrac{24x^5}{3y^2}}$

112. $\sqrt[3]{\dfrac{xy^2}{10z}}$

113. $\dfrac{\sqrt{x} + 5}{-3}$

(7.6) *Solve each equation for the variable.*

114. $\sqrt{y - 7} = 5$

115. $\sqrt{2x} + 10 = 4$

116. $\sqrt[3]{2x - 6} = 4$

117. $\sqrt{x + 6} = \sqrt{x + 2}$

118. $2x - 5\sqrt{x} = 3$

119. $\sqrt{x + 9} = 2 + \sqrt{x - 7}$

Find each unknown length.

△ **120.**

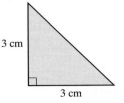

3 cm

3 cm

△ **121.**

7 ft

$8\sqrt{3}$ ft

122. Beverly Hillis wants to determine the distance x across a pond on her property. She is able to measure the distances shown on the following diagram. Find how wide the lake is at the crossing point, indicated by the triangle, to the nearest tenth of a foot.

65 ft

40 ft

△ **123.** A pipe fitter needs to connect two underground pipelines that are offset by 3 feet, as pictured in the diagram. Neglecting the joints needed to join the pipes, find the length of the shortest possible connecting pipe rounded to the nearest hundredth of a foot.

?

3 feet

3 feet

(7.7) *Perform the indicated operation and simplify. Write the result in the form $a + bi$.*

124. $\sqrt{-8}$

125. $-\sqrt{-6}$

126. $\sqrt{-4} + \sqrt{-16}$

127. $\sqrt{-2} \cdot \sqrt{-5}$

128. $(12 - 6i) + (3 + 2i)$

129. $(-8 - 7i) - (5 - 4i)$

130. $(2i)^6$

131. $-3i(6 - 4i)$

132. $(3 + 2i)(1 + i)$

133. $(2 - 3i)^2$

134. $(\sqrt{6} - 9i)(\sqrt{6} + 9i)$

135. $\dfrac{2 + 3i}{2i}$

136. $\dfrac{1 + i}{-3i}$

MIXED REVIEW

Simplify. Use absolute value bars when necessary.

137. $\sqrt[3]{x^3}$

138. $\sqrt{(x + 2)^2}$

Simplify. Assume that all variables represent positive real numbers. If necessary, write answers with positive exponents only.

139. $-\sqrt{100}$

140. $\sqrt[3]{-x^{12}y^3}$

141. $\sqrt[4]{\dfrac{y^{20}}{16x^{12}}}$

142. $9^{1/2}$

143. $64^{-1/2}$

144. $\left(\dfrac{27}{64}\right)^{-2/3}$

145. $\dfrac{(x^{2/3}x^{-3})^3}{x^{-1/2}}$

146. $\sqrt{200x^9}$

147. $\sqrt{\dfrac{3n^3}{121m^{10}}}$

148. $3\sqrt{20} - 7x\sqrt[3]{40} + 3\sqrt[3]{5x^3}$

149. $(2\sqrt{x} - 5)^2$

150. Find the distance between $(-3, 5)$ and $(-8, 9)$.

151. Find the midpoint of the line segment joining $(-3, 8)$ and $(11, 24)$.

Rationalize each denominator.

152. $\dfrac{7}{\sqrt{13}}$

153. $\dfrac{2}{\sqrt{x} + 3}$

Solve.

154. $\sqrt{x + 2} = x$

CHAPTER 7 TEST TEST PREP VIDEO

Remember to use the Chapter Test Prep Video CD to see the fully worked-out solutions to any of the exercises you want to review.

Raise to the power or find the root. Assume that all variables represent positive numbers. Write with only positive exponents.

1. $\sqrt{216}$

2. $-\sqrt[4]{x^{64}}$

3. $\left(\dfrac{1}{125}\right)^{1/3}$

4. $\left(\dfrac{1}{125}\right)^{-1/3}$

5. $\left(\dfrac{8x^3}{27}\right)^{2/3}$

6. $\sqrt[3]{-a^{18}b^9}$

7. $\left(\dfrac{64c^{4/3}}{a^{-2/3}b^{5/6}}\right)^{1/2}$

8. $a^{-2/3}(a^{5/4} - a^3)$

Find the root. Use absolute value bars when necessary.

9. $\sqrt[4]{(4xy)^4}$

10. $\sqrt[3]{(-27)^3}$

Rationalize the denominator. Assume that all variables represent positive numbers.

11. $\sqrt{\dfrac{9}{y}}$

12. $\dfrac{4 - \sqrt{x}}{4 + 2\sqrt{x}}$

13. $\dfrac{\sqrt[3]{ab}}{\sqrt[3]{ab^2}}$

14. Rationalize the numerator of $\dfrac{\sqrt{6} + x}{8}$ and simplify.

Perform the indicated operations. Assume that all variables represent positive numbers.

15. $\sqrt{125x^3} - 3\sqrt{20x^3}$

16. $\sqrt{3}(\sqrt{16} - \sqrt{2})$

17. $(\sqrt{x} + 1)^2$

18. $(\sqrt{2} - 4)(\sqrt{3} + 1)$

19. $(\sqrt{5} + 5)(\sqrt{5} - 5)$

Use a calculator to approximate each to three decimal places.

20. $\sqrt{561}$

21. $386^{-2/3}$

Solve.

22. $x = \sqrt{x - 2} + 2$

23. $\sqrt{x^2 - 7} + 3 = 0$

24. $\sqrt[3]{x + 5} = \sqrt[3]{2x - 1}$

Perform the indicated operation and simplify. Write the result in the form $a + bi$.

25. $\sqrt{-2}$

26. $-\sqrt{-8}$

27. $(12 - 6i) - (12 - 3i)$

28. $(6 - 2i)(6 + 2i)$

29. $(4 + 3i)^2$

30. $\dfrac{1 + 4i}{1 - i}$

31. Find x.

32. Identify the domain of $g(x)$. Then complete the accompanying table and graph $g(x)$.

$$g(x) = \sqrt{x + 2}$$

x	-2	-1	2	7
$g(x)$				

33. Find the distance between the points $(-6, 3)$ and $(-8, -7)$.

34. Find the distance between the points $(-2\sqrt{5}, \sqrt{10})$ and $(-\sqrt{5}, 4\sqrt{10})$.

35. Find the midpoint of the line segment whose endpoints are $(-2, -5)$ and $(-6, 12)$.

36. Find the midpoint of the line segment whose endpoints are $\left(-\dfrac{2}{3}, -\dfrac{1}{5}\right)$ and $\left(-\dfrac{1}{3}, \dfrac{4}{5}\right)$.

Solve.

37. The function $V(r) = \sqrt{2.5r}$ can be used to estimate the maximum safe velocity V in miles per hour at which a car can travel if it is driven along a curved road with a *radius of curvature r* in feet. To the nearest whole number, find the maximum safe speed if a cloverleaf exit on an expressway has a radius of curvature of 300 feet.

38. Use the formula from Exercise 37 to find the radius of curvature if the safe velocity is 30 mph.

CHAPTER 7 CUMULATIVE REVIEW

1. Simplify each expression.

   a. $3xy - 2xy + 5 - 7 + xy$

   b. $7x^2 + 3 - 5(x^2 - 4)$

   c. $(2.1x - 5.6) - (-x - 5.3)$

   d. $\frac{1}{2}(4a - 6b) - \frac{1}{3}(9a + 12b - 1) + \frac{1}{4}$

2. Simplify each expression.

   a. $2(x - 3) + (5x + 3)$

   b. $4(3x + 2) - 3(5x - 1)$

   c. $7x + 2(x - 7) - 3x$

3. Solve for x: $\dfrac{x + 5}{2} + \dfrac{1}{2} = 2x - \dfrac{x - 3}{8}$

4. Solve: $\dfrac{a - 1}{2} + a = 2 - \dfrac{2a + 7}{8}$

5. A part-time salesperson earns $600 per month plus a commission of 20% of sales. Find the minimum amount of sales needed to receive a total income of at least $1500 per month.

6. The Smith family owns a lake house 121.5 miles from home. If it takes them $4\frac{1}{2}$ hours round-trip to drive from their house to their lake house, find their average speed.

7. Solve: $2|x| + 25 = 23$

8. Solve: $|3x - 2| + 5 = 5$

9. Solve: $\left|\dfrac{x}{3} - 1\right| - 7 \geq -5$

10. Solve: $\left|\dfrac{x}{2} - 1\right| \leq 0$.

11. Graph the equation $y = |x|$.

12. Graph $y = |x - 2|$.

13. Determine the domain and range of each relation.

   a. $\{(2, 3), (2, 4), (0, -1), (3, -1)\}$

   b.

   c.
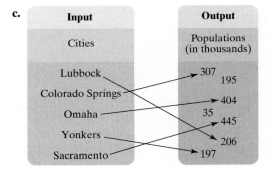

14. Find the domain and the range of each relation. Use the vertical line test to determine whether each graph is the graph of a function.

   a.

   b.
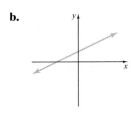

c.

15. Graph $y = -3$.

16. Graph $f(x) = -2$.

17. Find the slope of the line $x = -5$.

18. Find the slope of $y = -3$.

19. Use the substitution method to solve the system.

$$\begin{cases} -\dfrac{x}{6} + \dfrac{y}{2} = \dfrac{1}{2} \\ \dfrac{x}{3} - \dfrac{y}{6} = -\dfrac{3}{4} \end{cases}$$

20. Use the substitution method to solve the system.

$$\begin{cases} \dfrac{x}{6} - \dfrac{y}{2} = 1 \\ \dfrac{x}{3} - \dfrac{y}{4} = 2 \end{cases}$$

21. Use the product rule to simplify.

  a. $2^2 \cdot 2^5$

  b. $x^7 x^3$

  c. $y \cdot y^2 \cdot y^4$

22. At a seasonal clearance sale, Nana Long spent $33.75. She paid $3.50 for tee-shirts and $4.25 for shorts. If she bought 9 items, how many of each item did she buy?

23. Use scientific notation to simplify $\dfrac{2000 \times 0.000021}{700}$.

24. Use scientific notation to simplify and write the answer in scientific notation $\dfrac{0.0000035 \times 4000}{0.28}$.

25. If $P(x) = 3x^2 - 2x - 5$, find the following.

  a. $P(1)$

  b. $P(-2)$

26. Subtract $(2x - 5)$ from the sum of $(5x^2 - 3x + 6)$ and $(4x^2 + 5x - 3)$.

27. Multiply and simplify the product if possible.

  a. $(x + 3)(2x + 5)$

  b. $(2x - 3)(5x^2 - 6x + 7)$

28. Multiply and simplify the product if possible.

  a. $(y - 2)(3y + 4)$

  b. $(3y - 1)(2y^2 + 3y - 1)$

29. Find the GCF of $20x^3 y$, $10x^2 y^2$, and $35x^3$.

30. Factor $x^3 - x^2 + 4x - 4$

31. Simplify each rational expression.

  a. $\dfrac{x^3 + 8}{2 + x}$

  b. $\dfrac{2y^2 + 2}{y^3 - 5y^2 + y - 5}$

32. Simplify each rational expression.

  a. $\dfrac{a^3 - 8}{2 - a}$

  b. $\dfrac{3a^2 - 3}{a^3 + 5a^2 - a - 5}$

33. Perform the indicated operation.

  a. $\dfrac{2}{x^2 y} + \dfrac{5}{3x^3 y}$

  b. $\dfrac{3}{x + 2} + \dfrac{2x}{x - 2}$

  c. $\dfrac{2x - 6}{x - 1} - \dfrac{4}{1 - x}$

34. Perform the indicated operations.

  a. $\dfrac{3}{xy^2} - \dfrac{2}{3x^2 y}$

  b. $\dfrac{5x}{x + 3} - \dfrac{2x}{x - 3}$

  c. $\dfrac{x}{x - 2} - \dfrac{5}{2 - x}$

35. Simplify each complex fraction.

  a. $\dfrac{\dfrac{5x}{x + 2}}{\dfrac{10}{x - 2}}$

  b. $\dfrac{\dfrac{x}{y^2} + \dfrac{1}{y}}{\dfrac{y}{x^2} + \dfrac{1}{x}}$

36. Simplify each complex fraction.

  a. $\dfrac{\dfrac{y - 2}{16}}{\dfrac{2y + 3}{12}}$

  b. $\dfrac{\dfrac{x}{16} - \dfrac{1}{x}}{1 - \dfrac{4}{x}}$

37. Divide $10x^3 - 5x^2 + 20x$ by $5x$.

38. Divide $x^3 - 2x^2 + 3x - 6$ by $x - 2$.

39. Use synthetic division to divide $2x^3 - x^2 - 13x + 1$ by $x - 3$.

40. Use synthetic division to divide $4y^3 - 12y^2 - y + 12$ by $y - 3$.

41. Solve: $\dfrac{x + 6}{x - 2} = \dfrac{2(x + 2)}{x - 2}$.

42. Solve: $\dfrac{28}{9 - a^2} = \dfrac{2a}{a - 3} + \dfrac{6}{a + 3}$.

43. Solve: $\dfrac{1}{x} + \dfrac{1}{y} = \dfrac{1}{z}$ for x.

44. Solve: $A = \dfrac{h(a + b)}{2}$ for a.

45. Suppose that u varies inversely as w. If u is 3 when w is 5, find the constant of variation and the inverse variation equation.

46. Suppose that y varies directly as x. If $y = 0.51$ when $x = 3$, find the constant of variation and the direct variation equation.

47. Write each expression with a positive exponent, and then simplify.

   a. $16^{-3/4}$

   b. $(-27)^{-2/3}$

48. Write each expression with a positive exponent, and then simplify.

   a. $(81)^{-3/4}$

   b. $(-125)^{-2/3}$

49. Rationalize the numerator of $\dfrac{\sqrt{x} + 2}{5}$.

50. Add or subtract.

   a. $\sqrt{36a^3} - \sqrt{144a^3} + \sqrt{4a^3}$

   b. $\sqrt[3]{128ab^3} - 3\sqrt[3]{2ab^3} + b\sqrt[3]{16a}$

   c. $\dfrac{\sqrt[3]{81}}{10} + \sqrt[3]{\dfrac{192}{125}}$

8

Quadratic Equations and Functions

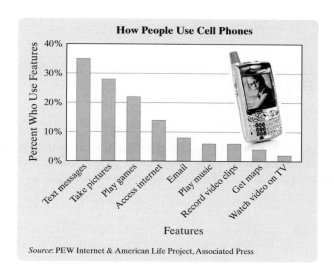

How People Use Cell Phones

Percent Who Use Features

Features

Source: PEW Internet & American Life Project, Associated Press

The growth of cell phones, shown below, can be approximated by a quadratic function. More interesting information is probably given on the graph above. As shown, the cell phone is certainly no longer just a phone.

Cell Phone Subscribers in the United States

Subscribers (in thousands)

$$f(x) = 668.7x^2 - 2990.7x + 938$$

Year
1985 ↔ 0

Source: CTIA – The Wireless Association

An important part of the study of algebra is learning to model and solve problems. Often, the model of a problem is a quadratic equation or a function containing a second-degree polynomial. In this chapter, we continue the work begun in Chapter 5, when we solved polynomial equations in one variable by factoring. Two additional methods of solving quadratic equations are analyzed, as well as methods of solving non-linear inequalities in one variable.

8.1 SOLVING QUADRATIC EQUATIONS BY COMPLETING THE SQUARE

OBJECTIVES

1 Use the square root property to solve quadratic equations.

2 Solve quadratic equations by completing the square.

3 Use quadratic equations to solve problems.

OBJECTIVE 1 ▶ Using the square root property. In Chapter 5, we solved quadratic equations by factoring. Recall that a **quadratic,** or **second-degree, equation** is an equation that can be written in the form $ax^2 + bx + c = 0$, where a, b, and c are real numbers and a is not 0. To solve a quadratic equation such as $x^2 = 9$ by factoring, we use the zero-factor theorem. To use the zero-factor theorem, the equation must first be written in standard form, $ax^2 + bx + c = 0$.

$$x^2 = 9$$
$$x^2 - 9 = 0 \qquad \text{Subtract 9 from both sides.}$$
$$(x + 3)(x - 3) = 0 \qquad \text{Factor.}$$
$$x + 3 = 0 \quad \text{or} \quad x - 3 = 0 \qquad \text{Set each factor equal to 0.}$$
$$x = -3 \qquad x = 3 \qquad \text{Solve.}$$

The solution set is $\{-3, 3\}$, the positive and negative square roots of 9. Not all quadratic equations can be solved by factoring, so we need to explore other methods. Notice that the solutions of the equation $x^2 = 9$ are two numbers whose square is 9.

$$3^2 = 9 \qquad \text{and} \qquad (-3)^2 = 9$$

Thus, we can solve the equation $x^2 = 9$ by taking the square root of both sides. Be sure to include both $\sqrt{9}$ and $-\sqrt{9}$ as solutions since both $\sqrt{9}$ and $-\sqrt{9}$ are numbers whose square is 9.

$$x^2 = 9$$
$$\sqrt{x^2} = \pm\sqrt{9} \qquad \text{The notation } \pm\sqrt{9} \text{ (read as "plus or minus } \sqrt{9}\text{")}$$
$$x = \pm 3 \qquad \text{indicates the pair of numbers } +\sqrt{9} \text{ and } -\sqrt{9}.$$

This illustrates the square root property.

> ▶ **Helpful Hint**
>
> The notation ± 3, for example, is read as "plus or minus 3." It is a shorthand notation for the pair of numbers $+3$ and -3.

> **Square Root Property**
> If b is a real number and if $a^2 = b$, then $a = \pm\sqrt{b}$.

EXAMPLE 1 Use the square root property to solve $x^2 = 50$.

Solution
$$x^2 = 50$$
$$x = \pm\sqrt{50} \qquad \text{Use the square root property.}$$
$$x = \pm 5\sqrt{2} \qquad \text{Simplify the radical.}$$

Check: Let $x = 5\sqrt{2}$.   Let $x = -5\sqrt{2}$.

$$x^2 = 50 \qquad\qquad x^2 = 50$$
$$\left(5\sqrt{2}\right)^2 \stackrel{?}{=} 50 \qquad \left(-5\sqrt{2}\right)^2 \stackrel{?}{=} 50$$
$$25 \cdot 2 \stackrel{?}{=} 50 \qquad\qquad 25 \cdot 2 \stackrel{?}{=} 50$$
$$50 = 50 \quad \text{True} \qquad\qquad 50 = 50 \quad \text{True}$$

The solutions are $5\sqrt{2}$ and $-5\sqrt{2}$, or the solution set is $\{-5\sqrt{2}, 5\sqrt{2}\}$. □

PRACTICE

1 Use the square root property to solve $x^2 = 18$.

EXAMPLE 2   Use the square root property to solve $2x^2 - 14 = 0$.

Solution   First we get the squared variable alone on one side of the equation.

$$2x^2 - 14 = 0$$
$$2x^2 = 14 \qquad \text{Add 14 to both sides.}$$
$$x^2 = 7 \qquad \text{Divide both sides by 2.}$$
$$x = \pm\sqrt{7} \qquad \text{Use the square root property.}$$

Check to see that the solutions are $\sqrt{7}$ and $-\sqrt{7}$, or the solution set is $\{-\sqrt{7}, \sqrt{7}\}$. ☐

PRACTICE
2   Use the square root property to solve $3x^2 - 30 = 0$.

EXAMPLE 3   Use the square root property to solve $(x + 1)^2 = 12$.

Solution
$$(x + 1)^2 = 12$$
$$x + 1 = \pm\sqrt{12} \qquad \text{Use the square root property.}$$
$$x + 1 = \pm 2\sqrt{3} \qquad \text{Simplify the radical.}$$
$$x = -1 \pm 2\sqrt{3} \qquad \text{Subtract 1 from both sides.}$$

Check: Below is a check for $-1 + 2\sqrt{3}$. The check for $-1 - 2\sqrt{3}$ is almost the same and is left for you to do on your own.

$$(x + 1)^2 = 12$$
$$\left(-1 + 2\sqrt{3} + 1\right)^2 \overset{?}{=} 12$$
$$\left(2\sqrt{3}\right)^2 \overset{?}{=} 12$$
$$4 \cdot 3 \overset{?}{=} 12$$
$$12 = 12 \quad \text{True}$$

The solutions are $-1 + 2\sqrt{3}$ and $-1 - 2\sqrt{3}$. ☐

PRACTICE
3   Use the square root property to solve $(x + 3)^2 = 20$.

EXAMPLE 4   Use the square root property to solve $(2x - 5)^2 = -16$.

Solution
$$(2x - 5)^2 = -16$$
$$2x - 5 = \pm\sqrt{-16} \qquad \text{Use the square root property.}$$
$$2x - 5 = \pm 4i \qquad \text{Simplify the radical.}$$
$$2x = 5 \pm 4i \qquad \text{Add 5 to both sides.}$$
$$x = \frac{5 \pm 4i}{2} \qquad \text{Divide both sides by 2.}$$

The solutions are $\dfrac{5 + 4i}{2}$ and $\dfrac{5 - 4i}{2}$. ☐

PRACTICE
4   Use the square root property to solve $(5x - 2)^2 = -9$.

Concept Check ☑

How do you know just by looking that $(x - 2)^2 = -4$ has complex, but not real solutions?

Answer to Concept Check:
answers may vary

OBJECTIVE 2 ▶ Solving by completing the square. Notice from Examples 3 and 4 that, if we write a quadratic equation so that one side is the square of a binomial, we can solve by using the square root property. To write the square of a binomial, we write perfect square trinomials. Recall that a perfect square trinomial is a trinomial that can be factored into two identical binomial factors.

Perfect Square Trinomials	*Factored Form*
$x^2 + 8x + 16$	$(x + 4)^2$
$x^2 - 6x + 9$	$(x - 3)^2$
$x^2 + 3x + \dfrac{9}{4}$	$\left(x + \dfrac{3}{2}\right)^2$

Notice that for each perfect square trinomial, **the constant term of the trinomial is the square of half the coefficient of the x-term.** For example,

$$\frac{1}{2}(8) = 4 \text{ and } 4^2 = 16 \qquad \frac{1}{2}(-6) = -3 \text{ and } (-3)^2 = 9$$

The process of writing a quadratic equation so that one side is a perfect square trinomial is called **completing the square.**

EXAMPLE 5 Solve $p^2 + 2p = 4$ by completing the square.

Solution First, add the square of half the coefficient of p to both sides so that the resulting trinomial will be a perfect square trinomial. The coefficient of p is 2.

$$\frac{1}{2}(2) = 1 \quad \text{and} \quad 1^2 = 1$$

Add 1 to both sides of the original equation.

$$
\begin{aligned}
p^2 + 2p &= 4 \\
p^2 + 2p + 1 &= 4 + 1 \qquad \text{Add 1 to both sides.} \\
(p + 1)^2 &= 5 \qquad \text{Factor the trinomial; simplify the right side.}
\end{aligned}
$$

We may now use the square root property and solve for p.

$$
\begin{aligned}
p + 1 &= \pm\sqrt{5} \qquad \text{Use the square root property.} \\
p &= -1 \pm \sqrt{5} \qquad \text{Subtract 1 from both sides.}
\end{aligned}
$$

Notice that there are two solutions: $-1 + \sqrt{5}$ and $-1 - \sqrt{5}$. □

PRACTICE
5 Solve $b^2 + 4b = 3$ by completing the square.

EXAMPLE 6 Solve $m^2 - 7m - 1 = 0$ for m by completing the square.

Solution First, add 1 to both sides of the equation so that the left side has no constant term.

$$
\begin{aligned}
m^2 - 7m - 1 &= 0 \\
m^2 - 7m &= 1
\end{aligned}
$$

Now find the constant term that makes the left side a perfect square trinomial by squaring half the coefficient of m. Add this constant to both sides of the equation.

$$\frac{1}{2}(-7) = -\frac{7}{2} \quad \text{and} \quad \left(-\frac{7}{2}\right)^2 = \frac{49}{4}$$

$$m^2 - 7m + \frac{49}{4} = 1 + \frac{49}{4} \qquad \text{Add } \frac{49}{4} \text{ to both sides of the equation.}$$

$$\left(m - \frac{7}{2}\right)^2 = \frac{53}{4} \qquad \text{Factor the perfect square trinomial and simplify the right side.}$$

$$m - \frac{7}{2} = \pm\sqrt{\frac{53}{4}} \qquad \text{Apply the square root property.}$$

$$m = \frac{7}{2} \pm \frac{\sqrt{53}}{2} \qquad \text{Add } \frac{7}{2} \text{ to both sides and simplify } \sqrt{\frac{53}{4}}.$$

$$m = \frac{7 \pm \sqrt{53}}{2} \qquad \text{Simplify.}$$

The solutions are $\dfrac{7 + \sqrt{53}}{2}$ and $\dfrac{7 - \sqrt{53}}{2}$.

PRACTICE

6 Solve $p^2 - 3p + 1 = 0$ by completing the square.

EXAMPLE 7   Solve: $2x^2 - 8x + 3 = 0$.

Solution   Our procedure for finding the constant term to complete the square works only if the coefficient of the squared variable term is 1. Therefore, to solve this equation, the first step is to divide both sides by 2, the coefficient of x^2.

$$2x^2 - 8x + 3 = 0$$

$$x^2 - 4x + \frac{3}{2} = 0 \qquad \text{Divide both sides by 2.}$$

$$x^2 - 4x = -\frac{3}{2} \qquad \text{Subtract } \frac{3}{2} \text{ from both sides.}$$

Next find the square of half of -4.

$$\frac{1}{2}(-4) = -2 \quad \text{and} \quad (-2)^2 = 4$$

Add 4 to both sides of the equation to complete the square.

$$x^2 - 4x + 4 = -\frac{3}{2} + 4$$

$$(x - 2)^2 = \frac{5}{2} \qquad \text{Factor the perfect square and simplify the right side.}$$

$$x - 2 = \pm\sqrt{\frac{5}{2}} \qquad \text{Apply the square root property.}$$

$$x - 2 = \pm\frac{\sqrt{10}}{2} \qquad \text{Rationalize the denominator.}$$

$$x = 2 \pm \frac{\sqrt{10}}{2} \qquad \text{Add 2 to both sides.}$$

$$= \frac{4}{2} \pm \frac{\sqrt{10}}{2} \qquad \text{Find the common denominator.}$$

$$= \frac{4 \pm \sqrt{10}}{2} \qquad \text{Simplify.}$$

The solutions are $\dfrac{4 + \sqrt{10}}{2}$ and $\dfrac{4 - \sqrt{10}}{2}$.

PRACTICE

7   Solve: $3x^2 - 12x + 1 = 0$.

The following steps may be used to solve a quadratic equation such as $ax^2 + bx + c = 0$ by completing the square. This method may be used whether or not the polynomial $ax^2 + bx + c$ is factorable.

> **Solving a Quadratic Equation in x by Completing the Square**
> **STEP 1.** If the coefficient of x^2 is 1, go to Step 2. Otherwise, divide both sides of the equation by the coefficient of x^2.
>
> **STEP 2.** Isolate all variable terms on one side of the equation.
>
> **STEP 3.** Complete the square for the resulting binomial by adding the square of half of the coefficient of x to both sides of the equation.
>
> **STEP 4.** Factor the resulting perfect square trinomial and write it as the square of a binomial.
>
> **STEP 5.** Use the square root property to solve for x.

EXAMPLE 8   Solve $3x^2 - 9x + 8 = 0$ by completing the square.

Solution $3x^2 - 9x + 8 = 0$

STEP 1. $x^2 - 3x + \dfrac{8}{3} = 0$ Divide both sides of the equation by 3.

STEP 2. $x^2 - 3x = -\dfrac{8}{3}$ Subtract $\dfrac{8}{3}$ from both sides.

Since $\dfrac{1}{2}(-3) = -\dfrac{3}{2}$ and $\left(-\dfrac{3}{2}\right)^2 = \dfrac{9}{4}$, we add $\dfrac{9}{4}$ to both sides of the equation.

STEP 3. $x^2 - 3x + \dfrac{9}{4} = -\dfrac{8}{3} + \dfrac{9}{4}$

STEP 4. $\left(x - \dfrac{3}{2}\right)^2 = -\dfrac{5}{12}$ Factor the perfect square trinomial.

STEP 5. $x - \dfrac{3}{2} = \pm\sqrt{-\dfrac{5}{12}}$ Apply the square root property.

$x - \dfrac{3}{2} = \pm\dfrac{i\sqrt{5}}{2\sqrt{3}}$ Simplify the radical.

$x - \dfrac{3}{2} = \pm\dfrac{i\sqrt{15}}{6}$ Rationalize the denominator.

$x = \dfrac{3}{2} \pm \dfrac{i\sqrt{15}}{6}$ Add $\dfrac{3}{2}$ to both sides.

$= \dfrac{9}{6} \pm \dfrac{i\sqrt{15}}{6}$ Find a common denominator.

$= \dfrac{9 \pm i\sqrt{15}}{6}$ Simplify.

The solutions are $\dfrac{9 + i\sqrt{15}}{6}$ and $\dfrac{9 - i\sqrt{15}}{6}$.   □

PRACTICE
8   Solve $2x^2 - 5x + 7 = 0$ by completing the square.

OBJECTIVE 3 ▶ Solving problems modeled by quadratic equations. Recall the **simple interest** formula $I = Prt$, where I is the interest earned, P is the principal, r is the rate of interest, and t is time in years. If $100 is invested at a simple interest rate of 5% annually, at the end of 3 years the total interest I earned is

$$I = P \cdot r \cdot t$$

or

$$I = 100 \cdot 0.05 \cdot 3 = \$15$$

and the new principal is

$$\$100 + \$15 = \$115$$

Most of the time, the interest computed on money borrowed or money deposited is **compound interest.** Compound interest, unlike simple interest, is computed on original principal *and* on interest already earned. To see the difference between simple interest and compound interest, suppose that $100 is invested at a rate of 5% compounded annually. To find the total amount of money at the end of 3 years, we calculate as follows.

$$I = P \cdot r \cdot t$$

First year: Interest $= \$100 \cdot 0.05 \cdot 1 = \$5.00$
             New principal $= \$100.00 + \$5.00 = \$105.00$

Second year: Interest $= \$105.00 \cdot 0.05 \cdot 1 = \$5.25$
             New principal $= \$105.00 + \$5.25 = \$110.25$

Third year: Interest $= \$110.25 \cdot 0.05 \cdot 1 \approx \$5.51$
             New principal $= \$110.25 + \$5.51 = \$115.76$

At the end of the third year, the total compound interest earned is $15.76, whereas the total simple interest earned is $15.

It is tedious to calculate compound interest as we did above, so we use a compound interest formula. The formula for calculating the total amount of money when interest is compounded annually is

$$A = P(1 + r)^t$$

where P is the original investment, r is the interest rate per compounding period, and t is the number of periods. For example, the amount of money A at the end of 3 years if $100 is invested at 5% compounded annually is

$$A = \$100(1 + 0.05)^3 \approx \$100(1.1576) = \$115.76$$

as we previously calculated.

EXAMPLE 9   Finding Interest Rates

Use the formula $A = P(1 + r)^t$ to find the interest rate r if $2000 compounded annually grows to $2420 in 2 years.

Solution

1. **UNDERSTAND** the problem. Since the $2000 is compounded annually, we use the compound interest formula. For this example, make sure that you understand the formula for compounding interest annually.

2. **TRANSLATE.** We substitute the given values into the formula.

$$A = P(1 + r)^t$$
$$2420 = 2000(1 + r)^2 \qquad \text{Let } A = 2420, P = 2000, \text{ and } t = 2.$$

3. **SOLVE.** Solve the equation for r.

$$2420 = 2000(1 + r)^2$$

$$\frac{2420}{2000} = (1 + r)^2 \qquad \text{Divide both sides by 2000.}$$

$$\frac{121}{100} = (1 + r)^2 \qquad \text{Simplify the fraction.}$$

$$\pm\sqrt{\frac{121}{100}} = 1 + r \qquad \text{Use the square root property.}$$

$$\pm \frac{11}{10} = 1 + r \qquad \text{Simplify.}$$

$$-1 \pm \frac{11}{10} = r$$

$$-\frac{10}{10} \pm \frac{11}{10} = r$$

$$\frac{1}{10} = r \quad \text{or} \quad -\frac{21}{10} = r$$

4. INTERPRET. The rate cannot be negative, so we reject $-\frac{21}{10}$.

Check: $\frac{1}{10} = 0.10 = 10\%$ per year. If we invest $2000 at 10% compounded annually, in 2 years the amount in the account would be $2000(1 + 0.10)^2 = 2420$ dollars, the desired amount.

State: The interest rate is 10% compounded annually.

PRACTICE
9 Use the formula from Example 9 to find the interest rate r if $5000 compounded annually grows to $5618 in 2 years.

Graphing Calculator Explorations

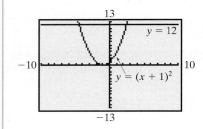

In Section 5.8, we showed how we can use a grapher to approximate real number solutions of a quadratic equation written in standard form. We can also use a grapher to solve a quadratic equation when it is not written in standard form. For example, to solve $(x + 1)^2 = 12$, the quadratic equation in Example 3, we graph the following on the same set of axes. Use Xmin $= -10$, Xmax $= 10$, Ymin $= -13$, and Ymax $= 13$.

$$Y_1 = (x + 1)^2 \quad \text{and} \quad Y_2 = 12$$

Use the Intersect feature or the Zoom and Trace features to locate the points of intersection of the graphs. (See your manuals for specific instructions.) The x-values of these points are the solutions of $(x + 1)^2 = 12$. The solutions, rounded to two decimal places, are 2.46 and -4.46.

Check to see that these numbers are approximations of the exact solutions $-1 \pm 2\sqrt{3}$.

Use a graphing calculator to solve each quadratic equation. Round all solutions to the nearest hundredth.

1. $x(x - 5) = 8$ **2.** $x(x + 2) = 5$

3. $x^2 + 0.5x = 0.3x + 1$ **4.** $x^2 - 2.6x = -2.2x + 3$

5. Use a graphing calculator and solve $(2x - 5)^2 = -16$, Example 4 in this section, using the window

$$\begin{aligned}
\text{Xmin} &= -20 \\
\text{Xmax} &= 20 \\
\text{Xscl} &= 1 \\
\text{Ymin} &= -20 \\
\text{Ymax} &= 20 \\
\text{Yscl} &= 1
\end{aligned}$$

Explain the results. Compare your results with the solution found in Example 4.

6. What are the advantages and disadvantages of using a graphing calculator to solve quadratic equations?

VOCABULARY & READINESS CHECK

Use the choices below to fill in each blank. Not all choices will be used.

binomial	$\sqrt{b}$	$\pm\sqrt{b}$	b^2	9	25	completing the square
quadratic	$-\sqrt{b}$	$\dfrac{b}{2}$	$\left(\dfrac{b}{2}\right)^2$	3	5	

1. By the square root property, if b is a real number, and $a^2 = b$, then $a =$ _____.

2. A _____ equation can be written in the form $ax^2 + bx + c = 0, a \neq 0$.

3. The process of writing a quadratic equation so that one side is a perfect square trinomial is called _____.

4. A perfect square trinomial is one that can be factored as a _____ squared.

5. To solve $x^2 + 6x = 10$ by completing the square, add _____ to both sides.

6. To solve $x^2 + bx = c$ by completing the square, add _____ to both sides.

Fill in the blank with the number needed to make the expression a perfect square trinomial.

7. $m^2 + 2m +$ _____   **8.** $m^2 - 2m +$ _____   **9.** $y^2 - 14y +$ _____   **10.** $z^2 + z +$ _____

8.1 EXERCISE SET

Use the square root property to solve each equation. These equations have real-number solutions. See Examples 1 through 3.

1. $x^2 = 16$ **2.** $x^2 = 49$

3. $x^2 - 7 = 0$ **4.** $x^2 - 11 = 0$

5. $x^2 = 18$ **6.** $y^2 = 20$

7. $3z^2 - 30 = 0$ **8.** $2x^2 - 4 = 0$

9. $(x + 5)^2 = 9$ **10.** $(y - 3)^2 = 4$

11. $(z - 6)^2 = 18$ **12.** $(y + 4)^2 = 27$

13. $(2x - 3)^2 = 8$ **14.** $(4x + 9)^2 = 6$

Use the square root property to solve each equation. See Examples 1 through 4.

15. $x^2 + 9 = 0$

16. $x^2 + 4 = 0$

17. $x^2 - 6 = 0$

18. $y^2 - 10 = 0$

19. $2z^2 + 16 = 0$

20. $3p^2 + 36 = 0$

21. $(x - 1)^2 = -16$

22. $(y + 2)^2 = -25$

23. $(z + 7)^2 = 5$

24. $(x + 10)^2 = 11$

25. $(x + 3)^2 = -8$

26. $(y - 4)^2 = -18$

Add the proper constant to each binomial so that the resulting trinomial is a perfect square trinomial. Then factor the trinomial.

27. $x^2 + 16x +$ _____   **28.** $y^2 + 2y +$ _____

29. $z^2 - 12z +$ _____   **30.** $x^2 - 8x +$ _____

31. $p^2 + 9p +$ _____   **32.** $n^2 + 5n +$ _____

33. $x^2 + x +$ _____   **34.** $y^2 - y +$ _____

MIXED PRACTICE

Solve each equation by completing the square. These equations have real number solutions. See Examples 5 through 7.

35. $x^2 + 8x = -15$

36. $y^2 + 6y = -8$

37. $x^2 + 6x + 2 = 0$

38. $x^2 - 2x - 2 = 0$

39. $x^2 + x - 1 = 0$

40. $x^2 + 3x - 2 = 0$

41. $x^2 + 2x - 5 = 0$

42. $y^2 + y - 7 = 0$

43. $3p^2 - 12p + 2 = 0$

44. $2x^2 + 14x - 1 = 0$

45. $4y^2 - 12y - 2 = 0$

46. $6x^2 - 3 = 6x$

47. $2x^2 + 7x = 4$

48. $3x^2 - 4x = 4$

49. $x^2 - 4x - 5 = 0$

50. $y^2 + 6y - 8 = 0$

51. $x^2 + 8x + 1 = 0$

52. $x^2 - 10x + 2 = 0$

53. $3y^2 + 6y - 4 = 0$

54. $2y^2 + 12y + 3 = 0$

55. $2x^2 - 3x - 5 = 0$

56. $5x^2 + 3x - 2 = 0$

Solve each equation by completing the square. See Examples 5 through 8.

57. $y^2 + 2y + 2 = 0$

58. $x^2 + 4x + 6 = 0$

59. $x^2 - 6x + 3 = 0$

60. $x^2 - 7x - 1 = 0$

61. $2a^2 + 8a = -12$

62. $3x^2 + 12x = -14$

63. $5x^2 + 15x - 1 = 0$

64. $16y^2 + 16y - 1 = 0$

65. $2x^2 - x + 6 = 0$

66. $4x^2 - 2x + 5 = 0$

67. $x^2 + 10x + 28 = 0$

68. $y^2 + 8y + 18 = 0$

69. $z^2 + 3z - 4 = 0$

70. $y^2 + y - 2 = 0$

71. $2x^2 - 4x = -3$

72. $9x^2 - 36x = -40$

73. $3x^2 + 3x = 5$

74. $5y^2 - 15y = 1$

Use the formula $A = P(1 + r)^t$ to solve Exercises 75 through 78. See Example 9.

75. Find the rate r at which $3000 compounded annually grows to $4320 in 2 years.

76. Find the rate r at which $800 compounded annually grows to $882 in 2 years.

77. Find the rate at which $15,000 compounded annually grows to $16,224 in 2 years.

78. Find the rate at which $2000 compounded annually grows to $2880 in 2 years.

79. In your own words, what is the difference between simple interest and compound interest?

Neglecting air resistance, the distance $s(t)$ in feet traveled by a freely falling object is given by the function $s(t) = 16t^2$, where t is time in seconds. Use this formula to solve Exercises 80 through 83. Round answers to two decimal places.

80. The Petronas Towers in Kuala Lumpur, built in 1997, are the tallest buildings in Malaysia. Each tower is 1483 feet tall. How long would it take an object to fall to the ground from the top of one of the towers? (*Source:* Council on Tall Buildings and Urban Habitat, Lehigh University)

81. The height of the Chicago Beach Tower Hotel, built in 1998 in Dubai, United Arab Emirates, is 1053 feet. How long would it take an object to fall to the ground from the top of the building? (*Source:* Council on Tall Buildings and Urban Habitat, Lehigh University)

82. The height of the Nurek Dam in Tajikistan (part of the former USSR that borders Afghanistan) is 984 feet. How long would it take an object to fall from the top to the base of the dam? (*Source:* U.S. Committee on Large Dams of the International Commission on Large Dams)

83. The Hoover Dam, located on the Colorado River on the border of Nevada and Arizona near Las Vegas, is 725 feet tall. How long would it take an object to fall from the top to the base of the dam? (*Source:* U.S. Committee on Large Dams of the International Commission on Large Dams)

84. If you are depositing money in an account that pays 4%, would you prefer the interest to be simple or compound? Explain why.

85. If you are borrowing money at a rate of 10%, would you prefer the interest to be simple or compound? Explain why.

REVIEW AND PREVIEW

Simplify each expression. See Section 7.1.

86. $\dfrac{3}{4} - \sqrt{\dfrac{25}{16}}$

87. $\dfrac{3}{5} + \sqrt{\dfrac{16}{25}}$

88. $\dfrac{1}{2} - \sqrt{\dfrac{9}{4}}$

89. $\dfrac{9}{10} - \sqrt{\dfrac{49}{100}}$

Simplify each expression. See Section 7.5.

90. $\dfrac{6 + 4\sqrt{5}}{2}$

91. $\dfrac{10 - 20\sqrt{3}}{2}$

92. $\dfrac{3 - 9\sqrt{2}}{6}$

93. $\dfrac{12 - 8\sqrt{7}}{16}$

Evaluate $\sqrt{b^2 - 4ac}$ for each set of values. See Section 7.3.

94. $a = 2, b = 4, c = -1$ **95.** $a = 1, b = 6, c = 2$

96. $a = 3, b = -1, c = -2$ **97.** $a = 1, b = -3, c = -1$

CONCEPT EXTENSIONS

Without solving, determine whether the solutions of each equation are real numbers or complex, but not real numbers. See the Concept Check in this section.

98. $(x + 1)^2 = -1$

99. $(y - 5)^2 = -9$

100. $3z^2 = 10$

101. $4x^2 = 17$

102. $(2y - 5)^2 + 7 = 3$

103. $(3m + 2)^2 + 4 = 1$

Find two possible missing terms so that each is a perfect square trinomial.

104. $x^2 + \underline{} + 16$ **105.** $y^2 + \underline{} + 9$

106. $z^2 + \underline{} + \dfrac{25}{4}$ **107.** $x^2 + \underline{} + \dfrac{1}{4}$

Solve.

△ **108.** The area of a square room is 225 square feet. Find the dimensions of the room.

△ **109.** The area of a circle is 36π square inches. Find the radius of the circle.

△ **110.** An isosceles right triangle has legs of equal length. If the hypotenuse is 20 centimeters long, find the length of each leg.

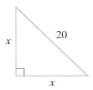

△ **111.** A 27-inch TV is advertised in the *Daily Sentry* newspaper. If 27 inches is the measure of the diagonal of the picture tube, find the measure of each side of the picture tube.

A common equation used in business is a demand equation. It expresses the relationship between the unit price of some commodity and the quantity demanded. For Exercises 112 and 113, p represents the unit price and x represents the quantity demanded in thousands.

112. A manufacturing company has found that the demand equation for a certain type of scissors is given by the equation $p = -x^2 + 47$. Find the demand for the scissors if the price is \$11 per pair.

113. Acme, Inc., sells desk lamps and has found that the demand equation for a certain style of desk lamp is given by the equation $p = -x^2 + 15$. Find the demand for the desk lamp if the price is \$7 per lamp.

8.2 SOLVING QUADRATIC EQUATIONS BY THE QUADRATIC FORMULA

OBJECTIVES

1 Solve quadratic equations by using the quadratic formula.

2 Determine the number and type of solutions of a quadratic equation by using the discriminant.

3 Solve geometric problems modeled by quadratic equations.

OBJECTIVE 1 ▶ Solving quadratic equations by using the quadratic formula. Any quadratic equation can be solved by completing the square. Since the same sequence of steps is repeated each time we complete the square, let's complete the square for a general quadratic equation, $ax^2 + bx + c = 0, a \neq 0$. By doing so, we find a pattern for the solutions of a quadratic equation known as the **quadratic formula.**

Recall that to complete the square for an equation such as $ax^2 + bx + c = 0$, we first divide both sides by the coefficient of x^2.

$$ax^2 + bx + c = 0$$

$$x^2 + \frac{b}{a}x + \frac{c}{a} = 0 \qquad \text{Divide both sides by } a, \text{ the coefficient of } x^2.$$

$$x^2 + \frac{b}{a}x = -\frac{c}{a} \qquad \text{Subtract the constant } \frac{c}{a} \text{ from both sides.}$$

Next, find the square of half $\dfrac{b}{a}$, the coefficient of x.

$$\frac{1}{2}\left(\frac{b}{a}\right) = \frac{b}{2a} \quad \text{and} \quad \left(\frac{b}{2a}\right)^2 = \frac{b^2}{4a^2}$$

Add this result to both sides of the equation.

$$x^2 + \frac{b}{a}x + \frac{b^2}{4a^2} = -\frac{c}{a} + \frac{b^2}{4a^2} \qquad \text{Add } \frac{b^2}{4a^2} \text{ to both sides.}$$

$$x^2 + \frac{b}{a}x + \frac{b^2}{4a^2} = \frac{-c \cdot 4a}{a \cdot 4a} + \frac{b^2}{4a^2} \qquad \text{Find a common denominator on the right side.}$$

$$x^2 + \frac{b}{a}x + \frac{b^2}{4a^2} = \frac{b^2 - 4ac}{4a^2} \qquad \text{Simplify the right side.}$$

$$\left(x + \frac{b}{2a}\right)^2 = \frac{b^2 - 4ac}{4a^2} \qquad \text{Factor the perfect square trinomial on the left side.}$$

$$x + \frac{b}{2a} = \pm\sqrt{\frac{b^2 - 4ac}{4a^2}} \qquad \text{Apply the square root property.}$$

$$x + \frac{b}{2a} = \pm\frac{\sqrt{b^2 - 4ac}}{2a} \qquad \text{Simplify the radical.}$$

$$x = -\frac{b}{2a} \pm \frac{\sqrt{b^2 - 4ac}}{2a} \qquad \text{Subtract } \frac{b}{2a} \text{ from both sides.}$$

$$x = \frac{-b \pm \sqrt{b^2 - 4ac}}{2a} \qquad \text{Simplify.}$$

This equation identifies the solutions of the general quadratic equation in standard form and is called the quadratic formula. It can be used to solve any equation written in standard form $ax^2 + bx + c = 0$ as long as a is not 0.

> **Quadratic Formula**
>
> A quadratic equation written in the form $ax^2 + bx + c = 0$ has the solutions
>
> $$x = \frac{-b \pm \sqrt{b^2 - 4ac}}{2a}$$

EXAMPLE 1 Solve $3x^2 + 16x + 5 = 0$ for x.

Solution This equation is in standard form, so $a = 3$, $b = 16$, and $c = 5$. Substitute these values into the quadratic formula.

$$x = \frac{-b \pm \sqrt{b^2 - 4ac}}{2a} \qquad \text{Quadratic formula}$$

$$= \frac{-16 \pm \sqrt{16^2 - 4(3)(5)}}{2 \cdot 3} \qquad \text{Use } a = 3, b = 16, \text{ and } c = 5.$$

$$= \frac{-16 \pm \sqrt{256 - 60}}{6}$$

$$= \frac{-16 \pm \sqrt{196}}{6} = \frac{-16 \pm 14}{6}$$

$$x = \frac{-16 + 14}{6} = -\frac{1}{3} \quad \text{or} \quad x = \frac{-16 - 14}{6} = -\frac{30}{6} = -5$$

The solutions are $-\dfrac{1}{3}$ and -5, or the solution set is $\left\{-\dfrac{1}{3}, -5\right\}$.

PRACTICE
1 Solve $3x^2 - 5x - 2 = 0$ for x.

> **Helpful Hint**

To replace $a, b,$ and c correctly in the quadratic formula, write the quadratic equation in standard form $ax^2 + bx + c = 0$.

EXAMPLE 2   Solve: $2x^2 - 4x = 3$.

Solution   First write the equation in standard form by subtracting 3 from both sides.

$$2x^2 - 4x - 3 = 0$$

Now $a = 2, b = -4,$ and $c = -3$. Substitute these values into the quadratic formula.

$$x = \frac{-b \pm \sqrt{b^2 - 4ac}}{2a}$$

$$= \frac{-(-4) \pm \sqrt{(-4)^2 - 4(2)(-3)}}{2 \cdot 2}$$

$$= \frac{4 \pm \sqrt{16 + 24}}{4}$$

$$= \frac{4 \pm \sqrt{40}}{4} = \frac{4 \pm 2\sqrt{10}}{4}$$

$$= \frac{2\left(2 \pm \sqrt{10}\right)}{2 \cdot 2} = \frac{2 \pm \sqrt{10}}{2}$$

The solutions are $\dfrac{2 + \sqrt{10}}{2}$ and $\dfrac{2 - \sqrt{10}}{2}$, or the solution set is $\left\{ \dfrac{2 - \sqrt{10}}{2}, \dfrac{2 + \sqrt{10}}{2} \right\}$.

PRACTICE

2   Solve: $3x^2 - 8x = 2$.

> **Helpful Hint**

To simplify the expression $\dfrac{4 \pm 2\sqrt{10}}{4}$ in the preceding example, note that 2 is factored out of both terms of the numerator *before* simplifying.

$$\frac{4 \pm 2\sqrt{10}}{4} = \frac{2\left(2 \pm \sqrt{10}\right)}{2 \cdot 2} = \frac{2 \pm \sqrt{10}}{2}$$

Concept Check ☑

For the quadratic equation $x^2 = 7$, which substitution is correct?

a. $a = 1, b = 0,$ and $c = -7$

b. $a = 1, b = 0,$ and $c = 7$

c. $a = 0, b = 0,$ and $c = 7$

d. $a = 1, b = 1,$ and $c = -7$

EXAMPLE 3   Solve: $\dfrac{1}{4}m^2 - m + \dfrac{1}{2} = 0$.

Solution   We could use the quadratic formula with $a = \dfrac{1}{4}, b = -1,$ and $c = \dfrac{1}{2}$. Instead, we find a simpler, equivalent standard form equation whose coefficients are not fractions. Multiply both sides of the equation by the LCD 4 to clear fractions.

$$4\left(\frac{1}{4}m^2 - m + \frac{1}{2} \right) = 4 \cdot 0$$

$$m^2 - 4m + 2 = 0 \qquad \text{Simplify.}$$

Substitute $a = 1$, $b = -4$, and $c = 2$ into the quadratic formula and simplify.

$$m = \frac{-(-4) \pm \sqrt{(-4)^2 - 4(1)(2)}}{2 \cdot 1} = \frac{4 \pm \sqrt{16 - 8}}{2}$$

$$= \frac{4 \pm \sqrt{8}}{2} = \frac{4 \pm 2\sqrt{2}}{2} = \frac{2(2 \pm \sqrt{2})}{2}$$

$$= 2 \pm \sqrt{2}$$

The solutions are $2 + \sqrt{2}$ and $2 - \sqrt{2}$. ☐

PRACTICE
3 Solve: $\frac{1}{8}x^2 - \frac{1}{4}x - 2 = 0$.

EXAMPLE 4 Solve: $x = -3x^2 - 3$.

Solution The equation in standard form is $3x^2 + x + 3 = 0$. Thus, let $a = 3$, $b = 1$, and $c = 3$ in the quadratic formula.

$$x = \frac{-1 \pm \sqrt{1^2 - 4(3)(3)}}{2 \cdot 3} = \frac{-1 \pm \sqrt{1 - 36}}{6} = \frac{-1 \pm \sqrt{-35}}{6} = \frac{-1 \pm i\sqrt{35}}{6}$$

The solutions are $\dfrac{-1 + i\sqrt{35}}{6}$ and $\dfrac{-1 - i\sqrt{35}}{6}$. ☐

PRACTICE
4 Solve: $x = -2x^2 - 2$.

Concept Check ☑

What is the first step in solving $-3x^2 = 5x - 4$ using the quadratic formula?

In Example 1, the equation $3x^2 + 16x + 5 = 0$ had 2 real roots, $-\frac{1}{3}$ and -5. In Example 4, the equation $3x^2 + x + 3 = 0$ (written in standard form) had no real roots. How do their related graphs compare? Recall that the x-intercepts of $f(x) = 3x^2 + 16x + 5$ occur where $f(x) = 0$ or where $3x^2 + 16x + 5 = 0$. Since this equation has 2 real roots, the graph has 2 x-intercepts. Similarly, since the equation $3x^2 + x + 3 = 0$ has no real roots, the graph of $f(x) = 3x^2 + x + 3$ has no x-intercepts.

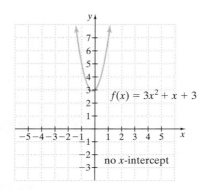

OBJECTIVE 2 ▶ Using the discriminant. In the quadratic formula, $x = \dfrac{-b \pm \sqrt{b^2 - 4ac}}{2a}$, the radicand $b^2 - 4ac$ is called the **discriminant** because, by knowing its value, we can **discriminate** among the possible number and type of solutions of a quadratic equation. Possible values of the discriminant and their meanings are summarized next.

Answer to Concept Check:
Write the equation in standard form.

Discriminant

The following table corresponds the discriminant $b^2 - 4ac$ of a quadratic equation of the form $ax^2 + bx + c = 0$ with the number and type of solutions of the equation.

$b^2 - 4ac$	*Number and Type of Solutions*
Positive	Two real solutions
Zero	One real solution
Negative	Two complex but not real solutions

EXAMPLE 5   Use the discriminant to determine the number and type of solutions of each quadratic equation.

a. $x^2 + 2x + 1 = 0$ **b.** $3x^2 + 2 = 0$ **c.** $2x^2 - 7x - 4 = 0$

Solution

a. In $x^2 + 2x + 1 = 0$, $a = 1$, $b = 2$, and $c = 1$. Thus,

$$b^2 - 4ac = 2^2 - 4(1)(1) = 0$$

Since $b^2 - 4ac = 0$, this quadratic equation has one real solution.

b. In this equation, $a = 3$, $b = 0$, $c = 2$. Then $b^2 - 4ac = 0 - 4(3)(2) = -24$. Since $b^2 - 4ac$ is negative, the quadratic equation has two complex but not real solutions.

c. In this equation, $a = 2$, $b = -7$, and $c = -4$. Then

$$b^2 - 4ac = (-7)^2 - 4(2)(-4) = 81$$

Since $b^2 - 4ac$ is positive, the quadratic equation has two real solutions.   □

PRACTICE
5   Use the discriminant to determine the number and type of solutions of each quadratic equation.

a. $x^2 - 6x + 9 = 0$ **b.** $x^2 - 3x - 1 = 0$ **c.** $7x^2 + 11 = 0$

The discriminant helps us determine the number and type of solutions of a quadratic equation, $ax^2 + bx + c = 0$. Recall that the solutions of this equation are the same as the x-intercepts of its related graph $f(x) = ax^2 + bx + c$. This means that the discriminant of $ax^2 + bx + c = 0$ also tells us the number of x-intercepts for the graph of $f(x) = ax^2 + bx + c$, or equivalently $y = ax^2 + bx + c$.

Graph of $f(x) = ax^2 + bx + c$ or $y = ax^2 + bx + c$

OBJECTIVE 3 ▶ Solving problems modeled by quadratic equations. The quadratic formula is useful in solving problems that are modeled by quadratic equations.

△ **EXAMPLE 6** **Calculating Distance Saved**

At a local university, students often leave the sidewalk and cut across the lawn to save walking distance. Given the diagram below of a favorite place to cut across the lawn, approximate how many feet of walking distance a student saves by cutting across the lawn instead of walking on the sidewalk.

Solution

1. UNDERSTAND. Read and reread the problem. In the diagram, notice that a triangle is formed. Since the corner of the block forms a right angle, we use the Pythagorean theorem for right triangles. You may want to review this theorem.

2. TRANSLATE. By the Pythagorean theorem, we have

$$\text{In words: } (\text{leg})^2 + (\text{leg})^2 = (\text{hypotenuse})^2$$
$$\text{Translate: } x^2 + (x + 20)^2 = 50^2$$

3. SOLVE. Use the quadratic formula to solve.

$$x^2 + x^2 + 40x + 400 = 2500 \quad \text{Square } (x + 20) \text{ and } 50.$$
$$2x^2 + 40x - 2100 = 0 \quad \text{Set the equation equal to } 0.$$
$$x^2 + 20x - 1050 = 0 \quad \text{Divide by } 2.$$

Here, $a = 1, b = 20, c = -1050$. By the quadratic formula,

$$x = \frac{-20 \pm \sqrt{20^2 - 4(1)(-1050)}}{2 \cdot 1}$$
$$= \frac{-20 \pm \sqrt{400 + 4200}}{2} = \frac{-20 \pm \sqrt{4600}}{2}$$
$$= \frac{-20 \pm \sqrt{100 \cdot 46}}{2} = \frac{-20 \pm 10\sqrt{46}}{2}$$
$$= -10 \pm 5\sqrt{46} \quad \text{Simplify.}$$

4. INTERPRET.

Check: Your calculations in the quadratic formula. The length of a side of a triangle can't be negative, so we reject $-10 - 5\sqrt{46}$. Since $-10 + 5\sqrt{46} \approx 24$ feet, the walking distance along the sidewalk is

$$x + (x + 20) \approx 24 + (24 + 20) = 68 \text{ feet.}$$

State: A student saves about $68 - 50$ or 18 feet of walking distance by cutting across the lawn. □

PRACTICE
6 Given the diagram, approximate to the nearest foot how many feet of walking distance a person can save by cutting across the lawn instead of walking on the sidewalk.

EXAMPLE 7 **Calculating Landing Time**

An object is thrown upward from the top of a 200-foot cliff with a velocity of 12 feet per second. The height h in feet of the object after t seconds is

$$h = -16t^2 + 12t + 200$$

How long after the object is thrown will it strike the ground? Round to the nearest tenth of a second.

200 ft

Solution

1. UNDERSTAND. Read and reread the problem.

2. TRANSLATE. Since we want to know when the object strikes the ground, we want to know when the height $h = 0$, or

$$0 = -16t^2 + 12t + 200$$

3. SOLVE. First we divide both sides of the equation by -4.

$$0 = 4t^2 - 3t - 50 \quad \text{Divide both sides by } -4.$$

Here, $a = 4$, $b = -3$, and $c = -50$. By the quadratic formula,

$$t = \frac{-(-3) \pm \sqrt{(-3)^2 - 4(4)(-50)}}{2 \cdot 4}$$

$$= \frac{3 \pm \sqrt{9 + 800}}{8}$$

$$= \frac{3 \pm \sqrt{809}}{8}$$

4. INTERPRET.

Check: We check our calculations from the quadratic formula. Since the time won't be negative, we reject the proposed solution

$$\frac{3 - \sqrt{809}}{8}.$$

State: The time it takes for the object to strike the ground is exactly

$$\frac{3 + \sqrt{809}}{8} \text{ seconds} \approx 3.9 \text{ seconds}. \qquad \square$$

PRACTICE

7 A toy rocket is shot upward at the edge of a building, 45 feet high, with an initial velocity of 20 feet per second. The height h in feet of the rocket after t seconds is

$$h = -16t^2 + 20t + 45$$

How long after the rocket is launched will it strike the ground? Round to the nearest tenth of a second.

VOCABULARY & READINESS CHECK

Fill in each blank.

1. The quadratic formula is _____ .

2. For $2x^2 + x + 1 = 0$, if $a = 2$, then $b = $ _____ and $c = $ _____ .

3. For $5x^2 - 5x - 7 = 0$, if $a = 5$, then $b = $ _____ and $c = $ _____ .

4. For $7x^2 - 4 = 0$, if $a = 7$, then $b = $ _____ and $c = $ _____ .

5. For $x^2 + 9 = 0$, if $c = 9$, then $a = $ _____ and $b = $ _____ .

6. The correct simplified form of $\dfrac{5 \pm 10\sqrt{2}}{5}$ is _____ .

   a. $1 \pm 10\sqrt{2}$ **b.** $2\sqrt{2}$ **c.** $1 \pm 2\sqrt{2}$ **d.** $\pm 5\sqrt{2}$

8.2 | EXERCISE SET

Use the quadratic formula to solve each equation. These equations have real number solutions only. See Examples 1 through 3.

1. $m^2 + 5m - 6 = 0$

2. $p^2 + 11p - 12 = 0$

3. $2y = 5y^2 - 3$

4. $5x^2 - 3 = 14x$

5. $x^2 - 6x + 9 = 0$

6. $y^2 + 10y + 25 = 0$

7. $x^2 + 7x + 4 = 0$

8. $y^2 + 5y + 3 = 0$

9. $8m^2 - 2m = 7$

10. $11n^2 - 9n = 1$

11. $3m^2 - 7m = 3$

12. $x^2 - 13 = 5x$

13. $\dfrac{1}{2}x^2 - x - 1 = 0$

14. $\dfrac{1}{6}x^2 + x + \dfrac{1}{3} = 0$

15. $\dfrac{2}{5}y^2 + \dfrac{1}{5}y = \dfrac{3}{5}$

16. $\dfrac{1}{8}x^2 + x = \dfrac{5}{2}$

17. $\dfrac{1}{3}y^2 = y + \dfrac{1}{6}$

18. $\dfrac{1}{2}y^2 = y + \dfrac{1}{2}$

19. $x^2 + 5x = -2$

20. $y^2 - 8 = 4y$

21. $(m + 2)(2m - 6) = 5(m - 1) - 12$

22. $7p(p - 2) + 2(p + 4) = 3$

MIXED PRACTICE

Use the quadratic formula to solve each equation. These equations have real solutions and complex, but not real, solutions. See Examples 1 through 4.

23. $x^2 + 6x + 13 = 0$

24. $x^2 + 2x + 2 = 0$

25. $(x + 5)(x - 1) = 2$

26. $x(x + 6) = 2$

27. $6 = -4x^2 + 3x$

28. $2 = -9x^2 - x$

29. $\dfrac{x^2}{3} - x = \dfrac{5}{3}$

30. $\dfrac{x^2}{2} - 3 = -\dfrac{9}{2}x$

31. $10y^2 + 10y + 3 = 0$

32. $3y^2 + 6y + 5 = 0$

33. $x(6x + 2) = 3$

34. $x(7x + 1) = 2$

35. $\dfrac{2}{5}y^2 + \dfrac{1}{5}y + \dfrac{3}{5} = 0$

36. $\dfrac{1}{8}x^2 + x + \dfrac{5}{2} = 0$

37. $\dfrac{1}{2}y^2 = y - \dfrac{1}{2}$

38. $\dfrac{2}{3}x^2 - \dfrac{20}{3}x = -\dfrac{100}{6}$

39. $(n - 2)^2 = 2n$

40. $\left(p - \dfrac{1}{2}\right)^2 = \dfrac{p}{2}$

Use the discriminant to determine the number and types of solutions of each equation. See Example 5.

41. $x^2 - 5 = 0$

42. $x^2 - 7 = 0$

43. $4x^2 + 12x = -9$

44. $9x^2 + 1 = 6x$

45. $3x = -2x^2 + 7$

46. $3x^2 = 5 - 7x$

47. $6 = 4x - 5x^2$

48. $8x = 3 - 9x^2$

49. $9x - 2x^2 + 5 = 0$

50. $5 - 4x + 12x^2 = 0$

Solve. See Examples 6 and 7.

51. Nancy, Thelma, and John Varner live on a corner lot. Often, neighborhood children cut across their lot to save walking distance. Given the diagram below, approximate to the nearest foot how many feet of walking distance is saved by cutting across their property instead of walking around the lot.

52. Given the diagram below, approximate to the nearest foot how many feet of walking distance a person saves by cutting across the lawn instead of walking on the sidewalk.

53. The hypotenuse of an isosceles right triangle is 2 centimeters longer than either of its legs. Find the exact length of each side. (*Hint:* An isosceles right triangle is a right triangle whose legs are the same length.)

54. The hypotenuse of an isosceles right triangle is one meter longer than either of its legs. Find the length of each side.

55. Bailey's rectangular dog pen for his Irish setter must have an area of 400 square feet. Also, the length must be 10 feet longer than the width. Find the dimensions of the pen.

56. An entry in the Peach Festival Poster Contest must be rectangular and have an area of 1200 square inches. Furthermore, its length must be 20 inches longer than its width. Find the dimensions each entry must have.

57. A holding pen for cattle must be square and have a diagonal length of 100 meters.

   a. Find the length of a side of the pen.

   b. Find the area of the pen.

58. A rectangle is three times longer than it is wide. It has a diagonal of length 50 centimeters.

   a. Find the dimensions of the rectangle.

   b. Find the perimeter of the rectangle.

59. The heaviest reported door in the world is the 708.6 ton radiation shield door in the National Institute for Fusion Science at Toki, Japan. If the height of the door is 1.1 feet longer than its width, and its front area (neglecting depth) is 1439.9 square feet, find its width and height [Interesting note: the door is 6.6 feet thick.] (*Source: Guiness World Records*)

60. Christi and Robbie Wegmann are constructing a rectangular stained glass window whose length is 7.3 inches longer than its width. If the area of the window is 569.9 square inches, find its width and length.

61. The base of a triangle is four more than twice its height. If the area of the triangle is 42 square centimeters, find its base and height.

62. If a point B divides a line segment such that the smaller portion is to the larger portion as the larger is to the whole, the whole is the length of the *golden ratio*.

$$\overbrace{\underset{A \qquad\quad B \qquad\quad C}{\underbrace{1}\quad\underbrace{x-1}}}^{x(\text{whole})}$$

The golden ratio was thought by the Greeks to be the most pleasing to the eye, and many of their buildings contained numerous examples of the golden ratio. The value of the golden ratio is the positive solution of

$$\underset{(\text{larger})}{\overset{(\text{smaller})}{\frac{x-1}{1}}} = \underset{(\text{whole})}{\overset{(\text{larger})}{\frac{1}{x}}}$$

Find this value.

The Wollomombi Falls in Australia have a height of 1100 feet. A pebble is thrown upward from the top of the falls with an initial velocity of 20 feet per second. The height of the pebble h after t seconds is given by the equation $h = -16t^2 + 20t + 1100$. Use this equation for Exercises 63 and 64.

63. How long after the pebble is thrown will it hit the ground? Round to the nearest tenth of a second.

64. How long after the pebble is thrown will it be 550 feet from the ground? Round to the nearest tenth of a second.

A ball is thrown downward from the top of a 180-foot building with an initial velocity of 20 feet per second. The height of the ball h after t seconds is given by the equation $h = -16t^2 - 20t + 180$. Use this equation to answer Exercises 65 and 66.

65. How long after the ball is thrown will it strike the ground? Round the result to the nearest tenth of a second.

66. How long after the ball is thrown will it be 50 feet from the ground? Round the result to the nearest tenth of a second.

REVIEW AND PREVIEW

Solve each equation. See Sections 6.6 and 7.6.

67. $\sqrt{5x - 2} = 3$

68. $\sqrt{y + 2} + 7 = 12$

69. $\dfrac{1}{x} + \dfrac{2}{5} = \dfrac{7}{x}$

70. $\dfrac{10}{z} = \dfrac{5}{z} - \dfrac{1}{3}$

Factor. See Section 5.7.

71. $x^4 + x^2 - 20$

72. $2y^4 + 11y^2 - 6$

73. $z^4 - 13z^2 + 36$

74. $x^4 - 1$

CONCEPT EXTENSIONS

For each quadratic equation, choose the correct substitution for a, b, and c in the standard form $ax^2 + bx + c = 0$.

75. $x^2 = -10$
   a. $a = 1, b = 0, c = -10$
   b. $a = 1, b = 0, c = 10$
   c. $a = 0, b = 1, c = -10$
   d. $a = 1, b = 1, c = 10$

76. $x^2 + 5 = -x$
   a. $a = 1, b = 5, c = -1$
   b. $a = 1, b = -1, c = 5$
   c. $a = 1, b = 5, c = 1$
   d. $a = 1, b = 1, c = 5$

77. Solve Exercise 1 by factoring. Explain the result.

78. Solve Exercise 2 by factoring. Explain the result.

Use the quadratic formula and a calculator to approximate each solution to the nearest tenth.

79. $2x^2 - 6x + 3 = 0$

80. $3.6x^2 + 1.8x - 4.3 = 0$

The accompanying graph shows the daily low temperatures for one week in New Orleans, Louisiana.

81. Which day of the week shows the greatest decrease in low temperature?

82. Which day of the week shows the greatest increase in low temperature?

83. Which day of the week had the lowest low temperature?

84. Use the graph to estimate the low temperature on Thursday.

Notice that the shape of the temperature graph is similar to the curve drawn. In fact, this graph can be modeled by the quadratic function f(x) = 3x² − 18x + 56, where f(x) is the temperature in degrees Fahrenheit and x is the number of days from Sunday. (This graph is shown in blue.) Use this function to answer Exercises 85 and 86.

85. Use the quadratic function given to approximate the temperature on Thursday. Does your answer agree with the graph?

86. Use the function given and the quadratic formula to find when the temperature was $35°$ F. [*Hint:* Let $f(x) = 35$ and solve for x.] Round your answer to one decimal place and interpret your result. Does your answer agree with the graph?

87. The number of Starbucks stores can be modeled by the quadratic function $f(x) = 115x^2 + 711x + 3946$, where $f(x)$ is the number of Starbucks and x is the number of years after 2000. (*Source: Starbuck's Annual Report 2006*)

   a. Find the number of Starbucks in 2004.

   b. If the trend described by the model continues, predict the years after 2000 in which the number of Starbucks will be 25,000. Round to the nearest whole year.

88. The number of visitors to U.S. theme parks can be modeled by the quadratic equation $v(x) = 0.25x^2 + 2.6x + 315.6$, where $v(x)$ is the number of visitors (in millions) and x is the number of years after 2000. (*Source:* Price Waterhouse Coopers)

   a. Find the number of visitors to U.S. theme parks in 2005. Round to the nearest million.

   b. Find the projected number of visitors to U.S. theme parks in 2010. Round to the nearest million.

The solutions of the quadratic equation $ax^2 + bx + c = 0$ are $\dfrac{-b + \sqrt{b^2 - 4ac}}{2a}$ *and* $\dfrac{-b - \sqrt{b^2 - 4ac}}{2a}$.

89. Show that the sum of these solutions is $\dfrac{-b}{a}$.

90. Show that the product of these solutions is $\dfrac{c}{a}$.

Use the quadratic formula to solve each quadratic equation.

91. $3x^2 - \sqrt{12}x + 1 = 0$,
   (*Hint:* $a = 3, b = -\sqrt{12}, c = 1$)

92. $5x^2 + \sqrt{20}x + 1 = 0$

93. $x^2 + \sqrt{2}x + 1 = 0$

94. $x^2 - \sqrt{2}x + 1 = 0$

95. $2x^2 - \sqrt{3}x - 1 = 0$

96. $7x^2 + \sqrt{7}x - 2 = 0$

97. Use a graphing calculator to solve Exercises 63 and 65.

98. Use a graphing calculator to solve Exercises 64 and 66.

Recall that the discriminant also tells us the number of x-intercepts of the related function.

99. Check the results of Exercise 49 by graphing $y = 9x - 2x^2 + 5$.

100. Check the results of Exercise 50 by graphing $y = 5 - 4x + 12x^2$.

📖 STUDY SKILLS BUILDER

How Well Do You Know Your Textbook?

Let's check to see whether you are familiar with your textbook yet. For help, see Section 1.1 in this text.

1. What does the 🖥 icon mean?

2. What does the ＼ icon mean?

3. What does the △ icon mean?

4. Where can you find a review for each chapter? What answers to this review can be found in the back of your text?

5. Each chapter contains an overview of the chapter along with examples. What is this feature called?

6. Each chapter contains a review of vocabulary. What is this feature called?

7. There are free CDs in your text. What content is contained on these CDs?

8. What is the location of the section that is entirely devoted to study skills?

9. There are Practice Problems that are contained in the margin of the text. What are they and how can they be used?

8.3 SOLVING EQUATIONS BY USING QUADRATIC METHODS

OBJECTIVE 1 ▶ Solving equations that are quadratic in form. In this section, we discuss various types of equations that can be solved in part by using the methods for solving quadratic equations.

Once each equation is simplified, you may want to use these steps when deciding what method to use to solve the quadratic equation.

Solving a Quadratic Equation

STEP 1. If the equation is in the form $(ax + b)^2 = c$, use the square root property and solve. If not, go to Step 2.

STEP 2. Write the equation in standard form: $ax^2 + bx + c = 0$.

STEP 3. Try to solve the equation by the factoring method. If not possible, go to Step 4.

STEP 4. Solve the equation by the quadratic formula.

The first example is a radical equation that becomes a quadratic equation once we square both sides.

EXAMPLE 1 Solve: $x - \sqrt{x} - 6 = 0$.

Solution Recall that to solve a radical equation, first get the radical alone on one side of the equation. Then square both sides.

$$x - 6 = \sqrt{x} \qquad \text{Add } \sqrt{x} \text{ to both sides.}$$
$$(x - 6)^2 = \left(\sqrt{x}\right)^2 \quad \text{Square both sides.}$$
$$x^2 - 12x + 36 = x$$
$$x^2 - 13x + 36 = 0 \qquad \text{Set the equation equal to 0.}$$
$$(x - 9)(x - 4) = 0$$
$$x - 9 = 0 \quad \text{or} \quad x - 4 = 0$$
$$x = 9 \qquad\qquad x = 4$$

Check:

Let $x = 9$	Let $x = 4$
$x - \sqrt{x} - 6 = 0$	$x - \sqrt{x} - 6 = 0$
$9 - \sqrt{9} - 6 \overset{?}{=} 0$	$4 - \sqrt{4} - 6 \overset{?}{=} 0$
$9 - 3 - 6 \overset{?}{=} 0$	$4 - 2 - 6 \overset{?}{=} 0$
$0 = 0$ True	$-4 = 0$ False

The solution is 9 or the solution set is {9}.

PRACTICE
1 Solve: $x - \sqrt{x + 1} - 5 = 0$.

EXAMPLE 2 Solve: $\dfrac{3x}{x - 2} - \dfrac{x + 1}{x} = \dfrac{6}{x(x - 2)}$.

Solution In this equation, x cannot be either 2 or 0, because these values cause denominators to equal zero. To solve for x, we first multiply both sides of the equation by

$x(x - 2)$ to clear the fractions. By the distributive property, this means that we multiply each term by $x(x - 2)$.

$$x(x - 2)\left(\frac{3x}{x - 2}\right) - x(x - 2)\left(\frac{x + 1}{x}\right) = x(x - 2)\left[\frac{6}{x(x - 2)}\right]$$

$$3x^2 - (x - 2)(x + 1) = 6 \quad \text{Simplify.}$$
$$3x^2 - (x^2 - x - 2) = 6 \quad \text{Multiply.}$$
$$3x^2 - x^2 + x + 2 = 6$$
$$2x^2 + x - 4 = 0 \quad \text{Simplify.}$$

This equation cannot be factored using integers, so we solve by the quadratic formula.

$$x = \frac{-1 \pm \sqrt{1^2 - 4(2)(-4)}}{2 \cdot 2} \quad \text{Use } a = 2, b = 1, \text{ and } c = -4 \text{ in the quadratic formula.}$$

$$= \frac{-1 \pm \sqrt{1 + 32}}{4} \quad \text{Simplify.}$$

$$= \frac{-1 \pm \sqrt{33}}{4}$$

Neither proposed solution will make the denominators 0.

The solutions are $\dfrac{-1 + \sqrt{33}}{4}$ and $\dfrac{-1 - \sqrt{33}}{4}$ or the solution set is $\left\{\dfrac{-1 + \sqrt{33}}{4}, \dfrac{-1 - \sqrt{33}}{4}\right\}$.

□

PRACTICE
2 Solve: $\dfrac{5x}{x + 1} - \dfrac{x + 4}{x} = \dfrac{3}{x(x + 1)}$.

EXAMPLE 3 Solve: $p^4 - 3p^2 - 4 = 0$.

Solution First we factor the trinomial.

$$p^4 - 3p^2 - 4 = 0$$
$$(p^2 - 4)(p^2 + 1) = 0 \quad \text{Factor.}$$
$$(p - 2)(p + 2)(p^2 + 1) = 0 \quad \text{Factor further.}$$
$$p - 2 = 0 \quad \text{or} \quad p + 2 = 0 \quad \text{or} \quad p^2 + 1 = 0 \quad \text{Set each factor equal to 0 and solve.}$$
$$p = 2 \qquad\qquad p = -2 \qquad\qquad p^2 = -1$$
$$p = \pm\sqrt{-1} = \pm i$$

The solutions are $2, -2, i$ and $-i$.

□

PRACTICE
3 Solve: $p^4 - 7p^2 - 144 = 0$.

> ▶ **Helpful Hint**
> Example 3 can be solved using substitution also. Think of $p^4 - 3p^2 - 4 = 0$ as
> $$(p^2)^2 - 3p^2 - 4 = 0 \quad \text{Then let } x = p^2, \text{ and solve and substitute back.}$$
> $$x^2 - 3x - 4 = 0 \quad \text{The solutions will be the same.}$$

Concept Check ☑

a. True or false? The maximum number of solutions that a quadratic equation can have is 2.

b. True or false? The maximum number of solutions that an equation in quadratic form can have is 2.

EXAMPLE 4   Solve: $(x - 3)^2 - 3(x - 3) - 4 = 0$.

Solution   Notice that the quantity $(x - 3)$ is repeated in this equation. Sometimes it is helpful to substitute a variable (in this case other than x) for the repeated quantity. We will let $y = x - 3$. Then

$$(x - 3)^2 - 3(x - 3) - 4 = 0$$

becomes

$$y^2 - 3y - 4 = 0 \quad \text{Let } x - 3 = y.$$
$$(y - 4)(y + 1) = 0 \quad \text{Factor.}$$

To solve, we use the zero factor property.

$$y - 4 = 0 \quad \text{or} \quad y + 1 = 0 \quad \text{Set each factor equal to 0.}$$
$$y = 4 \qquad\qquad y = -1 \quad \text{Solve.}$$

> ▶ **Helpful Hint**
> When using substitution, don't forget to substitute back to the original variable.

To find values of x, we substitute back. That is, we substitute $x - 3$ for y.

$$x - 3 = 4 \quad \text{or} \quad x - 3 = -1$$
$$x = 7 \qquad\qquad x = 2$$

Both 2 and 7 check. The solutions are 2 and 7.   □

PRACTICE
4   Solve: $(x + 2)^2 - 2(x + 2) - 3 = 0$.

EXAMPLE 5   Solve: $x^{2/3} - 5x^{1/3} + 6 = 0$.

Solution   The key to solving this equation is recognizing that $x^{2/3} = (x^{1/3})^2$. We replace $x^{1/3}$ with m so that

$$(x^{1/3})^2 - 5x^{1/3} + 6 = 0$$

becomes

$$m^2 - 5m + 6 = 0$$

Now we solve by factoring.

$$m^2 - 5m + 6 = 0$$
$$(m - 3)(m - 2) = 0 \qquad\qquad \text{Factor.}$$
$$m - 3 = 0 \quad \text{or} \quad m - 2 = 0 \quad \text{Set each factor equal to 0.}$$
$$m = 3 \qquad\qquad m = 2$$

Since $m = x^{1/3}$, we have

$$x^{1/3} = 3 \qquad \text{or} \quad x^{1/3} = 2$$
$$x = 3^3 = 27 \quad \text{or} \qquad x = 2^3 = 8$$

Both 8 and 27 check. The solutions are 8 and 27.   □

PRACTICE
5   Solve: $x^{2/3} - 5x^{1/3} + 4 = 0$.

OBJECTIVE 2 ▶ Solving problems that lead to quadratic equations. The next example is a work problem. This problem is modeled by a rational equation that simplifies to a quadratic equation.

EXAMPLE 6   **Finding Work Time**

Together, an experienced word processor and an apprentice word processor can create a word document in 6 hours. Alone, the experienced word processor can create the document 2 hours faster than the apprentice word processor can. Find the time in which each person can create the word document alone.

Solution

1. UNDERSTAND. Read and reread the problem. The key idea here is the relationship between the *time* (hours) it takes to complete the job and the *part of the job* completed in one unit of time (hour). For example, because they can complete the job together in 6 hours, the *part of the job* they can complete in 1 hour is $\frac{1}{6}$.

   Let

   $x =$ the *time* in hours it takes the apprentice word processor to complete the job alone

   $x - 2 =$ the *time* in hours it takes the experienced word processor to complete the job alone

   We can summarize in a chart the information discussed

	Total Hours to Complete Job	*Part of Job Completed in 1 Hour*
Apprentice Word Processor	x	$\frac{1}{x}$
Experienced Word Processor	$x - 2$	$\frac{1}{x - 2}$
Together	6	$\frac{1}{6}$

2. TRANSLATE.

In words:	part of job completed by apprentice word processor in 1 hour	added to	part of job completed by experienced word processor in 1 hour	is equal to	part of job completed together in 1 hour
	↓	↓	↓	↓	↓
Translate:	$\frac{1}{x}$	$+$	$\frac{1}{x - 2}$	$=$	$\frac{1}{6}$

3. SOLVE.

$$\frac{1}{x} + \frac{1}{x - 2} = \frac{1}{6}$$

$$6x(x - 2)\left(\frac{1}{x} + \frac{1}{x - 2}\right) = 6x(x - 2) \cdot \frac{1}{6} \qquad \text{Multiply both sides by the LCD } 6x(x - 2).$$

$$6x(x - 2) \cdot \frac{1}{x} + 6x(x - 2) \cdot \frac{1}{x - 2} = 6x(x - 2) \cdot \frac{1}{6} \qquad \text{Use the distributive property.}$$

$$6(x - 2) + 6x = x(x - 2)$$

$$6x - 12 + 6x = x^2 - 2x$$

$$0 = x^2 - 14x + 12$$

Now we can substitute $a = 1$, $b = -14$, and $c = 12$ into the quadratic formula and simplify.

$$x = \frac{-(-14) \pm \sqrt{(-14)^2 - 4(1)(12)}}{2 \cdot 1} = \frac{14 \pm \sqrt{148}}{2}{}^*$$

(*This expression can be simplified further, but this will suffice as we are approximating.)

Using a calculator or a square root table, we see that $\sqrt{148} \approx 12.2$ rounded to one decimal place. Thus,

$$x \approx \frac{14 \pm 12.2}{2}$$

$$x \approx \frac{14 + 12.2}{2} = 13.1 \quad \text{or} \quad x \approx \frac{14 - 12.2}{2} = 0.9$$

4. INTERPRET.

Check: If the apprentice word processor completes the job alone in 0.9 hours, the experienced word processor completes the job alone in $x - 2 = 0.9 - 2 = -1.1$ hours. Since this is not possible, we reject the solution of 0.9. The approximate solution thus is 13.1 hours.

State: The apprentice word processor can complete the job alone in approximately 13.1 hours, and the experienced word processor can complete the job alone in approximately

$$x - 2 = 13.1 - 2 = 11.1 \text{ hours.} \qquad \square$$

PRACTICE

6 Together, Katy and Steve can groom all the dogs at the Barkin' Doggie Day Care in 4 hours. Alone, Katy can groom the dogs 1 hour faster than Steve can groom the dogs alone. Find the time in which each of them can groom the dogs alone.

EXAMPLE 7 **Finding Driving Speeds**

Beach and Fargo are about 400 miles apart. A salesperson travels from Fargo to Beach one day at a certain speed. She returns to Fargo the next day and drives 10 mph faster. Her total travel time was $14\frac{2}{3}$ hours. Find her speed to Beach and the return speed to Fargo.

Solution

1. UNDERSTAND. Read and reread the problem. Let

$$x = \text{the speed to Beach, so}$$
$$x + 10 = \text{the return speed to Fargo.}$$

Then organize the given information in a table.

> **▶ Helpful Hint**
>
> Since $d = rt$, then $t = \dfrac{d}{r}$. The time column was completed using $\dfrac{d}{r}$.

	distance	=	rate	·	time	
To Beach	400		x		$\dfrac{400}{x}$	; distance ; rate
Return to Fargo	400		$x + 10$		$\dfrac{400}{x + 10}$	; distance ; rate

2. TRANSLATE.

In words:

time to Beach	+	return time to Fargo	=	$14\dfrac{2}{3}$ hours

Translate:
$$\dfrac{400}{x} \quad + \quad \dfrac{400}{x+10} \quad = \quad \dfrac{44}{3}$$

3. SOLVE.

$$\dfrac{400}{x} + \dfrac{400}{x+10} = \dfrac{44}{3}$$

$$\dfrac{100}{x} + \dfrac{100}{x+10} = \dfrac{11}{3} \qquad \text{Divide both sides by 4.}$$

$$3x(x+10)\left(\dfrac{100}{x} + \dfrac{100}{x+10}\right) = 3x(x+10)\cdot\dfrac{11}{3} \qquad \text{Multiply both sides by the LCD } 3x(x+10).$$

$$3x(x+10)\cdot\dfrac{100}{x} + 3x(x+10)\cdot\dfrac{100}{x+10} = 3x(x+10)\cdot\dfrac{11}{3} \qquad \text{Use the distributive property.}$$

$$3(x+10)\cdot100 + 3x\cdot100 = x(x+10)\cdot11$$

$$300x + 3000 + 300x = 11x^2 + 110x$$

$$0 = 11x^2 - 490x - 3000 \qquad \text{Set equation equal to 0.}$$

$$0 = (11x+60)(x-50) \qquad \text{Factor.}$$

$$11x + 60 = 0 \quad \text{or} \quad x - 50 = 0 \qquad \text{Set each factor equal to 0.}$$

$$x = -\dfrac{60}{11} \text{ or } -5\dfrac{5}{11}; \quad x = 50$$

4. INTERPRET.

Check: The speed is not negative, so it's not $-5\dfrac{5}{11}$. The number 50 does check.

State: The speed to Beach was 50 mph and her return speed to Fargo was 60 mph. □

PRACTICE
7 The 36-km S-shaped Hangzhou Bay Bridge is the longest cross-sea bridge in the world, linking Ningbo and Shanghai, China. A merchant drives over the bridge one morning from Ningbo to Shanghai in very heavy traffic and returns home that night driving 50 km per hour faster. The total travel time was 1.3 hours. Find the speed to Shanghai and the return speed to Ningbo.

8.3 | EXERCISE SET

MyMathLab®   PRACTICE   WATCH   DOWNLOAD   READ   REVIEW

Solve. See Example 1.

1. $2x = \sqrt{10+3x}$

2. $3x = \sqrt{8x+1}$

3. $x - 2\sqrt{x} = 8$

4. $x - \sqrt{2x} = 4$

5. $\sqrt{9x} = x+2$

6. $\sqrt{16x} = x+3$

Solve. See Example 2.

7. $\dfrac{2}{x} + \dfrac{3}{x-1} = 1$

8. $\dfrac{6}{x^2} = \dfrac{3}{x+1}$

9. $\dfrac{3}{x} + \dfrac{4}{x+2} = 2$

10. $\dfrac{5}{x-2} + \dfrac{4}{x+2} = 1$

11. $\dfrac{7}{x^2-5x+6} = \dfrac{2x}{x-3} - \dfrac{x}{x-2}$

12. $\dfrac{11}{2x^2+x-15} = \dfrac{5}{2x-5} - \dfrac{x}{x+3}$

Solve. See Example 3.

13. $p^4 - 16 = 0$

14. $x^4 + 2x^2 - 3 = 0$

15. $4x^4 + 11x^2 = 3$

16. $z^4 = 81$

17. $z^4 - 13z^2 + 36 = 0$

18. $9x^4 + 5x^2 - 4 = 0$

Solve. See Examples 4 and 5.

19. $x^{2/3} - 3x^{1/3} - 10 = 0$

20. $x^{2/3} + 2x^{1/3} + 1 = 0$

21. $(5n + 1)^2 + 2(5n + 1) - 3 = 0$

22. $(m - 6)^2 + 5(m - 6) + 4 = 0$

23. $2x^{2/3} - 5x^{1/3} = 3$

24. $3x^{2/3} + 11x^{1/3} = 4$

25. $1 + \dfrac{2}{3t - 2} = \dfrac{8}{(3t - 2)^2}$

26. $2 - \dfrac{7}{x + 6} = \dfrac{15}{(x + 6)^2}$

27. $20x^{2/3} - 6x^{1/3} - 2 = 0$

28. $4x^{2/3} + 16x^{1/3} = -15$

MIXED PRACTICE

Solve. See Examples 1 through 5.

29. $a^4 - 5a^2 + 6 = 0$

30. $x^4 - 12x^2 + 11 = 0$

31. $\dfrac{2x}{x - 2} + \dfrac{x}{x + 3} = -\dfrac{5}{x + 3}$

32. $\dfrac{5}{x - 3} + \dfrac{x}{x + 3} = \dfrac{19}{x^2 - 9}$

33. $(p + 2)^2 = 9(p + 2) - 20$

34. $2(4m - 3)^2 - 9(4m - 3) = 5$

35. $2x = \sqrt{11x + 3}$

36. $4x = \sqrt{2x + 3}$

37. $x^{2/3} - 8x^{1/3} + 15 = 0$

38. $x^{2/3} - 2x^{1/3} - 8 = 0$

39. $y^3 + 9y - y^2 - 9 = 0$

40. $x^3 + x - 3x^2 - 3 = 0$

41. $2x^{2/3} + 3x^{1/3} - 2 = 0$

42. $6x^{2/3} - 25x^{1/3} - 25 = 0$

43. $x^{-2} - x^{-1} - 6 = 0$

44. $y^{-2} - 8y^{-1} + 7 = 0$

45. $x - \sqrt{x} = 2$

46. $x - \sqrt{3x} = 6$

47. $\dfrac{x}{x - 1} + \dfrac{1}{x + 1} = \dfrac{2}{x^2 - 1}$

48. $\dfrac{x}{x - 5} + \dfrac{5}{x + 5} = -\dfrac{1}{x^2 - 25}$

49. $p^4 - p^2 - 20 = 0$

50. $x^4 - 10x^2 + 9 = 0$

51. $(x + 3)(x^2 - 3x + 9) = 0$

52. $(x - 6)(x^2 + 6x + 36) = 0$

53. $1 = \dfrac{4}{x - 7} + \dfrac{5}{(x - 7)^2}$

54. $3 + \dfrac{1}{2p + 4} = \dfrac{10}{(2p + 4)^2}$

55. $27y^4 + 15y^2 = 2$

56. $8z^4 + 14z^2 = -5$

Solve. See Examples 6 and 7.

57. A jogger ran 3 miles, decreased her speed by 1 mile per hour, and then ran another 4 miles. If her total time jogging was $1\dfrac{3}{5}$ hours, find her speed for each part of her run.

58. Mark Keaton's workout consists of jogging for 3 miles, and then riding his bike for 5 miles at a speed 4 miles per hour faster than he jogs. If his total workout time is 1 hour, find his jogging speed and his biking speed.

59. A Chinese restaurant in Mandeville, Louisiana, has a large goldfish pond around the restaurant. Suppose that an inlet pipe and a hose together can fill the pond in 8 hours. The inlet pipe alone can complete the job in one hour less time than the hose alone. Find the time that the hose can complete the job alone and the time that the inlet pipe can complete the job alone. Round each to the nearest tenth of an hour.

60. A water tank on a farm in Flatonia, Texas, can be filled with a large inlet pipe and a small inlet pipe in 3 hours. The large inlet pipe alone can fill the tank in 2 hours less time than the small inlet pipe alone. Find the time to the nearest tenth of an hour each pipe can fill the tank alone.

61. Roma Sherry drove 330 miles from her hometown to Tucson. During her return trip, she was able to increase her speed by 11 mph. If her return trip took 1 hour less time, find her original speed and her speed returning home.

62. A salesperson drove to Portland, a distance of 300 miles. During the last 80 miles of his trip, heavy rainfall forced him to decrease his speed by 15 mph. If his total driving time was 6 hours, find his original speed and his speed during the rainfall.

63. Bill Shaughnessy and his son Billy can clean the house together in 4 hours. When the son works alone, it takes him an hour longer to clean than it takes his dad alone. Find how long to the nearest tenth of an hour it takes the son to clean alone.

64. Together, Noodles and Freckles eat a 50-pound bag of dog food in 30 days. Noodles by himself eats a 50-pound bag in 2 weeks less time than Freckles does by himself. How many days to the nearest whole day would a 50-pound bag of dog food last Freckles?

65. The product of a number and 4 less than the number is 96. Find the number.

66. A whole number increased by its square is two more than twice itself. Find the number.

△ **67.** Suppose that an open box is to be made from a square sheet of cardboard by cutting out squares from each corner as shown and then folding along the dotted lines. If the box is to have a volume of 300 cubic centimeters, find the original dimensions of the sheet of cardboard.

a. The ? in the drawing above will be the length (and also the width) of the box as shown. Represent this length in terms of x.

b. Use the formula for volume of a box, $V = l \cdot w \cdot h$, to write an equation in x.

c. Solve the equation for x and give the dimensions of the sheet of cardboard. Check your solution.

△ **68.** Suppose that an open box is to be made from a square sheet of cardboard by cutting out squares from each corner as shown and then folding along the dotted lines. If the box is to have a volume of 128 cubic inches, find the original dimensions of the sheet of cardboard.

a. The ? in the drawing above will be the length (and also the width) of the box as shown. Represent this length in terms of x.

b. Use the formula for volume of a box, $V = l \cdot w \cdot h$, to write an equation in x.

c. Solve the equation for x and give the dimensions of the sheet of cardboard. Check your solution.

△ **69.** A sprinkler that sprays water in a circular motion is to be used to water a square garden. If the area of the garden is 920 square feet, find the smallest whole number *radius* that the sprinkler can be adjusted to so that the entire garden is watered.

△ **70.** Suppose that a square field has an area of 6270 square feet. See Exercise 69 and find a new sprinkler radius.

REVIEW AND PREVIEW

Solve each inequality. See Section 2.4.

71. $\dfrac{5x}{3} + 2 \le 7$

72. $\dfrac{2x}{3} + \dfrac{1}{6} \ge 2$

73. $\dfrac{y-1}{15} > -\dfrac{2}{5}$

74. $\dfrac{z-2}{12} < \dfrac{1}{4}$

Find the domain and range of each graphed relation. Decide which relations are also functions. See Section 3.2.

75.

76.

77.

78.

CONCEPT EXTENSIONS

Solve.

79. $y^3 + 9y - y^2 - 9 = 0$

80. $x^3 + x - 3x^2 - 3 = 0$

81. $x^{-2} - x^{-1} - 6 = 0$

82. $y^{-2} - 8y^{-1} + 7 = 0$

83. $2x^3 = -54$

84. $y^3 - 216 = 0$

85. Write a polynomial equation that has three solutions: 2, 5, and −7.

86. Write a polynomial equation that has three solutions: 0, 2*i*, and −2*i*.

87. At the 2007 Grand Prix of Long Beach auto race, Simon Pagenaud posted the fastest lap speed, but Sebastian Bourdais won the race. One lap through the streets of Long Beach is 10,391 feet (1.968 miles) long. Pagenaud's fastest lap speed was 0.55 foot per second faster than Bourdais's fastest lap speed. Traveling at these fastest speeds, Bourdais would have taken 0.25 second longer than Pagenaud to complete a lap. (*Source:* Championship Auto Racing Teams, Inc.)

    a. Find Sebastian Bourdais's fastest lap speed during the race. Round to two decimal places.

    b. Find Simon Pagenaud's fastest last speed during the race. Round to two decimal places.

    c. Convert each speed to miles per hour. Round to one decimal place.

88. Use a graphing calculator to solve Exercise 29. Compare the solution with the solution from Exercise 29. Explain any differences.

INTEGRATED REVIEW SUMMARY ON SOLVING QUADRATIC EQUATIONS

Sections 8.1–8.3

Use the square root property to solve each equation.

1. $x^2 - 10 = 0$

2. $x^2 - 14 = 0$

3. $(x - 1)^2 = 8$

4. $(x + 5)^2 = 12$

Solve each equation by completing the square.

5. $x^2 + 2x - 12 = 0$

6. $x^2 - 12x + 11 = 0$

7. $3x^2 + 3x = 5$

8. $16y^2 + 16y = 1$

Use the quadratic formula to solve each equation

9. $2x^2 - 4x + 1 = 0$

10. $\frac{1}{2}x^2 + 3x + 2 = 0$

11. $x^2 + 4x = -7$

12. $x^2 + x = -3$

Solve each equation. Use a method of your choice.

13. $x^2 + 3x + 6 = 0$

14. $2x^2 + 18 = 0$

15. $x^2 + 17x = 0$

16. $4x^2 - 2x - 3 = 0$

17. $(x - 2)^2 = 27$

18. $\frac{1}{2}x^2 - 2x + \frac{1}{2} = 0$

19. $3x^2 + 2x = 8$

20. $2x^2 = -5x - 1$

21. $x(x - 2) = 5$

22. $x^2 - 31 = 0$

23. $5x^2 - 55 = 0$

24. $5x^2 + 55 = 0$

25. $x(x + 5) = 66$

26. $5x^2 + 6x - 2 = 0$

27. $2x^2 + 3x = 1$

△ **28.** The diagonal of a square room measures 20 feet. Find the exact length of a side of the room. Then approximate the length to the nearest tenth of a foot.

20 ft

x

29. Together, Jack and Lucy Hoag can prepare a crawfish boil for a large party in 4 hours. Lucy alone can complete the job in 2 hours less time than Jack alone. Find the time that each person can prepare the crawfish boil alone. Round each time to the nearest tenth of an hour.

30. Diane Gray exercises at Total Body Gym. On the treadmill, she runs 5 miles, then increases her speed by 1 mile per hour and runs an additional 2 miles. If her total time on the tread mill is $1\frac{1}{3}$ hours, find her speed during each part of her run.

CHAPTER 8 GROUP ACTIVITY

Fitting a Quadratic Model to Data

Throughout the twentieth century, the eating habits of Americans changed noticeably. Americans started consuming less whole milk and butter, and started consuming more skim and low-fat milk and margarine. We also started eating more poultry and fish. In this project, you will have the opportunity to investigate trends in per capita consumption of poultry during the twentieth century. This project may be completed by working in groups or individually.

We will start by finding a quadratic model, $y = ax^2 + bx + c$, that has ordered pair solutions that correspond to the data for U.S. per capita consumption of poultry given in the table. To do so, substitute each data pair into the equation. Each time, the result is an equation in three unknowns: a, b, and c. Because there are three pairs of data, we can form a system of three linear equations in three unknowns. Solving for the values of a, b, and c gives a quadratic model that represents the given data.

U.S. per Capita Consumption of Poultry (in Pounds)

Year	x	Poultry Consumption, y (in pounds)
1909	9	11
1957	57	22
2005	105	66

(*Source:* Economic Research Service, U.S. Department of Agriculture)

1. Write the system of equations that must be solved to find the values of a, b, and c needed for a quadratic model of the given data.

2. Solve the system of equations for a, b, and c. Recall the various methods of solving linear systems used in Chapter 4. You might consider using matrices, Cramer's rule, or a graphing calculator to do so. Round to the nearest thousandth.

3. Write the quadratic model for the data. Note that the variable x represents the number of years after 1900.

4. In 1939, the actual U.S. per capita consumption of poultry was 12 pounds per person. Based on this information, how accurate do you think this model is for years other than those given in the table?

5. Use your model to estimate the per capita consumption of poultry in 1950.

6. According to the model, in what year was per capita consumption of poultry 50 pounds per person?

7. In what year was the per capita consumption of poultry at its lowest level? What was that level?

8. Who might be interested in a model like this and how would it be helpful?

STUDY SKILLS BUILDER

Are You Preparing for a Test on Chapter 8?

Below I have listed some common trouble areas for students in Chapter 8. After studying for your test—but before taking your test—read these.

- Don't forget that to solve a quadratic equation such as $x^2 + 6x = 1$, by completing the square, add the square of half of 6 to both sides.

$$x^2 + 6x = 1$$
$$x^2 + 6x + 9 = 1 + 9 \qquad \text{Add 9 to both sides,} \left(\frac{1}{2}(6) = 3 \text{ and } 3^2 = 9\right)$$
$$(x + 3)^2 = 10$$
$$x + 3 = \pm\sqrt{10}$$
$$x = -3 \pm \sqrt{10}$$

- Remember to write a quadratic equation in standard form $(ax^2 + bx + c = 0)$ before using the quadratic formula to solve.

$$x(4x - 1) = 1$$
$$4x^2 - x - 1 = 0 \qquad \text{Write in standard form.}$$

$$x = \frac{-(-1) \pm \sqrt{(-1)^2 - 4(4)(-1)}}{2 \cdot 4} \qquad \text{Use the quadratic formula with } a = 4, b = -1, \text{ and } c = -1.$$

$$x = \frac{1 \pm \sqrt{17}}{8} \qquad \text{Simplify.}$$

- Review the steps for solving a quadratic equation in general on page 500.
- Don't forget how to graph a quadratic function in the form $f(x) = a(x - h)^2 + k$.

The graph of $f(x) = -2(x - 3)^2 - 1$

opens downward, narrower | shift 3 units right | shift 1 unit down

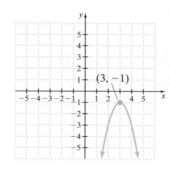

Remember: This is simply a checklist of common trouble areas. For a review of Chapter 8, see the Highlights and Chapter Review at the end of this chapter.

CHAPTER 8 VOCABULARY CHECK

Fill in each blank with one of the words or phrases listed below.

quadratic formula	quadratic	discriminant	$\pm\sqrt{b}$
completing the square	quadratic inequality	(h, k)	$(0, k)$
$(h, 0)$	$\dfrac{-b}{2a}$		

1. The _____ helps us find the number and type of solutions of a quadratic equation.
2. If $a^2 = b$, then $a =$ _____
3. The graph of $f(x) = ax^2 + bx + c$ where a is not 0 is a parabola whose vertex has x-value of _____.

4. A(n) _____ is an inequality that can be written so that one side is a quadratic expression and the other side is 0.

5. The process of writing a quadratic equation so that one side is a perfect square trinomial is called _____.

6. The graph of $f(x) = x^2 + k$ has vertex _____.

7. The graph of $f(x) = (x - h)^2$ has vertex _____.

8. The graph of $f(x) = (x - h)^2 + k$ has vertex _____.

9. The formula $x = \dfrac{-b \pm \sqrt{b^2 - 4ac}}{2a}$ is called the _____.

10. A _____ equation is one that can be written in the form $ax^2 + bx + c = 0$ where $a, b,$ and c are real numbers and a is not 0.

> ▶ **Helpful Hint**
>
> Are you preparing for your test? Don't forget to take the Chapter 8 Test on page 481. Then check your answers at the back of the text and use the Chapter Test Prep Video CD to see the fully worked-out solutions to any of the exercises you want to review.

CHAPTER 8 HIGHLIGHTS

DEFINITIONS AND CONCEPTS	**EXAMPLES**

SECTION 8.1   SOLVING QUADRATIC EQUATIONS BY COMPLETING THE SQUARE

Square root property	Solve: $(x + 3)^2 = 14$.
If b is a real number and if $a^2 = b$, then $a = \pm\sqrt{b}$.	$x + 3 = \pm\sqrt{14}$
	$x = -3 \pm \sqrt{14}$
To solve a quadratic equation in x by completing the square	Solve: $3x^2 - 12x - 18 = 0$.
Step 1. If the coefficient of x^2 is not 1, divide both sides of the equation by the coefficient of x^2.	**1.** $x^2 - 4x - 6 = 0$
Step 2. Isolate the variable terms.	**2.** $x^2 - 4x = 6$
Step 3. Complete the square by adding the square of half of the coefficient of x to both sides.	**3.** $\dfrac{1}{2}(-4) = -2$ and $(-2)^2 = 4$
	$x^2 - 4x + 4 = 6 + 4$
Step 4. Write the resulting trinomial as the square of a binomial.	**4.** $(x - 2)^2 = 10$
Step 5. Apply the square root property and solve for x.	**5.** $x - 2 = \pm\sqrt{10}$
	$x = 2 \pm \sqrt{10}$

SECTION 8.2   SOLVING QUADRATIC EQUATIONS BY THE QUADRATIC FORMULA

A quadratic equation written in the form $ax^2 + bx + c = 0$ has solutions	Solve: $x^2 - x - 3 = 0$.
$$x = \frac{-b \pm \sqrt{b^2 - 4ac}}{2a}$$	$a = 1, b = -1, c = -3$
	$x = \dfrac{-(-1) \pm \sqrt{(-1)^2 - 4(1)(-3)}}{2 \cdot 1}$
	$x = \dfrac{1 \pm \sqrt{13}}{2}$

DEFINITIONS AND CONCEPTS	**EXAMPLES**

SECTION 8.3   SOLVING EQUATIONS BY USING QUADRATIC METHODS

Substitution is often helpful in solving an equation that contains a repeated variable expression.

Solve: $(2x + 1)^2 - 5(2x + 1) + 6 = 0$.

Let $m = 2x + 1$. Then

$$m^2 - 5m + 6 = 0 \qquad \text{Let } m = 2x + 1.$$

$$(m - 3)(m - 2) = 0$$

$$m = 3 \quad \text{or} \qquad m = 2$$

$$2x + 1 = 3 \quad \text{or} \quad 2x + 1 = 2 \quad \text{Substitute back.}$$

$$x = 1 \quad \text{or} \qquad x = \frac{1}{2}$$

CHAPTER 8 REVIEW

(8.1) Solve by factoring.

1. $x^2 - 15x + 14 = 0$ **2.** $7a^2 = 29a + 30$

Solve by using the square root property.

3. $4m^2 = 196$ **4.** $(5x - 2)^2 = 2$

Solve by completing the square.

5. $z^2 + 3z + 1 = 0$

6. $(2x + 1)^2 = x$

7. If P dollars are originally invested, the formula $A = P(1 + r)^2$ gives the amount A in an account paying interest rate r compounded annually after 2 years. Find the interest rate r such that $2500 increases to $2717 in 2 years. Round the result to the nearest hundredth of a percent.

△ **8.** Two ships leave a port at the same time and travel at the same speed. One ship is traveling due north and the other due east. In a few hours, the ships are 150 miles apart. How many miles has each ship traveled? Give an exact answer and a one-decimal-place approximation.

(8.2) If the discriminant of a quadratic equation has the given value, determine the number and type of solutions of the equation.

9. -8 **10.** 48

11. 100   **12.** 0

Solve by using the quadratic formula.

13. $x^2 - 16x + 64 = 0$ **14.** $x^2 + 5x = 0$

15. $2x^2 + 3x = 5$ **16.** $9a^2 + 4 = 2a$

17. $6x^2 + 7 = 5x$ **18.** $(2x - 3)^2 = x$

19. Cadets graduating from military school usually toss their hats high into the air at the end of the ceremony. One cadet threw his hat so that its distance $d(t)$ in feet above the ground t seconds after it was thrown was $d(t) = -16t^2 + 30t + 6$.

a. Find the distance above the ground of the hat 1 second after it was thrown.

b. Find the time it takes the hat to hit the ground. Give an exact time and a one-decimal-place approximation.

△ **20.** The hypotenuse of an isosceles right triangle is 6 centimeters longer than either of the legs. Find the length of the legs.

(8.3) Solve each equation for the variable.

21. $x^3 = 27$

22. $y^3 = -64$

23. $\dfrac{5}{x} + \dfrac{6}{x - 2} = 3$

24. $x^4 - 21x^2 - 100 = 0$

25. $x^{2/3} - 6x^{1/3} + 5 = 0$

26. $5(x + 3)^2 - 19(x + 3) = 4$

27. $a^6 - a^2 = a^4 - 1$

28. $y^{-2} + y^{-1} = 20$

29. Two postal workers, Jerome Grant and Tim Bozik, can sort a stack of mail in 5 hours. Working alone, Tim can sort the mail in 1 hour less time than Jerome can. Find the time that each postal worker can sort the mail alone. Round the result to one decimal place.

30. A negative number decreased by its reciprocal is $-\dfrac{24}{5}$. Find the number.

MIXED REVIEW

Solve each equation.

57. $x^2 - x - 30 = 0$

58. $10x^2 = 3x + 4$

59. $9y^2 = 36$

60. $(9n + 1)^2 = 9$

61. $x^2 + x + 7 = 0$

62. $(3x - 4)^2 = 10x$

63. $x^2 + 11 = 0$

64. $(5a - 2)^2 - a = 0$

65. $\dfrac{7}{8} = \dfrac{8}{x^2}$

CHAPTER 8 TEST TEST PREP VIDEO

Remember to use the Chapter Test Prep Video CD to see the fully worked-out solutions to any of the exercises you want to review.

Solve each equation for the variable.

1. $5x^2 - 2x = 7$

2. $(x + 1)^2 = 10$

3. $m^2 - m + 8 = 0$

4. $u^2 - 6u + 2 = 0$

5. $7x^2 + 8x + 1 = 0$

6. $y^2 - 3y = 5$

7. $\dfrac{4}{x + 2} + \dfrac{2x}{x - 2} = \dfrac{6}{x^2 - 4}$

8. $x^5 + 3x^4 = x + 3$

9. $x^6 + 1 = x^4 + x^2$

10. $(x + 1)^2 - 15(x + 1) + 56 = 0$

Solve the equation for the variable by completing the square.

11. $x^2 - 6x = -2$

12. $2a^2 + 5 = 4a$

CHAPTER 8 CUMULATIVE REVIEW

1. Write each sentence using mathematical symbols.

   a. The sum of 5 and y is greater than or equal to 7.

   b. 11 is not equal to z.

   c. 20 is less than the difference of 5 and twice x.

2. Solve $|3x - 2| = -5$.

3. Find the slope of the line containing the points $(0, 3)$ and $(2, 5)$. Graph the line.

4. Use the elimination method to solve the system.
   $$\begin{cases} -6x + y = 5 \\ 4x - 2y = 6 \end{cases}$$

5. Use the elimination method to solve the system:
   $$\begin{cases} x - 5y = -12 \\ -x + y = 4 \end{cases}$$

6. Simplify. Use positive exponents to write each answer.

   a. $(a^{-2}bc^3)^{-3}$

   b. $\left(\dfrac{a^{-4}b^2}{c^3}\right)^{-2}$

   c. $\left(\dfrac{3a^8b^2}{12a^5b^5}\right)^{-2}$

7. Multiply.

   a. $(2x - 7)(3x - 4)$

   b. $(3x^2 + y)(5x^2 - 2y)$

8. Multiply.

   a. $(4a - 3)(7a - 2)$

   b. $(2a + b)(3a - 5b)$

9. Factor.

   a. $8x^2 + 4$

   b. $5y - 2z^4$

   c. $6x^2 - 3x^3 + 12x^4$

10. Factor.

    a. $9x^3 + 27x^2 - 15x$

    b. $2x(3y - 2) - 5(3y - 2)$

    c. $2xy + 6x - y - 3$

Factor the polynomials in Exercises 11 through 14.

11. $x^2 - 12x + 35$

12. $x^2 - 2x - 48$.

13. $3a^2x - 12abx + 12b^2x$

14. Factor. $2ax^2 - 12axy + 18ay^2$

15. Solve $3(x^2 + 4) + 5 = -6(x^2 + 2x) + 13$.

16. Solve $2(a^2 + 2) - 8 = -2a(a - 2) - 5$.

17. Solve $x^3 = 4x$.

18. Find the vertex and any intercepts of $f(x) = x^2 + x - 12$.

19. Simplify $\dfrac{2x^2}{10x^3 - 2x^2}$.

20. Simplify $\dfrac{x^2 - 4x + 4}{2 - x}$.

21. Add $\dfrac{2x - 1}{2x^2 - 9x - 5} + \dfrac{x + 3}{6x^2 - x - 2}$.

22. Subtract $\dfrac{a+1}{a^2-6a+8} - \dfrac{3}{16-a^2}$

23. Simplify $\dfrac{x^{-1}+2xy^{-1}}{x^{-2}-x^{-2}y^{-1}}$.

24. Simplify $\dfrac{(2a)^{-1}+b^{-1}}{a^{-1}+(2b)^{-1}}$.

25. Divide $\dfrac{3x^5y^2-15x^3y-x^2y-6x}{x^2y}$.

26. Divide $x^3 - 3x^2 - 10x + 24$ by $x + 3$.

27. If $P(x) = 2x^3 - 4x^2 + 5$
   a. Find $P(2)$ by substitution.
   b. Use synthetic division to find the remainder when $P(x)$ is divided by $x - 2$.

28. If $P(x) = 4x^3 - 2x^2 + 3$,
   a. Find $P(-2)$ by substitution.
   b. Use synthetic division to find the remainder when $P(x)$ is divided by $x + 2$.

29. Solve $\dfrac{4x}{5} + \dfrac{3}{2} = \dfrac{3x}{10}$.

30. Solve $\dfrac{x+3}{x^2+5x+6} = \dfrac{3}{2x+4} - \dfrac{1}{x+3}$.

31. If a certain number is subtracted from the numerator and added to the denominator of $\dfrac{9}{19}$, the new fraction is equivalent to $\dfrac{1}{3}$. Find the number.

32. Mr. Briley can roof his house in 24 hours. His son can roof the same house in 40 hours. If they work together, how long will it take to roof the house?

35. Simplify.
   a. $\sqrt{(-3)^2}$ **b.** $\sqrt{x^2}$
   c. $\sqrt[4]{(x-2)^4}$ **d.** $\sqrt[3]{(-5)^3}$
   e. $\sqrt[5]{(2x-7)^5}$ **f.** $\sqrt{25x^2}$
   g. $\sqrt{x^2+2x+1}$

36. Simplify. Assume that the variables represent any real number.
   a. $\sqrt{(-2)^2}$ **b.** $\sqrt{y^2}$
   c. $\sqrt[4]{(a-3)^4}$ **d.** $\sqrt[3]{(-6)^3}$
   e. $\sqrt[5]{(3x-1)^5}$

37. Use rational exponents to simplify. Assume that variables represent positive numbers.
   a. $\sqrt[8]{x^4}$ **b.** $\sqrt[6]{25}$
   c. $\sqrt[4]{r^2s^6}$

38. Use rational exponents to simplify. Assume that variables represent positive numbers.
   a. $\sqrt[4]{5^2}$ **b.** $\sqrt[12]{x^3}$
   c. $\sqrt[6]{x^2y^4}$

39. Use the product rule to simplify.
   a. $\sqrt{25x^3}$ **b.** $\sqrt[3]{54x^6y^8}$
   c. $\sqrt[4]{81z^{11}}$

40. Use the product rule to simplify. Assume that variables represent positive numbers.
   a. $\sqrt{64a^5}$ **b.** $\sqrt[3]{24a^7b^9}$
   c. $\sqrt[4]{48x^9}$

41. Rationalize the denominator of each expression.
   a. $\dfrac{2}{\sqrt{5}}$ **b.** $\dfrac{2\sqrt{16}}{\sqrt{9x}}$
   c. $\sqrt[3]{\dfrac{1}{2}}$

42. Multiply. Simplify if possible.
   a. $(\sqrt{3}-4)(2\sqrt{3}+2)$
   b. $(\sqrt{5}-x)^2$
   c. $(\sqrt{a}+b)(\sqrt{a}-b)$

43. Solve $\sqrt{2x+5} + \sqrt{2x} = 3$.

44. Solve $\sqrt{x-2} = \sqrt{4x+1} - 3$.

45. Divide. Write in the form $a + bi$.
   a. $\dfrac{2+i}{1-i}$ **b.** $\dfrac{7}{3i}$

46. Write each product in the form of $a + bi$.
   a. $3i(5-2i)$
   b. $(6-5i)^2$
   c. $(\sqrt{3}+2i)(\sqrt{3}-2i)$

47. Use the square root property to solve $(x+1)^2 = 12$.

48. Use the square root property to solve $(y-1)^2 = 24$.

49. Solve $x - \sqrt{x} - 6 = 0$.

50. Use the quadratic formula to solve $m^2 = 4m + 8$.

Appendix A

The Bigger Picture/Practice Final Exam

A.1 THE BIGGER PICTURE—SOLVING EQUATIONS AND INEQUALITIES

I. Equations

A. Linear Equations (Sec. 2.1)

$$5(x - 2) = \frac{4(2x + 1)}{3}$$
$$3 \cdot 5(x - 2) = \cancel{3} \cdot \frac{4(2x + 1)}{\cancel{3}}$$
$$15x - 30 = 8x + 4$$
$$7x = 34$$
$$x = \frac{34}{7}$$

B. Absolute Value Equations (Sec. 2.6)

$$|3x - 1| = 8$$

$3x - 1 = 8$ or	$3x - 1 = -8$
$3x = 9$ or	$3x = -7$
$x = 3$ or	$x = -\dfrac{7}{3}$

$$|x - 5| = |x + 1|$$

$x - 5 = x + 1$ or	$x - 5 = -(x + 1)$
$\underline{-5 = 1}$ or	$x - 5 = -x - 1$
No solution or	$2x = 4$
	$x = 2$

C. Quadratic and Higher-Degree Equations (Secs. 5.8, 8.1, 8.2, 8.3)

$$2x^2 - 7x = 9$$
$$2x^2 - 7x - 9 = 0$$
$$(2x - 9)(x + 1) = 0$$
$$2x - 9 = 0 \quad \text{or} \quad x + 1 = 0$$
$$x = \frac{9}{2} \quad \text{or} \quad x = -1$$

$$2x^2 + x - 2 = 0$$
$$a = 2, \quad b = 1, \quad c = -2$$
$$x = \frac{-1 \pm \sqrt{1^2 - 4(2)(-2)}}{2 \cdot 2}$$
$$x = \frac{-1 \pm \sqrt{17}}{4}$$

D. Equations with Rational Expressions (Sec. 6.5)

$$\frac{7}{x - 1} + \frac{3}{x + 1} = \frac{x + 3}{x^2 - 1}$$
$$\cancel{(x - 1)}(x + 1) \cdot \frac{7}{\cancel{x - 1}} + (x - 1)\cancel{(x + 1)} \cdot \frac{3}{\cancel{x + 1}}$$
$$= \cancel{(x - 1)}\cancel{(x + 1)} \cdot \frac{x + 3}{\cancel{(x - 1)}\cancel{(x + 1)}}$$
$$7(x + 1) + 3(x - 1) = x + 3$$
$$7x + 7 + 3x - 3 = x + 3$$
$$9x = -1$$
$$x = -\frac{1}{9}$$

484

E. Equations with Radicals (Sec. 7.6)

$$\sqrt{5x + 10} - 2 = x$$
$$\sqrt{5x + 10} = x + 2$$
$$(\sqrt{5x + 10})^2 = (x + 2)^2$$
$$5x + 10 = x^2 + 4x + 4$$
$$0 = x^2 - x - 6$$
$$0 = (x - 3)(x + 2)$$
$$x - 3 = 0 \quad \text{or} \quad x + 2 = 0$$
$$x = 3 \quad \text{or} \qquad x = -2$$

Both solutions check.

F. Exponential Equations

$$9^x = 27^{x+1}$$
$$(3^2)^x = (3^3)^{x+1}$$
$$3^{2x} = 3^{3x+3}$$
$$2x = 3x + 3$$
$$-3 = x$$

$$5^x = 7$$
$$\log 5^x = \log 7$$
$$x \log 5 = \log 7$$
$$x = \frac{\log 7}{\log 5}$$

G. Logarithmic Equations

$$\log 7 + \log(x + 3) = \log 5$$
$$\log 7(x + 3) = \log 5$$
$$7(x + 3) = 5$$
$$7x + 21 = 5$$
$$7x = -16$$
$$x = \frac{-16}{7}$$

II. Inequalities

A. Linear Inequalities (Sec. 2.4)

$$-3(x + 2) \geq 6$$
$$-3x - 6 \geq 6$$
$$-3x \geq 12$$
$$\frac{-3x}{-3} \leq \frac{12}{-3}$$
$$x \leq -4 \quad \text{or} \quad (-\infty, -4]$$

B. Compound Inequalities (Sec. 2.5)

$$x \leq 3 \quad \text{and} \quad x < -7$$

$$(-\infty, -7)$$

$$x \leq 3 \quad \text{or} \quad x < -7$$

$$(-\infty, 3]$$

C. Absolute Value Inequalities (Sec. 2.7)

$$|x - 5| - 8 < -2$$
$$|x - 5| < 6$$
$$-6 < x - 5 < 6$$
$$-1 < x < 11$$
$$(-1, 11)$$

$$|2x + 1| \geq 17$$
$$2x + 1 \geq 17 \quad \text{or} \quad 2x + 1 \leq -17$$
$$2x \geq 16 \quad \text{or} \qquad 2x \leq -18$$
$$x \geq 8 \quad \text{or} \qquad x \leq -9$$
$$(-\infty, -9] \cup [8, \infty)$$

A.2 PRACTICE FINAL EXAM

Simplify. If needed, write answers with positive exponents only.

1. $\sqrt{216}$

2. $\dfrac{(4 - \sqrt{16}) - (-7 - 20)}{-2(1 - 4)^2}$

3. $\left(\dfrac{1}{125}\right)^{-1/3}$

4. $(-9x)^{-2}$

5. $\dfrac{\dfrac{5}{x} - \dfrac{7}{3x}}{\dfrac{9}{8x} - \dfrac{1}{x}}$

6. $\dfrac{6^{-1}a^2b^{-3}}{3^{-2}a^{-5}b^2}$

7. $\left(\dfrac{64c^{4/3}}{a^{-2/3}b^{5/6}}\right)^{1/2}$

Factor completely.

8. $3x^2y - 27y^3$

9. $16y^3 - 2$

10. $x^2y - 9y - 3x^2 + 27$

Perform the indicated operations and simplify if possible.

11. $(4x^3y - 3x - 4) - (9x^3y + 8x + 5)$

12. $(6m + n)^2$

13. $(2x - 1)(x^2 - 6x + 4)$

14. $\dfrac{3x^2 - 12}{x^2 + 2x - 8} \div \dfrac{6x + 18}{x + 4}$

15. $\dfrac{2x^2 + 7}{2x^4 - 18x^2} - \dfrac{6x + 7}{2x^4 - 18x^2}$

16. $\dfrac{3}{x^2 - x - 6} + \dfrac{2}{x^2 - 5x + 6}$

17. $\sqrt{125x^3} - 3\sqrt{20x^3}$

18. $(\sqrt{5} + 5)(\sqrt{5} - 5)$

19. $(4x^3 - 5x) \div (2x + 1)$ [Use long division.]

Solve each equation or inequality. Write inequality solutions using interval notation.

20. $9(x + 2) = 5[11 - 2(2 - x) + 3]$

21. $|6x - 5| - 3 = -2$

22. $3n(7n - 20) = 96$

23. $-3 < 2(x - 3) \le 4$

24. $|3x + 1| > 5$

25. $\dfrac{x^2 + 8}{x} - 1 = \dfrac{2(x + 4)}{x}$

26. $y^2 - 3y = 5$

27. $x = \sqrt{x - 2} + 2$

28. $2x^2 - 7x > 15$

29. Solve the system: $\begin{cases} \dfrac{x}{2} + \dfrac{y}{4} = -\dfrac{3}{4} \\ x + \dfrac{3}{4}y = -4 \end{cases}$

Graph the following.

30. $4x + 6y = 7$

31. $2x - y > 5$

32. $y = -3$

Write equations of the following lines. Write each equation using function notation.

36. through $(4, -2)$ and $(6, -3)$

37. through $(-1, 2)$ and perpendicular to $3x - y = 4$

Find the distance or midpoint.

38. Find the distance between the points $(-6, 3)$ and $(-8, -7)$.

39. Find the midpoint of the line segment whose endpoints are $(-2, -5)$ and $(-6, 12)$.

Rationalize each denominator. Assume that variables represent positive numbers.

40. $\sqrt{\dfrac{9}{y}}$

41. $\dfrac{4 - \sqrt{x}}{4 + 2\sqrt{x}}$

Solve.

42. The most populous city in the United States is New York, although it is only the third most populous city in the world. Tokyo is the most populous city in the world. Second place is held by Seoul, Korea. Seoul's population is 1.3 million more than New York's and Tokyo's is 10.2 million less than twice the population of New York. If the sum of the populations of these three cities is 78.3 million, find the population of each city.

43. Write the area of the shaded region as a factored polynomial.

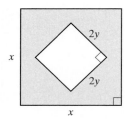

44. The product of one more than a number and twice the reciprocal of the number is $\dfrac{12}{5}$. Find the number.

48. The research department of a company that manufactures children's fruit drinks is experimenting with a new flavor. A 17.5% fructose solution is needed, but only 10% and 20% solutions are available. How many gallons of a 10% fructose solution should be mixed with a 20% fructose solution to obtain 20 gallons of a 17.5% fructose solution?

Complex Numbers: Chapter 7

Perform the indicated operation and simplify. Write the result in the form a + bi.

49. $-\sqrt{-8}$

Answers to Selected Exercises

CHAPTER 1 REAL NUMBERS AND ALGEBRAIC EXPRESSIONS

Section 1.2
Practice Exercises
1. 14 sq cm   **2.** 31   **3. a.** $\{6, 7, 8, 9\}$ **b.** $\{41, 42, 43, \dots\}$ **4. a.** true   **b.** true   **5. a.** true   **b.** false   **c.** true   **d.** false

6. a. 4   **b.** $\frac{1}{2}$ **c.** 1   **d.** -6.8 **e.** -4 **7. a.** -5.4 **b.** $\frac{3}{5}$ **c.** -18 **8. a.** $3x$ **b.** $2x - 5$ **c.** $3\frac{5}{8} + x$ **d.** $\frac{x}{2}$ **e.** $x - 14$ **f.** $5(x + 10)$

Vocabulary and Readiness Check 1.2
1. variables   **3.** absolute value   **5.** natural numbers   **7.** integers   **9.** rational number

Exercise Set 1.2
1. 35   **3.** 30.38   **5.** $\frac{3}{8}$ **7.** 22   **9.** 2000 mi   **11.** 20.4 sq. ft   **13.** $10,612.80   **15.** $\{1, 2, 3, 4, 5\}$ **17.** $\{11, 12, 13, 14, 15, 16\}$ **19.** $\{0\}$

21. $\{0, 2, 4, 6, 8\}$ **23.**   **25.**   **27.**

29. answers may vary   **31.** $\{3, 0, \sqrt{36}\}$ **33.** $\{3, \sqrt{36}\}$ **35.** $\{\sqrt{7}\}$ **37.** $\in$ **39.** $\notin$ **41.** $\notin$ **43.** $\notin$ **45.** true   **47.** true
49. false   **51.** false   **53.** true   **55.** false   **57.** answers may vary   **59.** -2 **61.** 4   **63.** 0   **65.** -3 **67.** answers may vary   **69.** 6.2

71. $-\frac{4}{7}$ **73.** $\frac{2}{3}$ **75.** 0   **77.** $2x$ **79.** $2x + 5$ **81.** $x - 10$ **83.** $x + 2$ **85.** $\frac{x}{11}$ **87.** $12 - 3x$ **89.** $x + 2.3$ or $x + 2\frac{3}{10}$ **91.** $1\frac{1}{3} - x$

93. $\frac{5}{4 - x}$ **95.** $2(x + 3)$ **97.** 137   **99.** 69   **101.** answers may vary

Section 1.3
Practice Exercises
1. a. -8 **b.** -3 **c.** 5   **d.** -8.1 **e.** $\frac{1}{15}$ **2. a.** -8 **b.** -3 **c.** -12 **d.** 7.7   **e.** $\frac{8}{21}$ **f.** 1.8   **g.** -7 **3. a.** 12   **b.** -4

4. a. -15 **b.** $\frac{1}{2}$ **c.** -10.2 **d.** 0   **e.** $-\frac{2}{13}$ **f.** 36   **g.** -11.5 **5. a.** -2 **b.** 5   **c.** $-\frac{1}{6}$ **d.** -6 **e.** $\frac{1}{9}$ **f.** 0   **6. a.** 8   **b.** $\frac{1}{9}$

c. -36 **d.** 36   **e.** -64 **f.** -64 **7. a.** 7   **b.** $\frac{1}{4}$ **c.** -8 **d.** not a real number   **e.** 10   **8. a.** 4   **b.** -1 **c.** 10   **9. a.** 2

b. 27   **c.** -29 **10.** 19   **11.** $-\frac{17}{44}$ **12. a.** 67   **b.** -100 **c.** $-\frac{39}{80}$ **13.** 23; 50; 77

Vocabulary and Readiness Check 1.3
1. b, c   **3.** b, d   **5.** b   **7.** 0   **9.** reciprocal   **11.** exponent   **13.** square root

Exercise Set 1.3
1. 5   **3.** -24 **5.** -11 **7.** -4 **9.** $\frac{4}{3}$ **11.** -2 **13.** $-\frac{1}{2}$ **15.** -6 **17.** -60 **19.** 0   **21.** 0   **23.** -3 **25.** 3   **27.** $-\frac{1}{6}$ **29.** 0.56

31. -7 **33.** -8 **35.** -49 **37.** 36   **39.** -8 **41.** $-\frac{1}{27}$ **43.** 7   **45.** $-\frac{2}{3}$ **47.** 4   **49.** 3   **51.** not a real number   **53.** 48   **55.** -1

57. -9 **59.** 17   **61.** -4 **63.** -2 **65.** 11   **67.** $-\frac{3}{4}$ **69.** 7   **71.** -11 **73.** -2.1 **75.** $-\frac{1}{3}$ **77.** $-\frac{79}{15}$ **79.** $-\frac{4}{5}$ **81.** -81

83. $-\frac{20}{33}$ **85.** 93   **87.** -12 **89.** $-\frac{23}{18}$ **91.** 5   **93.** $-\frac{3}{19}$ **95.** 18; 22; 28; 208   **97.** 600; 150; 105   **99.** $\frac{5}{2}$ **101.** $\frac{13}{35}$ **103.** 4205 m
105. $(2 + 7) \cdot (1 + 3)$ **107.** answers may vary   **109.** 3.1623   **111.** 2.8107   **113.** -0.5876 **115.** 15.6%   **117.** 17.7%
119. Long-term. Short-term is very volatile.

Integrated Review
1. 16   **2.** -16 **3.** 0   **4.** -11 **5.** -5 **6.** $-\frac{1}{60}$ **7.** undefined   **8.** -2.97 **9.** 4   **10.** -50 **11.** 35   **12.** 92   **13.** $-15 - 2x$

14. $3x + 5$ **15.** 0   **16.** true

Section 1.4
Practice Exercises

1. $-4x = 20$ **2.** $3(z - 3) = 9$ **3.** $x + 5 = 2x - 3$ **4.** $y + 2 = 4 + \dfrac{z}{8}$ **5. a.** $<$ **b.** $=$ **c.** $>$ **d.** $>$ **6. a.** $x - 3 \le 5$ **b.** $y \ne -4$

c. $2 < 4 + \dfrac{1}{2}z$ **7. a.** 7 **b.** -4.7 **c.** $\dfrac{3}{8}$ **8. a.** $-\dfrac{3}{5}$ **b.** $\dfrac{1}{14}$ **c.** $-\dfrac{1}{2}$ **9.** $13x + 8$ **10.** $(3 \cdot 11)b = 33b$ **11. a.** $4x + 20y$ **b.** $-3 + 2z$

c. $0.3xy - 0.9x$ **12. a.** $0.10x$ **b.** $26y$ **c.** $1.75z$ **d.** $0.15t$ **13. a.** $16 - x$ **b.** $180 - x$ **c.** $x + 2$ **d.** $x + 9$ **14. a.** $5ab$

b. $10x - 5$ **c.** $17p - 9$ **15. a.** $-pq + 7$ **b.** $x^2 + 19$ **c.** $5.8x + 3.8$ **d.** $-c - 8d + \dfrac{1}{4}$

Vocabulary and Readiness Check 1.4

1. $<$ **3.** $\ne$ **5.** $\ge$ **7.** $-a$ **9.** commutative   **11.** distributive   **13.** terms

Exercise Set 1.4

1. $10 + x = -12$ **3.** $2x + 5 = -14$ **5.** $\dfrac{n}{5} = 4n$ **7.** $z - \dfrac{1}{2} = \dfrac{1}{2}z$ **9.** $7x \le -21$ **11.** $2(x - 6) > \dfrac{1}{11}$ **13.** $2(x - 6) = -27$

15. $>$ **17.** $=$ **19.** $<$ **21.** $<$ **23.** $<$ **25.** $-5; \dfrac{1}{5}$ **27.** $8; -\dfrac{1}{8}$ **29.** $\dfrac{1}{7}; -7$ **31.** $0;$ undefined   **33.** $\dfrac{7}{8}; -\dfrac{7}{8}$

35. Zero. For every real number $x, 0 \cdot x \ne 1$, so 0 has no reciprocal. It is the only real number that has no reciprocal because if $x \ne 0$, then $x \cdot \dfrac{1}{x} = 1$

by definition.   **37.** $y + 7x$ **39.** $w \cdot z$ **41.** $\dfrac{x}{5} \cdot \dfrac{1}{3}$ **43.** no; answers may vary   **45.** $(5 \cdot 7)x$ **47.** $x + (1.2 + y)$ **49.** $14(z \cdot y)$

51. 10 and 4. Subtraction is not associative.   **53.** $3x + 15$ **55.** $-2a - b$ **57.** $12x + 10y + 4z$ **59.** $-4x + 8y - 28$ **61.** $3xy - 1.5x$
63. $6 + 3x$ **65.** 0 **67.** 7 **69.** $(10 \cdot 2)y$ **71.** $a(b + c) = ab + ac$ **73.** $0.1d$ **75.** $112 - x$ **77.** $90 - 5x$ **79.** $\$35.61y$ **81.** $2x + 2$

83. $-8y - 14$ **85.** $-9c - 4$ **87.** $4 - 8y$ **89.** $y^2 - 11yz - 11$ **91.** $3t - 14$ **93.** 0 **95.** $13n - 20$ **97.** $8.5y - 20.8$ **99.** $\dfrac{3}{8}a - \dfrac{1}{12}$

101. $20y + 48$ **103.** $-5x + \dfrac{5}{6}y - 1$ **105.** $-x - 6y - \dfrac{11}{24}$ **107.** $(5 \cdot 7)y$ **109.** $6.5y - 7.92x + 25.47$ **111.** no   **113.** 80 million

115. 35 million   **117.** 20.25%

Chapter 1 Vocabulary Check

1. algebraic expression   **2.** opposite   **3.** distributive   **4.** absolute value   **5.** exponent   **6.** variable   **7.** inequality   **8.** reciprocals
9. commutative   **10.** associative   **11.** whole   **12.** real

Chapter 1 Review

1. 21 **3.** $324{,}000$ **5.** $\{-2, 0, 2, 4, 6\}$ **7.** $\varnothing$ **9.** $\{\ldots, -1, 0, 1, 2\}$ **11.** false   **13.** true   **15.** true   **17.** true   **19.** true

21. true   **23.** true   **25.** true   **27.** true   **29.** $\left\{5, \dfrac{8}{2}, \sqrt{9}\right\}$ **31.** $\{\sqrt{7}, \pi\}$ **33.** $\left\{5, \dfrac{8}{2}, \sqrt{9}, -1\right\}$ **35.** -0.6 **37.** -1 **39.** $\dfrac{1}{0.6}$

41. 1 **43.** -35 **45.** 0.31 **47.** 13.3 **49.** 0 **51.** 0 **53.** -5 **55.** 4 **57.** 9 **59.** 3 **61.** $-\dfrac{32}{135}$ **63.** $-\dfrac{5}{4}$ **65.** $\dfrac{5}{8}$ **67.** -1

69. 1 **71.** -4 **73.** $\dfrac{5}{7}$ **75.** $\dfrac{1}{5}$ **77.** -5 **79.** 5 **81. a.** $6.28; 62.8; 628$ **b.** increase   **83.** $-5x - 9$ **85.** $-15x^2 + 6$ **87.** $5.7x + 1.1$

89. $n + 2n = -15$ **91.** $6(t - 5) = 4$ **93.** $9x - 10 = 5$ **95.** $-4 < 7y$ **97.** $t + 6 \le -12$ **99.** distributive property
101. commutative property of addition   **103.** multiplicative inverse property   **105.** associative property of multiplication

107. multiplicative identity property   **109.** $(3 + x) + (7 + y)$ **111.** $2 \cdot \dfrac{1}{2}$, for example   **113.** $7 + 0$ **115.** $>$ **117.** $=$ **119.** $>$

121. $5; \dfrac{1}{5}$ **123.** 9 **125.** 15 **127.** $\dfrac{1}{11}$ **129.** $1.8, 1.0, 0.4, 0.7, 0.2, 0.7, 1.0$

Chapter 1 Test

1. true   **2.** false   **3.** false   **4.** false   **5.** true   **6.** false   **7.** -3 **8.** -56 **9.** -225 **10.** 3 **11.** 1 **12.** $-\dfrac{3}{2}$ **13.** 12 **14.** 1

15. a. $5.75; 17.25; 57.50; 115.00$ **b.** increase   **16.** $2(x + 5) = 30$ **17.** $\dfrac{(6 - y)^2}{7} < -2$ **18.** $\dfrac{9z}{|-12|} \ne 10$ **19.** $3\left(\dfrac{n}{5}\right) = -n$

20. $20 = 2x - 6$ **21.** $-2 = \dfrac{x}{x + 5}$ **22.** distributive property   **23.** associative property of addition   **24.** additive inverse property

25. multiplication property of zero   **26.** $0.05n + 0.1d$ **27.** $-6x - 14$ **28.** $\dfrac{1}{2}a - \dfrac{9}{8}$ **29.** $2y - 10$ **30.** $-1.3x + 1.9$

CHAPTER 2 EQUATIONS, INEQUALITIES, AND PROBLEM SOLVING

Section 2.1
Practice Exercises
1. 5 **2.** 0.2 **3.** −5 **4.** −4 **5.** $\frac{5}{6}$ **6.** $\frac{5}{4}$ **7.** −3 **8.** { } or ∅ **9.** all real numbers or $\{x|x$ is a real number$\}$

Vocabulary and Readiness Check 2.1
1. equivalent **3.** addition **5.** expression **7.** equation **9.** all real numbers **11.** no solution

Exercise Set 2.1
1. 6 **3.** −22 **5.** 4.7 **7.** 10 **9.** −1.1 **11.** −5 **13.** −2 **15.** 0 **17.** 2 **19.** −9 **21.** $-\frac{10}{7}$ **23.** $\frac{9}{10}$ **25.** 4 **27.** 1 **29.** 5
31. $\frac{40}{3}$ **33.** 17 **35.** all real numbers **37.** ∅ **39.** all real numbers **41.** ∅ **43.** $\frac{1}{8}$ **45.** 0 **47.** all real numbers **49.** 4 **51.** $\frac{4}{5}$
53. 8 **55.** ∅ **57.** −8 **59.** $-\frac{5}{4}$ **61.** −2 **63.** 23 **65.** $-\frac{2}{9}$ **67.** $\frac{8}{x}$ **69.** $8x$ **71.** $2x - 5$ **73.** subtract 19 instead of adding; −3
75. $0.4 - 1.6 = -1.2$, not 1.2; −0.24 **77. a.** $4x + 5$ **b.** −3 **c.** answers may vary **79.** answers may vary **81.** $K = -11$ **83.** $K = -23$
85. answers may vary **87.** 1 **89.** 3 **91.** −4.86 **93.** 1.53

Section 2.2
Practice Exercises
1. a. $3x + 6$ **b.** $6x - 1$ **2.** $3x + 17.3$ **3.** 14, 34, 70 **4.** $450 **5.** width: 32 in.; length: 48 in. **6.** 25, 27, 29

Vocabulary and Readiness Check 2.2
1. > **3.** = **5.** 31, 32, 33, 34 **7.** 18, 20, 22 **9.** $y, y + 1, y + 2$ **11.** $p, p + 1, p + 2, p + 3$

Exercise Set 2.2
1. $4y$ **3.** $3z + 3$ **5.** $(65x + 30)$ cents **7.** $10x + 3$ **9.** $2x + 14$ **11.** −5 **13.** 45, 145, 225 **15.** approximately 1612.41 million acres
17. 2344 earthquakes **19.** 1275 shoppers **21.** 22% **23.** 417 employees **25.** 29.98 million **27.** 29°, 35°, 116° **29.** 28 m, 36 m, 38 m
31. 18 in., 18 in., 27 in., 36 in. **33.** 75, 76, 77 **35.** Fallon's zip code is 89406; Fernley's zip code is 89408; Gardnerville Ranchos' zip code is 89410
37. 317 thousand; 279 thousand; 184 thousand **39.** medical assistant: 215 thousand; postsecondary teacher jobs: 603 thousand; registered nurses: 623
thousand **41.** 757-200: 190 seats; 737-200: 113 seats; 737-300: 134 seats **43.** $430.00 **45.** 41.7 million **47.** 40°, 140° **49.** 64°, 32°, 84°
51. square: 18 cm; triangle: 24 cm **53.** 76, 78, 80 **55.** 40.5 ft; 202.5 ft; 240 ft **57.** Los Angeles: 61.0 million, Atlanta: 74.3 million, Chicago: 62.3 million
59. incandescent: 1500 bulb hours; fluorescent: 100,000 bulb hours; halogen: 4000 bulb hours **61.** height: 48 in.; width: 108 in.
63. a. $4.9 billion **b.** $1.23 billion **65.** Russia: 5.6%; China: 19.3%; U.S.: 9.9% **67.** 309 pages **69.** Germany: 11; U.S.: 9; Canada: 7
71. −54 **73.** 155 **75.** 557.424 **77.** answers may vary **79.** 50° **81. a.** 2032 **b.** 1015.8 **c.** 3 cigarettes per day; answers may vary
83. 500 boards; $30,000 **85.** company makes a profit

Section 2.3
Practice Exercises
1. $t = \frac{I}{Pr}$ **2.** $y = \frac{7}{2}x - \frac{5}{2}$ **3.** $r = \frac{A - P}{Pt}$ **4.** $10,134.16 **5.** 25.6 hr; 25 hr 36 min

Exercise Set 2.3
1. $t = \frac{D}{r}$ **3.** $R = \frac{I}{PT}$ **5.** $y = \frac{9x - 16}{4}$ **7.** $W = \frac{P - 2L}{2}$ **9.** $A = \frac{J + 3}{C}$ **11.** $g = \frac{W}{h - 3t^2}$ **13.** $B = \frac{T - 2C}{AC}$ **15.** $r = \frac{C}{2\pi}$
17. $r = \frac{E - IR}{I}$ **19.** $L = \frac{2s - an}{n}$ **21.** $v = \frac{3st^4 - N}{5s}$ **23.** $H = \frac{S - 2LW}{2L + 2W}$ **25.** $4703.71; $4713.99; $4719.22; $4722.74; $4724.45
27. a. $7313.97 **b.** $7321.14 **c.** $7325.98 **29.** 40°C **31.** 3.6 hr, or 3 hr and 36 min **33.** 171 packages **35.** 9 ft **37.** 2 gal
39. a. 1174.86 cu. m **b.** 310.34 cu. m **c.** 1485.20 cu. m **41.** 128.3 mph **43.** 0.42 ft **45.** 41.125π ft ≈ 129.1325 ft **47.** $1831.96
49. $f = \frac{C - 4h - 4p}{9}$ **51.** 178 cal **53.** 1.5 g **55.** −3, −2, −1 **57.** −3, −2, −1, 0, 1 **59.** answers may vary
61. 0.388; 0.723; 1.00; 1.523; 5.202; 9.538; 19.193; 30.065; 39.505 **63.** $6.80 per person **65.** 4 times a year; answers may vary **67.** 0.25 sec **69.** $\frac{1}{4}$
71. $\frac{3}{8}$ **73.** $\frac{3}{8}$ **75.** $\frac{3}{4}$ **77.** 1 **79.** 1

Section 2.4
Practice Exercises

1. a. $\xrightarrow{\qquad}$ $(-\infty, 3.5)$ **b.** $\xleftarrow{\qquad}$ $[-3, \infty)$ **c.** $\xleftarrow{\qquad}$ $[-1, 4)$ **2.** $\xleftarrow{\qquad}$ $(4, \infty)$

3. $\xrightarrow{\qquad}$ $(-\infty, -4]$ **4. a.** $\xleftarrow{\qquad}$ $\left[\dfrac{2}{3}, \infty\right)$ **b.** $\xleftarrow{\qquad}$ $(-4, \infty)$ **5.** $\xleftarrow{\qquad}$ $\left[-\dfrac{3}{2}, \infty\right)$

6. $\xrightarrow{\qquad}$ $(-\infty, 13]$ **7.** $\xleftarrow{\qquad\qquad}$ $(-\infty, \infty)$ **8.** Sales must be $\geq \$10{,}000$ per month.   **9.** the entire year 2021 and after

Vocabulary and Readiness Check 2.4
1. d   **3.** b   **5.** $[-0.4, \infty)$ **7.** $(-\infty, -0.4]$ **9.** no   **11.** yes

Exercise Set 2.4

1. $\xrightarrow{\qquad}$ $(-\infty, -3)$ **3.** $\xleftarrow{\qquad}$ $[0.3, \infty)$ **5.** $\xleftarrow{\qquad}$ $[-7, \infty)$ **7.** $\xleftarrow{\qquad}$ $(-2, 5)$

9. $\xleftarrow{\qquad}$ $(-1, 5]$ **11.** $\xleftarrow{\qquad}$ $[-2, \infty)$ **13.** $\xleftarrow{\qquad}$ $(-\infty, 1)$ **15.** $\xleftarrow{\qquad}$ $(-\infty, 2]$

17. $\xleftarrow{\qquad}$ $[8, \infty)$ **19.** $\xleftarrow{\qquad}$ $(-\infty, -4.7)$ **21.** $\xleftarrow{\qquad}$ $(-\infty, -3]$ **23.** $(-\infty, -1]$ **25.** $(-\infty, 11]$

27. $(0, \infty)$ **29.** $(-13, \infty)$ **31.** $\left[-\dfrac{79}{3}, \infty\right)$ **33.** $\left(-\infty, -\dfrac{35}{6}\right)$ **35.** $(-\infty, -6)$ **37.** $(4, \infty)$ **39.** $[-0.5, \infty)$ **41.** $(-\infty, 7]$ **43.** $[0, \infty)$

45. $(-\infty, -29]$ **47.** $[3, \infty)$ **49.** $(-\infty, -1]$ **51.** $[-31, \infty)$ **53.** $(-\infty, -2]$ **55.** $(-\infty, -15)$ **57.** $\left[-\dfrac{37}{3}, \infty\right)$ **59.** $(-\infty, 5)$

61. $(-\infty, 9)$ **63.** $\left(-\infty, -\dfrac{11}{2}\right]$ **65.** $(-\infty, \infty)$ **67.** $\varnothing$ **69. a.** $\{x \mid x \geq 81\}$ **b.** A final exam grade of 81 or higher will result in an average of 77 or higher.   **71. a.** $\{x \mid x \leq 1040\}$ **b.** The luggage and cargo must weight 1040 pounds or less.   **73. a.** $\{x \mid x \leq 20\}$

b. She can move at most 20 whole boxes at one time.   **75. a.** $\{x \mid x > 200\}$ **b.** If you make more than 200 calls, plan 1 is more economical.
77. $\{F \mid F \geq 932°\}$ **79. a.** 2011   **b.** answers may vary   **81.** decreasing; answers may vary   **83.** 5.7 gal   **85.** during 2008

87. answers may vary   **89.** 2, 3, 4   **91.** 2, 3, 4, ...   **93.** 5   **95.** $\dfrac{13}{6}$ **97.** $\{x \mid x \geq 2\}$; $[2, \infty)$ **99.** $\xleftarrow{\qquad}$; $(-\infty, 0)$

101. $\{x \mid -2 < x \leq 1.5\}$; $\xleftarrow{\qquad}$ **103.** $\{4\}$ **105.** $(4, \infty)$ **107.** answers may vary   **109.** answers may vary   **111.** answers may vary

The Bigger Picture

1. $-\dfrac{8}{3}$ **2.** 0   **3.** $(-1, \infty)$ **4.** 3   **5.** 6   **6.** $\varnothing$ **7.** $\left(-\infty, \dfrac{3}{2}\right]$ **8.** all real numbers or $(-\infty, \infty)$

Integrated Review

1. -5 **2.** $(-5, \infty)$ **3.** $\left[\dfrac{8}{3}, \infty\right)$ **4.** $[-1, \infty)$ **5.** 0   **6.** $\left[-\dfrac{1}{10}, \infty\right)$ **7.** $\left(-\infty, -\dfrac{1}{6}\right]$ **8.** 0   **9.** $\varnothing$ **10.** $\left[-\dfrac{3}{5}, \infty\right)$ **11.** 4.2   **12.** 6

13. -8 **14.** $(-\infty, -16)$ **15.** $\dfrac{20}{11}$ **16.** 1   **17.** $(38, \infty)$ **18.** -5.5 **19.** $\dfrac{3}{5}$ **20.** $(-\infty, \infty)$ **21.** 29   **22.** all real numbers

23. $(-\infty, 1)$ **24.** $\dfrac{9}{13}$ **25.** $(23, \infty)$ **26.** $(-\infty, 6]$ **27.** $\left(-\infty, \dfrac{3}{5}\right]$ **28.** $\left(-\infty, -\dfrac{19}{32}\right)$

Section 2.5
Practice Exercises

1. $\{1, 3\}$ **2.** $(-\infty, 2)$ **3.** $\{\ \}$ or $\varnothing$ **4.** $(-4, 2)$ **5.** $[-6, 8]$ **6.** $\{1, 2, 3, 4, 5, 6, 7, 9\}$ **7.** $\left(-\infty, \dfrac{3}{8}\right] \cup [3, \infty)$ **8.** $(-\infty, \infty)$

Vocabulary and Readiness Check 2.5
1. compound   **3.** or   **5.** $\cup$ **7.** and

Exercise Set 2.5

1. $\{2, 3, 4, 5, 6, 7\}$ **3.** $\{4, 6\}$ **5.** $\{\ldots, -2, -1, 0, 1, \ldots\}$ **7.** $\{5, 7\}$ **9.** $\{x \mid x$ is an odd integer or $x = 2$ or $x = 4\}$ **11.** $\{2, 4\}$

13. $\xleftarrow{\qquad}$ $(-3, 1)$ **15.** $\xleftarrow{\qquad}$ $\varnothing$ **17.** $\xleftarrow{\qquad}$ $(-\infty, -1)$ **19.** $[6, \infty)$ **21.** $(-\infty, -3]$ **23.** $(4, 10)$

25. $(11, 17)$ **27.** $[1, 4]$ **29.** $\left[-3, \dfrac{3}{2}\right]$ **31.** $\left[-\dfrac{7}{3}, 7\right]$ **33.** $\xleftarrow{\qquad}$ $(-\infty, 5)$ **35.** $\xleftarrow{\qquad}$ $(-\infty, -4] \cup [1, \infty)$

37. $\xleftarrow{\qquad}$ $(-\infty, \infty)$ **39.** $[2, \infty)$ **41.** $(-\infty, -4) \cup (-2, \infty)$ **43.** $(-\infty, \infty)$ **45.** $\left(-\dfrac{1}{2}, \dfrac{2}{3}\right)$ **47.** $(-\infty, \infty)$ **49.** $\left[\dfrac{3}{2}, 6\right]$

51. $\left(\dfrac{5}{4}, \dfrac{11}{4}\right)$ **53.** $\varnothing$ **55.** $\left(-\infty, -\dfrac{56}{5}\right) \cup \left(\dfrac{5}{3}, \infty\right)$ **57.** $\left(-5, \dfrac{5}{2}\right)$ **59.** $\left(0, \dfrac{14}{3}\right]$ **61.** $(-\infty, -3]$ **63.** $(-\infty, 1] \cup \left(\dfrac{29}{7}, \infty\right)$ **65.** $\varnothing$

67. $\left[-\dfrac{1}{2}, \dfrac{3}{2}\right)$ **69.** $\left(-\dfrac{4}{3}, \dfrac{7}{3}\right)$ **71.** $(6, 12)$ **73.** -12 **75.** -4 **77.** $-7, 7$ **79.** 0 **81.** $2003, 2004, 2005$ **83.** $-20.2° \le F \le 95°$

85. $67 \le \text{final score} \le 94$ **87.** $(6, \infty)$ **89.** $[3, 7]$ **91.** $(-\infty, -1)$

The Bigger Picture
1. $[-1, 3]$ **2.** $(-1, 6)$ **3.** 5.1 **4.** $(-\infty, -4)$ **5.** $(-\infty, -3]$ **6.** $(-\infty, -2) \cup (2, \infty)$ **7.** 4 **8.** $[19, \infty)$

Section 2.6
Practice Exercises

1. $-7, 7$ **2.** $-1, 4$ **3.** $-80, 70$ **4.** $-2, 2$ **5.** 0 **6.** $\{\ \}$ or $\varnothing$ **7.** $\{\ \}$ or $\varnothing$ **8.** $-\dfrac{3}{5}, 5$ **9.** 5

Vocabulary and Readiness Check 2.6
1. C   **3.** B   **5.** D

Exercise Set 2.6

1. $7, -7$ **3.** $4.2, -4.2$ **5.** $7, -2$ **7.** $8, 4$ **9.** $5, -5$ **11.** $3, -3$ **13.** 0 **15.** $\varnothing$ **17.** $\dfrac{1}{5}$ **19.** $|x| = 5$ **21.** $9, -\dfrac{1}{2}$ **23.** $-\dfrac{5}{2}$

25. answers may vary   **27.** $4, -4$ **29.** 0 **31.** $\varnothing$ **33.** $0, \dfrac{14}{3}$ **35.** $2, -2$ **37.** $\varnothing$ **39.** $7, -1$ **41.** $\varnothing$ **43.** $\varnothing$ **45.** $-\dfrac{1}{8}$ **47.** $\dfrac{1}{2}, -\dfrac{5}{6}$

49. $2, -\dfrac{12}{5}$ **51.** $3, -2$ **53.** $-8, \dfrac{2}{3}$ **55.** $\varnothing$ **57.** 4 **59.** $13, -8$ **61.** $3, -3$ **63.** $8, -7$ **65.** $2, 3$ **67.** $2, -\dfrac{10}{3}$ **69.** $\dfrac{3}{2}$ **71.** $\varnothing$

73. answers may vary   **75.** 34% **77.** 39.6 lb   **79.** answers may vary   **81.** no solution   **83.** $|x - 7| = 2$ **85.** $|2x - 1| = 4$ **87. a.** $c = 0$
b. c is a negative number   **c.** c is a positive number

Section 2.7
Practice Exercises

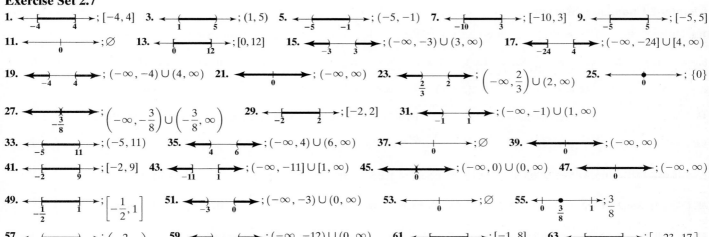

1. $(-2, 2)$ **2.** $(-4, 2)$ **3.** $\left[-\dfrac{2}{3}, 2\right]$ **4.** $\{\ \}$ or $\varnothing$ **5.** $(-\infty, -10] \cup [2, \infty)$

6. $(-\infty, \infty)$ **7.** $(-\infty, 0) \cup (12, \infty)$ **8.** 2

Vocabulary and Readiness Check 2.7
1. D   **3.** C   **5.** A

Exercise Set 2.7

1. ; $[-4, 4]$ **3.** ; $(1, 5)$ **5.** ; $(-5, -1)$ **7.** ; $[-10, 3]$ **9.** ; $[-5, 5]$

11. ; $\varnothing$ **13.** ; $[0, 12]$ **15.** ; $(-\infty, -3) \cup (3, \infty)$ **17.** ; $(-\infty, -24] \cup [4, \infty)$

19. ; $(-\infty, -4) \cup (4, \infty)$ **21.** ; $(-\infty, \infty)$ **23.** ; $\left(-\infty, \dfrac{2}{3}\right) \cup (2, \infty)$ **25.** ; $\{0\}$

27. ; $\left(-\infty, -\dfrac{3}{8}\right) \cup \left(-\dfrac{3}{8}, \infty\right)$ **29.** ; $[-2, 2]$ **31.** ; $(-\infty, -1) \cup (1, \infty)$

33. ; $(-5, 11)$ **35.** ; $(-\infty, 4) \cup (6, \infty)$ **37.** ; $\varnothing$ **39.** ; $(-\infty, \infty)$

41. ; $[-2, 9]$ **43.** ; $(-\infty, -11] \cup [1, \infty)$ **45.** ; $(-\infty, 0) \cup (0, \infty)$ **47.** ; $(-\infty, \infty)$

49. ; $\left[-\dfrac{1}{2}, 1\right]$ **51.** ; $(-\infty, -3) \cup (0, \infty)$ **53.** ; $\varnothing$ **55.** ; $\dfrac{3}{8}$

57. ; $\left(-\dfrac{2}{3}, 0\right)$ **59.** ; $(-\infty, -12) \cup (0, \infty)$ **61.** ; $[-1, 8]$ **63.** ; $\left[-\dfrac{23}{8}, \dfrac{17}{8}\right]$

65. $(-2, 5)$ **67.** $5, -2$ **69.** $(-\infty, -7] \cup [17, \infty)$ **71.** $-\dfrac{9}{4}$ **73.** $(-2, 1)$ **75.** $2, \dfrac{4}{3}$ **77.** $\varnothing$ **79.** $\dfrac{19}{2}, -\dfrac{17}{2}$ **81.** $\left(-\infty, -\dfrac{25}{3}\right) \cup \left(\dfrac{35}{3}, \infty\right)$

83. $\dfrac{1}{6}$ **85.** 0 **87.** $\dfrac{1}{3}$ **89.** -1.5 **91.** 0 **93.** $|x| < 7$ **95.** $|x| \le 5$ **97.** answers may vary   **99.** $3.45 < x < 3.55$

The Bigger Picture

1. -8 **2.** $-13, 21$ **3.** $(-\infty, 6]$ **4.** $(-7, 5]$ **5.** $-\dfrac{13}{2}$ **6.** $\varnothing$ **7.** -50 **8.** -5 **9.** $\left[-\dfrac{9}{5}, 1\right]$ **10.** $(\infty, -13) \cup (-9, \infty)$ **11.** $-3, \dfrac{23}{9}$

12. $-11, -\dfrac{9}{7}$

Chapter 2 Vocabulary Check

1. compound inequality **2.** contradiction **3.** intersection **4.** union **5.** identity **6.** formula **7.** absolute value **8.** solution
9. consecutive integers **10.** linear inequality in one variable **11.** linear equation in one variable

Chapter 2 Review

1. 3 **3.** $-\dfrac{45}{14}$ **5.** 0 **7.** 6 **9.** all real number **11.** $\varnothing$ **13.** -3 **15.** $\dfrac{96}{5}$ **17.** 32 **19.** 8 **21.** $\varnothing$ **23.** -7 **25.** 52

27. 940.5 million **29.** no such integers exist **31.** 258 mi **33.** $W = \dfrac{V}{LH}$ **35.** $y = \dfrac{5x + 12}{4}$ **37.** $m = \dfrac{y - y_1}{x - x_1}$ **39.** $r = \dfrac{E - IR}{I}$

41. $g = \dfrac{T}{r + vt}$ **43. a.** \$3695.27 **b.** \$3700.81 **45.** length: 10 in.; width: 8 in. **47.** $(3, \infty)$ **49.** $(-4, \infty)$ **51.** $(-\infty, 7]$ **53.** $(-\infty, 1)$

55. more economical to use housekeeper for more than 35 pounds per week **57.** 9.6 **59.** $\left[2, \dfrac{5}{2}\right]$ **61.** $\left(\dfrac{1}{8}, 2\right)$ **63.** $\left(\dfrac{7}{8}, \dfrac{27}{20}\right]$ **65.** $\left(\dfrac{11}{3}, \infty\right)$

67. 5, 11 **69.** $-1, \dfrac{11}{3}$ **71.** $-\dfrac{1}{6}$ **73.** $\varnothing$ **75.** $5, -\dfrac{1}{3}$ **77.** $\left(-\dfrac{8}{5}, 2\right)$ **79.** $(-\infty, -3) \cup (3, \infty)$

81. $\varnothing$ **83.** $(-\infty, -27) \cup (-9, \infty)$ **85.** 2 **87.** China: 137 million; USA: 102 million; France: 93 million

89. $h = \dfrac{3V}{\pi r^2}$ **91.** 58 mph **93.** $(2, \infty)$ **95.** $(-\infty, \infty)$ **97.** $3, -3$ **99.** $-10, -\dfrac{4}{3}$ **101.** $\left(-\dfrac{1}{2}, 2\right)$

Chapter 2 Test

1. 10 **2.** -32 **3.** $\varnothing$ **4.** all real numbers **5.** $-\dfrac{80}{29}$ **6.** $\dfrac{29}{4}$ **7.** $1, \dfrac{2}{3}$ **8.** $\varnothing$ **9.** $-4, -\dfrac{1}{3}$ **10.** $\dfrac{3}{2}$ **11.** $y = \dfrac{3x - 8}{4}$ **12.** $g = \dfrac{S}{t^2 + vt}$

13. $C = \dfrac{5}{9}(F - 32)$ **14.** $(5, \infty)$ **15.** $\left(-\infty, -\dfrac{11}{3}\right]$ **16.** $\left(\dfrac{3}{2}, 5\right]$ **17.** $(-\infty, -2) \cup \left(\dfrac{4}{3}, \infty\right)$ **18.** $(3, 7)$ **19.** $[5, \infty)$ **20.** $[4, \infty)$

21. $\left[1, \dfrac{11}{2}\right)$ **22.** $(-\infty, \infty)$ **23.** 9.6 **24.** 230,323 people **25.** approximately 8 hunting dogs **26.** more than 850 sunglasses
27. \$3542.27 **28.** New York: 21.8 million; Seoul: 23.1 million; Tokyo: 33.4 million

Chapter 2 Cumulative Review

1. a. $\{101, 102, 103, \ldots\}$ **b.** $\{2, 3, 4, 5\}$; Sec. 1.2, Ex. 3 **3. a.** 3 **b.** $\dfrac{1}{7}$ **c.** -2.7 **d.** -8 **e.** 0; Sec. 1.2, Ex. 6 **5. a.** -14

b. -4 **c.** 5 **d.** -10.2 **e.** $-\dfrac{5}{21}$; Sec. 1.3, Ex. 1 **7. a.** 3 **b.** 5 **c.** $\dfrac{1}{2}$ **d.** -6 **e.** not a real number; Sec. 1.3, Ex. 7 **9. a.** 33 **b.** -18

c. $\dfrac{1}{12}$; Sec. 1.3, Ex. 12 **11. a.** $x + 5 = 20$ **b.** $2(3 + y) = 4$ **c.** $x - 8 = 2x$ **d.** $\dfrac{z}{9} = 9 + z$; Sec. 1.4, Ex. 1 **13.** $5 + 7x$; Sec. 1.4, Ex. 9

15. 2; Sec. 2.1, Ex. 1 **17.** all real numbers; Sec. 2.1, Ex. 9 **19. a.** $3x + 3$ **b.** $12x - 3$; Sec. 2.2, Ex. 1 **21.** 23, 49, 92; Sec. 2.2, Ex. 3

23. $y = \dfrac{2x + 7}{3}$ or $y = \dfrac{2x}{3} + \dfrac{7}{3}$; Sec. 2.3, Ex. 2 **25.** $b = \dfrac{2A - Bh}{h}$; Sec. 2.3, Ex. 3 **27. a.** ; $[2, \infty)$ **b.** ; $(-\infty, -1)$

c. ; $(0.5, 3]$; Sec. 2.4, Ex. 1 **29.** $\left[\dfrac{5}{2}, \infty\right)$; Sec. 2.4, Ex. 5 **31.** $(-\infty, \infty)$; Sec. 2.4, Ex. 7 **33.** $\{4, 6\}$; Sec. 2.5, Ex. 1

35. $(-\infty, 4)$; Sec. 2.5, Ex. 2 **37.** $\{2, 3, 4, 5, 6, 8\}$; Sec. 2.5, Ex. 6 **39.** $(-\infty, \infty)$; Sec. 2.5, Ex. 8 **41.** $2, -2$; Sec. 2.6, Ex. 1

43. $24, -20$; Sec. 2.6, Ex. 3 **45.** 4; Sec. 2.6, Ex. 9 **47.** $[-3, 3]$; Sec. 2.7, Ex. 1 **49.** $(-\infty, \infty)$; Sec. 2.7, Ex. 6

CHAPTER 3 GRAPHS AND FUNCTIONS

Section 3.1
Practice Exercises

1.   **a.** Quadrant IV **b.** y-axis **c.** Quadrant II **d.** x-axis **e.** Quadrant III **f.** Quadrant I
2. yes, no, yes **3. a.** \$4200 **b.** more than \$9000

4. $y = -3x - 2$ **5.**   **6.** $y = 2x^2$ **7.** $y = -|x|$

Graphing Calculator Explorations 3.1

1.   **3.**   **5.**   **7.**

Vocabulary and Readiness Check 3.1

1. $(5, 2)$ **3.** $(3, 0)$ **5.** $(-5, -2)$ **7.** $(-1, 0)$ **9.** QI **11.** QII **13.** QIII **15.** y-axis **17.** QIII **19.** x-axis

Exercise Set 3.1

1. Quadrant I **3.** Quadrant II **5.** Quadrant IV **7.** y-axis **9.** Quadrant III

11. Quadrant IV **13.** x-axis **15.** Quadrant III **17.** no; yes **19.** yes; yes **21.** yes; yes **23.** yes; no **25.** yes; yes
27. linear **29.** linear **31.** linear **33.** not linear **35.** linear **37.** not linear

39. not linear **41.** linear **43.** linear **45.** not linear **47.** not linear **49.** not linear

51. linear **53.** linear **55.** -5 **57.** $-\dfrac{1}{10}$ **59.** $(-\infty, -5]$ **61.** $(-\infty, -4)$ **63.** b **65.** b **67.** c

69. 1991   **71.** answers may vary   **73.**

75. a.

b. 14 in.   **77.** $7000   **79.** $500

81. Depreciation is the same from year to year.   **83.**

; answers may vary   **85.** answers may vary

87. $y = -3 - 2x$;

89. $y = 5 - x^2$;

91.

93.

Section 3.2

Practice Exercises

1. a. Domain: $\{4, 5\}$; Range: $\{1, -3, -2, 6\}$ **b.** Domain: $\{3\}$; Range: $\{-4, -3, -2, -1, 0, 1, 2, 3, 4\}$ **c.** Domain: $\{$Administrative Secretary, Game Developer, Engineer, Restaurant Manager, Marketing$\}$; Range: $\{27, 50, 73, 35\}$ **2. a.** yes, a function   **b.** not a function   **c.** yes, a function
3. yes, a function   **4.** yes, a function   **5. a.** yes, a function   **b.** yes, a function   **c.** no, not a function   **d.** yes, a function   **e.** no, not a function
6. a. Domain: $[-1, 2]$; Range: $[-2, 9]$; yes, a function   **b.** Domain: $[-1, 1]$; Range: $[-4, 4]$; not a function
c. Domain: $(-\infty, \infty)$; Range: $(-\infty, 4]$; yes, a function   **d.** Domain: $(-\infty, \infty)$; Range: $(-\infty, \infty)$; yes, a function
7. a. 1   **b.** 6   **c.** -2   **d.** 15   **8. a.** -3   **b.** -2   **c.** 3   **d.** 1   **e.** -1 and 3   **f.** -3   **9.** $35 billion   **10.** $57.224 billion

Graphing Calculator Explorations 3.2

1.

3.

5.

Vocabulary and Readiness Check 3.2

1. origin   **3.** $x; y$ **5.** V-shaped   **7.** relation   **9.** domain   **11.** vertical

Exercise Set 3.2

1. domain: $\{-1, 0, -2, 5\}$; range: $\{7, 6, 2\}$; function   **3.** domain: $\{-2, 6, -7\}$; range: $\{4, -3, -8\}$; not a function

5. domain: $\{1\}$; range: $\{1, 2, 3, 4\}$; not a function   **7.** domain: $\left\{\frac{3}{2}, 0\right\}$; range: $\left\{\frac{1}{2}, -7, \frac{4}{5}\right\}$; not a function

9. domain: $\{-3, 0, 3\}$; range: $\{-3, 0, 3\}$; function   **11.** domain: $\{-1, 1, 2, 3\}$; range: $\{2, 1\}$; function   **13.** domain: $\{$Iowa, Alaska, Delaware, Illinois, Connecticut, New York$\}$; range: $\{5, 1, 19, 29\}$; function   **15.** domain: $\{32°, 104°, 212°, 50°\}$; range: $\{0°, 40°, 10°, 100°\}$; function
17. domain: $\{0\}$; range: $\{2, -1, 5, 100\}$; not a function   **19.** function   **21.** not a function   **23.** function   **25.** not a function   **27.** function
29. domain: $[0, \infty)$; range: $(-\infty, \infty)$; not a function   **31.** domain: $[-1, 1]$; range: $(-\infty, \infty)$; not a function   **33.** domain: $(-\infty, \infty)$; range: $(-\infty, -3] \cup [3, \infty)$; not a function   **35.** domain: $[2, 7]$; range $[1, 6]$; not a function   **37.** domain: $\{-2\}$; range: $(-\infty, \infty)$; not a function
39. domain: $(-\infty, \infty)$; range: $(-\infty, 3]$; function   **41.** answers may vary   **43.** yes   **45.** no   **47.** yes   **49.** yes   **51.** yes   **53.** no

55. 15   **57.** 38   **59.** 7   **61.** 3   **63. a.** 0   **b.** 1   **c.** -1   **65. a.** 246   **b.** 6   **c.** $\frac{9}{2}$ **67. a.** -5   **b.** -5   **c.** -5   **69. a.** 5.1
b. 15.5   **c.** 9.533   **71.** $(1, -10)$ **73.** $(4, 56)$ **75.** $f(-1) = -2$ **77.** $g(2) = 0$ **79.** -4, 0   **81.** 3   **83.** infinite number
85. a. $17 billion   **b.** $15.592 billion   **87.** $15.54 billion   **89.** $f(x) = x + 7$ **91.** 25π sq cm   **93.** 2744 cu in.   **95.** 166.38 cm
97. 163.2 mg   **99. a.** 106.26; per capita consumption of poultry was 106.26 lb in 2006.   **b.** 108.54 lb   **101.** 5, -5, 6

103. $2, \dfrac{8}{7}, \dfrac{12}{7}$ **105.** $0, 0, -6$

107. yes; 170 m **109.** false **111.** true **113. a.** $-3s + 12$ **b.** $-3r + 12$
115. a. 132 **b.** $a^2 - 12$ **117.** answers may vary

Section 3.3
Practice Exercises

1.   **2.**   **3. a.** $\left(0, -\dfrac{2}{5}\right)$ **b.** $(0, 4.1)$ **4.**   **5.**

6.   **7.**

Graphing Calculator Explorations 3.3

1. $y = \dfrac{x}{3.5}$ 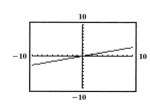 **3.** $y = -\dfrac{5.78}{2.31}x + \dfrac{10.98}{2.31}$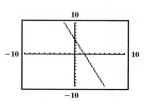

5. $y = |x| + 3.78$ **7.** $y = 5.6x^2 + 7.7x + 1.5$

Vocabulary and Readiness Check 3.3
1. linear **3.** vertical; $(c, 0)$ **5.** y; $f(x)$; x

Exercise Set 3.3

1.   **3.**   **5.**   **7.**   **9.** C **11.** D **13.**

15.   **17.**   **19.**   **21.** answers may vary **23.**   **25.**

27.   **29.** C **31.** A **33.** The vertical line $x = 0$ has y-intercepts. **35.**   **37.**

39.

41.

43.

45.

47.

49. $x = -3$

51.

53.

55.

57.

59. $x = -3$

61. $9, -3$ **63.** $(-\infty, -4) \cup (-1, \infty)$ **65.** $\left[\dfrac{2}{3}, 2\right]$ **67.** $\dfrac{3}{2}$ **69.** 6 **71.** $-\dfrac{6}{5}$

73. a. $(0, 500)$; if no tables are produced, 500 chairs can be produced   **b.** $(750, 0)$; if no chairs are produced, 750 tables can be produced   **c.** 466 chairs

75. a. \$64   **b.**   **c.** The line moves upward from left to right.   **77. a.** \$2855.12   **b.** 2012   **c.** answers may vary

79.

81.

83. a. a line parallel to $y = -4x$ but with y-intercept $(0, 2)$ **b.** a line parallel to $y = -4x$ but with y-intercept $(0, -5)$ **85.** B   **87.** A

Chapter 3 Vocabulary Check

1. relation   **3.** linear inequality   **5.** range   **7.** slope-intercept   **9.** slope   **11.** y **13.** linear function   **15.** point-slope

Chapter 3 Review

1.

3. no, yes   **5.** yes, yes   **7.** linear

9. linear

11. nonlinear

13. linear

15. linear

17. linear

19. domain: $\left\{-\dfrac{1}{2}, 6, 0, 25\right\}$; range: $\left\{\dfrac{3}{4} \text{ or } 0.75, -12, 25\right\}$; function   **21.** domain: $\{2, 4, 6, 8\}$; range: $\{2, 4, 5, 6\}$; not a function

23. domain: $(-\infty, \infty)$; range: $(-\infty, -1] \cup [1, \infty)$; not a function   **25.** domain: $(-\infty, \infty)$; range: $\{4\}$; function   **27.** -3 **29.** 18

31. -3 **33.** 381 lb   **35.** 0   **37.** $-2, 4$ **39.**

41.

43. A   **45.** D   **47.**

49.

51. $x = -2$

53.

55. -3 **57.** $\dfrac{5}{2}$ **59.** $m = \dfrac{2}{5}, b = -\dfrac{4}{3}$ **61.** 0   **63.** l_2 **65.** l_2

67. a. $m = 0.3$; The cost increases by \$0.30 for each additional mile driven.   **b.** $b = 42$; The cost for 0 miles driven is \$42.   **69.** parallel

71.   **73.**   **75.** $x = -2$ **77.** $y = 5$ **79.** $2x - y = 12$ **81.** $11x + y = -52$ **83.** $y = -5$

85. $f(x) = -x - 2$ **87.** $f(x) = -\frac{3}{2}x - 8$ **89.** $f(x) = -\frac{3}{2}x - 1$

91. a. $y = \frac{17}{22}x + 43$ **b.** 52 million

Chapter 3 Test

1. A: quadrant IV   B: x-axis   C: quadrant II   **2.**   **3.**   **4.**

5.   **6.** $-\frac{3}{2}$ **7.** $m = -\frac{1}{4}, b = \frac{2}{3}$ **8.**   **9.**   **10.** $y = -8$
11. $x = -4$
12. $y = -2$
13. $3x + y = 11$

14. $5x - y = 2$ **15.** $f(x) = -\frac{1}{2}x$ **16.** $f(x) = -\frac{1}{3}x + \frac{5}{3}$ **17.** $f(x) = -\frac{1}{2}x - \frac{1}{2}$ **18.** neither

19.   **20.**   **21.**   **22.** domain: $(-\infty, \infty)$; range: $\{5\}$; function
23. domain: $\{-2\}$; range: $(-\infty, \infty)$; not a function
24. domain: $(-\infty, \infty)$; range: $[0, \infty)$; function
25. domain: $(-\infty, \infty)$; range: $(-\infty, \infty)$; function
26. a. \$25,193   **b.** \$32,410   **c.** 2015   **d.** The average yearly earnings for high school graduates increases \$1031 per year.   **e.** The average yearly earnings for a high school graduate in 2000 was \$25,193.

Chapter 3 Cumulative Review

1. 41; Sec. 1.2, Ex. 2   **3. a.** true   **b.** false   **c.** false   **d.** false; Sec. 1.2, Ex. 5   **5. a.** -6 **b.** -7 **c.** -16 **d.** 20.5
e. $\frac{1}{6}$ **f.** 0.94   **g.** -3; Sec. 1.3, Ex. 2   **7. a.** 9   **b.** $\frac{1}{16}$ **c.** -25 **d.** 25   **e.** -125 **f.** -125; Sec. 1.3, Ex. 6
9. a. $>$ **b.** $=$ **c.** $<$ **d.** $<$; Sec. 1.4, Ex. 5   **11. a.** $\frac{1}{11}$ **b.** $-\frac{1}{9}$ **c.** $\frac{4}{7}$; Sec. 1.4, Ex. 8   **13.** 0.4; Sec. 2.1, Ex. 2
15. $\{\ \}$ or $\varnothing$; Sec. 2.1, Ex. 8   **17. a.** $3x + 3$ **b.** $12x - 3$; Sec. 2.2, Ex. 1   **19.** 86, 88 and 90; Sec. 2.2, Ex. 7   **21.** $\frac{V}{lw} = h$; Sec. 2.3, Ex. 1
23. $\{x \mid x < 7\}$ or $(-\infty, 7)$; ; Sec. 2.4, Ex. 2   **25.** $\left(-\infty, -\frac{7}{3}\right]$; Sec. 2.4, Ex. 6   **27.** $\varnothing$; Sec. 2.5, Ex. 3
29. $\left(-\infty, \frac{13}{5}\right] \cup [4, \infty)$; Sec. 2.5, Ex. 7   **31.** $-2, \frac{4}{5}$; Sec. 2.6, Ex. 2   **33.** $\frac{3}{4}, 5$; Sec. 2.6, Ex. 8   **35.** $\left[-2, \frac{8}{5}\right]$; Sec. 2.7, Ex. 3
37. $(-\infty, -4) \cup (10, \infty)$; Sec. 2.7, Ex. 5   **39.** solutions: $(2, -6), (0, -12)$; not a solution $(1, 9)$; Sec. 3.1, Ex. 2   **41.** yes; Sec. 3.2, Ex. 3
43. a. $\left(0, \frac{3}{7}\right)$ **b.** $(0, -3.2)$; Sec. 3.3, Ex. 3   **45.** $\frac{2}{3}$; Sec. 3.4, Ex. 3   **47.** $y = \frac{1}{4}x - 3$; Sec. 3.5 Ex. 1

CHAPTER 4 SYSTEMS OF EQUATIONS

Section 4.1
Practice Exercises

1. a. yes   **b.** no   **2. a.** infinite number of solutions of the form $\{(x, y) \mid 3x - 2y = 4\}$ or $\{(x, y) \mid -9x + 6y = -12\}$

2. b. solution: $(1, 5)$ **c.** no solution   **3.** $\left(-\frac{1}{2}, 5\right)$ **4.** $\left(-\frac{9}{5}, -\frac{2}{5}\right)$ **5.** $(2, 1)$ **6.** $(-2, 0)$

7. $\varnothing$ or $\{\ \}$ **8.** $\{(x, y) \mid -3x + 2y = -1\}$ or $\{(x, y) \mid 9x - 6y = 3\}$

Graphing Calculator Explorations 4.1

1. $(2.11, 0.17)$ **3.** $(0.57, -1.97)$

Vocabulary and Readiness Check 4.1

1. B   **3.** A

Exercise Set 4.1

1. yes   **3.** no   **5.** no   **7.** $(2, -1)$ **9.** $(1, 2)$ **11.** $\varnothing$ **13.** No; answers may vary

15. $(2, 8)$ **17.** $(0, -9)$ **19.** $(1, -1)$ **21.** $(-5, 3)$ **23.** $\left(\dfrac{5}{2}, \dfrac{5}{4}\right)$ **25.** $(1, -2)$ **27.** $(8, 2)$ **29.** $(7, 2)$ **31.** $\varnothing$ **33.** $\{(x, y) \mid 3x + y = 1\}$

35. $\left(\dfrac{3}{2}, 1\right)$ **37.** $(2, -1)$ **39.** $(-5, 3)$ **41.** $\{(x, y) \mid 3x + 9y = 12\}$ **43.** $\varnothing$ **45.** $\left(\dfrac{1}{2}, \dfrac{1}{5}\right)$ **47.** $(9, 9)$ **49.** $\{(x, y) \mid x = 3y + 2\}$

51. $\left(-\dfrac{1}{4}, \dfrac{1}{2}\right)$ **53.** $(3, 2)$ **55.** $(7, -3)$ **57.** $\varnothing$ **59.** $(3, 4)$ **61.** $(-2, 1)$ **63.** $(1.2, -3.6)$ **65.** true   **67.** false   **69.** $6y - 4z = 25$

71. $x + 10y = 2$ **73.** 5000 DVDs; \$21   **75.** supply greater than demand   **77.** $(1875, 4687.5)$ **79.** makes money

81. for x-values greater than 1875   **83.** answers may vary; One possibility: $\begin{cases} -2x + y = 1 \\ x - 2y = -8 \end{cases}$

85. a. Consumption of red meat is decreasing while consumption of poultry is increasing.   **b.** $(35, 103)$ **c.** In the year 2035, red meat and poultry consumption will each be about 103 pounds per person.   **87.** $\left(\dfrac{1}{4}, 8\right)$ **89.** $\left(\dfrac{1}{3}, \dfrac{1}{2}\right)$ **91.** $\left(\dfrac{1}{4}, -\dfrac{1}{3}\right)$ **93.** $\varnothing$

Section 4.2
Practice Exercises

1. $(-1, 2, 1)$ **2.** $\{\ \}$ or $\varnothing$ **3.** $\left(\dfrac{2}{3}, -\dfrac{1}{2}, 0\right)$ **4.** $\{(x, y, z) \mid 2x + y - 3z = 6\}$ **5.** $(6, 15, -5)$

Exercise Set 4.2

1. a, b, d   **3.** Yes; answers may vary   **5.** $(-1, 5, 2)$ **7.** $(-2, 5, 1)$ **9.** $(-2, 3, -1)$ **11.** $\{(x, y, z) \mid x - 2y + z = -5\}$ **13.** $\varnothing$
15. $(0, 0, 0)$ **17.** $(-3, -35, -7)$ **19.** $(6, 22, -20)$ **21.** $\varnothing$ **23.** $(3, 2, 2)$ **25.** $\{(x, y, z) \mid x + 2y - 3z = 4\}$ **27.** $(-3, -4, -5)$
29. $\left(0, \dfrac{1}{2}, -4\right)$ **31.** $(12, 6, 4)$ **33.** 15 and 30   **35.** 5   **37.** $-\dfrac{5}{3}$ **39.** answers may vary   **41.** answers may vary   **43.** $(1, 1, -1)$
45. $(1, 1, 0, 2)$ **47.** $(1, -1, 2, 3)$ **49.** answers may vary

Section 4.3
Practice Exercises

1. a. 2037   **b.** yes; answers may vary   **2.** 12 and 17   **3.** Atlantique: 500 kph; V150: 575 kph   **4.** 0.95 liter of water; 0.05 liter of 99% HCL
5. 1500 packages   **6.** $40°, 60°, 80°$

Exercise Set 4.3

1. 10 and 8   **3. a.** Enterprise class: 1101 ft; Nimitz class: 1092 ft   **b.** 3.67 foot ball fields   **5.** plane: 520 mph; wind: 40 mph   **7.** 20 qt of 4%; 40 qt
of 1%   **9.** United Kingdom: 32,071 students; Italy: 24,858 students   **11.** 9 large frames; 13 small frames   **13.** -10 and -8 **15.** 2007
17. tablets: \$0.80; pens: \$0.20   **19.** B737: 450 mph; Piper: 90 mph   **21. a.** answers may vary but notice the slope of each function   **b.** 1991
23. 28 cm; 28 cm; 37 cm   **25.** 600 mi   **27.** $x = 75; y = 105$ **29.** 625 units   **31.** 3000 units   **33.** 1280 units   **35. a.** $R(x) = 450x$
b. $C(x) = 200x + 6000$ **c.** 24 desks   **37.** 2 units of Mix A; 3 units of Mix B; 1 unit of Mix C   **39.** 5 in.; 7 in.; 10 in.   **41.** 18, 13, and 9
43. 143 free throws; 177 two-point field goals; 121 three-point field goals   **45.** $x = 60; y = 55; z = 65$ **47.** $5x + 5z = 10$ **49.** $-5y + 2z = 2$
51. 1996: 1,059,444; 2006: 1,085,209   **53. a.** $(112, 137)$ **b.** June 2019   **55.** $a = 1, b = -2, c = 3$
57. $a = 0.28, b = -3.71, c = 12.83$; 2.12 in. in Sept.

Integrated Review

1. C   **2.** D   **3.** A   **4.** B   **5.** $(1, 3)$ **6.** $\left(\dfrac{4}{3}, \dfrac{16}{3}\right)$ **7.** $(2, -1)$ **8.** $(5, 2)$ **9.** $\left(\dfrac{3}{2}, 1\right)$ **10.** $\left(-2, \dfrac{3}{4}\right)$ **11.** $\varnothing$

12. $\{(x, y) \mid 2x - 5y = 3\}$ **13.** $\left(1, \dfrac{1}{3}\right)$ **14.** $\left(3, \dfrac{3}{4}\right)$ **15.** $(-1, 3, 2)$ **16.** $(1, -3, 0)$ **17.** $\varnothing$ **18.** $\{(x, y, z) \mid x - y + 3z = 2\}$

19. $\left(2, 5, \dfrac{1}{2}\right)$ **20.** $\left(1, 1, \dfrac{1}{3}\right)$ **21.** 19 and 27   **22.** $70°; 70°; 100°; 120°$

Chapter 4 Review

1. $(-3, 1)$ **2.** $\left(0, \dfrac{2}{3}\right)$ **3.** $\varnothing$ **4.** $\{(x, y) \mid 3x - 6y = 12\}$ **5.** $\left(3, \dfrac{8}{3}\right)$ **6.** 1500 backpacks   **7.** $(2, 0, 2)$ **8.** $(2, 0, -3)$

9. $\left(-\dfrac{1}{2}, \dfrac{3}{4}, 1\right)$ **10.** $(-1, 2, 0)$ **11.** $\varnothing$ **12.** $(5, 3, 0)$ **13.** $(1, 1, -2)$ **14.** $(3, 1, 1)$ **15.** 10, 40, and 48   **16.** 63 and 21

17. 58 mph; 65 mph   **18.** width: 37 ft; length: 111 ft   **19.** 20 L of 10% solution; 30 L of 60% solution   **20.** 30 lb of creme-filled; 5 lb of chocolate-covered nuts; 10 lb of chocolate-covered raisins   **21.** 17 pennies; 20 nickels; 16 dimes   **22.** larger investment: 9.5%; smaller investment: 7.5%

23. two sides: 22 cm each; third side; 29 cm   **24.** 120, 115, and 60   **25.** $(-3, 1)$ **26.** $\{(x, y) \mid x - 2y = 4\}$ **27.** $\left(-\dfrac{2}{3}, 3\right)$

Chapter 4 Test

1. $(1, 3)$ **2.** $\varnothing$ **3.** $(2, -3)$ **4.** $\{(x, y) \mid 10x + 4y = 10\}$ **5.** $(-1, -2, 4)$ **6.** $\varnothing$ **7.** $\left(\dfrac{7}{2}, -10\right)$

8. $\{(x, y) \mid x - y = -2\}$ **9.** $(5, -3)$ **10.** $(-1, -1, 0)$ **11.** 53 double rooms; 27 single rooms   **12.** 5 gal of 10%; 15 gal of 20%

13. 800 packages   **14.** $23°, 45°, 112°$

Chapter 4 Cumulative Review

1. a. true   **b.** true; Sec. 1.2, Ex. 4   **3. a.** 6   **b.** -7; Sec. 1.3, Ex. 3   **5. a.** -4 **b.** $-\dfrac{3}{7}$ **c.** 11.2; Sec. 1.4, Ex. 7   **7. a.** $6x + 3y$

b. $-3x + 1$ **c.** $0.7\,ab - 1.4a$; Sec. 1.4, Ex. 11   **9. a.** $-2x + 4$ **b.** $8yz$ **c.** $4z + 6.1$; Sec. 1.4, Ex. 14   **11.** -4; Sec. 2.1, Ex. 3

13. -4; Sec. 2.1, Ex. 7   **15.** 25 cm, 62 cm, 62 cm; Sec. 2.2, Ex. 6   **17.** $[-10, \infty)$ ⟵———▶ ; Sec. 2.4, Ex. 3   **19.** $(-3, 2)$; Sec. 2.5, Ex. 4
$\qquad\qquad\qquad\qquad\qquad\qquad\qquad\qquad\qquad\qquad\qquad -10$

21. $1, -1$; Sec. 2.6, Ex. 4   **23.** $(4, 8)$; Sec. 2.7, Ex. 2   **25. a.** IV   **b.** y-axis   **c.** II   **d.** x-axis   **e.** III   **f.** I; ; Sec. 3.1, Ex. 1

27. no; Sec. 3.2, Ex. 4   **29. a.** 5   **b.** 1   **c.** 35   **d.** -2; Sec. 3.2, Ex. 7   **31.** ; Sec. 3.3, Ex. 1   **33.** slope: $\dfrac{3}{4}$; y-intercept: $(0, -1)$; Sec. 3.4, Ex. 4

35. a. parallel   **b.** neither; Sec. 3.4, Ex. 8   **37.** $f(x) = \dfrac{5}{8}x - \dfrac{5}{2}$; Sec. 3.5, Ex. 5   **39.** ; Sec. 3.6, Ex. 2   **41. a.** yes   **b.** no; Sec. 4.1, Ex. 1

43. $(-4, 2, -1)$; Sec. 4.2, Ex. 1   **45.** $(-1, 2)$; Sec. 4.4, Ex. 1

CHAPTER 5 EXPONENTS, POLYNOMIALS, AND POLYNOMIAL FUNCTIONS

Section 5.1

Practice Exercises

1. a. 3^6 **b.** x^7 **c.** y^9 **2. a.** $35z^4$ **b.** $-20.5\,t^6 q^8$ **3. a.** 1   **b.** -1 **c.** 1   **d.** 3   **4. a.** z^5 **b.** 3^6 **c.** $9x^4$ **d.** $\dfrac{4a^7}{3}$ or $\dfrac{4}{3}a^7$

5. a. $\dfrac{1}{36}$ **b.** $\dfrac{1}{64}$ **c.** $\dfrac{3}{x^5}$ **d.** $\dfrac{1}{5y}$ **e.** $\dfrac{1}{k^7}$ **f.** $\dfrac{1}{25}$ **g.** $\dfrac{9}{20}$ **h.** z^8 **6. a.** $\dfrac{1}{z^{11}}$ **b.** $7t^8$ **c.** 9   **d.** $\dfrac{b^7}{3a^7}$ **e.** $\dfrac{2}{x^4}$ **7. a.** x^{3a+4} **b.** x^{2t+1}

8. a. 6.5×10^4 **b.** 3.8×10^{-5} **9. a.** 620,000   **b.** 0.03109

Graphing Calculator Explorations 5.1

1. 6×10^{43} **3.** 3.796×10^{28}

Vocabulary and Readiness Check 5.1

1. x **3.** 3   **5.** y^7 **7.** $\dfrac{5}{xy^2}$ **9.** $\dfrac{a^2}{bc^5}$ **11.** $\dfrac{x^4}{y^2}$

Exercise Set 5.1

1. 4^5 **3.** x^8 **5.** m^{14} **7.** $-20x^2y$ **9.** $-16x^6y^3p^2$ **11.** -1 **13.** 1   **15.** -1 **17.** 9   **19.** a^3 **21.** $-13z^4$ **23.** x **25.** $\dfrac{4}{3}x^3y^2$

27. $-6a^4b^4c^6$ **29.** $\dfrac{1}{16}$ **31.** $-\dfrac{1}{27}$ **33.** $\dfrac{1}{x^8}$ **35.** $\dfrac{5}{a^4}$ **37.** $\dfrac{y^2}{x^7}$ **39.** $\dfrac{1}{x^7}$ **41.** $4r^8$ **43.** 1   **45.** $\dfrac{b^7}{9a^7}$ **47.** $\dfrac{6x^{16}}{5}$ **49.** $-140x^{12}$

51. x^{16} **53.** $10x^{10}$ **55.** 6   **57.** $\dfrac{1}{z^3}$ **59.** -2 **61.** y^4 **63.** $\dfrac{13}{36}$ **65.** $\dfrac{3}{x}$ **67.** r^8 **69.** $\dfrac{1}{x^9y^4}$ **71.** $24x^7y^6$ **73.** $\dfrac{x}{16}$ **75.** 625

77. $\dfrac{1}{8}$ **79.** $\dfrac{a^5}{81}$ **81.** $\dfrac{7}{x^3z^5}$ **83.** x^{7a+5} **85.** x^{2t-1} **87.** x^{4a+7} **89.** z^{6x-7} **91.** x^{6t-1} **93.** 3.125×10^7 **95.** 1.6×10^{-2} **97.** 6.7413×10^4

99. 1.25×10^{-2} **101.** 5.3×10^{-5} **103.** 3.44992×10^{11} **105.** 3.5×10^6 **107.** 1.24×10^{11} **109.** 1.0×10^{-3} **111.** 0.0000000036

113. 93,000,000   **115.** 1,278,000   **117.** 7,350,000,000,000   **119.** 0.000000403   **121.** 300,000,000   **123.** \$153,000,000,000   **125.** 100   **127.** $\dfrac{27}{64}$

129. 64   **131.** answers may vary   **133.** answers may vary   **135. a.** x^{2a} **b.** $2x^a$ **c.** x^{a-b} **d.** x^{a+b} **e.** $x^a + x^b$ **137.** 7^{13} **139.** 7^{-11}

Section 5.2

Practice Exercises

1. a. z^{15} **b.** 625   **c.** $\dfrac{1}{27}$ **d.** x^{24} **2. a.** $32x^{15}$ **b.** $\dfrac{9}{25}$ **c.** $\dfrac{16a^{20}}{b^{28}}$ **d.** $9x$ **e.** $\dfrac{a^4b^{10}}{c^8}$ **3. a.** $\dfrac{b^{15}}{27a^3}$ **b.** y^{15} **c.** $\dfrac{64}{9}$ **d.** $\dfrac{b^8}{81a^6}$

4. a. $\dfrac{c^3}{125a^{36}b^3}$ **b.** $\dfrac{16x^{16}y^4}{25}$ **5. a.** $27x^a$ **b.** y^{5b+3} **6. a.** 1.7×10^{-2} **b.** 1.4×10^{10} **7.** 4.2×10^{-6}

Vocabulary and Readiness Check 5.2

1. x^{20} **3.** x^9 **5.** y^{42} **7.** z^{36} **9.** z^{18}

Exercise Set 5.2

1. $\dfrac{1}{9}$ **3.** $\dfrac{1}{x^{36}}$ **5.** $\dfrac{1}{y^5}$ **7.** $9x^4y^6$ **9.** $16x^{20}y^{12}$ **11.** $\dfrac{c^{18}}{a^{12}b^6}$ **13.** $\dfrac{y^{15}}{x^{35}z^{20}}$ **15.** $\dfrac{1}{125}$ **17.** x^{15} **19.** $\dfrac{8}{x^{12}y^{18}}$ **21.** $\dfrac{y^{16}}{64x^5}$ **23.** $\dfrac{64}{p^9}$

25. $-\dfrac{1}{x^9a^9}$ **27.** $\dfrac{x^5y^{10}}{5^{15}}$ **29.** $\dfrac{1}{x^{63}}$ **31.** $\dfrac{343}{512}$ **33.** $16x^4$ **35.** $-\dfrac{y^3}{64}$ **37.** $4^8x^2y^6$ **39.** 64   **41.** $\dfrac{x^4}{16}$ **43.** $\dfrac{1}{y^{15}}$ **45.** $\dfrac{x^9}{8y^3}$

47. $\dfrac{16a^2b^9}{9}$ **49.** $\dfrac{3}{8x^8y^7}$ **51.** $\dfrac{1}{x^{30}b^6c^6}$ **53.** $\dfrac{25}{8x^5y^4}$ **55.** $\dfrac{2}{x^4y^{10}}$ **57.** x^{9a+18} **59.** x^{12a+2} **61.** b^{10x-4} **63.** y^{15a+3} **65.** $16x^{4t+4}$

67. $5x^{-a}y^{-a+2}$ **69.** 1.45×10^9 **71.** 8×10^{15} **73.** 4×10^{-7} **75.** 3×10^{-1} **77.** 2×10^1 **79.** 1×10^1 **81.** 8×10^{-5} **83.** 1.1×10^7

85. 3.5×10^{22} **87.** 2×10^{-3} sec   **89.** 6.232×10^{-11} cu m   **91.** $-3m - 15$ **93.** $-3y - 5$ **95.** $-3x + 5$ **97.** $\dfrac{15y^3}{x^8}$ sq ft   **99.** 1.331928×10^{13}

101. no   **103.** 85 people per sq mi   **105.** 6.4 times   **107.** 31.7%

Section 5.3

Practice Exercises

1. a. 5   **b.** 3   **c.** 1   **d.** 11   **e.** 0   **2. a.** degree 4; trinomial   **b.** degree 5; monomial   **c.** degree 5; binomial   **3.** 5

4. a. -15 **b.** -47 **5.** 290 feet; 226 feet   **6. a.** $3x^4 - 5x$ **b.** $7ab - 3b$ **7. a.** $3a^4b + 4ab^2 - 5$ **b.** $2x^5 + y - x - 9$

8. $6x^3 + 6x^2 - 7x - 8$ **9.** $15a^4 - 15a^3 + 3$ **10.** $6x^2y^2 - 4xy^2 - 5y^3$ **11.** C

Graphing Calculator Explorations 5.3

1. $x^3 - 4x^2 + 7x - 8$ **3.** $-2.1x^2 - 3.2x - 1.7$ **5.** $7.69x^2 - 1.26x + 5.3$

Vocabulary and Readiness Check 5.3

1. coefficient   **3.** binomial   **5.** trinomial   **7.** degree   **9.** $6x$ **11.** $2y$ **13.** $7xy^2 - y^2$

Exercise Set 5.3

1. 0   **3.** 2   **5.** 3   **7.** 3   **9.** 9   **11.** degree 1; binomial   **13.** degree 2; trinomial   **15.** degree 3; monomial   **17.** degree 4; none of these
19. 57   **21.** 499   **23.** $-\dfrac{11}{16}$ **25.** 1061 ft   **27.** 549 ft   **29.** $6y$ **31.** $11x - 3$ **33.** $xy + 2x - 1$ **35.** $6x^2 - xy + 16y^2$ **37.** $18y^2 - 17$
39. $3x^2 - 3xy + 6y^2$ **41.** $x^2 - 4x + 8$ **43.** $y^2 + 3$ **45.** $-2x^2 + 5x$ **47.** $-2x^2 - 4x + 15$ **49.** $4x - 13$ **51.** $x^2 + 2$ **53.** $12x^3 + 8x + 8$
55. $7x^3 + 4x^2 + 8x - 10$ **57.** $-18y^2 + 11yx + 14$ **59.** $-x^3 + 8a - 12$ **61.** $5x^2 - 9x - 3$ **63.** $-3x^2 + 3$ **65.** $8xy^2 + 2x^3 + 3x^2 - 3$
67. $7y^2 - 3$ **69.** $5x^2 + 22x + 16$ **71.** $\dfrac{3}{4}x^2 - \dfrac{1}{3}x^2y - \dfrac{8}{3}x^2y^2 + \dfrac{3}{2}y^3$ **73.** $-q^4 + q^2 - 3q + 5$ **75.** $15x^2 + 8x - 6$ **77.** $x^4 - 7x^2 + 5$
79. $\dfrac{1}{3}x^2 - x + 1$ **81.** 202 sq in.   **83. a.** 284 ft   **b.** 536 ft   **c.** 756 ft   **d.** 944 ft   **e.** answers may vary   **f.** 19 sec   **85.** \$80,000
87. \$40,000   **89.** A   **91.** D   **93.** $15x - 10$ **95.** $-2x^2 + 10x - 12$ **97.** a and c
99. $(12x - 1.7) - (15x + 6.2) = 12x - 1.7 - 15x - 6.2 = -3x - 7.9$ **101.** answers may vary   **103.** answers may vary
105. $3x^{2a} + 2x^a + 0.7$ **107.** $4x^{2y} + 2x^y - 11$ **109.** $(6x^2 + 14y)$ units   **111.** $4x^2 - 3x + 6$ **113.** $-x^2 - 6x + 10$ **115.** $3x^2 - 12x + 13$
117. $15x^2 + 12x - 9$ **119. a.** $2a - 3$ **b.** $-2x - 3$ **c.** $2x + 2h - 3$ **121. a.** $4a$ **b.** $-4x$ **c.** $4x + 4h$
123. a. $4a - 1$ **b.** $-4x - 1$ **c.** $4x + 4h - 1$ **125. a.** 2.9 million   **b.** 57.3 million   **c.** 247.4 million   **d.** answers may vary
127. a. 42.4 million   **b.** 29.5 million   **129. a.** 4.4 million   **b.** 6.2 million

Section 5.4

Practice Exercises

1. a. $6x^6$ **b.** $40m^5n^2p^8$ **2. a.** $21x^2 - 3x$ **b.** $-15a^4 + 30a^3 - 25a^2$ **c.** $-5m^3n^5 - 2m^2n^4 + 5m^2n^3$
3. a. $2x^2 + 13x + 15$ **b.** $3x^3 - 19x^2 + 12x - 2$ **4.** $3x^4 - 12x^3 - 13x^2 - 8x - 10$ **5.** $x^2 - 2x - 15$
6. a. $6x^2 - 31x + 35$ **b.** $8x^4 - 10x^2y - 3y^2$ **7. a.** $x^2 + 12x + 36$ **b.** $x^2 - 4x + 4$ **c.** $9x^2 + 30xy + 25y^2$ **d.** $9x^4 - 48x^2b + 64b^2$
8. a. $x^2 - 49$ **b.** $4a^2 - 25$ **c.** $25x^4 - \dfrac{1}{16}$ **d.** $a^6 - 16b^4$ **9.** $4 + 12x - 4y + 9x^2 - 6xy + y^2$ **10.** $9x^2 - 6xy + y^2 - 25$
11. $x^4 - 32x^2 + 256$ **12.** $h^2 - h + 3$

Graphing Calculator Explorations 5.4

1. $x^2 - 16$ **3.** $9x^2 - 42x + 49$ **5.** $5x^3 - 14x^2 - 13x - 2$

Vocabulary and Readiness Check 5.4

1. b   **3.** b   **5.** d

Exercise Set 5.4

1. $-12x^5$ **3.** $12x^2 + 21x$ **5.** $-24x^2y - 6xy^2$ **7.** $-4a^3bx - 4a^3by + 12ab$ **9.** $2x^2 - 2x - 12$ **11.** $2x^4 + 3x^3 - 2x^2 + x + 6$
13. $15x^2 - 7x - 2$ **15.** $15m^3 + 16m^2 - m - 2$ **17.** $x^2 + x - 12$ **19.** $10x^2 + 11xy - 8y^2$ **21.** $3x^2 + 8x - 3$
23. $9x^2 - \dfrac{1}{4}$ **25.** $5x^4 - 17x^2y^2 + 6y^4$ **27.** $x^2 + 8x + 16$ **29.** $36y^2 - 1$ **31.** $9x^2 - 6xy + y^2$ **33.** $25b^2 - 36y^2$ **35.** $16b^2 + 32b + 16$
37. $4s^2 - 12s + 8$ **39.** $x^2y^2 - 4xy + 4$ **41.** answers may vary   **43.** $x^4 - 2x^2y^2 + y^4$ **45.** $x^4 - 8x^3 + 24x^2 - 32x + 16$ **47.** $x^4 - 625$
49. $9x^2 + 18x + 5$ **51.** $10x^5 + 8x^4 + 2x^3 + 25x^2 + 20x + 5$ **53.** $49x^2 - 9$ **55.** $9x^3 + 30x^2 + 12x - 24$ **57.** $16x^2 - \dfrac{2}{3}x - \dfrac{1}{6}$
59. $36x^2 + 12x + 1$ **61.** $x^4 - 4y^2$ **63.** $-30a^4b^4 + 36a^3b^2 + 36a^2b^3$ **65.** $2a^2 - 12a + 16$ **67.** $49a^2b^2 - 9c^2$ **69.** $m^2 - 8m + 16$
71. $9x^2 + 6x + 1$ **73.** $y^2 - 7y + 12$ **75.** $2x^3 + 2x^2y + x^2 + xy - x - y$ **77.** $9x^4 + 12x^3 - 2x^2 - 4x + 1$ **79.** $12x^3 - 2x^2 + 13x + 5$
81. $a^2 - 3a$ **83.** $a^2 + 2ah + h^2 - 3a - 3h$ **85.** $b^2 - 7b + 10$ **87.** -2 **89.** $\dfrac{3}{5}$ **91.** function   **93.** $7y(3z - 2) + 1 = 21yz - 14y + 1$
95. answers may vary   **97. a.** $a^2 + 2ah + h^2 + 3a + 3h + 2$ **b.** $a^2 + 3a + 2$ **c.** $2ah + h^2 + 3h$ **99.** $30x^2y^{2n+1} - 10x^2y^n$
101. $x^{3a} + 5x^{2a} - 3x^a - 15$ **103.** $\pi(25x^2 - 20x + 4)$ sq km   **105.** $(8x^2 - 12x + 4)$ sq in.   **107. a.** $6x + 12$
b. $9x^2 + 36x + 35$; one operation is addition, the other is multiplication.   **109.** $5x^2 + 25x$ **111.** $x^4 - 4x^2 + 4$ **113.** $x^3 + 5x^2 - 2x - 10$

Section 5.5

Practice Exercises

1. $8y$ **2. a.** $3(2x^2 + 3 + 5x)$ **b.** $3x - 8y^3$ **c.** $2a^3(4a - 1)$ **3.** $8x^3y^2(8x^2 - 1)$ **4.** $-xy^2(9x^3 - 5x - 7)$ **5.** $(3 + 5b)(x + 4)$
6. $(8b - 1)(a^3 + 2y)$ **7.** $(x + 2)(y - 5)$ **8.** $(a + 2)(a^2 + 5)$ **9.** $(x^2 + 3)(y^2 - 5)$ **10.** $(q + 3)(p - 1)$

Vocabulary and Readiness Check 5.5

1. factoring   **3.** least   **5.** false   **7.** false   **9.** 6   **11.** 5   **13.** x **15.** $7x$

Exercise Set 5.5

1. a^3 **3.** y^2z^2 **5.** $3x^2y$ **7.** $5xz^3$ **9.** $6(3x - 2)$ **11.** $4y^2(1 - 4xy)$ **13.** $2x^3(3x^2 - 4x + 1)$ **15.** $4ab(2a^2b^2 - ab + 1 + 4b)$
17. $(x + 3)(6 + 5a)$ **19.** $(z + 7)(2x + 1)$ **21.** $(x^2 + 5)(3x - 2)$ **23.** answers may vary   **25.** $(a + 2)(b + 3)$
27. $(a - 2)(c + 4)$ **29.** $(x - 2)(2y - 3)$ **31.** $(4x - 1)(3y - 2)$ **33.** $3(2x^3 + 3)$ **35.** $x^2(x + 3)$ **37.** $4a(2a^2 - 1)$

39. $-4xy(5x - 4y^2)$ or $4xy(-5x + 4y^2)$ **41.** $5ab^2(2ab + 1 - 3b)$ **43.** $3b(3ac^2 + 2a^2c - 2a + c)$ **45.** $(y - 2)(4x - 3)$
47. $(2x + 3)(3y + 5)$ **49.** $(x + 3)(y - 5)$ **51.** $(2a - 3)(3b - 1)$ **53.** $(6x + 1)(2y + 3)$ **55.** $(n - 8)(2m - 1)$ **57.** $3x^2y^2(5x - 6)$
59. $(2x + 3y)(x + 2)$ **61.** $(5x - 3)(x + y)$ **63.** $(x^2 + 4)(x + 3)$ **65.** $(x^2 - 2)(x - 1)$ **67.** $55x^7$ **69.** $125x^6$ **71.** $x^2 - 3x - 10$
73. $x^2 + 5x + 6$ **75.** $y^2 - 4y + 3$ **77.** d   **79.** $2\pi r(r + h)$ **81.** $A = 5600(1 + rt)$ **83.** answers may vary   **85.** none   **87.** a
89. $A = P(1 + RT)$ **91.** $y^n(3 + 3y^n + 5y^{7n})$ **93.** $3x^{2a}(x^{3a} - 2x^a + 3)$ **95. a.** $h(t) = -16(t^2 - 14)$ **b.** 160   **c.** answers may vary

Section 5.6
Practice Exercises
1. $(x + 3)(x + 2)$ **2.** $(x - 3)(x - 8)$ **3.** $3x(x - 5)(x + 2)$ **4.** $2(b^2 - 9b - 11)$ **5.** $(2x + 1)(x + 6)$ **6.** $(4x - 3)(x + 2)$
7. $3b^2(2b - 5)(3b - 2)$ **8.** $(5x + 2y)^2$ **9.** $(5x + 2)(4x + 3)$ **10.** $(5x + 3)(3x - 1)$ **11.** $(x - 3)(3x + 8)$ **12.** $(3x^2 + 2)(2x^2 - 5)$

Vocabulary and Readiness Check 5.6
1. 5 and 2   **3.** 8 and 3

Exercise Set 5.6
1. $(x + 3)(x + 6)$ **3.** $(x - 8)(x - 4)$ **5.** $(x + 12)(x - 2)$ **7.** $(x - 6)(x + 4)$ **9.** $3(x - 2)(x - 4)$ **11.** $4z(x + 2)(x + 5)$
13. $2(x^2 - 12x - 32)$ **15.** $(5x + 1)(x + 3)$ **17.** $(2x - 3)(x - 4)$ **19.** prime polynomial   **21.** $(2x - 3)^2$ **23.** $2(3x - 5)(2x + 5)$
25. $y^2(3y + 5)(y - 2)$ **27.** $2x(3x^2 + 4x + 12)$ **29.** $(2x + y)(x - 3y)$ **31.** $2(7y + 2)(2y + 1)$ **33.** $(2x - 3)(x + 9)$
35. $(x^2 + 3)(x^2 - 2)$ **37.** $(5x + 8)(5x + 2)$ **39.** $(x^3 - 4)(x^3 - 3)$ **41.** $(a - 3)(a + 8)$ **43.** $(x - 27)(x + 3)$ **45.** $(x - 18)(x + 3)$
47. $3(x - 1)^2$ **49.** $(3x + 1)(x - 2)$ **51.** $(4x - 3)(2x - 5)$ **53.** $3x^2(2x + 1)(3x + 2)$ **55.** $(x + 7z)(x + z)$ **57.** $(x - 4)(x + 3)$
59. $3(a + 2b)^2$ **61.** prime polynomial   **63.** $(2x + 13)(x + 3)$ **65.** $(3x - 2)(2x - 15)$ **67.** $(x^2 - 6)(x^2 + 1)$ **69.** $x(3x + 1)(2x - 1)$
71. $(4a - 3b)(3a - 5b)$ **73.** $(3x + 5)^2$ **75.** $y(3x - 8)(x - 1)$ **77.** $2(x + 3)(x - 2)$ **79.** $(x + 2)(x - 7)$ **81.** $(2x^3 - 3)(x^3 + 3)$
83. $2x(6y^2 - z)^2$ **85.** $2xy(x + 3)(x - 2)$ **87.** $(x + 5y)(x + y)$ **89.** $x^2 - 9$ **91.** $4x^2 + 4x + 1$ **93.** $x^3 - 8$ **95.** $\pm 5, \pm 7$
97. $x(x + 4)(x - 2)$ **99. a.** 576 ft; 672 ft; 640 ft; 480 ft   **b.** answers may vary   **c.** $-16(t + 4)(t - 9)$ **101.** $(x^n + 2)(x^n + 8)$
103. $(x^n - 6)(x^n + 3)$ **105.** $(2x^n + 1)(x^n + 5)$ **107.** $(2x^n - 3)^2$ **109.** $x^2(x + 5)(x + 1)$ **111.** $3x(5x - 1)(2x + 1)$

Section 5.7
Practice Exercises
1. $(b + 8)^2$ **2.** $5b(3x - 1)^2$ **3. a.** $(x + 4)(x - 4)$ **b.** $(5b - 7)(5b + 7)$ **c.** $5(3 - 2x)(3 + 2x)$ **d.** $\left(y - \dfrac{1}{9}\right)\left(y + \dfrac{1}{9}\right)$

4. a. $(x^2 + 100)(x + 10)(x - 10)$ **b.** $(x + 9)(x - 5)$ **5.** $(m + 3 + n)(m + 3 - n)$ **6.** $(x + 4)(x^2 - 4x + 16)$
7. $(a + 2b)(a^2 - 2ab + 4b^2)$ **8.** $(3 - y)(9 + 3y + y^2)$ **9.** $x^2(b - 2)(b^2 + 2b + 4)$

Vocabulary and Readiness Check 5.7
1. $(9y)^2$ **3.** $(8x^3)^2$ **5.** 5^3 **7.** $(2x)^3$ **9.** $(4x^2)^3$

Exercise Set 5.7
1. $(x + 3)^2$ **3.** $(2x - 3)^2$ **5.** $3(x - 4)^2$ **7.** $x^2(3y + 2)^2$ **9.** $(x + 5)(x - 5)$ **11.** $(3 + 2z)(3 - 2z)$ **13.** $(y + 9)(y - 5)$
15. $4(4x + 5)(4x - 5)$ **17.** $(x + 3)(x^2 - 3x + 9)$ **19.** $(z - 1)(z^2 + z + 1)$ **21.** $(m + n)(m^2 - mn + n^2)$ **23.** $y^2(x - 3)(x^2 + 3x + 9)$
25. $b(a + 2b)(a^2 - 2ab + 4b^2)$ **27.** $(5y - 2x)(25y^2 + 10yx + 4x^2)$ **29.** $(x + 3 + y)(x + 3 - y)$ **31.** $(x - 5 + y)(x - 5 - y)$
33. $(2x + 1 + z)(2x + 1 - z)$ **35.** $(3x + 7)(3x - 7)$ **37.** $(x - 6)^2$ **39.** $(x^2 + 9)(x + 3)(x - 3)$ **41.** $(x + 4 + 2y)(x + 4 - 2y)$
43. $(x + 2y + 3)(x + 2y - 3)$ **45.** $(x - 6)(x^2 + 6x + 36)$ **47.** $(x + 5)(x^2 - 5x + 25)$ **49.** prime polynomial   **51.** $(2a + 3)^2$
53. $2y(3x + 1)(3x - 1)$ **55.** $(2x + y)(4x^2 - 2xy + y^2)$ **57.** $(x^2 - y)(x^4 + x^2y + y^2)$ **59.** $(x + 8 + x^2)(x + 8 - x^2)$

61. $3y^2(x^2 + 3)(x^4 - 3x^2 + 9)$ **63.** $(x + y + 5)(x^2 + 2xy + y^2 - 5x - 5y + 25)$ **65.** $(2x - 1)(4x^2 + 20x + 37)$ **67.** 5   **69.** $-\dfrac{1}{3}$ **71.** 0

73. 5   **75.** no; $x^2 - 4$ can be factored further   **77.** yes   **79.** $\pi R^2 - \pi r^2 = \pi(R + r)(R - r)$ **81.** $x^3 - y^2x$; $x(x + y)(x - y)$ **83.** $c = 9$
85. $c = 49$ **87.** $c = \pm 8$ **89. a.** $(x + 1)(x^2 - x + 1)(x - 1)(x^2 + x + 1)$ **b.** $(x + 1)(x - 1)(x^4 + x^2 + 1)$ **c.** answers may vary
91. $(x^n + 6)(x^n - 6)$ **93.** $(5x^n + 9)(5x^n - 9)$ **95.** $(x^{2n} + 25)(x^n + 5)(x^n - 5)$

Integrated Review Practice Exercises
1. a. $3xy(4x - 1)$ **b.** $(7x + 2)(7x - 2)$ **c.** $(5x - 3)(x + 1)$ **d.** $(3 + x)(x^2 + 2)$ **e.** $(2x + 5)^2$ **f.** cannot be factored
2. a. $(4x + y)(16x^2 - 4xy + y^2)$ **b.** $7y^2(x - 3y)(x + 3y)$ **c.** $3(x + 2 + b)(x + 2 - b)$ **d.** $x^2y(xy + 3)(x^2y^2 - 3xy + 9)$
e. $(x + 7 + 9y)(x + 7 - 9y)$

Integrated Review
1. $2y^2 + 2y - 11$ **2.** $-2z^4 - 6z^2 + 3z$ **3.** $x^2 - 7x + 7$ **4.** $7x^2 - 4x - 5$ **5.** $25x^2 - 30x + 9$ **6.** $x - 3$

7. $2x^3 - 4x^2 + 5x - 5 + \dfrac{8}{x + 2}$ **8.** $4x^3 - 13x^2 - 5x + 2$ **9.** $(x - 4 + y)(x - 4 - y)$ **10.** $2(3x + 2)(2x - 5)$ **11.** $x(x - 1)(x^2 + x + 1)$
12. $2x(2x - 1)$ **13.** $2xy(7x - 1)$ **14.** $6ab(4b - 1)$ **15.** $4(x + 2)(x - 2)$ **16.** $9(x + 3)(x - 3)$ **17.** $(3x - 11)(x + 1)$
18. $(5x + 3)(x - 1)$ **19.** $4(x + 3)(x - 1)$ **20.** $6(x + 1)(x - 2)$ **21.** $(2x + 9)^2$ **22.** $(5x + 4)^2$ **23.** $(2x + 5y)(4x^2 - 10xy + 25y^2)$

24. $(3x - 4y)(9x^2 + 12xy + 16y^2)$ **25.** $8x^2(2y - 1)(4y^2 + 2y + 1)$ **26.** $27x^2y(xy - 2)(x^2y^2 + 2xy + 4)$
27. $(x + 5 + y)(x^2 + 10x - xy - 5y + y^2 + 25)$ **28.** $(y - 1 + 3x)(y^2 - 2y + 1 - 3xy + 3x + 9x^2)$ **29.** $(5a - 6)^2$ **30.** $(4r + 5)^2$
31. $7x(x - 9)$ **32.** $(4x + 3)(5x + 2)$ **33.** $(a + 7)(b - 6)$ **34.** $20(x - 6)(x - 5)$ **35.** $(x^2 + 1)(x - 1)(x + 1)$ **36.** $5x(3x - 4)$
37. $(5x - 11)(2x + 3)$ **38.** $9m^2n^2(5mn - 3)$ **39.** $5a^3b(b^2 - 10)$ **40.** $x(x + 1)(x^2 - x + 1)$ **41.** prime   **42.** $20(x + y)(x^2 - xy + y^2)$
43. $10x(x - 10)(x - 11)$ **44.** $(3y - 7)^2$ **45.** $a^3b(4b - 3)(16b^2 + 12b + 9)$ **46.** $(y^2 + 4)(y + 2)(y - 2)$ **47.** $2(x - 3)(x^2 + 3x + 9)$
48. $(2s - 1)(r + 5)$ **49.** $(y^4 + 2)(3y - 5)$ **50.** prime   **51.** $100(z + 1)(z^2 - z + 1)$ **52.** $2x(5x - 2)(25x^2 + 10x + 4)$ **53.** $(2b - 9)^2$
54. $(a^4 + 3)(2a - 1)$ **55.** $(y - 4)(y - 5)$ **56.** $(c - 3)(c + 1)$ **57.** $A = 9 - 4x^2 = (3 + 2x)(3 - 2x)$

Section 5.8
Practice Exercises
1. $-8, 5$ **2.** $-4, \dfrac{2}{3}$ **3.** $-4, -\dfrac{2}{3}$ **4.** $-\dfrac{3}{4}$ **5.** $-\dfrac{1}{8}, 2$ **6.** $0, 3, -1$ **7.** $3, -3, -2$ **8.** 6 seconds   **9.** $6, 8, 10$ units   **10.** $f(x): C; g(x): A; h(x): B$

Graphing Calculator Explorations 5.8
1. $-3.562, 0.562$ **3.** $-0.874, 2.787$ **5.** $-0.465, 1.910$

Vocabulary and Readiness Check 5.8
1. $3, -5$ **3.** $3, -7$ **5.** $0, 9$

Exercise Set 5.8
1. $-3, \dfrac{4}{3}$ **3.** $\dfrac{5}{2}, -\dfrac{3}{4}$ **5.** $-3, -8$ **7.** $\dfrac{1}{4}, -\dfrac{2}{3}$ **9.** $1, 9$ **11.** $\dfrac{3}{5}, -1$ **13.** 0 **15.** $6, -3$ **17.** $\dfrac{2}{5}, -\dfrac{1}{2}$ **19.** $\dfrac{3}{4}, -\dfrac{1}{2}$ **21.** $-2, 7, \dfrac{8}{3}$

23. $0, 3, -3$ **25.** $2, 1, -1$ **27.** answers may vary   **29.** $-\dfrac{7}{2}, 10$ **31.** $0, 5$ **33.** $-3, 5$ **35.** $-\dfrac{1}{2}, \dfrac{1}{3}$ **37.** $-4, 9$ **39.** $\dfrac{4}{5}$ **41.** $-5, 0, 2$

43. $-3, 0, \dfrac{4}{5}$ **45.** $\varnothing$ **47.** $-7, 4$ **49.** $4, 6$ **51.** $-\dfrac{1}{2}$ **53.** $-4, -3, 3$ **55.** $-5, 0, 5$ **57.** $-6, 5$ **59.** $-\dfrac{1}{3}, 0, 1$ **61.** $-\dfrac{1}{3}, 0$ **63.** $-\dfrac{7}{8}$

65. $\dfrac{31}{4}$ **67.** 1 **69. a.** incorrect   **b.** correct   **c.** correct   **d.** incorrect   **71.** -11 and -6 or 6 and 11 **73.** 75 ft   **75.** 105 units

77. 12 cm and 9 cm   **79.** 2 in.   **81.** 10 sec   **83.** width: $7\dfrac{1}{2}$ ft; length: 12 ft   **85.** 10 in. sq tier   **87.** 9 sec   **89.** E   **91.** F   **93.** B
95. $(-3, 0), (0, 2)$; function   **97.** $(-4, 0), (0, 2), (4, 0), (0, -2)$; not a function   **99.** answers may vary

101. $x - 5 = 0$ or $x + 2 = 0$ **103.** $y(y - 5) = -6$ **105.** $-3, -\dfrac{1}{3}, 2, 5$ **107.** no; answers may vary   **109.** answers may vary
$\qquad x = 5$ or $x = -2$ $\qquad\qquad y^2 - 5y + 6 = 0$
$\qquad\qquad\qquad (y - 2)(y - 3) = 0$ **111.** answers may vary
$\qquad\qquad\qquad y - 2 = 0$ or $y - 3 = 0$
$\qquad\qquad\qquad\quad y = 2$ or $\quad y = 3$

The Bigger Picture
1. $-\dfrac{1}{2}, 6$ **2.** $(-7, 3)$ **3.** $-\dfrac{5}{3}$ **4.** $-\dfrac{3}{2}, 6$ **5.** $(-\infty, \infty)$ **6.** $-8, 3$ **7.** $-3, 10$ **8.** $(-\infty, 0]$

Chapter 5 Vocabulary Check
1. polynomial   **2.** factoring   **3.** exponents   **4.** degree of a term   **5.** monomial   **6.** 1   **7.** trinomial
8. quadratic equation   **9.** scientific notation   **10.** degree of a polynomial   **11.** binomial   **12.** 0

Chapter 5 Review
1. 4 **3.** -4 **5.** 1 **7.** $-\dfrac{1}{16}$ **9.** $-x^2y^7z$ **11.** $\dfrac{1}{a^9}$ **13.** $\dfrac{1}{x^{11}}$ **15.** $\dfrac{1}{y^5}$ **17.** -3.62×10^{-4} **19.** $410{,}000$ **21.** $\dfrac{a^2}{16}$ **23.** $\dfrac{1}{16x^2}$

25. $\dfrac{1}{8^{18}}$ **27.** $-\dfrac{1}{8x^9}$ **29.** $\dfrac{-27y^6}{x^6}$ **31.** $\dfrac{xz}{4}$ **33.** $\dfrac{2}{27z^3}$ **35.** $2y^{x-7}$ **37.** -2.21×10^{-11} **39.** $\dfrac{x^3y^{10}}{3z^{12}}$ **41.** 5 **43.** $12x - 6x^2 - 6x^2y$
45. $4x^2 + 8y + 6$ **47.** $8x^2 + 2b - 22$ **49.** $12x^2y - 7xy + 3$ **51.** $x^3 + x - 2xy^2 - y - 7$ **53.** 58 **55.** $x^2 + 4x - 6$
57. $(6x^2y - 12x + 12)$ cm   **59.** $-12a^2b^5 - 28a^2b^3 - 4ab^2$ **61.** $9x^2a^2 - 24xab + 16b^2$ **63.** $15x^2 + 18xy - 81y^2$
65. $x^4 + 18x^3 + 83x^2 + 18x + 1$ **67.** $16x^2 + 72x + 81$ **69.** $16 - 9a^2 + 6ab - b^2$ **71.** $(9y^2 - 49z^2)$ sq units
73. $16x^2y^2z - 8xy^2b + b^2$ **75.** $8x^2(2x - 3)$ **77.** $2ab(3b + 4 - 2ab)$ **79.** $(a + 3b)(6a - 5)$ **81.** $(x - 6)(y + 3)$ **83.** $(p - 5)(q - 3)$
85. $x(2y - x)$ **87.** $(x - 4)(x + 20)$ **89.** $3(x + 2)(x + 9)$ **91.** $(3x + 8)(x - 2)$ **93.** $(15x - 1)(x - 6)$ **95.** $3(x - 2)(3x + 2)$
97. $(x + 7)(x + 9)$ **99.** $(x^2 - 2)(x^2 + 10)$ **101.** $(x + 9)(x - 9)$ **103.** $6(x + 3)(x - 3)$ **105.** $(4 + y^2)(2 + y)(2 - y)$ **107.** $(x - 7)(x + 1)$
109. $(y + 8)(y^2 - 8y + 64)$ **111.** $(1 - 4y)(1 + 4y + 16y^2)$ **113.** $2x^2(x + 2y)(x^2 - 2xy + 4y^2)$ **115.** $(x - 3 - 2y)(x - 3 + 2y)$

117. $(4a - 5b)^2$ **119.** $\dfrac{1}{3}, -7$ **121.** $0, 4, \dfrac{9}{2}$ **123.** $0, 6$ **125.** $-\dfrac{1}{3}, 2$ **127.** $-4, 1$ **129.** $0, 6, -3$ **131.** $0, -2, 1$ **133.** $-\dfrac{15}{2}, 7$ **135.** 5 sec

137. $3x^3 + 13x^2 - 9x + 5$ **139.** $8x^2 + 3x + 4.5$ **141.** -24 **143.** $6y^4(2y - 1)$ **145.** $2(3x + 1)(x - 6)$ **147.** $z^5(2z + 7)(2z - 7)$ **149.** $0, 3$

Chapter 5 Test

1. $\dfrac{1}{81x^2}$ **2.** $-12x^2z$ **3.** $\dfrac{3a^7}{2b^5}$ **4.** $-\dfrac{y^{40}}{z^5}$ **5.** 6.3×10^8 **6.** 1.2×10^{-2} **7.** 0.000005 **8.** 0.0009 **9.** $-5x^3y - 11x - 9$

10. $-12x^2y - 3xy^2$ **11.** $12x^2 - 5x - 28$ **12.** $25a^2 - 4b^2$ **13.** $36m^2 + 12mn + n^2$ **14.** $2x^3 - 13x^2 + 14x - 4$ **15.** $4x^2y(4x - 3y^3)$

16. $(x - 15)(x + 2)$ **17.** $(2y + 5)^2$ **18.** $3(2x + 1)(x - 3)$ **19.** $(2x + 5)(2x - 5)$ **20.** $(x + 4)(x^2 - 4x + 16)$

21. $3y(x + 3y)(x - 3y)$ **22.** $6(x^2 + 4)$ **23.** $2(2y - 1)(4y^2 + 2y + 1)$ **24.** $(x + 3)(x - 3)(y - 3)$ **25.** $4, -\dfrac{8}{7}$ **26.** $-3, 8$

27. $-\dfrac{5}{2}, -2, 2$ **28.** $(x + 2y)(x - 2y)$ **29. a.** 960 ft **b.** 953.44 ft **c.** 11 sec

Chapter 5 Cumulative Review

1. a. 3 **b.** 1 **c.** 2; Sec. 1.3, Ex. 8 **3.** 1; Sec. 2.1, Ex. 4 **5.** \$11,607.55; Sec. 2.3, Ex. 4 **7. a.** $\left(-\infty, \dfrac{3}{2}\right]$

b. $(-3, \infty)$; Sec. 2.4, Ex. 4 **9.** $\left[-9, -\dfrac{9}{2}\right]$; Sec. 2.5, Ex. 5 **11.** 0; Sec. 2.6, Ex. 5 **13.** $\varnothing$; Sec. 2.7, Ex. 4

15. ; Sec. 3.1, Ex. 5 **17.** $(2, -3), (-6, -9), (0, 3)$; Sec. 3.6, Ex. 1 **19.** ; Sec. 3.3, Ex. 6 **21.** 0; Sec. 3.4, Ex. 7

23. $y = 3$; Sec. 3.5, Ex. 8 **25.** ; Sec. 3.7, Ex. 4 **27.** $\left(-4, \dfrac{1}{2}\right)$; Sec. 4.1, Ex. 3 **29.** $\left(\dfrac{1}{2}, 0, \dfrac{3}{4}\right)$; Sec. 4.2, Ex. 3

31. 7, 11; Sec. 4.3, Ex. 2 **33.** $\varnothing$; Sec. 4.4, Ex. 2 **35.** $30°, 40°, 110°$; Sec. 4.3, Ex. 6 **37. a.** 7.3×10^5 **b.** 1.04×10^{-6}; Sec. 5.1, Ex. 8

39. a. $\dfrac{y^6}{4}$ **b.** x^9 **c.** $\dfrac{49}{4}$ **d.** $\dfrac{y^{16}}{25x^5}$; Sec. 5.2, Ex. 3 **41.** 4; Sec. 5.3, Ex. 3 **43. a.** $10x^9$ **b.** $-7xy^{15}z^9$; Sec. 5.4, Ex. 1

45. $17x^3y^2(1 - 2x)$; Sec. 5.5, Ex. 3 **47.** $(x + 2)(x + 8)$; Sec. 5.6, Ex. 1 **49.** $-5, \dfrac{1}{2}$; Sec. 5.8, Ex. 2

CHAPTER 6 RATIONAL EXPRESSIONS

Section 6.1
Practice Exercises

1. a. $\{x \mid x \text{ is a real number}\}$ **b.** $\{x \mid x \text{ is a real number and } x \neq -3\}$ **c.** $\{x \mid x \text{ is a real number and } x \neq 2, x \neq 3\}$

2. a. $\dfrac{1}{2z - 1}$ **b.** $\dfrac{5x + 3}{6x - 5}$ **3. a.** 1 **b.** -1 **4.** $-\dfrac{5(2 + x)}{x + 3}$ **5. a.** $x^2 - 4x + 16$ **b.** $\dfrac{5}{z - 3}$ **6. a.** $\dfrac{2n + 1}{n(n - 1)}$ **b.** $-x^2$

7. a. $\dfrac{-y^3}{21(y + 3)}$ **b.** $\dfrac{7x + 2}{x + 2}$ **8.** $\dfrac{5}{3(x - 3)}$ **9. a.** \$7.20 **b.** \$3.60

Graphing Calculator Explorations 6.1

1. $\{x \mid x \text{ is a real number and } x \neq -2, x \neq 2\}$

3. $\left\{x \mid x \text{ is a real number and } x \neq -4, x \neq \dfrac{1}{2}\right\}$

Vocabulary and Readiness Check 6.1

1. rational   **3.** domain   **5.** 1   **7.** $\dfrac{-a}{b}; \dfrac{a}{-b}$ **9.** $\dfrac{xy}{10}$ **11.** $\dfrac{2y}{3x}$ **13.** $\dfrac{m^2}{36}$

Exercise Set 6.1

1. $\{x \mid x \text{ is a real number}\}$ **3.** $\{t \mid t \text{ is a real number and } t \neq 0\}$ **5.** $\{x \mid x \text{ is a real number and } x \neq 7\}$

7. $\left\{x \;\middle|\; x \text{ is a real number and } x \neq \dfrac{1}{3}\right\}$ **9.** $\{x \mid x \text{ is a real number and } x \neq -2, x \neq 0, x \neq 1\}$ **11.** $\{x \mid x \text{ is a real number and } x \neq 2, x \neq -2\}$

13. $1 - 2x$ **15.** $x - 3$ **17.** $\dfrac{9}{7}$ **19.** $x - 4$ **21.** -1 **23.** $-(x + 7)$ **25.** $\dfrac{2x + 1}{x - 1}$ **27.** $\dfrac{x^2 + 5x + 25}{2}$ **29.** $\dfrac{x - 2}{2x^2 + 1}$

31. $\dfrac{1}{3x + 5}$ **33.** $-\dfrac{4}{5}$ **35.** $-\dfrac{6a}{2a + 1}$ **37.** $\dfrac{3}{2(x - 1)}$ **39.** $\dfrac{x + 2}{x + 3}$ **41.** $\dfrac{3a}{5(a - b)}$ **43.** $\dfrac{1}{6}$ **45.** $\dfrac{x}{3}$ **47.** $\dfrac{4a^2}{a - b}$

49. $\dfrac{4}{(x + 2)(x + 3)}$ **51.** $\dfrac{1}{2}$ **53.** -1 **55.** $\dfrac{8(a - 2)}{3(a + 2)}$ **57.** $\dfrac{(x + 2)(x + 3)}{4}$ **59.** $\dfrac{2(x + 3)(x - 3)}{5(x^2 - 8x - 15)}$ **61.** $r^2 - rs + s^2$

63. $\dfrac{8}{x^2 y}$ **65.** $\dfrac{(y + 5)(2x - 1)}{(y + 2)(5x + 1)}$ **67.** $\dfrac{5(3a + 2)}{a}$ **69.** $\dfrac{5x^2 - 2}{(x - 1)^2}$ **71.** $\dfrac{10}{3}, -8, -\dfrac{7}{3}$ **73.** $-\dfrac{17}{48}, \dfrac{2}{7}, -\dfrac{3}{8}$

75. a. \$200 million   **b.** \$500 million   **c.** \$300 million   **d.** $\{x \mid x \text{ is a real number}\}$ **77.** $\dfrac{7}{5}$ **79.** $\dfrac{1}{12}$ **81.** $\dfrac{11}{16}$

83. b and d   **85.** no; answers may vary   **87.** $\dfrac{5}{x - 2}$ sq m   **89.** $\dfrac{(x + 2)(x - 1)^2}{x^5}$ ft   **91.** answers may vary

93. a. 1   **b.** -1 **c.** neither   **d.** -1 **e.** -1 **f.** 1   **95.** $(x - 5)(2x + 7)$ **97.** $0, \dfrac{20}{9}, \dfrac{60}{7}, 20, \dfrac{140}{3}, 180, 380, 1980;$

99. $2x^2(x^n + 2)$ **101.** $\dfrac{1}{10y(y^n + 3)}$ **103.** $\dfrac{y^n + 1}{2(y^n - 1)}$

Section 6.2
Practice Exercises

1. a. $\dfrac{9 + x}{11z^2}$ **b.** $\dfrac{3x}{4}$ **c.** $x - 4$ **d.** $\dfrac{-3}{2a^2}$ **2. a.** $18x^3 y^5$ **b.** $(x - 2)(x + 3)$ **c.** $(b - 4)^2(b + 4)(2b + 3)$ **d.** $-4(y - 3)(y + 3)$

3. a. $\dfrac{20p + 3}{5p^4 q}$ **b.** $\dfrac{5y^2 + 19y - 12}{(y + 3)(y - 3)}$ **c.** 3   **4.** $\dfrac{t^2 - t - 15}{(t + 5)(t - 5)(t + 2)}$ **5.** $\dfrac{5x^2 - 12x - 3}{(3x + 1)(x - 2)(2x - 5)}$ **6.** $\dfrac{4}{x - 2}$

Vocabulary and Readiness Check 6.2

1. a, b   **3.** c   **5.** $\dfrac{12}{y}$ **7.** $\dfrac{35}{y^2}$ **9.** $\dfrac{-x + 4}{2x}$ **11.** $\dfrac{16}{y - 2}$

Exercise Set 6.2

1. $-\dfrac{3}{xz^2}$ **3.** $\dfrac{x + 2}{x - 2}$ **5.** $x - 2$ **7.** $\dfrac{-1}{x - 2}$ or $\dfrac{1}{2 - x}$ **9.** $-\dfrac{5}{x}$ **11.** $35x$ **13.** $x(x + 1)$ **15.** $(x + 7)(x - 7)$ **17.** $6(x + 2)(x - 2)$

19. $(a + b)(a - b)^2$ **21.** $-4x(x + 3)(x - 3)$ **23.** $\dfrac{17}{6x}$ **25.** $\dfrac{35 - 4y}{14y^2}$ **27.** $\dfrac{-13x + 4}{(x + 4)(x - 4)}$ **29.** $\dfrac{3}{x + 4}$ **31.** 0   **33.** $-\dfrac{x}{x - 1}$

35. $\dfrac{-x + 1}{x - 2}$ **37.** $\dfrac{y^2 + 2y + 10}{(y + 4)(y - 4)(y - 2)}$ **39.** $\dfrac{5(x^2 + x - 4)}{(3x + 2)(x + 3)(2x - 5)}$ **41.** $\dfrac{-x^2 + 10x + 19}{(x - 2)(x + 1)(x + 3)}$ **43.** $\dfrac{x^2 + 4x + 2}{(2x + 5)(x - 7)(x - 1)}$

45. $\dfrac{5a + 1}{(a + 1)^2(a - 1)}$ **47.** $\dfrac{3}{x^2 y^3}$ **49.** $-\dfrac{5}{x}$ **51.** $\dfrac{25}{6(x + 5)}$ **53.** $\dfrac{-2x - 1}{x^2(x - 3)}$ **55.** $\dfrac{b(2a - b)}{(a + b)(a - b)}$ **57.** $\dfrac{2(x + 8)}{(x + 2)^2(x - 2)}$

59. $\dfrac{3x^2 + 23x - 7}{(2x - 1)(x - 5)(x + 3)}$ **61.** $\dfrac{5 - 2x}{2(x + 1)}$ **63.** $\dfrac{2(x^2 + x - 21)}{(x + 3)^2(x - 3)}$ **65.** $\dfrac{6x}{(x + 3)(x - 3)^2}$ **67.** $\dfrac{4}{3}$ **69.** $\dfrac{2x^2 + 9x - 18}{6x^2}$ or $\dfrac{(x + 6)(2x - 3)}{6x^2}$

71. $\dfrac{4a^2}{9(a - 1)}$ **73.** 4   **75.** $-\dfrac{4}{x - 1}$ **77.** $-\dfrac{32}{x(x + 2)(x - 2)}$ **79.** 10   **81.** $4 + x^2$ **83.** 10   **85.** 2   **87.** 3   **89.** 5 m

91. $\dfrac{2x - 3}{x^2 + 1} - \dfrac{x - 6}{x^2 + 1} = \dfrac{2x - 3 - x + 6}{x^2 + 1} = \dfrac{x + 3}{x^2 + 1}$ **93.** $\dfrac{4x}{x + 5}$ ft; $\dfrac{x^2}{(x + 5)^2}$ sq ft   **95.** answers may vary   **97.** answers may vary

99. answers may vary   **101.** $\dfrac{3}{2x}$ **103.** $\dfrac{4 - 3x}{x^2}$ **105.**

Section 6.3
Practice Exercises
1. a. $\dfrac{1}{12m}$ **b.** $\dfrac{8x(x+4)}{3(x-4)}$ **c.** $\dfrac{b^2}{a^2}$ **2. a.** $\dfrac{8x(x+4)}{3(x-4)}$ **b.** $\dfrac{b^2}{a^2}$ **3.** $\dfrac{y(3xy+1)}{x^2(1+xy)}$ **4.** $\dfrac{1-6x}{15+6x}$

Vocabulary and Readiness Check 6.3
1. $\dfrac{7}{1+z}$ **3.** $\dfrac{1}{x^2}$ **5.** $\dfrac{2}{x}$ **7.** $\dfrac{1}{9y}$

Exercise Set 6.3
1. 4 **3.** $\dfrac{7}{13}$ **5.** $\dfrac{4}{x}$ **7.** $\dfrac{9(x-2)}{9x^2+4}$ **9.** $2x+y$ **11.** $\dfrac{2(x+1)}{2x-1}$ **13.** $\dfrac{2x+3}{4-9x}$ **15.** $\dfrac{1}{x^2-2x+4}$ **17.** $\dfrac{x}{5(x-2)}$

19. $\dfrac{x-2}{2x-1}$ **21.** $\dfrac{x}{2-3x}$ **23.** $-\dfrac{y}{x+y}$ **25.** $-\dfrac{2x^3}{y(x-y)}$ **27.** $\dfrac{2x+1}{y}$ **29.** $\dfrac{x-3}{9}$ **31.** $\dfrac{1}{x+2}$ **33.** 2

35. $\dfrac{xy^2}{x^2+y^2}$ **37.** $\dfrac{2b^2+3a}{b(b-a)}$ **39.** $\dfrac{x}{(x+1)(x-1)}$ **41.** $\dfrac{1+a}{1-a}$ **43.** $\dfrac{x(x+6y)}{2y}$ **45.** $\dfrac{5a}{2(a+2)}$ **47.** $xy(5y+2x)$

49. $\dfrac{xy}{2x+5y}$ **51.** $\dfrac{x^2y^2}{4}$ **53.** $-9x^3y^4$ **55.** $-4, 14$ **57.** a and c **59.** $\dfrac{770a}{770-s}$ **61.** a, b **63.** $\dfrac{1+x}{2+x}$ **65.** $x(x+1)$

67. $\dfrac{x-3y}{x+3y}$ **69.** $3a^2+4a+4$ **71. a.** $\dfrac{1}{a+h}$ **b.** $\dfrac{1}{a}$ **c.** $\dfrac{\dfrac{1}{a+h}-\dfrac{1}{a}}{h}$ **d.** $\dfrac{-1}{a(a+h)}$ **73. a.** $\dfrac{3}{a+h+1}$

b. $\dfrac{3}{a+1}$ **c.** $\dfrac{\dfrac{3}{a+h+1}-\dfrac{3}{a+1}}{h}$ **d.** $\dfrac{-3}{(a+h+1)(a+1)}$

Section 6.4
Practice Exercises
1. $3a^2-2a+5$ **2.** $5a^2b^2-8ab+1-\dfrac{8}{ab}$ **3.** $3x-2$ **4.** $3x-2$ **5.** $5x^2-6x+8+\dfrac{6}{x+3}$ **6.** $2x^2+3x-2+\dfrac{-8x+4}{x^2+1}$

7. $16x^2+20x+25$ **8.** $4x^2+x+7+\dfrac{12}{x-1}$ **9.** $x^3-5x+21-\dfrac{51}{x+3}$ **10. a.** -4 **b.** -4 **11.** 15

Exercise Set 6.4
1. $2a+4$ **3.** $3ab+4$ **5.** $2y+\dfrac{3y}{x}-\dfrac{2y}{x^2}$ **7.** $x+1$ **9.** $2x-8$ **11.** $x-\dfrac{1}{2}$ **13.** $2x^2-\dfrac{1}{2}x+5$ **15.** $2x^2-6$

17. $3x^3+5x+4-\dfrac{2x}{x^2-2}$ **19.** $2x^3+\dfrac{9}{2}x^2+10x+21+\dfrac{42}{x-2}$ **21.** $x+8$ **23.** $x-1$ **25.** $x^2-5x-23-\dfrac{41}{x-2}$

27. $4x+8+\dfrac{7}{x-2}$ **29.** $x^6y+\dfrac{2}{y}+1$ **31.** $5x^2-6-\dfrac{5}{2x-1}$ **33.** $2x^2+2x+8+\dfrac{28}{x-4}$ **35.** $2x^3-3x^2+x-4$

37. $3x^2+4x-8+\dfrac{20}{x+1}$ **39.** $3x^2+3x-3$ **41.** x^2+x+1 **43.** $-\dfrac{5y}{x}-\dfrac{15z}{x}-25z$ **45.** $3x^4-2x$ **47.** 1 **49.** -133

51. 3 **53.** $-\dfrac{187}{81}$ **55.** $\dfrac{95}{32}$ **57.** $-\dfrac{5}{6}$ **59.** 2 **61.** 54 **63.** $(x-1)(x^2+x+1)$ **65.** $(5z+2)(25z^2-10z+4)$ **67.** $(y+2)(x+3)$

69. $x(x+3)(x-3)$ **71.** yes **73.** no **75.** a or d **77.** (x^4+2x^2-6) m **79.** $(3x-7)$ in. **81.** (x^3-5x^2+2x-1) cm

83. $x^3+\dfrac{5}{3}x^2+\dfrac{5}{3}x+\dfrac{8}{3}+\dfrac{8}{3(x-1)}$ **85.** $\dfrac{3}{2}x^3+\dfrac{1}{4}x^2+\dfrac{1}{8}x-\dfrac{7}{16}+\dfrac{1}{16(2x-1)}$ **87.** $x^3-\dfrac{2}{5}x$ **89.** $5x-1+\dfrac{6}{x}; x\neq 0$

91. $7x^3+14x^2+25x+50+\dfrac{102}{x-2}; x\neq 2$ **93.** answers may vary **95.** answers may vary

97. $(x+3)(x^2+4)=x^3+3x^2+4x+12$ **99.** 0 **101.** $x^3+2x^2+7x+28$

Section 6.5
Practice Exercises
1. 4 **2.** 7 **3.** $\{\ \}$ or $\varnothing$ **4.** -1 **5.** 1 **6.** 12, -1

Vocabulary and Readiness Check 6.5
1. c **3.** a

Exercise Set 6.5

1. 72   **3.** 2   **5.** 6   **7.** 2, −2   **9.** ∅   **11.** $-\dfrac{28}{3}$ **13.** 3   **15.** −8   **17.** 3   **19.** ∅   **21.** 1   **23.** 3   **25.** −1   **27.** 6   **29.** $\dfrac{1}{3}$

31. −5, 5   **33.** 3   **35.** 7   **37.** ∅   **39.** $\dfrac{4}{3}$ **41.** −12   **43.** 1, $\dfrac{11}{4}$ **45.** −5, −1   **47.** $-\dfrac{7}{5}$ **49.** 5   **51.** length, 15 in.; width, 10 in.

53. 36%   **55.** 12–19   **57.** 40,000 students   **59.** answers may vary   **61.** 800 pencil sharpeners   **63.** $\dfrac{1}{9}, -\dfrac{1}{4}$ **65.** 3, 2   **67.** 1.39

69. −0.08   **71.** 1, 2   **73.** −3, $-\dfrac{3}{4}$ **75.**   **77.**

The Bigger Picture

1. $\left(-2, \dfrac{16}{7}\right)$ **2.** −2, $\dfrac{16}{7}$ **3.** ±11   **4.** 5   **5.** $-\dfrac{8}{5}$ **6.** $(-\infty, 2]$ **7.** $(-\infty, -5]$ **8.** (7, 10]   **9.** $(-\infty, -17) \cup (18, \infty)$ **10.** 0, $-\dfrac{1}{3}, \dfrac{7}{5}$

Integrated Review

1. $\dfrac{1}{2}$ **2.** 10   **3.** $\dfrac{1 + 2x}{8}$ **4.** $\dfrac{15 + x}{10}$ **5.** $\dfrac{2(x - 4)}{(x + 2)(x - 1)}$ **6.** $-\dfrac{5(x - 8)}{(x - 2)(x + 4)}$ **7.** 4   **8.** 8   **9.** −5   **10.** $-\dfrac{2}{3}$ **11.** $\dfrac{2x + 5}{x(x - 3)}$

12. $\dfrac{5}{2x}$ **13.** −2   **14.** $-\dfrac{y}{x}$ **15.** $\dfrac{(a + 3)(a + 1)}{a + 2}$ **16.** $\dfrac{-a^2 + 31a + 10}{5(a - 6)(a + 1)}$ **17.** $-\dfrac{1}{5}$ **18.** $-\dfrac{3}{13}$ **19.** $\dfrac{4a + 1}{(3a + 1)(3a - 1)}$

20. $\dfrac{-a - 8}{4a(a - 2)}$ or $-\dfrac{a + 8}{4a(a - 2)}$ **21.** −1, $\dfrac{3}{2}$ **22.** $\dfrac{x^2 - 3x + 10}{2(x + 3)(x - 3)}$ **23.** $\dfrac{3}{x + 1}$ **24.** $\{x \mid x$ is a real number and $x \neq 2, x \neq -1\}$ **25.** −1

26. $\dfrac{22z - 45}{3z(z - 3)}$ **27. a.** $\dfrac{x}{5} - \dfrac{x}{4} + \dfrac{1}{10}$ **b.** Write each rational expression term so that the denominator is the LCD, 20.   **c.** $\dfrac{-x + 2}{20}$

28. a. $\dfrac{x}{5} - \dfrac{x}{4} = \dfrac{1}{10}$ **b.** Clear the equation of fractions by multiplying each term by the LCD, 20.   **c.** −2   **29.** b   **30.** d   **31.** d   **32.** a   **33.** d

Section 6.6
Practice Exercises

1. $a = \dfrac{bc}{b + c}$ **2.** 7   **3.** 3000   **4.** $1\dfrac{1}{5}$ hr   **5.** 50 mph

Exercise Set 6.6

1. $C = \dfrac{5}{9}(F - 32)$ **3.** $I = A - QL$ **5.** $R = \dfrac{R_1 R_2}{R_1 + R_2}$ **7.** $n = \dfrac{2S}{a + L}$ **9.** $b = \dfrac{2A - ah}{h}$ **11.** $T_2 = \dfrac{P_2 V_2 T_1}{P_1 V_1}$ **13.** $f_2 = \dfrac{f_1 f}{f_1 - f}$

15. $L = \dfrac{n\lambda}{2}$ **17.** $c = \dfrac{2L\omega}{\theta}$ **19.** 1 and 5   **21.** 5   **23.** 4.5 gal   **25.** 4470 women   **27.** 15.6 hr   **29.** 10 min   **31.** 200 mph

33. 15 mph   **35.** −8 and −7   **37.** 36 min   **39.** 45 mph; 60 mph   **41.** 5.9 hr   **43.** 2 hr   **45.** 135 mph   **47.** 12 mi   **49.** $\dfrac{7}{8}$

51. $1\dfrac{1}{2}$ min   **53.** $2\dfrac{2}{9}$ hr   **55.** 10 mph; 8 mph   **57.** 2 hr   **59.** by jet: 3 hr; by car: 4 hr   **61.** 428 movies   **63.** 6

65. 22   **67.** answers may vary; 60 in. or 5 ft   **69.** 6 ohms   **71.** $\dfrac{1}{R} = \dfrac{1}{R_1} + \dfrac{1}{R_2} + \dfrac{1}{R_3}; R = \dfrac{15}{13}$ ohms

Exercise Set 6.7

1. $k = \dfrac{1}{5}; y = \dfrac{1}{5}x$ **3.** $k = \dfrac{3}{2}; y = \dfrac{3}{2}x$ **5.** $k = 14; y = 14x$ **7.** $k = 0.25; y = 0.25x$ **9.** 4.05 lb   **11.** 204,706 tons   **13.** $k = 30; y = \dfrac{30}{x}$

15. $k = 700; y = \dfrac{700}{x}$ **17.** $k = 2; y = \dfrac{2}{x}$ **19.** $k = 0.14; y = \dfrac{0.14}{x}$ **21.** 54 mph   **23.** 72 amps   **25.** divided by 4   **27.** $x = kyz$

29. $r = kst^3$ **31.** $k = \dfrac{1}{3}; y = \dfrac{1}{3}x^3$ **33.** $k = 0.2; y = 0.2\sqrt{x}$ **35.** $k = 1.3; y = \dfrac{1.3}{x^2}$ **37.** $k = 3; y = 3xz^3$ **39.** 22.5 tons

41. 15π cu in.   **43.** 8 ft   **45.** $y = kx$ **47.** $a = \dfrac{k}{b}$ **49.** $y = kxz$ **51.** $y = \dfrac{k}{x^3}$ **53.** $y = \dfrac{kx}{p^2}$ **55.** $C = 8\pi$ in.; $A = 16\pi$ sq in.

57. $C = 18\pi$ cm; $A = 81\pi$ sq cm   **59.** 9   **61.** 1   **63.** $\dfrac{1}{2}$ **65.** $\dfrac{2}{3}$ **67.** a   **69.** c   **71.** multiplied by 8   **73.** multiplied by 2

75. 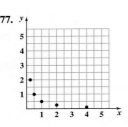 **77.**

Chapter 6 Vocabulary Check

1. complex fraction   **2.** long division   **3.** directly   **4.** inversely   **5.** least common denominator
6. synthetic division   **7.** jointly   **8.** opposites   **9.** rational expression   **10.** equation, expression

Chapter 6 Review

1. $\{x|x \text{ is a real number}\}$ **3.** $\{x|x \text{ is a real number and } x \neq 5\}$ **5.** $\{x|x \text{ is a real number and } x \neq 0, x \neq -8\}$ **7.** -1 **9.** $\dfrac{1}{x-1}$

11. $\dfrac{2(x-3)}{x-4}$ **13.** $-\dfrac{3}{2}$ **15.** $\dfrac{a-b}{2a}$ **17.** $\dfrac{12}{5}$ **19.** $\dfrac{a-b}{5a}$ **21.** $-\dfrac{1}{x}$ **23.** $60x^2y^5$ **25.** $5x(x-5)$ **27.** $\dfrac{4+x}{x-4}$

29. $\dfrac{3}{2(x-2)}$ **31.** $\dfrac{-7x-6}{5(x-3)(x+3)}$ **33.** $\dfrac{5a-1}{(a-1)^2(a+1)}$ **35.** $\dfrac{5-2x}{2(x-1)}$ **37.** $\dfrac{4-3x}{8+x}$ **39.** $\dfrac{5(4x-3)}{2(5x^2-2)}$ **41.** $\dfrac{x(5y+1)}{3y}$

43. $\dfrac{1+x}{1-x}$ **45.** $\dfrac{3}{a+h}$ **47.** $\dfrac{\frac{3}{a+h}-\frac{3}{a}}{h}$ **49.** $1+\dfrac{x}{2y}-\dfrac{9}{4xy}$ **51.** $3x^3+9x^2+2x+6-\dfrac{2}{x-3}$ **53.** $x^2-1+\dfrac{5}{2x+3}$

55. $3x^2+6x+24+\dfrac{44}{x-2}$ **57.** $x^2+3x+9-\dfrac{54}{x-3}$ **59.** 3043 **61.** $\dfrac{365}{32}$ **63.** 6 **65.** $\dfrac{3}{2}$ **67.** $\dfrac{2x+5}{x(x-7)}$ **69.** $\dfrac{-5(x+6)}{2x(x-3)}$

71. $R_2=\dfrac{RR_1}{R_1-R}$ **73.** $r=\dfrac{A-P}{Pt}$ **75.** $1, 2$ **77.** $1\dfrac{23}{37}$ hr   **79.** 8 mph   **83.** 2 **85.** $\dfrac{3}{5x}$ **87.** $\dfrac{5(a-2)}{7}$ **89.** $\dfrac{13}{3x}$

91. $\dfrac{1}{x-2}$ **93.** $\dfrac{2}{15-2x}$ **95.** $\dfrac{2(x-1)}{x+6}$ **97.** 2 **99.** $\dfrac{23}{25}$ **101.** 10 hr   **103.** $63\dfrac{2}{3}$ mph; 45 mph

Chapter 6 Test

1. $\{x|x \text{ is a real number and } x \neq 1\}$ **2.** $\{x|x \text{ is a real number and } x \neq -3, x \neq -1\}$ **3.** $-\dfrac{7}{8}$ **4.** $\dfrac{x}{x+9}$ **5.** x^2+2x+4

6. $\dfrac{5}{3x}$ **7.** $\dfrac{3}{x^3}$ **8.** $\dfrac{x+2}{2(x+3)}$ **9.** $-\dfrac{4(2x+9)}{5}$ **10.** -1 **11.** $\dfrac{1}{x(x+3)}$ **12.** $\dfrac{5x-2}{(x-3)(x+2)(x-2)}$ **13.** $\dfrac{-x+30}{6(x-7)}$

14. $\dfrac{3}{2}$ **15.** $\dfrac{64}{3}$ **16.** $\dfrac{(x-3)^2}{x-2}$ **17.** $\dfrac{4xy}{3z}+\dfrac{3}{z}+1$ **18.** $2x^2-x-2+\dfrac{2}{2x+1}$ **19.** $4x^3-15x^2+45x-136+\dfrac{407}{x+3}$

20. 91 **21.** 8 **22.** $\dfrac{2}{7}$ **23.** 3 **24.** $x=\dfrac{7a^2+b^2}{4a-b}$ **25.** 5 **26.** $\dfrac{6}{7}$ hr

Chapter 6 Cumulative Review

1. a. $8x$ **b.** $8x+3$ **c.** $x \div -7$ or $\dfrac{x}{-7}$ **d.** $2x-1.6$ **e.** $x-6$ **f.** $2(4+x)$; Sec. 1.2, Ex. 8   **3.** 2; Sec. 2.1, Ex. 5
5. 2026 and after; Sec. 2.4, Ex. 9   **7.** $\varnothing$; Sec. 2.6, Ex. 7   **9.** -1; Sec. 2.7, Ex. 8   **11.** ; Sec. 3.1, Ex. 4

13. a. function   **b.** not a function   **c.** function; Sec. 3.2, Ex. 2   **15.** ; Sec. 3.3, Ex. 4   **17.** $y=-3x-2$; Sec. 3.5, Ex. 4

19. $\dfrac{x \geq 1 \text{ and}}{y \geq 2x - 1}$; Sec. 3.7, Ex. 3   **21.** $(0, -5)$; Sec. 4.1, Ex. 6   **23.** $\varnothing$; Sec. 4.2, Ex. 2   **25.** $30°, 110°, 40°$; Sec. 4.3, Ex. 6

27. $(1, -1, 3)$; Sec. 4.4, Ex. 3   **29. a.** 1   **b.** -1 **c.** 1   **d.** 2; Sec. 5.1, Ex. 3   **31. a.** $4x^b$ **b.** y^{5a+6}; Sec 5.2, Ex. 5

33. a. 2   **b.** 5   **c.** 1   **d.** 6   **e.** 0; Sec. 5.3, Ex. 1   **35.** $9 + 12a + 6b + 4a^2 + 4ab + b^2$; Sec. 5.4, Ex. 9   **37.** $(b - 6)(a + 2)$; Sec 5.5, Ex. 7

39. $2(n^2 - 19n + 40)$; Sec. 5.6, Ex. 4   **41.** $(x + 2 + y)(x + 2 - y)$; Sec. 5.7, Ex. 5   **43.** $-2, 6$; Sec. 5.8, Ex. 1   **45. a.** $\dfrac{1}{5x - 1}$

b. $\dfrac{9x + 4}{8x - 7}$; Sec. 6.1, Ex. 2   **47.** $\dfrac{5k^2 - 7k + 4}{(k + 2)(k - 2)(k - 1)}$; Sec. 6.2, Ex. 4   **49.** -2; Sec. 6.5, Ex. 2

CHAPTER 7 RATIONAL EXPONENTS, RADICALS, AND COMPLEX NUMBERS

Section 7.1
Practice Exercises

1. a. 7   **b.** 0   **c.** $\dfrac{4}{9}$ **d.** 0.8   **e.** z^4 **f.** $4b^2$ **g.** -6 **h.** not a real number   **2.** 6.708   **3. a.** -1 **b.** 3   **c.** $\dfrac{3}{4}$ **d.** x^4 **e.** $-2x$

4. a. 10   **b.** -1 **c.** -9 **d.** not a real number   **e.** $3x^3$ **5. a.** 4   **b.** $|x^7|$ **c.** $|x + 7|$ **d.** -7 **e.** $3x - 5$ **f.** $7|x|$ **g.** $|x + 2|$

6. a. 4   **b.** 2   **c.** 2   **d.** -2 **7.** **8.**

Vocabulary and Readiness Check 7.1

1. index; radical sign; radicand   **3.** is not   **5.** $[0, \infty)$ **7.** $(16, 4)$ **9.** d   **11.** d

Exercise Set 7.1

1. 10   **3.** $\dfrac{1}{2}$ **5.** 0.01   **7.** -6 **9.** x^5 **11.** $4y^3$ **13.** 2.646   **15.** 6.164   **17.** 14.142   **19.** 4   **21.** $\dfrac{1}{2}$

23. -1 **25.** x^4 **27.** $-3x^3$ **29.** -2 **31.** not a real number   **33.** -2 **35.** x^4 **37.** $2x^2$ **39.** $9x^2$ **41.** $4x^2$

43. 8   **45.** -8 **47.** $2|x|$ **49.** x **51.** $|x - 5|$ **53.** $|x + 2|$ **55.** -11 **57.** $2x$ **59.** y^6 **61.** $5ab^{10}$

63. $-3x^4y^3$ **65.** a^4b **67.** $-2x^2y$ **69.** $\dfrac{5}{7}$ **71.** $\dfrac{x}{2y}$ **73.** $-\dfrac{z^7}{3x}$ **75.** $\dfrac{x}{2}$ **77.** $\sqrt{3}$ **79.** -1 **81.** -3 **83.** $\sqrt{7}$

85. $[0, \infty)$;   **87.** $[3, \infty)$; 0, 1, 2, 3   **89.** $(-\infty, \infty)$;   **91.** $(-\infty, \infty)$; 0, 1, -1, 2, -2

93. $-32x^{15}y^{10}$ **95.** $-60x^7y^{10}z^5$ **97.** $\dfrac{x^9y^5}{2}$ **99.** not a real number   **101.** not a real number   **103.** answers may vary   **105.** 13   **107.** 18

109. 1.69 sq m   **111.** answers may vary   **113.**   **115.**

Section 7.2
Practice Exercises

1. a. 6 **b.** 10 **c.** $\sqrt[5]{x}$ **d.** 1 **e.** -8 **f.** $5x^3$ **g.** $\sqrt[4]{3x}$ **2. a.** 64 **b.** -1 **c.** -27 **d.** $\dfrac{1}{125}$ **e.** $\sqrt[9]{(3x+2)^5}$

3. a. $\dfrac{1}{27}$ **b.** $\dfrac{1}{16}$ **4. a.** $y^{10/3}$ **b.** $x^{17/20}$ **c.** $\dfrac{1}{9}$ **d.** $b^{2/9}$ **e.** $\dfrac{81}{x^3 y^{11/3}}$ **5. a.** $x^{14/15} - x^{13/5}$ **b.** $x + 4x^{1/2} - 12$ **6.** $x^{-1/5}(2 - 7x)$

7. a. $\sqrt[3]{x}$ **b.** $\sqrt{6}$ **c.** $\sqrt[4]{a^2 b}$ **8. a.** $\sqrt[12]{x^7}$ **b.** $\sqrt[15]{y^2}$ **c.** $\sqrt[6]{675}$

Vocabulary and Readiness Check 7.2

1. true **3.** true **5.** multiply **7.** A **9.** C **11.** B

Exercise Set 7.2

1. 7 **3.** 3 **5.** $\dfrac{1}{2}$ **7.** 13 **9.** $2\sqrt[3]{m}$ **11.** $3x^2$ **13.** -3 **15.** -2 **17.** 8 **19.** 16 **21.** not a real number **23.** $\sqrt[5]{(2x)^3}$

25. $\sqrt[3]{(7x+2)^2}$ **27.** $\dfrac{64}{27}$ **29.** $\dfrac{1}{16}$ **31.** $\dfrac{1}{16}$ **33.** not a real number **35.** $\dfrac{1}{x^{1/4}}$ **37.** $a^{2/3}$ **39.** $\dfrac{5x^{3/4}}{7}$ **41.** $a^{7/3}$ **43.** x **45.** $3^{5/8}$

47. $y^{1/6}$ **49.** $8u^3$ **51.** $-b$ **53.** $\dfrac{1}{x^2}$ **55.** $27x^{2/3}$ **57.** $\dfrac{y}{z^{1/6}}$ **59.** $\dfrac{1}{x^{7/4}}$ **61.** $y - y^{7/6}$ **63.** $x^{5/3} - 2x^{2/3}$ **65.** $4x^{2/3} - 9$ **67.** $x^{8/3}(1 + x^{2/3})$

69. $x^{1/5}(x^{1/5} - 3)$ **71.** $x^{-1/3}(5 + x)$ **73.** $\sqrt{x}$ **75.** $\sqrt[3]{2}$ **77.** $2\sqrt{x}$ **79.** $\sqrt{xy}$ **81.** $\sqrt[3]{a^2 b}$ **83.** $\sqrt{x+3}$ **85.** $\sqrt[15]{y^{11}}$

87. $\sqrt[12]{b^5}$ **89.** $\sqrt[24]{x^{23}}$ **91.** $\sqrt{a}$ **93.** $\sqrt[6]{432}$ **95.** $\sqrt[15]{343y^5}$ **97.** $\sqrt[6]{125r^3 s^2}$ **99.** $25 \cdot 3$ **101.** $16 \cdot 3$ or $4 \cdot 12$ **103.** $8 \cdot 2$ **105.** $27 \cdot 2$

107. 1509 calories **109.** 210.1 million **111.** $a^{1/3}$ **113.** $x^{1/5}$ **115.** 1.6818 **117.** 5.6645 **119.** $\dfrac{t^{1/2}}{u^{1/2}}$

Section 7.3
Practice Exercises

1. a. $\sqrt{35}$ **b.** $\sqrt{13z}$ **c.** 5 **d.** $\sqrt[3]{15x^2 y}$ **e.** $\sqrt{\dfrac{5t}{2m}}$ **2. a.** $\dfrac{6}{7}$ **b.** $\dfrac{\sqrt{z}}{4}$ **c.** $\dfrac{5}{2}$ **d.** $\dfrac{\sqrt[4]{5}}{3x^2}$ **3. a.** $7\sqrt{2}$ **b.** $3\sqrt[3]{2}$ **c.** $\sqrt{35}$ **d.** $3\sqrt[4]{3}$

4. a. $6z^3\sqrt{z}$ **b.** $2pq^2\sqrt[3]{4pq}$ **c.** $2x^3\sqrt[4]{x^3}$ **5. a.** 4 **b.** $\dfrac{7}{3}\sqrt{z}$ **c.** $10xy^2\sqrt[3]{x^2}$ **d.** $6x^2 y\sqrt[5]{2y}$ **6.** $\sqrt{17} \approx 4.123$ **7.** $\left(\dfrac{13}{2}, -4\right)$

Vocabulary and Readiness Check 7.3

1. midpoint; point **3.** midpoint **5.** false **7.** true **9.** false

Exercise Set 7.3

1. $\sqrt{14}$ **3.** 2 **5.** $\sqrt[3]{36}$ **7.** $\sqrt{6x}$ **9.** $\sqrt{\dfrac{14}{xy}}$ **11.** $\sqrt[4]{20x^3}$ **13.** $\dfrac{\sqrt{6}}{7}$ **15.** $\dfrac{\sqrt{2}}{7}$ **17.** $\dfrac{\sqrt[4]{x^3}}{2}$ **19.** $\dfrac{\sqrt[3]{4}}{3}$ **21.** $\dfrac{\sqrt[4]{8}}{x^2}$ **23.** $\dfrac{\sqrt[3]{2x}}{3y^4\sqrt[3]{3}}$

25. $\dfrac{x\sqrt{y}}{10}$ **27.** $\dfrac{x\sqrt{5}}{2y}$ **29.** $-\dfrac{z^2\sqrt[3]{z}}{3x}$ **31.** $4\sqrt{2}$ **33.** $4\sqrt[3]{3}$ **35.** $25\sqrt{3}$ **37.** $2\sqrt{6}$ **39.** $10x^2\sqrt{x}$ **41.** $2y^2\sqrt[3]{2y}$ **43.** $a^2 b\sqrt[4]{b^3}$

45. $y^2\sqrt{y}$ **47.** $5ab\sqrt{b}$ **49.** $-2x^2\sqrt[5]{y}$ **51.** $x^4\sqrt[3]{50x^2}$ **53.** $-4a^4 b^3\sqrt{2b}$ **55.** $3x^3 y^4\sqrt{xy}$ **57.** $5r^3 s^4$ **59.** $\sqrt{2}$ **61.** 2 **63.** 10

65. $x^2 y$ **67.** $24m^2$ **69.** $\dfrac{15x\sqrt{2x}}{2}$ or $\dfrac{15x}{2}\sqrt{2x}$ **71.** $2a^2\sqrt[4]{2}$ **73.** 5 units **75.** $\sqrt{41}$ units ≈ 6.403 **77.** $\sqrt{10}$ units ≈ 3.162

79. $\sqrt{5}$ units ≈ 2.236 **81.** $\sqrt{192.58}$ units ≈ 13.877 **83.** $(4, -2)$ **85.** $\left(-5, \dfrac{5}{2}\right)$ **87.** $(3, 0)$ **89.** $\left(-\dfrac{1}{2}, \dfrac{1}{2}\right)$ **91.** $\left(\sqrt{2}, \dfrac{\sqrt{5}}{2}\right)$

93. $(6.2, -6.65)$ **95.** $14x$ **97.** $2x^2 - 7x - 15$ **99.** y^2 **101.** $-3x - 15$ **103.** $x^2 - 8x + 16$ **105.** $\dfrac{\sqrt[3]{64}}{\sqrt{64}} = \dfrac{4}{8} = \dfrac{1}{2}$ **107.** x^7 **109.** $a^3 bc^5$

111. $z^{10}\sqrt[3]{z^2}$ **113.** $q^2 r^5 s\sqrt{q^3 r^5}$ **115.** $r = 1.6$ meters **117. a.** 3.8 times **b.** 2.9 times **c.** answers may vary

Section 7.4
Practice Exercises

1. a. $8\sqrt{17}$ **b.** $-5\sqrt[3]{5z}$ **c.** $3\sqrt{2} + 5\sqrt[3]{2}$ **2. a.** $11\sqrt{6}$ **b.** $-9\sqrt[3]{3}$ **c.** $-2\sqrt{3x}$ **d.** $2\sqrt{10} + 2\sqrt{5}$ **e.** $4x\sqrt[3]{3x}$ **3. a.** $\dfrac{5\sqrt{7}}{12}$

b. $\dfrac{13\sqrt[3]{6y}}{4}$ **4. a.** $2\sqrt{5} + 5\sqrt{3}$ **b.** $2\sqrt{3} + 2\sqrt{2} - \sqrt{30} - 2\sqrt{5}$ **c.** $6z + \sqrt{z} - 12$ **d.** $-6\sqrt{6} + 15$ **e.** $5x - 9$ **f.** $6\sqrt{x+2} + x + 11$

Vocabulary and Readiness Check 7.4

1. Unlike **3.** Like **5.** $6\sqrt{3}$ **7.** $7\sqrt{x}$ **9.** $8\sqrt[3]{x}$ **11.** $\sqrt{11} + \sqrt[3]{11}$ **13.** $10\sqrt[3]{2x}$

Exercise Set 7.4

1. $-2\sqrt{2}$ **3.** $10x\sqrt{2x}$ **5.** $17\sqrt{2} - 15\sqrt{5}$ **7.** $-\sqrt[3]{2x}$ **9.** $5b\sqrt{b}$ **11.** $\dfrac{31\sqrt{2}}{15}$ **13.** $\dfrac{\sqrt[3]{11}}{3}$ **15.** $\dfrac{5\sqrt{5x}}{9}$ **17.** $14 + \sqrt{3}$ **19.** $7 - 3y$

21. $6\sqrt{3} - 6\sqrt{2}$ **23.** $-23\sqrt[3]{5}$ **25.** $2b\sqrt{b}$ **27.** $20y\sqrt{2y}$ **29.** $2y\sqrt[3]{2x}$ **31.** $6\sqrt[3]{11} - 4\sqrt{11}$ **33.** $4x\sqrt[4]{x^3}$ **35.** $\dfrac{2\sqrt{3}}{3}$ **37.** $\dfrac{5x\sqrt[3]{x}}{7}$

39. $\dfrac{5\sqrt{7}}{2x}$ **41.** $\dfrac{\sqrt[3]{2}}{6}$ **43.** $\dfrac{14x\sqrt[3]{2x}}{9}$ **45.** $15\sqrt{3}$ in. **47.** $\sqrt{35} + \sqrt{21}$ **49.** $7 - 2\sqrt{10}$ **51.** $3\sqrt{x} - x\sqrt{3}$ **53.** $6x - 13\sqrt{x} - 5$

55. $\sqrt[3]{a^2} + \sqrt[3]{a} - 20$ **57.** $6\sqrt{2} - 12$ **59.** $2 + 2x\sqrt{3}$ **61.** $-16 - \sqrt{35}$ **63.** $x - y^2$ **65.** $3 + 2x\sqrt{3} + x^2$ **67.** $23x - 5x\sqrt{15}$

69. $2\sqrt[3]{2} - \sqrt[3]{4}$ **71.** $x + 1$ **73.** $x + 24 + 10\sqrt{x - 1}$ **75.** $2x + 6 - 2\sqrt{2x + 5}$ **77.** $x - 7$ **79.** $\dfrac{7}{x + y}$ **81.** $2a - 3$ **83.** $\dfrac{-2 + \sqrt{3}}{3}$

85. $22\sqrt{5}$ ft; 150 sq ft **87. a.** $2\sqrt{3}$ **b.** 3 **c.** answers may vary **89.** answers may vary

Section 7.5
Practice Exercises

1. a. $\dfrac{5\sqrt{3}}{3}$ **b.** $\dfrac{15\sqrt{x}}{2x}$ **c.** $\dfrac{\sqrt[3]{6}}{3}$ **2.** $\dfrac{\sqrt{15yz}}{5y}$ **3.** $\dfrac{\sqrt[3]{z^2x^2}}{3x^2}$ **4. a.** $\dfrac{5(3\sqrt{5} - 2)}{41}$ **b.** $\dfrac{\sqrt{6} + 5\sqrt{3} + \sqrt{10} + 5\sqrt{5}}{-2}$ **c.** $\dfrac{6x - 3\sqrt{xy}}{4x - y}$

5. $\dfrac{2}{\sqrt{10}}$ **6.** $\dfrac{5b}{\sqrt[3]{50ab^2}}$ **7.** $\dfrac{x - 9}{4(\sqrt{x} + 3)}$

Vocabulary and Readiness Check 7.5

1. conjugate **3.** rationalizing the numerator **5.** $\sqrt{2} - x$ **7.** $5 + \sqrt{a}$ **9.** $-7\sqrt{5} - 8\sqrt{x}$

Exercise Set 7.5

1. $\dfrac{\sqrt{14}}{7}$ **3.** $\dfrac{\sqrt{5}}{5}$ **5.** $\dfrac{2\sqrt{x}}{x}$ **7.** $\dfrac{4\sqrt[3]{9}}{3}$ **9.** $\dfrac{3\sqrt{2x}}{4x}$ **11.** $\dfrac{3\sqrt[3]{2x}}{2x}$ **13.** $\dfrac{3\sqrt{3a}}{a}$ **15.** $\dfrac{3\sqrt[3]{4}}{2}$ **17.** $\dfrac{2\sqrt{21}}{7}$ **19.** $\dfrac{\sqrt{10xy}}{5y}$ **21.** $\dfrac{\sqrt[3]{75}}{5}$

23. $\dfrac{\sqrt{6x}}{10}$ **25.** $\dfrac{\sqrt{3z}}{6z}$ **27.** $\dfrac{\sqrt[3]{6xy^2}}{3x}$ **29.** $\dfrac{3\sqrt[4]{2}}{2}$ **31.** $\dfrac{2\sqrt[4]{9x}}{3x^2}$ **33.** $\dfrac{5a\sqrt[5]{4ab^4}}{2a^2b^3}$ **35.** $-2(2 + \sqrt{7})$ **37.** $\dfrac{7(3 + \sqrt{x})}{9 - x}$ **39.** $-5 + 2\sqrt{6}$

41. $\dfrac{2a + 2\sqrt{a} + \sqrt{ab} + \sqrt{b}}{4a - b}$ **43.** $-\dfrac{8(1 - \sqrt{10})}{9}$ **45.** $\dfrac{x - \sqrt{xy}}{x - y}$ **47.** $\dfrac{5 + 3\sqrt{2}}{7}$ **49.** $\dfrac{5}{\sqrt{15}}$ **51.** $\dfrac{6}{\sqrt{10}}$ **53.** $\dfrac{2x}{7\sqrt{x}}$ **55.** $\dfrac{5y}{\sqrt[3]{100xy}}$

57. $\dfrac{2}{\sqrt{10}}$ **59.** $\dfrac{2x}{11\sqrt{2x}}$ **61.** $\dfrac{7}{2\sqrt[3]{49}}$ **63.** $\dfrac{3x^2}{10\sqrt[3]{9x}}$ **65.** $\dfrac{6x^2y^3}{\sqrt{6z}}$ **67.** answers may vary **69.** $\dfrac{-7}{12 + 6\sqrt{11}}$ **71.** $\dfrac{3}{10 + 5\sqrt{7}}$

73. $\dfrac{x - 9}{x - 3\sqrt{x}}$ **75.** $\dfrac{1}{3 + 2\sqrt{2}}$ **77.** $\dfrac{x - 1}{x - 2\sqrt{x} + 1}$ **79.** 5 **81.** $-\dfrac{1}{2}, 6$ **83.** $2, 6$ **85.** $\sqrt[3]{25}$ **87.** $r = \dfrac{\sqrt{A\pi}}{2\pi}$ **89.** answers may vary

Integrated Review

1. 9 **2.** -2 **3.** $\dfrac{1}{2}$ **4.** x^3 **5.** y^3 **6.** $2y^5$ **7.** $-2y$ **8.** $3b^3$ **9.** 6 **10.** $\sqrt[4]{3y}$ **11.** $\dfrac{1}{16}$ **12.** $\sqrt[5]{(x + 1)^3}$ **13.** y **14.** $16x^{1/2}$

15. $x^{5/4}$ **16.** $4^{11/15}$ **17.** $2x^2$ **18.** $\sqrt[4]{a^3b^2}$ **19.** $\sqrt[4]{x^3}$ **20.** $\sqrt[6]{500}$ **21.** $2\sqrt{10}$ **22.** $2xy^2\sqrt[4]{x^3y^2}$ **23.** $3x\sqrt[3]{2x}$ **24.** $-2b^2\sqrt[5]{2}$

25. $\sqrt{5x}$ **26.** $4x$ **27.** $7y^2\sqrt{y}$ **28.** $2a^2\sqrt[4]{3}$ **29.** $2\sqrt{5} - 5\sqrt{3} + 5\sqrt{7}$ **30.** $y\sqrt[3]{2y}$ **31.** $\sqrt{15} - \sqrt{6}$ **32.** $10 + 2\sqrt{21}$

33. $4x^2 - 5$ **34.** $x + 2 - 2\sqrt{x + 1}$ **35.** $\dfrac{\sqrt{21}}{3}$ **36.** $\dfrac{5\sqrt[3]{4x}}{2x}$ **37.** $\dfrac{13 - 3\sqrt{21}}{5}$ **38.** $\dfrac{7}{\sqrt{21}}$ **39.** $\dfrac{3y}{\sqrt[3]{33y^2}}$ **40.** $\dfrac{x - 4}{x + 2\sqrt{x}}$

Section 7.6
Practice Exercises

1. 18 **2.** $\dfrac{3}{8}, -\dfrac{1}{2}$ **3.** 10 **4.** 9 **5.** $\dfrac{3}{25}$ **6.** $6\sqrt{3}$ meters **7.** $\sqrt{193}$ in. ≈ 13.89

Graphing Calculator Explorations 7.6

1. 3.19 **3.** $\varnothing$ **5.** 3.23

Vocabulary and Readiness Check 7.6

1. extraneous solution **3.** $x^2 - 10x + 25$

Exercise Set 7.6

1. 8 **3.** 7 **5.** ∅ **7.** 7 **9.** 6 **11.** $-\dfrac{9}{2}$ **13.** 29 **15.** 4 **17.** -4 **19.** ∅ **21.** 7 **23.** 9 **25.** 50 **27.** ∅ **29.** $\dfrac{15}{4}$

31. 13 **33.** 5 **35.** -12 **37.** 9 **39.** -3 **41.** 1 **43.** 1 **45.** $\dfrac{1}{2}$ **47.** 0, 4 **49.** $\dfrac{37}{4}$ **51.** $3\sqrt{5}$ ft **53.** $2\sqrt{10}$ m

55. $2\sqrt{131}$ m ≈ 22.9 m **57.** $\sqrt{100.84}$ mm ≈ 10.0 mm **59.** 17 ft **61.** 13 ft **63.** 14,657,415 sq mi **65.** 100 ft **67.** 100

69. $\dfrac{\pi}{2}$ sec ≈ 1.57 sec **71.** 12.97 ft **73.** answers may vary **75.** $15\sqrt{3}$ sq mi ≈ 25.98 sq mi **77.** answers may vary **79.** 0.51 km

81. function **83.** function **85.** not a function **87.** $\dfrac{x}{4x + 3}$ **89.** $-\dfrac{4z + 2}{3z}$

91. $\sqrt{5x - 1} + 4 = 7$
$\sqrt{5x - 1} = 3$
$\left(\sqrt{5x - 1}\right)^2 = 3^2$
$5x - 1 = 9$
$5x = 10$
$x = 2$

93. 1 **95. a.–b.** answers may vary **97.** $-1, 2$ **99.** $-8, -6, 0, 2$

The Bigger Picture

1. -19 **2.** $-\dfrac{5}{3}, 5$ **3.** $-\dfrac{9}{2}, 5$ **4.** $\left[\dfrac{-11}{5}, 1\right]$ **5.** $\left(-\dfrac{7}{5}, \infty\right)$ **6.** 25 **7.** $(-5, \infty)$ **8.** ∅ **9.** $(-\infty, -13) \cup (17, \infty)$ **10.** $\dfrac{17}{25}$

Section 7.7

Practice Exercises

1. a. $2i$ **b.** $i\sqrt{7}$ **c.** $-3i\sqrt{2}$ **2. a.** $-\sqrt{30}$ **b.** -3 **c.** $25i$ **d.** $3i$ **3. a.** $-1 - 4i$ **b.** $-3 + 5i$ **c.** $3 - 2i$ **4. a.** 20 **b.** $-5 + 10i$

c. $15 + 16i$ **d.** $8 - 6i$ **e.** 85 **5. a.** $\dfrac{11}{10} - \dfrac{7i}{10}$ **b.** $0 - \dfrac{5i}{2}$ **6. a.** i **b.** 1 **c.** -1 **d.** 1

Vocabulary and Readiness Check 7.7

1. complex **3.** -1 **5.** real **7.** $9i$ **9.** $i\sqrt{7}$ **11.** -4 **13.** $8i$

Exercise Set 7.7

1. $2i\sqrt{6}$ **3.** $-6i$ **5.** $24i\sqrt{7}$ **7.** $-3\sqrt{6}$ **9.** $-\sqrt{14}$ **11.** $-5\sqrt{2}$ **13.** $4i$ **15.** $i\sqrt{3}$ **17.** $2\sqrt{2}$ **19.** $6 - 4i$ **21.** $-2 + 6i$

23. $-2 - 4i$ **25.** -40 **27.** $18 + 12i$ **29.** 7 **31.** $12 - 16i$ **33.** $-4i$ **35.** $\dfrac{28}{25} - \dfrac{21}{25}i$ **37.** $4 + i$ **39.** $\dfrac{17}{13} + \dfrac{7}{13}i$ **41.** 63

43. $2 - i$ **45.** $27 + 3i$ **47.** $-\dfrac{5}{2} - 2i$ **49.** $18 + 13i$ **51.** 20 **53.** 10 **55.** 2 **57.** $-5 + \dfrac{16}{3}i$ **59.** $17 + 144i$ **61.** $\dfrac{3}{5} - \dfrac{1}{5}i$

63. $5 - 10i$ **65.** $\dfrac{1}{5} - \dfrac{8}{5}i$ **67.** $8 - i$ **69.** 7 **71.** $12 - 16i$ **73.** 1 **75.** i **77.** $-i$ **79.** -1 **81.** -64 **83.** $-243i$ **85.** 40°

87. $x^2 - 5x - 2 - \dfrac{6}{x - 1}$ **89.** 5 people **91.** 14 people **93.** 16.7% **95.** $-1 - i$ **97.** 0 **99.** $2 + 3i$ **101.** $2 + i\sqrt{2}$ **103.** $\dfrac{1}{2} - \dfrac{\sqrt{3}}{2}i$

105. answers may vary **107.** $6 - 6i$ **109.** yes

Chapter 7 Vocabulary Check

1. conjugate **2.** principal square root **3.** rationalizing **4.** imaginary unit **5.** cube root **6.** index, radicand **7.** like radicals
8. complex number **9.** distance **10.** midpoint

Chapter 7 Review

1. 9 **3.** -2 **5.** $-\dfrac{1}{7}$ **7.** -6 **9.** $-a^2b^3$ **11.** $2ab^2$ **13.** $\dfrac{x^6}{6y}$ **15.** $|-x|$ **17.** -27 **19.** $-x$ **21.** $5|(x - y)^5|$ **23.** $-x$

25. $(-\infty, \infty)$; $-2, -1, 0, 1, 2$ **27.** $-\dfrac{1}{3}$ **29.** $-\dfrac{1}{4}$ **31.** $\dfrac{1}{4}$ **33.** $\dfrac{343}{125}$ **35.** not a real number **37.** $5^{1/5}x^{2/5}y^{3/5}$ **39.** $5\sqrt[3]{xy^2z^5}$

41. $a^{13/6}$ **43.** $\dfrac{1}{a^{9/2}}$ **45.** a^4b^6 **47.** $\dfrac{b^{5/6}}{49a^{1/4}c^{5/3}}$ **49.** 4.472 **51.** 5.191 **53.** -26.246 **55.** $\sqrt[6]{1372}$

57. $2\sqrt{6}$ **59.** $2x$ **61.** $2\sqrt{15}$ **63.** $3\sqrt[3]{6}$ **65.** $6x^3\sqrt{x}$ **67.** $\dfrac{p^8\sqrt{p}}{11}$ **69.** $\dfrac{y\sqrt[4]{xy^2}}{3}$ **71. a.** $\dfrac{5}{\sqrt{\pi}}$ m or $\dfrac{5\sqrt{\pi}}{\pi}$ m

b. 5.75 in. **73.** $\sqrt{130}$ units ≈ 11.402 **75.** $7\sqrt{2}$ units ≈ 9.899 **77.** $\sqrt{275.6}$ units ≈ 16.601 **79.** $\left(-\dfrac{15}{2}, 1\right)$ **81.** $\left(\dfrac{1}{20}, -\dfrac{3}{16}\right)$

83. $\left(\sqrt{3}, -3\sqrt{6}\right)$ **85.** $2x\sqrt{3xy}$ **87.** $3a\sqrt[4]{2a}$ **89.** $\dfrac{3\sqrt{2}}{4x}$ **91.** $-4ab\sqrt[4]{2b}$ **93.** $x - 6\sqrt{x} + 9$ **95.** $4x - 9y$ **97.** $\sqrt[3]{a^2} + 4\sqrt[3]{a} + 4$

99. $a + 64$ **101.** $\dfrac{\sqrt{3x}}{6}$ **103.** $\dfrac{2x^2\sqrt{2x}}{y}$ **105.** $-\dfrac{10 + 5\sqrt{7}}{3}$ **107.** $-5 + 2\sqrt{6}$ **109.** $\dfrac{6}{\sqrt{2y}}$ **111.** $\dfrac{4x^3}{y\sqrt{2x}}$ **113.** $\dfrac{x - 25}{-3\sqrt{x} + 15}$

115. $\varnothing$ **117.** $\varnothing$ **119.** 16 **121.** $\sqrt{241}$ **123.** 4.24 ft **125.** $-i\sqrt{6}$ **127.** $-\sqrt{10}$ **129.** $-13 - 3i$ **131.** $-12 - 18i$ **133.** $-5 - 12i$

135. $\dfrac{3}{2} - i$ **137.** x **139.** -10 **141.** $\dfrac{y^5}{2x^3}$ **143.** $\dfrac{1}{8}$ **145.** $\dfrac{1}{x^{13/2}}$ **147.** $\dfrac{n\sqrt{3n}}{11m^5}$ **149.** $4x - 20\sqrt{x} + 25$ **151.** $(4, 16)$ **153.** $\dfrac{2\sqrt{x} - 6}{x - 9}$

Chapter 7 Test

1. $6\sqrt{6}$ **2.** $-x^{16}$ **3.** $\dfrac{1}{5}$ **4.** 5 **5.** $\dfrac{4x^2}{9}$ **6.** $-a^6b^3$ **7.** $\dfrac{8a^{1/3}c^{2/3}}{b^{5/12}}$ **8.** $a^{7/12} - a^{7/3}$ **9.** $|4xy|$ or $4|xy|$ **10.** -27 **11.** $\dfrac{3\sqrt{y}}{y}$

12. $\dfrac{8 - 6\sqrt{x} + x}{8 - 2x}$ **13.** $\dfrac{\sqrt[3]{b^2}}{b}$ **14.** $\dfrac{6 - x^2}{8(\sqrt{6} - x)}$ **15.** $-x\sqrt{5x}$ **16.** $4\sqrt{3} - \sqrt{6}$ **17.** $x + 2\sqrt{x} + 1$ **18.** $\sqrt{6} - 4\sqrt{3} + \sqrt{2} - 4$

19. -20 **20.** 23.685 **21.** 0.019 **22.** 2, 3 **23.** $\varnothing$ **24.** 6 **25.** $i\sqrt{2}$ **26.** $-2i\sqrt{2}$ **27.** $-3i$ **28.** 40 **29.** $7 + 24i$ **30.** $-\dfrac{3}{2} + \dfrac{5}{2}i$

31. $\dfrac{5\sqrt{2}}{2}$ **32.** $[-2, \infty)$; 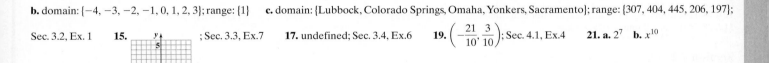 $; 0, 1, 2, 3$ **33.** $2\sqrt{26}$ units **34.** $\sqrt{95}$ units **35.** $\left(-4, \dfrac{7}{2}\right)$ **36.** $\left(-\dfrac{1}{2}, \dfrac{3}{10}\right)$

37. 27 mph **38.** 360 ft

Chapter 7 Cumulative Review

1. a. $2xy - 2$ **b.** $2x^2 + 23$ **c.** $3.1x - 0.3$ **d.** $-a - 7b + \dfrac{7}{12}$; Sec. 1.4, Ex. 15 **3.** $\dfrac{21}{11}$; Sec. 2.1, Ex. 6 **5.** \$4500 per month; Sec. 2.4, Ex. 8

7. $\varnothing$; Sec. 2.6, Ex. 6 **9.** $(-\infty, -3] \cup [9, \infty)$; Sec. 2.7, Ex. 7 **11.** ; Sec. 3.1, Ex.7 **13. a.** domain: $\{2, 0, 3\}$; range: $\{3, 4, -1\}$

b. domain: $\{-4, -3, -2, -1, 0, 1, 2, 3\}$; range: $\{1\}$ **c.** domain: {Lubbock, Colorado Springs, Omaha, Yonkers, Sacramento}; range: $\{307, 404, 445, 206, 197\}$;

Sec. 3.2, Ex. 1 **15.** ; Sec. 3.3, Ex.7 **17.** undefined; Sec. 3.4, Ex.6 **19.** $\left(-\dfrac{21}{10}, \dfrac{3}{10}\right)$; Sec. 4.1, Ex.4 **21. a.** 2^7 **b.** x^{10}

c. y^7; Sec. 5.1, Ex. 1 **23.** 6×10^{-5}; Sec. 5.2, Ex. 7 **25. a.** -4 **b.** 11; Sec. 5.3, Ex. 4 **27. a.** $2x^2 + 11x + 15$ **b.** $10x^3 - 27x^2 + 32x - 21$;

Sec. 5.4, Ex. 3 **29.** $5x^2$; Sec. 5.5, Ex. 1 **31. a.** $x^2 - 2x + 4$ **b.** $\dfrac{2}{y - 5}$; Sec. 6.1, Ex. 5 **33. a.** $\dfrac{6x + 5}{3x^3y}$ **b.** $\dfrac{2x^2 + 7x - 6}{(x + 2)(x - 2)}$ **c.** 2; Sec. 6.2, Ex. 3

35. a. $\dfrac{x(x - 2)}{2(x + 2)}$ **b.** $\dfrac{x^2}{y^2}$; Sec. 6.3, Ex. 2 **37.** $2x^2 - x + 4$; Sec. 6.4, Ex. 1 **39.** $2x^2 + 5x + 2 + \dfrac{7}{x - 3}$; Sec. 6.4, Ex. 8 **41.** $\varnothing$; Sec. 6.5, Ex. 3

43. $x = \dfrac{yz}{y - z}$; Sec. 6.6, Ex. 1 **45.** constant of variation: 15; $u = \dfrac{15}{w}$; Sec. 6.7, Ex. 3 **47. a.** $\dfrac{1}{8}$ **b.** $\dfrac{1}{9}$; Sec. 7.2, Ex. 3

49. $\dfrac{x - 4}{5(\sqrt{x} - 2)}$; Sec. 7.5, Ex. 7

CHAPTER 8 QUADRATIC EQUATIONS AND FUNCTIONS

Section 8.1

Practice Exercises

1. $-3\sqrt{2}, 3\sqrt{2}$ **2.** $\pm\sqrt{10}$ **3.** $-3 \pm 2\sqrt{5}$ **4.** $\dfrac{2 + 3i}{5}, \dfrac{2 - 3i}{5}$ **5.** $-2 \pm \sqrt{7}$ **6.** $\dfrac{3 \pm \sqrt{5}}{2}$ **7.** $\dfrac{6 \pm \sqrt{33}}{3}$ **8.** $\dfrac{5 \pm i\sqrt{31}}{4}$ **9.** 6%

Graphing Calculator Explorations 8.1

1. $-1.27,\ 6.27$ **3.** $-1.10, 0.90$ **5.** no real solutions

Vocabulary and Readiness Check 8.1

1. $\pm\sqrt{b}$ **3.** completing the square   **5.** 9   **7.** 1   **9.** 49

Exercise Set 8.1

1. $-4, 4$ **3.** $-\sqrt{7}, \sqrt{7}$ **5.** $-3\sqrt{2}, 3\sqrt{2}$ **7.** $-\sqrt{10}, \sqrt{10}$ **9.** $-8, -2$ **11.** $6 - 3\sqrt{2}, 6 + 3\sqrt{2}$ **13.** $\dfrac{3 - 2\sqrt{2}}{2}, \dfrac{3 + 2\sqrt{2}}{2}$

15. $-3i, 3i$ **17.** $-\sqrt{6}, \sqrt{6}$ **19.** $-2i\sqrt{2}, 2i\sqrt{2}$ **21.** $1 - 4i, 1 + 4i$ **23.** $-7 - \sqrt{5}, -7 + \sqrt{5}$ **25.** $-3 - 2i\sqrt{2}, -3 + 2i\sqrt{2}$

27. $x^2 + 16x + 64 = (x + 8)^2$ **29.** $z^2 - 12z + 36 = (z - 6)^2$ **31.** $p^2 + 9p + \dfrac{81}{4} = \left(p + \dfrac{9}{2}\right)^2$ **33.** $x^2 + x + \dfrac{1}{4} = \left(x + \dfrac{1}{2}\right)^2$ **35.** $-5, -3$

37. $-3 - \sqrt{7}, -3 + \sqrt{7}$ **39.** $\dfrac{-1 - \sqrt{5}}{2}, \dfrac{-1 + \sqrt{5}}{2}$ **41.** $-1 - \sqrt{6}, -1 + \sqrt{6}$ **43.** $\dfrac{6 - \sqrt{30}}{3}, \dfrac{6 + \sqrt{30}}{3}$ **45.** $\dfrac{3 - \sqrt{11}}{2}, \dfrac{3 + \sqrt{11}}{2}$

47. $-4, \dfrac{1}{2}$ **49.** $-1, 5$ **51.** $-4 - \sqrt{15}, -4 + \sqrt{15}$ **53.** $\dfrac{-3 - \sqrt{21}}{3}, \dfrac{-3 + \sqrt{21}}{3}$ **55.** $-1, \dfrac{5}{2}$ **57.** $-1 - i, -1 + i$ **59.** $3 - \sqrt{6}, 3 + \sqrt{6}$

61. $-2 - i\sqrt{2}, -2 + i\sqrt{2}$ **63.** $\dfrac{-15 - 7\sqrt{5}}{10}, \dfrac{-15 + 7\sqrt{5}}{10}$ **65.** $\dfrac{1 - i\sqrt{47}}{4}, \dfrac{1 + i\sqrt{47}}{4}$ **67.** $-5 - i\sqrt{3}, -5 + i\sqrt{3}$ **69.** $-4, 1$

71. $\dfrac{2 - i\sqrt{2}}{2}, \dfrac{2 + i\sqrt{2}}{2}$ **73.** $\dfrac{-3 - \sqrt{69}}{6}, \dfrac{-3 + \sqrt{69}}{6}$ **75.** 20%   **77.** 4%   **79.** answers may vary   **81.** 8.11 sec   **83.** 6.73 sec

85. simple; answers may vary   **87.** $\dfrac{7}{5}$ **89.** $\dfrac{1}{5}$ **91.** $5 - 10\sqrt{3}$ **93.** $\dfrac{3 - 2\sqrt{7}}{4}$ **95.** $2\sqrt{7}$ **97.** $\sqrt{13}$ **99.** complex, but not real numbers

101. real solutions   **103.** complex, but not real numbers   **105.** $-6y, 6y$ **107.** $-x, x$ **109.** 6 in.   **111.** 16.2 in. $\times$ 21.6 in.
113. 2.828 thousand units or 2828 units

Section 8.2

Practice Exercises

1. $2, -\dfrac{1}{3}$ **2.** $\dfrac{4 \pm \sqrt{22}}{3}$ **3.** $1 \pm \sqrt{17}$ **4.** $\dfrac{-1 \pm i\sqrt{15}}{4}$ **5. a.** one real solution   **b.** two real solutions   **c.** two complex, but not real
solutions   **6.** 6 ft   **7.** 2.4 sec

Vocabulary and Readiness Check 8.2

1. $x = \dfrac{-b \pm \sqrt{b^2 - 4ac}}{2a}$ **3.** $-5; -7$ **5.** $1; 0$

Exercise Set 8.2

1. $-6, 1$ **3.** $-\dfrac{3}{5}, 1$ **5.** 3   **7.** $\dfrac{-7 - \sqrt{33}}{2}, \dfrac{-7 + \sqrt{33}}{2}$ **9.** $\dfrac{1 - \sqrt{57}}{8}, \dfrac{1 + \sqrt{57}}{8}$ **11.** $\dfrac{7 - \sqrt{85}}{6}, \dfrac{7 + \sqrt{85}}{6}$ **13.** $1 - \sqrt{3}, 1 + \sqrt{3}$

15. $-\dfrac{3}{2}, 1$ **17.** $\dfrac{3 - \sqrt{11}}{2}, \dfrac{3 + \sqrt{11}}{2}$ **19.** $\dfrac{-5 - \sqrt{17}}{2}, \dfrac{-5 + \sqrt{17}}{2}$ **21.** $\dfrac{5}{2}, 1$ **23.** $-3 - 2i, -3 + 2i$ **25.** $-2 - \sqrt{11}, -2 + \sqrt{11}$

27. $\dfrac{3 - i\sqrt{87}}{8}, \dfrac{3 + i\sqrt{87}}{8}$ **29.** $\dfrac{3 - \sqrt{29}}{2}, \dfrac{3 + \sqrt{29}}{2}$ **31.** $\dfrac{-5 - i\sqrt{5}}{10}, \dfrac{-5 + i\sqrt{5}}{10}$ **33.** $\dfrac{-1 - \sqrt{19}}{6}, \dfrac{-1 + \sqrt{19}}{6}$

35. $\dfrac{-1 - i\sqrt{23}}{4}, \dfrac{-1 + i\sqrt{23}}{4}$ **37.** 1   **39.** $3 + \sqrt{5}, 3 - \sqrt{5}$ **41.** two real solutions   **43.** one real solution   **45.** two real solutions

47. two complex but not real solutions   **49.** two real solutions   **51.** 14 ft   **53.** $2 + 2\sqrt{2}$ cm, $2 + 2\sqrt{2}$ cm, $4 + 2\sqrt{2}$ cm

55. width: $-5 + 5\sqrt{17}$ ft; length: $5 + 5\sqrt{17}$ ft   **57. a.** $50\sqrt{2}$ m   **b.** 5000 sq m   **59.** 37.4 ft by 38.5 ft   **61.** base, $2 + 2\sqrt{43}$ cm;

height, $-1 + \sqrt{43}$ cm   **63.** 8.9 sec   **65.** 2.8 sec   **67.** $\dfrac{11}{5}$ **69.** 15   **71.** $(x^2 + 5)(x + 2)(x - 2)$ **73.** $(z + 3)(z - 3)(z + 2)(z - 2)$

75. b   **77.** answers may vary   **79.** 0.6, 2.4   **81.** Sunday to Monday   **83.** Wednesday   **85.** 32; yes   **87. a.** 8630 stores   **b.** 2011

89. answers may vary   **91.** $\dfrac{\sqrt{3}}{3}$ **93.** $\dfrac{-\sqrt{2} - i\sqrt{2}}{2}, \dfrac{-\sqrt{2} + i\sqrt{2}}{2}$ **95.** $\dfrac{\sqrt{3} - \sqrt{11}}{4}, \dfrac{\sqrt{3} + \sqrt{11}}{4}$

97. 8.9 sec: 1200   2.8 sec: 200   **99.** two real solutions

Section 8.3

Practice Exercises

1. 8   **2.** $\dfrac{5 \pm \sqrt{137}}{8}$ **3.** $4, -4, 3i, -3i$ **4.** $1, -3$ **5.** $1, 64$ **6.** Katy: $\dfrac{7 + \sqrt{65}}{2} \approx 7.5$ hr; Steve: $\dfrac{9 + \sqrt{65}}{2} \approx 8.5$ hr

7. to Shanghai: 40 km/hr; to Ningbo: 90 km/hr

Exercise Set 8.3

1. 2   **3.** 16   **5.** $1, 4$ **7.** $3 - \sqrt{7}, 3 + \sqrt{7}$ **9.** $\dfrac{3 - \sqrt{57}}{4}, \dfrac{3 + \sqrt{57}}{4}$ **11.** $\dfrac{1 - \sqrt{29}}{2}, \dfrac{1 + \sqrt{29}}{2}$ **13.** $-2, 2, -2i, 2i$

15. $-\dfrac{1}{2}, \dfrac{1}{2}, -i\sqrt{3}, i\sqrt{3}$ **17.** $-3, 3, -2, 2$ **19.** $125, -8$ **21.** $-\dfrac{4}{5}, 0$ **23.** $-\dfrac{1}{8}, 27$ **25.** $-\dfrac{2}{3}, \dfrac{4}{3}$ **27.** $-\dfrac{1}{125}, \dfrac{1}{8}$ **29.** $-\sqrt{2}, \sqrt{2}, -\sqrt{3}, \sqrt{3}$

31. $\dfrac{-9 - \sqrt{201}}{6}, \dfrac{-9 + \sqrt{201}}{6}$ **33.** $2, 3$ **35.** 3   **37.** $27, 125$ **39.** $1, -3i, 3i$ **41.** $\dfrac{1}{8}, -8$ **43.** $-\dfrac{1}{2}, \dfrac{1}{3}$ **45.** 4

47. -3 **49.** $-\sqrt{5}, \sqrt{5}, -2i, 2i$ **51.** $-3, \dfrac{3 - 3i\sqrt{3}}{2}, \dfrac{3 + 3i\sqrt{3}}{2}$ **53.** $6, 12$ **55.** $-\dfrac{1}{3}, \dfrac{1}{3}, -\dfrac{i\sqrt{6}}{3}, \dfrac{i\sqrt{6}}{3}$ **57.** 5 mph, then 4 mph

59. inlet pipe: 15.5 hr; hose: 16.5 hr   **61.** 55 mph, 66 mph   **63.** 8.5 hr   **65.** 12 or -8 **67. a.** $(x - 6)$ in.   **b.** $300 = (x - 6) \cdot (x - 6) \cdot 3$

c. 16 cm by 16 cm   **69.** 22 feet   **71.** $(-\infty, 3]$ **73.** $(-5, \infty)$ **75.** domain: $(-\infty, \infty)$; range: $(-\infty, \infty)$; function

77. domain: $(-\infty, \infty)$; range: $[-1, \infty)$; function   **79.** $1, -3i, 3i$ **81.** $-\dfrac{1}{2}, \dfrac{1}{3}$ **83.** $-3, \dfrac{3 - 3i\sqrt{3}}{2}, \dfrac{3 + 3i\sqrt{3}}{2}$ **85.** answers may vary

87. a. 150.94 ft/sec   **b.** 151.49 ft/sec   **c.** Bourdais: 102.9 mph; Pagenaud: 103.3 mph

Integrated Review

1. $-\sqrt{10}, \sqrt{10}$ **2.** $-\sqrt{14}, \sqrt{14}$ **3.** $1 - 2\sqrt{2}, 1 + 2\sqrt{2}$ **4.** $-5 - 2\sqrt{3}, -5 + 2\sqrt{3}$ **5.** $-1 - \sqrt{13}, -1 + \sqrt{13}$

6. $1, 11$ **7.** $\dfrac{-3 - \sqrt{69}}{6}, \dfrac{-3 + \sqrt{69}}{6}$ **8.** $\dfrac{-2 - \sqrt{5}}{4}, \dfrac{-2 + \sqrt{5}}{4}$ **9.** $\dfrac{2 - \sqrt{2}}{2}, \dfrac{2 + \sqrt{2}}{2}$ **10.** $-3 - \sqrt{5}, -3 + \sqrt{5}$

11. $-2 + i\sqrt{3}, -2 - i\sqrt{3}$ **12.** $\dfrac{-1 - i\sqrt{11}}{2}, \dfrac{-1 + i\sqrt{11}}{2}$ **13.** $\dfrac{-3 + i\sqrt{15}}{2}, \dfrac{-3 - i\sqrt{15}}{2}$ **14.** $3i, -3i$ **15.** $0, -17$

16. $\dfrac{1 + \sqrt{13}}{4}, \dfrac{1 - \sqrt{13}}{4}$ **17.** $2 + 3\sqrt{3}, 2 - 3\sqrt{3}$ **18.** $2 + \sqrt{3}, 2 - \sqrt{3}$ **19.** $-2, \dfrac{4}{3}$ **20.** $\dfrac{-5 + \sqrt{17}}{4}, \dfrac{-5 - \sqrt{17}}{4}$ **21.** $1 - \sqrt{6}, 1 + \sqrt{6}$

22. $-\sqrt{31}, \sqrt{31}$ **23.** $-\sqrt{11}, \sqrt{11}$ **24.** $-i\sqrt{11}, i\sqrt{11}$ **25.** $-11, 6$ **26.** $\dfrac{-3 + \sqrt{19}}{5}, \dfrac{-3 - \sqrt{19}}{5}$ **27.** $\dfrac{-3 + \sqrt{17}}{4}, \dfrac{-3 - \sqrt{17}}{4}$

28. $10\sqrt{2}$ ft ≈ 14.1 ft   **29.** Jack: 9.1 hr; Lucy: 7.1 hr   **30.** 5 mph during the first part, then 6 mph

Vocabulary and Readiness Check 8.6

1. (h, k)　　**3.** $0; 1$　　**5.** $2; 1$　　**7.** $1; 1$　　**9.** down　　**11.** up

Exercise Set 8.6

1. $(-4, -9)$　　**3.** $(5, 30)$　　**5.** $(1, -2)$　　**7.** $\left(\dfrac{1}{2}, \dfrac{5}{4}\right)$　　**9.** D　　**11.** B

13. 　　**15.** 　　**17.** 　　**19.** 　　**21.**

23. 　　**25.** 　　**27.** 　　**29.** 　　**31.**

33. 　　**35.**   　　**37.** 　　**39.**

41. 　　**43.**　　**45.** 144 ft　　**47. a.** 200 bicycles　　**b.** \$12,000　　**49.** 30 and 30　　**51.** 5, −5
53. length, 20 units; width, 20 units

55.　　**57.**　　**59.**　　**61.**　　**63.**

65. minimum value　　**67.** maximum value　　**69.**　　**71.**　　**73.** −0.84　　**75.** 1.43

77. a. maximum; answers may vary　　**b.** 2005　　**c.** 31,523　　**79.** 　　**81.**

Chapter 8 Vocabulary Check

1. discriminant　　**2.** $\pm\sqrt{b}$　　**3.** $\dfrac{-b}{2a}$　　**4.** quadratic inequality　　**5.** completing the square　　**6.** $(0, k)$　　**7.** $(h, 0)$　　**8.** (h, k)
9. quadratic formula　　**10.** quadratic

Chapter 8 Review

1. 14, 1   **3.** $-7, 7$ **5.** $\dfrac{-3 - \sqrt{5}}{2}, \dfrac{-3 + \sqrt{5}}{2}$ **7.** 4.25%   **9.** two complex but not real solutions   **11.** two real solutions   **13.** 8   **15.** $-\dfrac{5}{2}, 1$

17. $\dfrac{5 - i\sqrt{143}}{12}, \dfrac{5 + i\sqrt{143}}{12}$ **19. a.** 20 ft   **b.** $\dfrac{15 + \sqrt{321}}{16}$ sec; 2.1 sec   **21.** $3, \dfrac{-3 + 3i\sqrt{3}}{2}, \dfrac{-3 - 3i\sqrt{3}}{2}$ **23.** $\dfrac{2}{3}, 5$ **25.** 1, 125   **27.** $-1, 1, -i, i$

29. Jerome: 10.5 hr; Tim: 9.5 hr

Chapter 8 Test

1. $\dfrac{7}{5}, -1$ **2.** $-1 - \sqrt{10}, -1 + \sqrt{10}$ **3.** $\dfrac{1 + i\sqrt{31}}{2}, \dfrac{1 - i\sqrt{31}}{2}$ **4.** $3 - \sqrt{7}, 3 + \sqrt{7}$ **5.** $-\dfrac{1}{7}, -1$ **6.** $\dfrac{3 + \sqrt{29}}{2}, \dfrac{3 - \sqrt{29}}{2}$

7. $-2 - \sqrt{11}, -2 + \sqrt{11}$ **8.** $-1, 1, -i, i, -3$ **9.** $-1, 1, -i, i$ **10.** 6, 7   **11.** $3 - \sqrt{7}, 3 + \sqrt{7}$ **12.** $\dfrac{2 - i\sqrt{6}}{2}, \dfrac{2 + i\sqrt{6}}{2}$

Chapter 8 Cumulative Review

1. a. $5 + y \geq 7$ **b.** $11 \neq z$ **c.** $20 < 5 - 2x$; Sec. 1.4, Ex. 6   **3.** slope: 1; ; Sec. 3.4, Ex. 1   **5.** $(-2, 2)$; Sec. 4.1, Ex. 5

7. a. $6x^2 - 29x + 28$ **b.** $15x^4 - x^2y - 2y^2$; Sec. 5.4, Ex. 6   **9. a.** $4(2x^2 + 1)$ **b.** prime polynomial   **c.** $3x^2(2 - x + 4x^2)$; Sec. 5.5, Ex. 2

11. $(x - 5)(x - 7)$; Sec. 5.6, Ex. 2   **13.** $3x(a - 2b)^2$; Sec. 5.7, Ex. 2   **15.** $-\dfrac{2}{3}$; Sec. 5.8, Ex. 4   **17.** $-2, 0, 2$; Sec. 5.8, Ex. 6

19. $\dfrac{1}{5x - 1}$; Sec. 6.1, Ex. 2a   **21.** $\dfrac{7x^2 - 9x - 13}{(2x + 1)(x - 5)(3x - 2)}$; Sec. 6.2, Ex. 5   **23.** $\dfrac{xy + 2x^3}{y - 1}$; Sec. 6.3, Ex. 3   **25.** $3x^3y - 15x - 1 - \dfrac{6}{xy}$; Sec. 6.4, Ex. 2

27. a. 5   **b.** 5; Sec. 6.4, Ex. 10   **29.** -3; Sec. 6.5, Ex. 1   **31.** 2; Sec. 6.6, Ex. 2   **35. a.** 3   **b.** $|x|$ **c.** $|x - 2|$

d. -5 **e.** $2x - 7$ **f.** $5|x|$ **g.** $|x + 1|$; Sec. 7.1, Ex. 5   **37. a.** $\sqrt{x}$ **b.** $\sqrt[3]{5}$ **c.** $\sqrt{rs^3}$; Sec. 7.2, Ex. 7   **39. a.** $5x\sqrt{x}$ **b.** $3x^2y^2\sqrt[3]{2y^2}$

c. $3z^2\sqrt[4]{z^3}$; Sec. 7.3, Ex. 4   **41. a.** $\dfrac{2\sqrt{5}}{5}$ **b.** $\dfrac{8\sqrt{x}}{3x}$ **c.** $\dfrac{\sqrt[3]{4}}{2}$; Sec. 7.5, Ex. 1   **43.** $\dfrac{2}{9}$; Sec. 7.6, Ex. 5   **45. a.** $\dfrac{1}{2} + \dfrac{3}{2}i$ **b.** $-\dfrac{7}{3}i$; Sec. 7.7, Ex. 5

47. $-1 + 2\sqrt{3}, -1 - 2\sqrt{3}$; Sec. 8.1, Ex. 3   **49.** 9; Sec. 8.3, Ex. 1

APPENDIX A.2 PRACTICE FINAL EXAM

1. $6\sqrt{6}$ **2.** $-\dfrac{3}{2}$ **3.** 5   **4.** $\dfrac{1}{81x^2}$ **5.** $\dfrac{64}{3}$ **6.** $\dfrac{3a^7}{2b^5}$ **7.** $\dfrac{8a^{1/3}c^{2/3}}{b^{5/12}}$ **8.** $3y(x + 3y)(x - 3y)$ **9.** $2(2y - 1)(4y^2 + 2y + 1)$

10. $(x + 3)(x - 3)(y - 3)$ **11.** $-5x^3y - 11x - 9$ **12.** $36m^2 + 12mn + n^2$ **13.** $2x^3 - 13x^2 + 14x - 4$ **14.** $\dfrac{x + 2}{2(x + 3)}$ **15.** $\dfrac{1}{x(x + 3)}$

16. $\dfrac{5x - 2}{(x - 3)(x + 2)(x - 2)}$ **17.** $-x\sqrt{5x}$ **18.** -20 **19.** $2x^2 - x - 2 + \dfrac{2}{2x + 1}$ **20.** -32 **21.** $1, \dfrac{2}{3}$

22. $4, -\dfrac{8}{7}$ **23.** $\left(\dfrac{3}{2}, 5\right]$ **24.** $(-\infty, -2) \cup \left(\dfrac{4}{3}, \infty\right)$ **25.** 3   **26.** $\dfrac{3 \pm \sqrt{29}}{2}$ **27.** 2, 3   **29.** $\left(\dfrac{7}{2}, -10\right)$

30.   **31.** $2x - y > 5$ **32.** $y = -3$

36. $f(x) = -\dfrac{1}{2}x$ **37.** $f(x) = -\dfrac{1}{3}x + \dfrac{5}{3}$ **38.** $2\sqrt{26}$ units   **39.** $\left(-4, \dfrac{7}{2}\right)$ **40.** $\dfrac{3\sqrt{y}}{y}$ **41.** $\dfrac{8 - 6\sqrt{x} + x}{8 - 2x}$

42. New York: 21.8 million; Seoul: 23.1 million; Tokyo: 33.4 million   **43.** $(x + 2y)(x - 2y)$ **44.** 5

48. 5 gal of 10%; 15 gal of 20%   **49.** $-2i\sqrt{2}$ **50.** $-3i$

Index